STAR WARS®

THE SCRIPTS

STAR WARS®

THE SCRIPTS

Star Wars®
Original screenplay by: George Lucas

The Empire Strikes Back™
Original screenplay by: Leigh Brackett and Lawrence Kasdan
Story by: George Lucas

Return of the Jedi™
Original screenplay by: Lawrence Kasdan and George Lucas
Story by: George Lucas

BOXTREE

First published in Great Britain in 1995 by Boxtree Limited
Broadwall House
21 Broadwall
London SE1 9PL

10 9 8 7 6 5 4 3 2 1

ISBN: 0 7522 0766 0

A CIP catalogue entry for this book is available from the British Library.

Cover artwork by John Alvin
Cover design by Shoot That Tiger!

Printed and bound in Great Britain by Butler & Tanner Ltd, Frome and London

STAR WARS®
THE COMPLETE CONTINUITY SCRIPTS

Star Wars® The complete continuity Scripts provides for the first time an accurate record of the scripts from three of the most astonishing and successful science-fiction films ever made. Published to coincide with the release of the three films under the THX Digital Mastering process, this is an opportunity for Star Wars enthusiasts and film fans alike to see this extraordinary, ground-breaking trilogy in a dynamic new way, and at the same time to see how the script was put together.

The scripts from *Star Wars, The Empire Strikes Back* and *Return of the Jedi* have never been published together before. Furthermore, the previously published script books carry the full script of each movie before it reached the screen; these are known as 'shooting scripts'. *Star Wars: The complete continuity Scripts* presents the script from each film as it appeared in the final version of the film itself. Decisions taken at the time of filming, and cutting decisions taken at the editing stage, mean that a shooting script is never an accurate representation of what we see in the cinema. The Star Wars scripts are no exception to this.

Also unique to this book is the time code that appears on each page; this allows a reader to follow, closely, the action as it unfolds on the screen.

STAR WARS

Episode IV

A NEW HOPE

STAR WARS

A long time ago in a galaxy far,
far away....

A vast sea of stars serves as the backdrop for the main title. War drums echo through the heavens as a roll-up slowly crawls into infinity.

Episode IV

A NEW HOPE

It is a period of civil war.
Rebel spaceships, striking
from a hidden base, have won
their first victory against
the evil Galactic Empire.

During the battle, Rebel
spies managed to steal secret
plans to the Empire's
ultimate weapon, the DEATH
STAR, an armored space
station with enough power to
destroy an entire planet.

Pursued by the Empire's
sinister agents, Princess
Leia races home aboard her
starship, custodian of the
stolen plans that can save
her people and restore
freedom to the galaxy....

The awesome yellow planet of Tatooine emerges from a total eclipse, her two moons glowing against the darkness. A tiny silver spacecraft, a Rebel Blockade Runner firing lasers from the back of the ship, races through space. It is pursued by a giant Imperial starship. Hundreds of deadly laserbolts streak from the Imperial Star Destroyer, causing the main solar fin of the Rebel craft to disintegrate.

INT. REBEL BLOCKADE RUNNER — MAIN PASSAGEWAY

An explosion rocks the ship as two robots, Artoo-Detoo (R2-D2) and See-Threepio (C-3PO) struggle to make their way through the shaking, bouncing passageway. Both robots are old and battered. Artoo is a short, claw-armed tripod. His face is a mass of computer lights surrounding a radar eye. Threepio, on the other hand, is a tall, slender robot of human proportions. He has a gleaming bronze-like metallic surface of an Art Deco design.
    Rebel troops rush past and another blast shakes them as they struggle along their way.

THREEPIO: Did you hear that? They've shut down the main reactor. We'll be destroyed for sure. This is madness!

Rebel troopers continue to rush past the robots and take up positions in the main passageway. They aim their weapons toward the door.

THREEPIO: We're doomed!

The little R2 unit makes a series of electronic sounds that only another robot could understand.

THREEPIO: There'll be no escape for the Princess this time.

Artoo continues making beeping sounds. Tension mounts as loud metallic latches clank and the screams of heavy equipment are heard moving around the outside hull of the ship.

THREEPIO: What's that?

EXT. SPACECRAFT IN SPACE

(CONT'D)

CONTINUED

The Imperial craft has easily overtaken the Rebel Blockade Runner. The smaller Rebel ship is being drawn into the underside dock of the giant Imperial starship.

INT. REBEL BLOCKADE RUNNER

The nervous Rebel troopers aim their weapons. Suddenly a tremendous blast opens up a hole in the main passageway and a score of fearsome armored spacesuited stormtroopers make their way into the smoke-filled corridor.

In a few minutes the entire passageway is ablaze with laserfire. The deadly bolts ricochet in wild random patterns creating huge explosions. Stormtroopers scatter and duck behind storage lockers. Laserbolts hit several Rebel soldiers who scream and stagger through the smoke, holding shattered arms and faces.

An explosion hits near the robots.

The awesome, seven-foot-tall Dark Lord of the Sith makes his way into the blinding light of the main passageway. This is Darth Vader, right hand of the Emperor. His face is obscured by his flowing black robes and grotesque breath mask, which stands out next to the fascist white armored suits of the Imperial stormtroopers.

Everyone instinctively backs away from the imposing warrior.

INT. REBEL BLOCKADE RUNNER

A woman's hand puts a card into an opening in Artoo's dome. Artoo makes beeping sounds.

INT. REBEL BLOCKADE RUNNER

Threepio stands in a hallway, somewhat bewildered. Artoo is nowhere in sight. Fighting can be heard in the distance.

THREEPIO: Artoo-Detoo, where are you?

A familiar beeping sound attracts Threepio's attention and he spots little Artoo at the end of the hallway in a smoke filled alcove. A beautiful young girl (about sixteen years old) stands in front of Artoo. Surreal and out of place, dreamlike and half hidden in the smoke, she finishes adjusting something on Artoo's computer face, then disappears as the little robot joins his companion. Stormtroopers can be heard battling in the distance.

THREEPIO: At last! Where have you been? They're heading in this direction. What are we going to do? We'll be sent to the spice mines of Kessel or smashed into who-knows-what!

Artoo scoots past his bronze friend and races down the subhallway. Threepio chases after him.

THREEPIO: Wait a minute, where are you going?

Artoo responds with electronic beeps.
The lovely young girl watches them go.

INT. REBEL BLOCKADE RUNNER – CORRIDOR

Captured Rebel troops are marched away. The evil Darth Vader holds a wounded Rebel Officer by the neck as an Imperial Officer rushes up to the Dark Lord.

IMPERIAL OFFICER: The Death Star plans are not in the main computer.

Vader squeezes the neck of the Rebel Officer, who struggles in vain.

VADER: Where are those transmissions you intercepted? What have you done with those plans?

Vader lifts the Rebel off his feet by his throat.

REBEL OFFICER: We intercepted no transmissions. Aaah ... This is a consular ship. We're on a diplomatic mission.

VADER: If this is a consular ship ... where is the Ambassador?

The Dark Lord begins to squeeze the officer's throat, creating a gruesome snapping and choking, until the soldier goes limp. Vader tosses the dead soldier against the wall and turns to his troops.

VADER: Commander, tear this ship apart until you've found those plans and bring me the passengers. I want them alive!

(CONT'D)

CONTINUED

The stormtroopers scurry into the subhallways.

INT. REBEL BLOCKADE RUNNER – SUBHALLWAY

The lovely young girl huddles in a small alcove as the stormtroopers search through the ship. She is Princess Leia Organa, a member of the Alderaan Senate. The stormtroopers approach. One of the troopers spots her.

TROOPER: There's one! Set for stun!

Leia steps from her hiding place and blasts a trooper with her laser pistol. She starts to run but is felled by a paralyzing ray. The troopers inspect her inert body.

TROOPER: She'll be all right. Inform Lord Vader we have a prisoner.

INT. REBEL BLOCKADE RUNNER – SUBHALLWAY

Artoo stops before the small hatch of an emergency lifepod. The stubby astro-robot works his way into the cramped four-man pod.

THREEPIO: Hey, you're not permitted in there. It's restricted. You'll be deactivated for sure.

Artoo beeps something to him.

THREEPIO: Don't you call me a mindless philosopher, you overweight glob of grease! Now come out before somebody sees you.

Artoo whistles something at his reluctant friend regarding the mission he is about to perform.

THREEPIO: Secret mission? What plans? What are you talking about? I'm not getting in there!

A new explosion, this time very close, sends dust and debris through the narrow subhallway. Flames lick at Threepio and, after a flurry of electronic swearing from Artoo, the lanky robot jumps into the lifepod.

THREEPIO: I'm going to regret this.

INT. REBEL BLOCKADE RUNNER

The safety door snaps shut, and with the thunder of exploding latches the tiny lifepod ejects from the disabled ship.

INT. IMPERIAL STAR DESTROYER

On the main viewscreen, the lifepod carrying the two terrified robots speeds away from the stricken Rebel spacecraft.

CHIEF PILOT: There goes another one.

CAPTAIN: Hold your fire. There's no life forms. It must have short-circuited.

INT. LIFEPOD

Artoo and Threepio look out at the receding Imperial starship. Stars circle as the pod rotates through the galaxy.

THREEPIO: That's funny, the damage doesn't look as bad from out here.

Artoo beeps an assuring response.

THREEPIO: Are you sure this thing is safe?

EXT. SPACE – PLANT TATOOINE

The lifepod disappears in the direction of the planet.

INT. REBEL BLOCKADE RUNNER – HALLWAY

Princess Leia is led down a low-ceilinged hallway by a squad of briskly marching armored stormtroopers. Her hands are bound. They stop in a smoky hallway as Darth Vader appears.

LEIA: Darth Vader. Only you could be so bold. The Imperial Senate will not sit still for this. When they hear you've attacked a diplomatic –

(CONT'D)

CONTINUED

VADER: Don't act so surprised, Your Highness. You weren't on any mercy mission this time. Several transmissions were beamed to this ship by Rebel spies. I want to know what happened to the plans they sent you.

LEIA: I don't know what you're talking about. I'm a member of the Imperial Senate on a diplomatic mission to Alderaan . . .

VADER: You are a part of the Rebel Alliance . . . and a traitor. Take her away!

Leia is marched away down the hallway. An Imperial Commander turns to Vader.

COMMANDER: Holding her is dangerous. If word of this gets out, it could generate sympathy for the Rebellion in the senate.

VADER: I have traced the Rebel spies to her. Now she is my only link to finding their secret base.

COMMANDER: She'll die before she'll tell you anything.

VADER: Leave that to me. Send a distress signal and then inform the senate that all aboard were killed!

Another Imperial Commander approaches Vader and the first Commander.

SECOND COMMANDER: Lord Vader, the battle station plans are not aboard this ship! And no transmissions were made. An escape pod was jettisoned during the fighting, but no life forms were aboard.

VADER: She must have hidden the plans in the escape pod. Send a detachment down to retrieve them. See to it personally, Commander. There'll be no one to stop us this time.

SECOND COMMANDER: Yes, sir.

EXT. SPACE

The Imperial Star Destroyer comes over the surface of the planet Tatooine.

EXT. TATTOINE – DESERT

Jundland, or "No Man's Land", where the rugged desert mesas meet the foreboding dune sea. The two helpless astro-robots kick up clouds of sand as they leave the lifepod and clumsily work their way across the desert wasteland. The lifepod in the distance rests half-buried in the sand.

THREEPIO: How did we get into his mess: I really don't know how. We seem to be made to suffer. It's our lot in life.

Artoo answers with beeping sounds.

THREEPIO: I've got to rest before I fall apart. My joints are almost frozen.

Artoo continues to respond with beeping sounds.

THREEPIO: What a desolate place this is.

Suddenly Artoo whistles, makes a sharp right turn and starts off in the direction of the rocky desert mesas. Threepio stops and yells at him.

THREEPIO: Where do you think you're going?

A stream of electronic noises continues to pour forth from the small robot.

THREEPIO: Well, I'm not going that way. It's much too rocky. This way is much easier.

Artoo counters with a beep.

THREEPIO: What makes you think there are settlements over there?

Artoo continues to make beeping sounds.

THREEPIO: Don't get technical with me.

Artoo continues to make beeping sounds.

(CONT'D)

CONTINUED

THREEPIO: What mission? What are you talking about? I've just about had enough of you! Go that way! You'll be malfunctioning within a day, you nearsighted scrap pile!

Threepio gives the little robot a kick and starts on in the direction of the vast dune sea.

THREEPIO: And don't let me catch you following me begging for help, because you won't get it.

Artoo's reply is a rather rude sound. He turns in the direction of the towering mesas.

THREEPIO: No more adventures. I'm not going that way.

Artoo beeps to himself as he makes his way toward the distant mountains.

EXT. TATOOINE — DUNE SEA

Threepio, hot and tired, struggles up over the ridge of a dune: only to find more dunes, which seem to go on for endless miles. He looks back in the direction of the now distant rock mesas.

THREEPIO: That malfunctioning little twerp. This is all his fault! He tricked me into going this way, but he'll do no better.

His plight seems hopeless, when a glint of reflected light in the distance reveals an object moving toward him.

THREEPIO: Wait, what's that? A transport! I'm saved!

The bronze droid waves frantically and yells at the approaching transport.

THREEPIO: Over here! Hey! Hey! Help! Please, help!

EXT. TATOOINE — ROCK CANYON — SUNSET

The gargantuan rock formations are shrouded in a strange foreboding mist and the ominous sounds of unearthly creatures fill the air. Artoo moves cautiously through the creepy rock canyon, inadvertently making a loud whirring noise as he goes.
A little further up the canyon a slight flicker of lights reveals a pair of eyes in the dark recesses only a few feet from the narrow path.
The unsuspecting robot waddles along the rugged trail until suddenly, out of nowhere, a powerful magnetic ray shoots out of the rocks and engulfs him in an eerie glow.
He manages a few electronic squeaks before he topples over, his bright computer lights extinguished. Out of the rocks scurry several Jawas, no taller than Artoo. They holster strange and complex weapons as they cautiously approach the robot. They wear grubby cloaks and their faces are shrouded so that only their glowing yellow eyes can be seen. They hiss and make odd guttural sounds as they heave the heavy robot on to their shoulders and carry him off down the trail.

EXT. TATOOINE — ROCK CANYON — SANDCRAWLER — SUNSET

The Jawas carry Artoo out of the canyon to a huge tank-like vehicle the size of a four-story house. They weld a small disk on the side of Artoo and then put him under a large tube on the side of the vehicle and the little robot is sucked into the giant machine.
The filthy little Jawas scurry like rats up a ladder and enter the main cabin of the behemoth transport.

INT. SANDCRAWLER — HOLD AREA

It is dim inside the hold area of the sandcrawler. Artoo switches on a small floodlight on his forehead and stumbles around the scrap heap. The narrow beam swings across rusty metal rocket parts and an array of grotesquely twisted and maimed astro-robots. He lets out a pathetic electronic whimper and stumbles off toward what appears to be a door at the end of the chamber.

INT. SANDCRAWLER — PRISON AREA

Artoo enters a wide room with a low ceiling. In the middle of the scrap heap sits a dozen or so robots of various shapes and sizes. Some are engaged in electronic conversation, while others simply mill about. A voice calls out from the gloom.

THREEPIO: Artoo? Artoo-Detoo! It is you! It is you!

A battered Threepio scrambles up to Artoo and embraces him.

(CONT'D)

CONTINUED

EXT. TATOOINE — ROCK CANYON — SANDCRAWLER — SUNSET

The enormous sandcrawler lumbers off.

EXT. TATOOINE — DESERT — DAY

Imperial stormtroopers mill about in front of the half-buried lifepod that brought Artoo and Threepio to Tatooine. A trooper radios to an officer some distance away.

FIRST TROOPER: Someone was in the pod. The tracks go off in this direction.

A second trooper picks up a small bit of metal out of the sand and gives it to the first trooper.

SECOND TROOPER: Look, sir — droids.

EXT. TATOOINE — DUNES

The sandcrawler moves slowly down a great sand dune.

INT. SANDCRAWLER

Threepio and Artoo travel along inside the cramped prison chamber. Artoo appears to be shut off.

THREEPIO: Wake up! Wake up!

As the sandcrawler stops, Threepio's fist bangs the head of Artoo whose computer lights pop on as he begins beeping. At the far end of the long chamber a hatch opens, filling the chamber with blinding white light. A dozen or so Jawas make their way through the odd assortment of robots.

THREEPIO: We're doomed.

A Jawa starts moving toward them.

THREEPIO: Do you think they'll melt us down?

Artoo responds, making beeping sounds.

THREEPIO: Don't shoot! Don't shoot! Will this never end?

EXT. TATOOINE — DESERT — LARS HOMESTEAD — AFTERNOON

The Jawas mutter gibberish as they busily line up their battered captives, including Artoo and Threepio, in front of the enormous sandcrawler, which is parked beside a small homestead consisting of three large holes in the ground surrounded by several tall moisture vaporators and one small adobe block house.

    The Jawas scurry around fussing over the robots, straightening them up or brushing some dust from a dented metallic elbow.

    Out of the shadows of a dingy side-building limps Owen Lars, a large burly man in his mid-fifties. His reddish eyes are sunken in a dust-covered face. As the farmer carefully inspects each of the robots, he is closely followed by his slump-shouldered nephew, Luke Skywalker. One of the vile little Jawas walks ahead of the farmer spouting an animated sales pitch in a queer, unintelligible language.

OWEN: Yeah, all right, fine. Let's go.

A voice calls out from one of the huge holes that form the homestead.

BERU: Luke! Luke!

Luke goes over to the edge and sees his aunt Beru standing in the main courtyard.

BERU: Luke, tell Uncle, if he gets a translator, be sure it speaks Bocce.

LUKE: Doesn't it look like we have much of a choice but I'll remind him.

Luke returns to his uncle as they look over the equipment for sale with the Jawa leader.

OWEN: No, not that one … *(addressing Threepio)* You, I suppose you're programmed for etiquette and protocol?

THREEPIO: Protocol? Why, it's my primary function, sir. I am well versed in all the customs —

OWEN: I have no need for a protocol droid.

(CONT'D)

CONTINUED

THREEPIO: *(quickly)* Of course you haven't, sir — not in an environment such as this — that's why I have been programmed —

OWEN: What I really need is a droid who understands the binary language of moisture vaporators.

THREEPIO: Vaporators! Sir — My first job was programming binary load lifters ... very similar to your vaporators in most respects ...

OWEN: Can you speak Bocce?

THREEPIO: Of course I can, sir. It's like a second language to me ... I'm as fluent in —

OWEN: All right; shut up! *(turning to Jawa)* I'll take this one.

THREEPIO: Shutting up, sir.

OWEN: Luke! Take these two over to the garage, will you? I want them cleaned up before dinner.

LUKE: But I was going into Toshi Station to pick up some power converters ...

OWEN: You can waste time with your friends when your chores are done. Now, come on, get to it!

LUKE: All right, come on. And the red one, come on. Well, come on, Red, let's go.

As the Jawas start to lead the remaining robots back into the sandcrawler, Artoo lets out a pathetic little beep and starts after his old friend Threepio. He is restrained by a slimy Jawa, who zaps him with a control box.

Owen is negotiating with the head Jawa. Luke and the two robots start for the garage when a plate pops off the head of the red astro-droid, throwing parts all over the ground.

LUKE: Uncle Owen ...

OWEN: Yeah?

LUKE: This R2 unit has a bad motivator. Look!

OWEN: *(to the head Jawa)* Hey, what're you trying to push on us?

The Jawa goes into a loud spiel. Meanwhile, Artoo is moving up and down trying to attract attention. He lets out with a low whistle. Threepio taps Luke on the shoulder.

THREEPIO: *(pointing to Artoo)* Excuse me, sir, but that R2 unit is in prime condition. A real bargain.

LUKE: Uncle Owen ...

OWEN: Yeah?

LUKE: What about that one?

OWEN: *(to Jawa)* What about that blue one? We'll take that one.

With a little reluctance the scruffy dwarf trades the damaged astro-robot for Artoo.

LUKE: Yeah, take this away.

THREEPIO: I'm quite sure you'll be very pleased with that one, sir. He really is in first-class condition. I've worked with him before. Here he comes.

The two robots trudge off toward a grimy homestead entry.

LUKE: Okay, let's go.

THREEPIO: *(to Artoo)* Now, don't you forget this! Why I should stick my neck out for you is quite beyond my capacity!

INT. LARS HOMESTEAD — GARAGE AREA — LATE AFTERNOON

The garage is cluttered and worn, but a friendly peaceful atmosphere permeates the low grey chamber. Threepio lowers himself into a large tub filled with warm oil. Near the battered landspeeder little Artoo rests on a large battery with a cord attached to his face.

(CONT'D)

CONTINUED

THREEPIO: Thank the maker! This oil bath is going to feel so good. I've got such a bad case of dust contamination, I can barely move!

Luke seems to be lost in thought as he plays with the damaged fin of a small two-man skyhopper spaceship. Finally Luke's frustrations get the better of him.

LUKE: It just isn't fair. Oh, Biggs is right. I'm never gonna get out of here!

THREEPIO: Is there anything I might do to help?

Luke glances at the battered robot. A bit of his anger drains.

LUKE: Well, not unless you can alter time, speed up the harvest, or teleport me off this rock!

THREEPIO: I don't think so, sir. I'm only a droid and not very knowledgeable about such things. Not on this planet, anyway. As a matter of fact, I'm not even sure which planet I'm on.

LUKE: Well, if there's a bright center to the universe, you're on the planet that it's farthest from.

THREEPIO: I see, sir.

LUKE: Uh, you can call me Luke.

THREEPIO: I see, Sir Luke.

LUKE: *(laughing)* Just Luke.

THREEPIO: *(climbing out of the oil tub)* Oh! And I am See-Threepio, human cyborg relations, and this is my counterpart, Artoo-Detoo.

LUKE: Hello.

Artoo beeps in response. Luke unplugs Artoo and begins to scrape several connectors on the robot's head with a chrome pick.

LUKE: You got a lot of carbon scoring here. It looks like you boys have seen a lot of action.

THREEPIO: Will all we've been through, sometimes I'm amazed we're in as good condition as we are, what with the Rebellion and all.

Luke sparks to life at the mention of the Rebellion.

LUKE: You know of the Rebellion against the Empire?

THREEPIO: That's how we came to be in your service, if you take my meaning, sir.

LUKE: Have you been in many battles?

THREEPIO: Several, I think. Actually, there's not much to tell. I'm not much more than an interpreter, and not very good at telling stories. Well, not at making them interesting, anyway.

Luke struggles to remove a small metal fragment from Artoo's neck joint. He uses a larger pick.

LUKE: Well, my little friend, you've got something jammed in here real good. Were you on a starcruiser or . . .

The fragment breaks loose with a snap, sending Luke tumbling head over heels. He sits up and sees a twelve-inch three-dimensional hologram of Leia Organa, the Rebel senator, being projected from the face of little Artoo. The image is a rainbow of colors as it flickers and jiggles in the dimly lit garage. Luke's mouth hangs open in awe.

LEIA: Help me, Obi-Wan Kenobi. You're my only hope.

LUKE: What's this?

Artoo looks around and sheepishly beeps an answer for Threepio to translate.

THREEPIO: What is what?!? He asked you a question . . . What is that?

Leia continues to repeat the sentence fragment over and over.

LEIA: Help me, Obi-Wan Kenobi. You're my only hope. Help me, Obi-Wan Kenobi. You're my only hope.

(CONT'D)

CONTINUED

Artoo whistles his surprise as he pretends to just notice the hologram. He looks around and sheepishly beeps an answer for Threepio to translate.

THREEPIO: Oh, he says it's nothing sir. Merely a malfunction. Old data. Pay it no mind.

Luke becomes intrigued by the beautiful young girl.

LUKE: Who is she? She's beautiful.

THREEPIO: I'm afraid I'm not quite sure, sir.

LEIA: Help me, Obi-Wan Kenobi. You're my only hope . . .

THREEPIO: I think she was a passenger on our last voyage. A person of some importance, sir — I believe. Our captain was attached to . . .

LUKE: Is there more to this recording?

Artoo lets out several squeaks.

THREEPIO: Behave yourself, Artoo. You're going to get us into trouble. It's all right, you can trust him. He's our new master.

Artoo whistles and beeps a long message to Threepio.

THREEPIO: He says that he's the property of Obi-Wan Kenobi, a resident of these parts. And it's a private message for him. Quite frankly, sir, I don't know what he's talking about. Our last master was Captain Antilles, but with all we've been through, this little R2 unit has become a bit eccentric.

LUKE: Obi-Wan Kenobi? I wonder if he means old Ben Kenobi?

THREEPIO: I beg your pardon, sir, but do you know what he's talking about?

LUKE: Well, I don't know anyone named Obi-Wan, but old Ben lives out beyond the dune sea. He's kind of a strange old hermit.

Luke gazes at the beautiful young princess for a few moments.

LUKE: I wonder who she is. It sounds like she's in trouble. I'd better play back the whole thing.

Artoo beeps something to Threepio.

THREEPIO: He says the restraining bolt has short-circuited his recording system. He suggests that if you remove the bolt, he might be able to play back the entire recording.

Luke has been looking longingly at the lovely, little princess and hasn't really heard what Threepio has been saying.

LUKE: H'm? Oh, yeah, well, I guess you're too small to run away on me if I take this off? Okay.

Luke takes a wedged bolt and pops the restraining bolt off Artoo's side.

LUKE: There you go.

The princess immediately disappears.

LUKE: Hey, wait a minute. Where'd she go? Bring her back! Play back the entire message.

Artoo beeps an innocent reply as Threepio sits up in embarrassment.

THREEPIO: What message. The one you've just been playing. The one you're carrying inside your rusty innards!

A woman's voice calls out from the other room.

AUNT BERU: Luke? Luke!

LUKE: All right, I'll be right there, Aunt Beru.

THREEPIO: I'm sorry, sir, but he appears to have picked up a slight flutter.

Luke gives Artoo's restraining bolt to Threepio.

(CONT'D)

CONTINUED

LUKE: Here, see what you can do with him. I'll be right back.

Luke hurries out of the room.

THREEPIO: *(to Artoo)* Just you reconsider playing that message for him.

Artoo beeps in response.

THREEPIO: No, I don't think he likes you at all.

Artoo beeps.

THREEPIO: No. I don't like you either.

INT. LARS HOMESTEAD – DINING AREA

Luke's Aunt Beru, a warm, motherly woman, fills a pitcher with blue fluid from a refrigerated container in the well-used kitchen. She puts the pitcher on a tray with some bowls of food in the dining area.
   Luke sits with his Uncle Owen and Aunt Beru before a table covered with bowls of food.

LUKE: You know, I think that R2 unit we bought might have been stolen.

OWEN: What makes you think that?

LUKE: Well, I stumbled across a recording while I was cleaning him. He says he belongs to someone called Obi-Wan Kenobi.

Owen is greatly alarmed at the mention of this name, but manages to control himself.

LUKE: I thought he might have meant old Ben. Do you know what he's talking about? Well, I wonder if he's related to Ben.

Owen breaks loose with a fit of uncontrolled anger.

OWEN: That wizard's just a crazy old man. Tomorrow I want you to take that R2 unit into Anchorhead and have its memory erased. That'll be the end of it. It belongs to us now.

LUKE: But what if this Obi-Wan comes looking for him?

OWEN: He won't. I don't think he exists anymore. He died about the same time as your father.

LUKE: He knew my father?

OWEN: I told you to forget it. Your only concern is to prepare those two new droids for tomorrow. In the morning I want them up there on the south ridge working on those condensers.

LUKE: Yes, sir. I think those new droids are going to work out fine. In fact, I, uh, was also thinking about our agreement, about me staying on another season. And if these new droids do work out, I want to transmit my application to the Academy this year.

Owen's face becomes a scowl, although he tries to suppress it.

OWEN: You mean the next semester before harvest?

LUKE: Sure. There's more than enough droids.

OWEN: Harvest is when I need you the most. It's only one season more. This year we'll make enough on the harvest that I'll be able to hire some more hands. And then you can go to the Academy next year. You must understand I need you here, Luke.

LUKE: But it's whole 'nother year.

OWEN: Look, it's only one more season.

Luke pushes his half-eaten plate of food aside and stands.

LUKE: Yeah, that's what you said last year when Biggs and Tank left.

AUNT BERU: Where are you going?

LUKE: It looks like I'm going nowhere. I have to go finish cleaning those droids.

(CONT'D)

0:24

CONTINUED

Resigned to his fate, Luke paddles out of the room.

AUNT BERU: Owen, he can't stay here for ever. Most of his friends have gone. It means so much to him.

OWEN: I'll make it up to him next year. I promise.

AUNT BERU: Luke's just not a farmer, Owen. He has too much of his father in him.

OWEN: That's what I'm afraid of.

EXT. TATOOINE – LARS HOMESTEAD

The giant twin suns of Tatooine slowly disappear behind a distant dune range. Luke stands watching them for a few moments, then reluctantly enters the domed entrance to the homestead.

INT. LARS HOMESTEAD – GARAGE

Luke enters the garage to discover the robots nowhere in sight. He takes a small control box from his utility belt similar to the one the Jawas were carrying. He activates the box, which creates a low buzz, and Threepio, letting out a short cry, pops up from behind the family landspeeder.

LUKE: What are you doing hiding back there?

Threepio stumbles forward, but Artoo is still nowhere in sight.

THREEPIO: It wasn't my fault, sir. Please don't deactivate me. I told him not to go, but he's faulty, malfunctioning; kept babbling on about his mission.

LUKE: Oh, no!

Luke races out of the garage followed by Threepio.

EXT. TATOOINE – LARS HOMESTEAD

Luke rushes out of the small domed entry to the homestead and searches the darkening horizon for the small tripod astro-robot. Threepio struggles out of the homestead and on the salt flat as Luke scans the landscape with his electrobinoculars.

THREEPIO: That R2 unit has always been a problem. These astro-droids are getting quite out of hand. Even I can't understand their logic at times.

LUKE: How could I be so stupid? He's nowhere in sight. Blast it!

THREEPIO: Pardon me, sir, but couldn't we go after him?

LUKE: It's too dangerous with all the Sand People around. We'll have to wait until morning.

Owen yells up from the homestead plaza.

OWEN: Luke, I'm shutting the power down.

LUKE: All right, I'll be there in a few minutes. Boy, am I gonna get it!

He takes one final look across the dim horizon.

LUKE: You know that little droid is going to cause me a lot of trouble.

THREEPIO: Oh, he excels at that, sir.

INT. LARS HOMESTEAD – PLAZA

Morning slowly creeps into the sparse but sparkling oasis of the open courtyard. The idyll is broken by the yelling of Uncle Owen, his voice echoing throughout the homestead.

OWEN: Luke? Luke? Luke?

INT. LARS HOMESTEAD – KITCHEN

The interior of the kitchen is a warm glow as Aunt Beru prepares the morning breakfast. Owen enters in a huff.

OWEN: Have you seen Luke this morning?

(CONT'D)

CONTINUED

AUNT BERU: He said he had some things to do before he started today, so he left early.

OWEN: Uh? Did he take those two new droids with him?

AUNT BERU: I think so.

OWEN: Well, he better have those units in the south range repaired by midday or there'll be hell to pay!

INT./EXT. LUKE'S SPEEDER – DESERT WASTELAND – TRAVELING – DAY

The rock and sand of the desert floor are a blur as Threepio pilots the sleek landspeeder gracefully across the vast wasteland.

LUKE: Look, there's a droid on the scanner. Dead ahead. Might be our little R2 unit. Hit the accelerator.

EXT. TATOOINE – ROCK MESA – DUNE SEA – COASTLINE – DAY

From high on a rock mesa, the tiny landspeeder can be seen gliding across the desert floor. Suddenly, in the foreground two weather-beaten Sand People shrouded in their grimy desert cloaks peer over the edge of the rock mesa. One of the marginally human creatures raises a long ominous laser rifle and points it at the speeder but the second creature grabs the gun before it can be fired.
The Sand People, or Tusken Raiders as they're sometimes called, speak in a coarse barbaric language as they get into an animated argument. The second Tusken Raider seems to get in the final word and the nomads scurry over the rocky terrain.

EXT. TATOOINE – ROCK MESA – CANYON

The Tusken Raiders approach two large banthas standing tied to a rock. The monstrous, bear-like creatures are as large as elephants, with huge red eyes, tremendous looped horns, and long, furry, dinosaur-like tails. The Tusken Raiders mount saddles strapped to the huge creatures' shaggy backs and ride off down the rugged bluff.

EXT. TATOOINE – ROCK CANYON – FLOOR

The speeder is parked on the floor of a massive canyon. Luke runs up to stand before little Artoo.

LUKE: Hey, whoa, just where do you think you're going?

The little droid whistles a feeble reply, as Threepio poses menacingly behind the little runaway.

THREEPIO: Master Luke is your rightful owner now. We'll have no more of this Obi-Wan Kenobi gibberish ... and don't talk to me of your mission, either. You're fortunate he doesn't blast you into a million pieces right here.

LUKE: No, it's all right but I think we better go.

Suddenly the little robot jumps to life with a mass of frantic whistles and screams.

LUKE: What's wrong with him now?

THREEPIO: There are several creatures approaching from the southeast.

Luke looks to the south, and fetches his long laser rifle from the landspeeder.

LUKE: Sand People! Or worse! Come on, let's go have a look. Come on.

EXT. TATOOINE – ROCK CANYON – RIDGE – DAY

Luke carefully makes his way to the top of a rock ridge and scans the canyon with his electrobinoculars.
He spots the two riderless banthas. Threepio struggles up behind the young adventurer.

LUKE: Well, there are two banthas down there but I don't see any ... wait a second, they're Sand People all right. I can see one of them now.

Luke watches the distant Tusken Raider through his electrobinoculars. Suddenly something huge moves in front of his field of view. Before Luke or Threepio can react, a large gruesome Tusken Raider looms over them. Threepio is startled and backs away, right off the side of the cliff. He can be heard for several moments as he clangs, bangs and rattles down the side of the mountain.
The towering creature brings down his curved, double-pointed gaderffii – the dreaded axe blade that has

(CONT'D)

CONTINUED

struck terror in the heart of the local settlers. But Luke manages to block the blow with his laser rifle, which is smashed to pieces. The terrified farm boy scrambles backward until he is forced to the edge of a deep crevice. The sinister Raider stands over him with his weapon raised and lets out a horrible shrieking laugh.

EXT. TATOOINE – ROCK CANYON FLOOR – DAY

Artoo forces himself into the shadows of a small alcove in the rocks as the vicious Sand People walk past carrying the inert Luke Skywalker, who is dropped in a heap before the speeder. The Sand People ransack the speeder, throwing parts and supplies in all directions. Suddenly, they stop. Then everything is quiet for a few moments. A great howling moan is heard echoing through the canyon which sends the Sand People fleeing in terror.

Artoo moves even tighter into the shadows as the slight swishing sound that frightened off the Sand People grows even closer, until a shabby old desert-rat-of-a-man appears and leans over Luke. His ancient leathery face, cracked and weathered by exotic climates is set off by dark, penetrating eyes and a scraggly white beard. Ben Kenobi squints his eyes as he scrutinizes the unconscious farm boy. Artoo makes a slight sound and Ben turns and looks right at him.

BEN: Hello there! Come here, my little friend. Don't be afraid.

Artoo begins to whistle and beep his concern about Luke. Luke begins to come around.

BEN: Oh, don't worry, he'll be all right. Rest easy, son, you've had a busy day. You're fortunate to be all in one piece.

LUKE: Ben? Ben Kenobi? Boy am I glad to see you!

BEN: The Jundland Wastes are not to be traveled lightly. Tell me, young Luke, what brings you out this far?

LUKE: Oh, this little droid! I think he's searching for his former master but I've never seen such devotion in a droid before ... Ah, he claims to be the property of an Obi-Wan Kenobi. Is he a relative of yours? Do you know who he's talking about?

Ben ponders this for a moment.

BEN: Obi-Wan Kenobi ... Obi-Wan? Now that's a name I've not heard in a long time ... a long time.

LUKE: I think my uncle knows him. He said he was dead ...

BEN: Oh, he's not dead, or ... not yet.

LUKE: You know him?

BEN: Well, of course I know him. He's me! I haven't gone by the name Obi-Wan since oh, before you were born.

LUKE: Well then, the droid does belong to you.

BEN: Don't seem to remember ever owning a droid. Very interesting ...

He suddenly looks up at the overhanging cliffs.

BEN: I think we better get indoors. The Sand People are easily startled but they will soon be back. And in greater numbers.

Luke gets up. Artoo lets out a pathetic beep causing Luke to remember something. He looks around.

LUKE: ... Threepio!

EXT. TATOOINE – SAND PIT – ROCK MESA – DAY

Luke and Ben stand over a very dented and tangled Threepio lying half-buried in the sand. One of his arms has broken off.

THREEPIO: Where am I? I must have taken a bad step ...

LUKE: Well, can you stand? We've got to get out of here before the Sand People return.

THREEPIO: I don't think I can make it. You go on Master Luke. There's no sense in you risking yourself on my account. I'm done for.

(CONT'D)

0:30

CONTINUED

Artoo makes a beeping sound.

LUKE: No, you're not. What kind of talk is that?

BEN: Quickly ... They're on the move.

Luke and Ben help the battered robot to his feet.

INT. KENOBI'S DWELLING

The small, spartan hovel is cluttered with desert junk but still manages to radiate an air of time-worn comfort and security. Luke is in one corner repairing Threepio's arm, as old Ben sits thinking.

LUKE: No, my father didn't fight in the wars. He was a navigator on a spice freighter.

BEN: That's what your uncle told you. He didn't hold with your father's ideals. Thought he should have stayed here and not gotten involved.

LUKE: You fought in the Clone Wars?

BEN: Yes. I was once a Jedi Knight the same as your father.

LUKE: I wish I'd known him.

BEN: He was the best star-pilot in the galaxy, and a cunning warrior. I understand you've become quite a good pilot yourself. And he was a good friend. Which reminds me ...

Ben gets up and goes to a chest where he rummages around as Luke finishes repairing Threepio.

BEN: I have something here for you. Your father wanted you to have this when you were old enough, but your uncle wouldn't allow it. He feared you might follow old Obi-Wan on some damned-fool idealistic crusade like your father did.

THREEPIO: Sir, if you'll not be needing me, I'll close down for a while.

LUKE: Sure, go ahead.

Ben shuffles up and presents Luke with a short handle with several electronic gadgets attached to it.

LUKE: What is it?

BEN: Your father's lightsaber. This is the weapon of a Jedi Knight. Not as clumsy or random as a blaster.

Luke pushes a button on the handle. A long beam shoots out about four feet and flickers there. The light plays across the ceiling.

BEN: An elegant weapon for a more civilized day. For over a thousand generations the Jedi Knights were the guardians of peace and justice in the Old Republic. Before the dark times, before the Empire.

Luke hasn't really been listening.

LUKE: How did my father die?

BEN: A young Jedi named Darth Vader, who was a pupil of mine until he turned to evil, helped the Empire hunt down and destroy the Jedi Knights. He betrayed and murdered your father. Now the Jedi are all but extinct. Vader was seduced by the dark side of the Force.

LUKE: The Force?

BEN: The Force is what gives the Jedi his power. It's an energy field created by all living things. It surrounds us and penetrates us. It binds the galaxy together.

Artoo makes beeping sounds.

BEN: Now, let's see if we can't figure out what you are, my little friend. And where you come from.

LUKE: I saw part of the message he was ...

Luke is cut short as the recorded image of the beautiful young Rebel princess is projected from Artoo's face.

BEN: I seem to have found it.

(CONT'D)

CONTINUED

The lovely girl's image flickers.

LEIA: General Kenobi, years ago you served my father in the Clone Wars. Now he begs you to help him in his struggle against the Empire. I regret that I am unable to present my father's request to you in person, but my ship has fallen under attack and I'm afraid my mission to bring you to Alderaan has failed. I have placed information vital to the survival of the Rebellion into the memory systems of this R2 unit. My father will know how to retrieve it. You must see this droid safely delivered to him on Alderaan. This is our most desperate hour. Help me, Obi-Wan Kenobi, you're my only hope.

There is a little static and the transmission is cut short. Old Ben leans back and scratches his beard. Luke has stars in his eyes.

BEN: You must learn the ways of the Force if you're to come with me to Alderaan.

LUKE: Alderaan? *(laughing)* I'm not going to Alderaan. I've got to get home. It's late, I'm in for it as it is.

BEN: I need your help, Luke. She needs your help. I'm getting too old for this sort of thing.

LUKE: I can't get involved! I've got work to do! It's not that I like the Empire! I hate it! But there's nothing I can do about it right now. It's such a long way from here.

BEN: That's your uncle talking.

LUKE: *(sighing)* Oh, boy, my uncle. How am I ever going to explain this?

BEN: Learn about the Force, Luke.

LUKE: Look, I can take you as far as Anchorhead. You can get a transport there to Mos Eisley or wherever you're going.

BEN: You must do what you feel is right, of course.

EXT. SPACE

An Imperial Star Destroyer heads towards the evil planet-like battle station: the Death Star!

INT. DEATH STAR – CONFERENCE ROOM

Imperial senators and generals sit around a black conference table. Imperial stormtroopers stand guard around the room. Commander Tagge, a young, slimy-looking general, is speaking.

TAGGE: Until this battle station is fully operational we are vulnerable. The Rebel Alliance is too well equipped. They're more dangerous than you realize.

The bitter Admiral Motti replies.

MOTTI: Dangerous to your starfleet, Commander; not to this battle station!

TAGGE: The Rebellion will continue to gain a support in the Imperial Senate as long as . . .

Suddenly all heads turn as Commander Tagge's speech is cut short and the Grand Moff Tarkin, governor of the Imperial outland regions, enters. He is followed by his powerful ally, the Sith Lord, Darth Vader. The thin, evil-looking governor takes his place at the head of the table. The Dark Lord stands behind him.

TARKIN: The Imperial Senate will no longer be of any concern to us. I have just received word that the Emperor has dissolved the council permanently. The last remnants of the Old Republic have been swept away.

TAGGE: That's impossible. How will the Emperor maintain control without the bureaucracy?

TARKIN: The regional governors now have direct control over their territories. Fear will keep the local systems in line. Fear of this battle station.

TAGGE: And what of the Rebellion? If the Rebels have obtained a complete technical readout of this station, it is possible, however unlikely, that they might find a weakness and exploit it.

VADER: The plans you refer to will soon be back in our hands.

MOTTI: Any attack made by the Rebels against this station would be a useless gesture, no matter what technical data they've obtained. This station is now the ultimate power in the universe. I suggest we use it!

(CONT'D)

CONTINUED

VADER: Don't be too proud of this technological terror you've constructed. The ability to destroy a planet is insignificant next to the power of the Force.

MOTTI: Don't try to frighten us with your sorcerer's ways, Lord Vader. Your sad devotion to that ancient religion has not helped you conjure up the stolen data tapes, or given you clairvoyance enough to find the Rebel's hidden fort . . .

Suddenly Motti chokes and starts to turn blue under Vader's spell.

VADER: I find your lack of faith disturbing.

TARKIN: Enough of this! Vader, release him!

VADER: As you wish.

TARKIN: This bickering is pointless. Lord Vader will provide us with the location of the Rebel fortress by the time this station is operational. We will then crush the Rebellion with one swift stroke.

EXT. TATOOINE — WASTELAND

Threepio, Artoo, Luke and Ben walk among the scattered bodies and rubble of what remains of the huge Jawa sandcrawler.

LUKE: It looks like the Sand People did this, all right. Look, there's gaffi sticks, bantha tracks. It's just . . . I never heard of them hitting anything this big before.

BEN: They didn't. But we are meant to think they did. These tracks are side by side. Sand People always ride single file to hide their numbers.

LUKE: These are the same Jawas that sold us Artoo and Threepio.

BEN: And these blast points, too accurate for Sand People. Only Imperial stormtroopers are so precise.

LUKE: But why would Imperial troops want to slaughter Jawas?

Luke looks back at the speeder where Artoo and Threepio are inspecting the dead Jawas, and puts two and two together.

LUKE: If they traced the robots here, they may have learned who they sold them to and that would lead them back home!

BEN: Wait, Luke! It's too dangerous!

Luke races off leaving Ben and the two robots alone with the burning sandcrawler.

EXT. TATOOINE — WASTELAND

Luke races across the flat landscape in his battered landspeeder.

EXT. TATOOINE — LARS HOMESTEAD

The speeder roars up to the homestead.
    Luke jumps out and runs to the smoking holes that were once his home. Debris is scattered everywhere and it looks as if a great battle has taken place.

LUKE: Uncle Owen! Aunt Beru! Uncle Owen!

Luke stumbles around in a daze looking for his aunt and uncle. Suddenly he comes upon their smouldering remains. He is stunned, and cannot speak. Hate replaces fear and a new resolve comes over him.

EXT. SPACE

Imperial TIE fighters race toward the Death Star.

INT. DEATH STAR — DETENTION CORRIDOR

Two stormtroopers open an electronic cell door and allow Darth Vader to enter. Princess Leia's face is filled with defiance.

VADER: And now, Your Highness, we will discuss the location of your hidden Rebel base.

(CONT'D)

CONTINUED

A black torture robot enters, giving off a steady beeping sound as it approaches Princess Leia and extends one of its mechanical arms bearing a large hypodermic needle. The door slides shut.

EXT. TATOOINE — WASTELAND

There is a large bonfire of Jawa bodies blazing in front of the sandcrawler as Ben and the robots finish burning the dead. Luke drives up in the speeder and walks over to Ben.

BEN: There's nothing you could have done, Luke, had you been there. You'd have been killed, too, and the droids would now be in the hands of the Empire.

LUKE: I want to come with you to Alderaan. There's nothing for me here now. I want to learn the ways of the Force and become a Jedi like my father.

EXT. TATOOINE — WASTELAND

The landspeeder with Luke, Artoo, Threepio, and Ben in it zooms across the desert. The speeder stops on a bluff overlooking the spaceport at Mos Eisley. It is a haphazard array of low, grey concrete structures and semi-domes. A harsh gale blows across the stark canyon floor. The four stand on the edge of the craggy bluff.

BEN: Mos Eisley Spaceport. You will never find a more wretched hive of scum and villainy. We must be cautious.

EXT. TATOOINE — MOS EISLEY — STREET

The speeder is stopped on a crowded street by several combat-hardened stormtroopers who look over the two robots. An Imperial trooper questions Luke.

TROOPER: How long have you had these droids?

LUKE: About three or four seasons.

BEN: They're up for sale if you want them.

TROOPER: Let me see your identification.

Ben speaks to the trooper in a very controlled voice.

BEN: You don't need to see his identification.

TROOPER: We don't need to see his identification.

BEN: These aren't the droids you're looking for.

TROOPER: These aren't the droids we're looking for.

BEN: He can go about his business.

TROOPER: You can go about your business.

BEN: *(to Luke)* Move along.

TROOPER: Move along. Move along.

EXT. TATOOINE — MOS EISLEY — STREET

The speeder pulls up in front of a rundown blockhouse cantina on the outskirts of the spaceport. A Jawa runs up and begins to fondle the speeder.

THREEPIO: I can't abide those Jawas. Disgusting creatures.

As Luke gets out of the speeder he tries to shoo the Jawa away.

LUKE: Go on, go on. I can't understand how we got by those troops. I thought we were dead.

BEN: The Force can have a strong influence on the weak-minded.

LUKE: Do you really think we're going to find a pilot here that'll take us to Alderaan?

BEN: Well, most of the best freighter pilots can be found here. Only watch your step. This place can be a little rough.

(CONT'D)

CONTINUED

LUKE: I'm ready for anything.

THREEPIO: Come along, Artoo.

INT. TATOOINE — MOS EISLEY — CANTINA

The young adventurer and his two mechanical servants follow Ben Kenobi into the smoke-filled cantina. The murky, moldy den is filled with a startling array of weird and exotic alien creatures and monsters at the long metallic bar. At first the sight is horrifying. One-eyed, thousand-eyed, slimy, furry, scaly, tentacled, and clawed creatures huddle over drinks. Ben moves to an empty spot at the bar. A huge, rough-looking Bartender calls out to Luke and points at the robots.

BARTENDER: Hey, we don't serve their kind here!

Luke, still recovering from the shock of seeing so many outlandish creatures, doesn't quite catch the bartender's drift.

LUKE: What?

BARTENDER: Your droids. They'll have to wait outside. We don't want them here.

LUKE: Listen, why don't you wait out by the speeder. We don't want any trouble.

Luke pats Threepio on the shoulder.

THREEPIO: I heartily agree with you sir.

Threepio and his stubby partner go outside and most of the creatures at the bar go back to their drinks.
    Luke is terrified but tries not to show it. He quietly sips his drink, looking over the crowd for a more sympathetic ear or whatever.
    Ben is standing next to Chewbacca, an eight-foot-tall savage-looking creature resembling a huge grey bushbaby monkey with fierce baboon-like fangs. His large blue eyes dominate a fur-covered face and soften his otherwise awesome appearance. Over his matted, furred body he wears two chrome bandoliers, and little else. He is a 200-year-old Wookiee and a sight to behold.
    A large-eyed creature gives Luke a rough shove.

CREATURE: Negola dewaghi wooldugger?!?

The hideous freak is obviously drunk. Luke tries to ignore the creature and turns back to his drink. A disfigured belligerent monstrosity.

HUMAN: He doesn't like you.

LUKE: I'm sorry.

The big creature is getting agitated and yells some unintelligible gibberish at the now rather nervous, young adventurer.

HUMAN: I don't like you either.

HUMAN: *(continuing)* You just watch yourself. We're wanted men. I have the death sentence on twelve systems.

LUKE: I'll be careful.

HUMAN: You'll be dead.

Old Ben moves in behind Luke.

BEN: This little one's not worth the effort. Come let me get you something.

A powerful throw from the unpleasant human sends the young would-be Jedi sailing across the room, crashing through tables. With a blood-curdling shriek the human draws a wicked chrome laser pistol from his belt and levels it at old Ben. The bartender panics.

BARTENDER: No blasters! No blasters!

With astounding agility old Ben's laser sword sparks to life and in a flash an arm lies on the floor. Ben carefully

(CONT'D)

CONTINUED

and precisely turns off his laser sword. Luke is totally amazed at the old man's abilities. The entire fight has lasted only a matter of seconds. The cantina goes back to normal as Ben helps Luke to his feet.

LUKE: I'm all right.

Ben nods to the Wookiee.

BEN: Chewbacca here is first mate on a ship that might suit us.

EXT. TATOOINE – MOS EISLEY – STREET

Threepio paces in front of the cantina as Artoo carries on an electronic conversation with another little red astro-droid. Someone last seen in the cantina approaches two stormtroopers in the street.

THREEPIO: I don't like the look of this.

INT. TATOOINE – MOS EISLEY – CANTINA

Strange creatures play exotic big band music on odd-looking instruments. Luke has followed Ben and Chewbacca to a booth where they are joined by Han Solo. Han is a tough, roguish starpilot about thirty years old. A mercenary on a starship, he is simple, sentimental, and cocksure.

HAN: Han Solo. I'm captain of the Millennium Falcon. Chewie here tells me you're looking for passage to the Alderaan system.

BEN: Yes, indeed. If it's a fast ship.

HAN: Fast ship? You've never heard of the Millennium Falcon?

BEN: Should I have?

HAN: It's the ship that made the Kessel run in less than twelve parsecs!

Ben reacts to Solo's stupid attempt to impress them with obvious misinformation.

HAN: *(continuing)* I've outrun Imperial starships, not the local bulk-cruises, mind you. I'm talking about the big Corellian ships now. She's fast enough for you, old man. What's the cargo?

BEN: Only passengers. Myself, the boy, two droids, and no questions asked.

HAN: What is it? Some kind of local trouble?

BEN: Let's just say we'd like to avoid any Imperial entanglements.

HAN: Well, that's the real trick, isn't it? And it's going to cost you something extra. Ten thousand, all in advance.

LUKE: Ten thousand? We could almost buy our own ship for that!

HAN: But who's going to fly it, kid! You?

LUKE: You bet I could. I'm not such a bad pilot myself! We don't have to sit here and listen . . .

BEN: We can pay you two thousand now, plus fifteen when we reach Alderaan.

HAN: Seventeen, huh!

Han ponders this for a few moments.

HAN: Okay. You guys got yourselves a ship. We'll leave as soon as you're ready. Docking Bay Ninety-four.

BEN: Ninety-four.

HAN: Looks like somebody's beginning to take an interest in your handiwork.

Ben and Luke turn around to see four Imperial stormtroopers looking at the dead bodies and asking the bartender some questions. The bartender points to the booth.

TROOPER: All right, we'll check it out.

The stormtroopers look over at the booth but Luke and Ben are gone.

(CONT'D)

0:47

CONTINUED

HAN: Seventeen thousand! Those guys must really be desperate. This could really save my neck. Get back to the ship and get her ready.

EXT. TATOOINE – MOS EISLEY – STREET

BEN: You'll have to sell your speeder.

LUKE: That's okay. I'm never coming back to this planet again.

INT. MOS EISLEY – CANTINA

As Han is about to leave, Greedo, a slimy green-faced alien with a short trunk-nose, pokes a gun in his chest. The creature speaks in a foreign tongue translated into English subtitles.

GREEDO: Going somewhere, Solo?

HAN: Yes, Greedo. As a matter of act, I was just going to see your boss. Tell Jabba that I've got his money.

Han sits down and the alien sits across from him holding the gun on him.

GREEDO: It's too late. You should have paid him when you had the chance. Jabba's put a price on your head so large every bounty hunter in the galaxy will be looking for you. I'm lucky I found you first.

HAN: Yeah, but this time I've got the money.

GREEDO: If you give it to me, I might forget I found you.

HAN: I don't have it with me. Tell Jabba . . .

GREEDO: Jabba's through with you. He has no time for smugglers who drop their shipments at the first sign of an Imperial cruiser.

HAN: Even I get boarded sometimes. Do you think I had a choice?

Han Solo reaches for his gun under the table.

GREEDO: You can tell that to Jabba. He may only take your ship.

HAN: Over my dead body.

GREEDO: That's the idea. I've been looking forward to this for a long time.

HAN: Yes, I'll bet you have.

Suddenly, the slimy alien disappears in a blinding flash of light. Han pulls his smoking gun from beneath the table as the other patrons look on in bemused amazement. Han gets up and starts out of the cantina, flipping the bartender some coins as he leaves.

HAN: Sorry about the mess.

EXT. SPACE

Two TIE fighters approach the Death Star.

INT. DEATH STAR – CONTROL ROOM

VADER: Her resistance to the mind probe is considerable. It will be some time before we can extract any information from her.

An Imperial Officer interrupts the meeting.

IMPERIAL OFFICER The final check-out is completed. All systems are operational. What course shall we set?

TARKIN: Perhaps she would respond to an alternative form of persuasion.

VADER: What do you mean?

TARKIN: I think it is time we demonstrated the full power of this station. *(to soldier)* Set your course for Alderaan.

IMPERIAL OFFICER With pleasure.

(CONT'D)

CONTINUED

EXT. TATOOINE – MOS EISLEY – STREET

Threepio is standing in a doorway.

THREEPIO: Lock the door, Artoo.

Heavily armed stormtroopers move menacingly along a narrow slum alleyway.

TROOPER: All right, check this side of the street. *(One of the troopers checks a tightly locked door.)* The door's locked? Move on to the next one.

The door opens. Threepio moves into the doorway.

THREEPIO: I would much rather have gone with Master Luke than stay here with you. I don't know what all this trouble is about, but I'm sure it must be your fault.

Artoo makes beeping sounds.

THREEPIO: You watch your language!

EXT. TATOOINE – MOS EISLEY – STREET – ALLEYWAY – USED SPEEDER LOT

Ben and Luke are standing in a sleazy used speeder lot, talking with a tall, grotesque, insect-like used speeder dealer. Strange exotic bodies and spindly-legged beasts pass by as the insect concludes the sale by giving Luke some coins.

LUKE: All right, give it to me, I'll take it. Look at this. Ever since the XP-38 came out, they just aren't in demand.

BEN: It will be enough.

Ben and Luke leave the speeder lot and walk down the dusty alleyway. A darkly clad creature moves out of the shadows as they pass and watches them as they disappear down another alley.

BEN: If the ship's as fast as he's boasting, we ought to do well.

EXT. DOCKING PORT ENTRY – ALLEYWAY

Chewbacca waits restlessly at the entrance to Docking Bay 94. Ben, Luke, and the robots make their way up the street. The darkly clad creature has followed them from the speeder lot. He stops in a nearby doorway and speaks into a small transmitter.

INT. MOS EISLEY SPACEPORT – DOCKING BAY 94

Chewbacca leads the group into the giant dirt pit that is Docking Bay 94. Resting in the middle of the huge hole is a large, round, beat-up, pieced-together hunk of junk that could only loosely be called a starship.

LUKE: What a piece of junk.

The tall figure of Han Solo comes down the boarding ramp.

HAN: She'll make point five past light-speed. She may not look like much, but she's got it where it counts, kid. I've made a lot of special modifications myself. But we're a little rushed, so if you'll just get on board we'll get out of here.

INT. MILLENNIUM FALCON

Chewbacca settles into the pilot's chair and starts the mighty engines of the starship.

INT. MOS EISLEY SPACE PORT – DOCKING BAY 94

Luke, Ben, Threepio, and Artoo move toward the Millennium Falcon passing Solo.

THREEPIO: Hello, sir.

EXT. TATOOINE – MOS EISLEY – STREET

Seven Imperial stormtroopers rush up to the darkly clad creature.

TROOPER: Which way?

(CONT'D)

CONTINUED

The darkly clad creature points to the door of the docking bay.

TROOPER: All right, men. Load your weapons!

INT. MOS EISLEY SPACEPORT – DOCKING BAY 94

The troops hold their guns at the ready and charge down the docking bay entrance.

TROOPER: Stop that ship!

Han Solo looks up and sees the Imperial stormtroopers rushing into the docking bay. Several of the troopers fire at Han as he ducks into the spaceship.

TROOPER: Blast 'em!

Han draws his laser pistol and pops off a couple of shots which force the stormtroopers to dive for safety. The pirateship engines whine as Han hits the release button that slams the overhead entry shut.

INT. MILLENNIUM FALCON

HAN: Chewie, get us out of here!

The group straps in for takeoff.

THREEPIO: Oh, my, I'd forgotten how much I hate space travel.

EXT. TATOOINE – MOS EISLEY – STREETS

The half-dozen stormtroopers at a checkpoint hear the general alarm and look to the sky as the huge starship rises above the dingy slum dwellings and quickly disappears into the morning sky.

INT. MILLENNIUM FALCON

Han sits in the pilot's chair, typing information into the ship's computer.

EXT. SPACE – PLANET TATOOINE

The starship climbs away from the planet.

INT. MILLENNIUM FALCON – CABIN

Chewbacca points out something on the radar scope.

HAN: Looks like an Imperial cruiser. Our passengers must be hotter than I thought. Try and hold them off. Angle the deflector shield while I make the calculations for the jump to light speed.

EXT. SPACE – PLANET TATOOINE

The Millennium Falcon pirateship races away from the yellow planet. It is followed by two huge Imperial Star Destroyers.

INT. MILLENNIUM FALCON – COCKPIT

Over the shoulders of Chewbacca and Han, we can see the galaxy spread before them. Luke and Ben make their way into the cramped cockpit where Han continues his calculation.

HAN: Stay sharp! There are two more coming in; they're going to try to cut us off.

LUKE: Why don't you outrun them? I thought you said this thing was fast.

HAN: Watch your mouth, kid, or you're going to find yourself floating home. We'll be safe enough once we make the jump to hyperspace. Besides, I know a few maneuvers. We'll lose them!

EXT. SPACE – PLANET TATOOINE

Imperial cruisers fire at the pirateship.

INT. MILLENNIUM FALCON – COCKPIT

The ship shudders as an explosion flashes outside the window.

HAN: Here's where the fun begins!

(CONT'D)

CONTINUED

BEN: How long before you can make the jump to light speed?

HAN: It'll take a few moments to get the coordinates from the navi-computer.

The ship begins to rock violently as lasers hit it.

LUKE: Are you kidding? At the rate they're gaining . . .

HAN: Traveling through hyperspace isn't like dusting crops, boy! Without precise calculations we could fly right through a star or bounce too close to a supernova and that'd end your trip real quick, wouldn't it?

The ship is now constantly battered with laserfire as a red warning light begins to flash.

LUKE: What's that flashing?

HAN: We're losing our deflector shield. Go strap yourselves in. I'm going to make the jump to light speed.

The galaxy brightens and they move faster, almost as if crashing a barrier. Stars become streaks as the pirateship makes the jump to hyperspace.

EXT. SPACE

The Millennium Falcon zooms into infinity in less than a second.

EXT. DEATH STAR

Alderaan looms behind the Death Star battle station.

INT. DEATH STAR – CONTROL ROOM – CORRIDOR

Governor Tarkin stands before the huge wall screen displaying a small green planet.
  Vader and two stormtroopers march Princess Leia towards the Control room.
  Admiral Motti reports to Governor Tarkin.

MOTTI: We've entered the Alderaan system.

Vader and two stormtroopers enter with Princess Leia. Her hands are bound.

LEIA: Governor Tarkin. I should have expected to find you holding Vader's leash. I recognized your foul stench when I was brought on board.

TARKIN: Charming to the last. You don't know how hard I found it signing the order to terminate your life!

LEIA: I'm surprised you had the courage to take the responsibility yourself!

TARKIN: Princess Leia, before your execution I would like you to be my guest at a ceremony that will make this battle station operational. No star system will dare oppose the Emperor now.

LEIA: The more you tighten your grip, Tarkin, the more star systems will slip through your fingers.

TARKIN: Not after we demonstrate the power of this station. In a way, you have determined the choice of the planet that'll be destroyed first. Since you are reluctant to provide us with the location of the Rebel base, I have chosen to test this station's destructive power . . . on your home planet of Alderaan.

LEIA: No! Alderaan is peaceful. We have no weapons. You can't possibly . . .

TARKIN: You would prefer another target? A military target? Then name the system!

Tarkin looks menacingly at Leia.

TARKIN: I grow tired of asking this. So it'll be the last time. Where is the Rebel base?

Leia sees Alderaan on the huge wall screen.

LEIA: (*softly*) Dantooine.

Leia lowers her head.

LEIA: They're on Dantooine.

(CONT'D)

CONTINUED

TARKIN: There. You see, Lord Vader, she can be reasonable. (*addressing Motti*) Continue with the operation. You may fire when ready.

LEIA: What?

TARKIN: You're far too trusting. Dantooine is too remote to make an effective demonstration. But don't worry. We will deal with your Rebel friends soon enough

LEIA: No!

INT. DEATH STAR – BLAST CHAMBER

DEATH STAR INTERCOM VOICE: Commence primary ignition.

A button is pressed which switches on a panel of lights. A hooded Imperial soldier reaches overhead and pulls a level. Another lever is pulled and a bank of lights on a panel and wall lights up. A huge beam of light emanates from within a cone-shaped area and converges into a single laser beam out toward Alderaan. The small green planet of Alderaan is blown into space dust.

INT. MILLENNIUM FALCON – CENTRAL HOLD AREA

Ben watches as Luke practices the lightsaber with a small 'seeker' robot. Ben suddenly turns away and sits down. He falters, seems almost faint.

LUKE: Are you all right? What's wrong?

BEN: I felt a great disturbance in the Force ... as if millions of voices suddenly cried out in terror and were suddenly silenced. I fear something terrible has happened.

Ben rubs his forehead. He seems to drift into a trance. Then he fixes his gaze on Luke.

BEN: You'd better get on with your exercises.

Han Solo enters the room.

HAN: Well, you can forget your troubles with those Imperial slugs. I told you I'd outrun 'em.

Luke is once again practicing with the lightsaber.

HAN: Don't everybody thank me at once.

Threepio watches Chewbacca and Artoo who are engrossed in a game in which three-dimensional holographic figures move along a chess-type board.

HAN: Anyway, we should be at Alderaan at about oh-two-hundred hours.

Chewbacca and the two robots sit around the lighted table covered with small holographic monsters. Each side of the table has a small computer monitor embedded in it. Chewbacca seems very pleased with himself.

THREEPIO: Now be careful, Artoo.

Artoo immediately reaches up and taps the computer with his stubby claw hand, causing one of the holographic creatures to walk to the new square. A sudden frown crosses Chewbacca's face and he begins yelling at the tiny robot. Threepio intercedes on behalf of his small companion and begins to argue with the huge Wookiee.

THREEPIO: He made a fair move. Screaming about it can't help you.

HAN: (*interrupting*) Let him have it. It's not wise to upset a Wookiee.

THREEPIO: But sir, nobody worries about upsetting a droid.

HAN: That's because a droid don't pull people's arms out of their sockets when they lose. Wookiees are known to do that.

THREEPIO: I see your point, sir. I suggest a new strategy, Artoo. Let the Wookiee win.

Luke stands in the middle of the small hold area: he seems frozen in place. A humming lightsaber is held out in front of him. Ben watches him from the corner, studying his movements.

BEN: Remember, a Jedi can feel the Force flowing through him.

(CONT'D)

CONTINUED

LUKE: You mean it controls your actions?

BEN: Partially. But it also obeys your commands.

Suspended at eye level, about ten feet in front of Luke, a "seeker", a chrome baseball-like robot covered with antennae, hovers slowly in a wide arc. The ball floats to one side of the youth then to the other. Suddenly it makes a lightning-swift lunge, emitting a blood red laser beam as it attacks. It hits Luke in the leg. Han lets loose with a burst of laughter.

HAN: *(laughing)* Hokey religions and ancient weapons are no match for a good blaster at your side, kid.

LUKE: You don't believe in the Force, do you?

HAN: Kid, I've flown from one side of this galaxy to the other. I've seen a lot of strange stuff, but I've never seen anything to make me believe there's one all-powerful force controlling everything. There's no mystical energy field that controls my destiny.

Ben smiles quietly.

HAN: It's all a lot of simple tricks and nonsense.

BEN: I suggest you try it again, Luke. This time, let go your conscious self and act on instinct.

Ben places a large helmet on Luke's head which covers his eyes.

LUKE: *(laughing)* With the blast shield down, I can't even see. How am I supposed to fight?

BEN: Your eyes can deceive you. Don't trust them.

The ball shoots straight up in the air. Luke swings the lightsaber around blindly missing the seeker, which fires off a laserbolt which hits Luke.

BEN: Stretch out with your feelings.

Luke stands in one place, seemingly frozen. The seeker fires at Luke and, incredibly, he manages to deflect the bolts. The ball ceases firing and moves back to its original position.

BEN: You see, you can do it.

HAN: I call it luck.

BEN: In my experience, there is no such thing as luck.

HAN: Look, good against remotes is one thing. Good against the living? That's something else.

Solo notes a small light flashing on the far side of the control panel.

HAN: Looks like we're coming up on Alderaan.

Han and Chewbacca head back to the cockpit.

LUKE: You know, I did feel something. I could almost see the remote.

BEN: That's good. You have taken your first step into a larger world.

INT. DEATH STAR – CONFERENCE ROOM

Imperial Officer Cass enters to stand before Governor Tarkin and the evil Dark Lord Darth Vader.

TARKIN: Yes.

OFFICER CASS: Our scout ships have reached Dantooine. They found the remains of a Rebel base, but they estimate that it has been deserted for some time. They are now conducting an extensive search of the surrounding systems.

TARKIN: She lied! She lied to us!

VADER: I told you she would never consciously betray the Rebellion.

TARKIN: Terminate her ... immediately!

(CONT'D)

CONTINUED

EXT. HYPERSPACE

The pirateship is just coming out of hyperspace: a strange surreal light show surrounds the ship.

INT. MILLENNIUM FALCON – COCKPIT

HAN: Stand by, Chewie, here we go. Cut in the sub-light engines.

Han pulls back on a control lever. Outside the cockpit window stars begin streaking past, seem to decrease in speed, then stop. Suddenly the starship begins to shudder and violently shake about. Asteroids begin to race toward them, battering the sides of the ship.

HAN: What the ... ? Aw, we've come out of hyperspace into a meteor shower. Some kind of asteroid collision. It's not on any of the charts.

The giant Wookiee flips off several controls and seems very cool in the emergency. Luke makes his way into the bouncing cockpit, followed by Ben.

LUKE: What's going on?

HAN: Our position is correct, except ... no Alderaan!

LUKE: What do you mean? Where is it?

HAN: That's what I'm trying to tell you, kid. It ain't there. It's been totally blown away.

LUKE: What? How?

The ship begins to settle down.

BEN: Destroyed ... by the Empire!

HAN: The entire starfleet couldn't destroy the whole planet. It'd take a thousand ships with more fire power than I've ...

A muffled alarm starts sounding on the control panel.

HAN: There's another ship coming in.

LUKE: Maybe they know what happened.

BEN: It's an Imperial fighter.

A huge explosion bursts outside the cockpit window, shaking the ship violently. A tiny, finned Imperial TIE fighter races past the cockpit window.

LUKE: It followed us!

BEN: No. It's a short-range fighter.

HAN: There aren't any bases around here. Where did it come from?

EXT. SPACE

The fighter races past the Corellian pirateship.

INT. MILLENNIUM FALCON – COCKPIT

LUKE: It sure is leaving in a big hurry. If they identify us, we're in big trouble.

HAN: Not if I can help it. Chewie ... jam its transmissions.

BEN: It'd be as well to let it go. It's too far out of range.

HAN: Not for long ...

EXT. SPACE

The pirateship zooms over the camera and away into the vastness of space after the Imperial TIE fighter.

INT. MILLENNIUM FALCON – COCKPIT

(CONT'D)

CONTINUED

The tension mounts as the pirateship gains on the tiny fighter. Ben stands behind Han.

BEN: A fighter that size couldn't get this deep into space on its own.

LUKE: Then me must have gotten lost, been part of a convoy, or something . . .

HAN: Well, he ain't going to be around long enough to tell anybody about us.

EXT. SPACE

The TIE fighter is losing ground to the larger pirateship as they race toward camera and disappear overhead.

INT. MILLENNIUM FALCON – COCKPIT

A distant star can now be distinguished as a small moon or planet.

LUKE: Look at him. He's heading for that small moon.

HAN: I think I can get him before he gets there . . . he's almost in range.

BEN: That's no moon! It's a space station.

HAN: It's too big to be a space station.

LUKE: I have a very bad feeling about this.

BEN: Turn the ship around!

HAN: Yeah. I think you're right. Full reverse! Chewie, lock in the auxiliary power.

The pirateship shudders and the TIE fighter accelerates away toward the gargantuan battle station.

HAN: Chewie, lock in the auxiliary power.

LUKE: Why are we still moving towards it?

HAN: We're caught in a tractor beam! It's pulling us in.

LUKE: There's gotta be something you can do!

HAN: There's nothin' I can do about it, kid. I'm full power. I'm going to have to shut down. But they're not going to get me without a fight!

BEN: You can't win. But there are alternatives to fighting.

INT. MILLENNIUM FALCON – DEATH STAR

As the battered starship is towed closer to the awesome metal moon, the immense size of the massive battle station becomes staggering. Running along the equator of the gigantic sphere is a mile-high band of huge docking ports into which the helpless pirateship is dragged.

INT. DEATH STAR – HUGE PORT DOORS

The helpless Millennium Falcon is pulled past a docking port control room and huge laser turret cannons.

VOICE OVER DEATH STAR INTERCOM: Clear Bay three-twenty-seven. We are opening the magnetic field.

INT. DEATH STAR – DOCKING BAY 2307

As the pirateship is pulled in through port doors of the Death Star, stormtroopers stand at attention in a central assembly area.

OFFICER: To your stations!

OFFICER: *(To another officer)* Come with me.

INT. DEATH STAR – HALLWAY

Stormtroopers run to their posts.

INT. DEATH STAR – HANGAR 2307

(CONT'D)

CONTINUED

A line of stormtroopers marches toward the pirateship, which has come to rest in a huge hangar, in readiness to board it, while other troopers stand with weapons ready to fire.

OFFICER: Close all outboard shields! Close all outboard shields!

INT. DEATH STAR – CONFERENCE ROOM

Tarkin responds to intercom buzz and pushes a button.

TARKIN: Yes.

VOICE: *(over intercom)* We've captured a freighter entering the remains of the Alderaan system. Its markings match those of a ship that blasted its way out of Mos Eisley.

VADER: They must be trying to return the stolen plans to the princess. She may yet be of some use to us.

INT. DEATH STAR – DOCKING BAY 2307

Vader and a commander approach the troops as an Officer and several heavily armed troops exit the spacecraft.

VOICE: *(over intercom)* Unlock one, five, seven and nine. Release charges.

OFFICER: *(to Vader)* There's no one on board sir. According to the log, the crew abandoned ship right after takeoff. It must be a decoy, sir. Several of the escape pods have been jettisoned.

VADER: Did you find any droids?'

OFFICER: No, sir. If there were any on board, they must also have been jettisoned.

VADER: Send a scanning crew aboard. I want every part of the this ship checked.

OFFICER: Yes, sir.

VADER: I sense something ... a presence I've not felt since ...

Vader turns quickly and exits the hangar.

OFFICER: Get me a scanning crew in here on the double. I want every part of this ship checked!

INT. MILLENNIUM FALCON – HALLWAY

A trooper strides through the hallway heading for the exit. In a few moments all is quiet. The muffled sounds of a distant officer giving orders finally fade. Two floor panels suddenly pop up revealing Han Solo and Luke. Ben Kenobi sticks his head out of a third locker.

LUKE: Boy, it's lucky you had these compartments.

HAN: I use them for smuggling. I never thought I'd be smuggling myself in them. This is ridiculous. Even if I could take off. I'd never get past the tractor beam.

BEN: Leave that to me!

HAN: Damn fool. I knew that you were going to say that!

BEN: Who's the more foolish ... the fool or the fool who follows him?

Han sighs. Chewbacca agrees.

INT. DEATH STAR – MAIN FORWARD BAY

Two crewmen bring a heavy box towards the ship.

TROOPER: The ship's all yours. If the scanners pick up anything, report it immediately. All right, let's go.

The crewmen enter the pirateship and a loud crashing sound is followed by a voice calling to the guard below.

HAN'S VOICE: Hey down there! Could you give us a hand with this?

The two stormtroopers guarding either side of the ramp enter the ship and a quick round of gunfire is heard.

INT. DEATH STAR – FORWARD BAY – COMMAND OFFICE

(CONT'D)

CONTINUED

In a very small command office near the entrance to the pirateship, a gantry officer looks out his window and notices the guards are missing. He speaks into the comlink.

GANTRY OFFICER: TK-four-two-one. Why aren't you at your post? TK-four-two-one, do you copy?

A stormtrooper comes down the ramp of the pirateship and waves to the gantry officer, pointing to his ear, indicating his comlink is not working. The gantry officer heads for the door, giving his aide instructions.

GANTRY OFFICER: Take over. We've got a bad transmitter. I'll see what I can do.

As the officer approaches the door, it slides open revealing the towering Chewbacca. The gantry officer, in a momentary state of shock, fails to react. With a bone-chilling howl, the giant Wookiee flattens the officer with one blow. The aide immediately reaches for his pistol, but is blasted by Han, dressed as an Imperial stormtrooper.

 Ben and the robots enter the room quickly, followed by Luke, also dressed as a stormtrooper. Luke quickly removes his helmet.

LUKE: You know, between his howling and your blasting everything in sight, it's a wonder the whole station doesn't know we're here.

HAN: Bring them on! I prefer a straight fight to all this sneaking around.

THREEPIO: We found the computer outlet, sir.

BEN: Plug in. He should be able to interpret the entire Imperial network.

Artoo punches his claw arm into the computer socket and the vast Imperial brain network comes to life, feeding information to the little robot. After a few moments, he beeps something.

THREEPIO: He says he's found the main controls to the power beam that's holding the ship here. He'll try to make the precise location appear on the monitor.

The computer monitor flashes readouts.

THREEPIO: The tractor beam is coupled to the main reactor in seven locations. A power loss at one of the terminals will allow the ship to leave.

Ben studies the data on the monitor readout.

BEN: I don't think you boys can help. I must go alone.

HAN: Whatever you say. I've done more than I bargained for on this trip already.

LUKE: I want to go with you.

BEN: Be patient, Luke. Stay and watch over the droids.

LUKE: But he can —

BEN: They must be delivered safely or other star systems will suffer the same fate as Alderaan. Your destiny lies along a different path from mine. The Force will be with you ... always!

Ben steps out of the command office, then disappears down a long grey hallway. Chewbacca barks a comment and Han agrees.

HAN: Boy, you said it, Chewie.

Han looks at Luke.

HAN: Where did you dig up that old fossil?

LUKE: Ben is a great man.

HAN: Yeah, great at getting us into trouble.

LUKE: I didn't hear you give any ideas ...

HAN: Well, anything's better than just hanging around waiting for them to pick us up ...

LUKE: Who do you think ...

(CONT'D)

CONTINUED

Suddenly Artoo begins to whistle and beep a blue streak. Luke goes over to him.

LUKE: What is it?

THREEPIO: I'm afraid I'm not quite sure, sir. He says 'I found her', and keeps repeating 'She's here.'

LUKE: Well, who … who has he found?

THREEPIO: Princess Leia.

LUKE: The princess? She's here?

HAN: Princess?

LUKE: Where … where is she?

HAN: Princess? What's going on?

THREEPIO: Level five, Detention block AA-twenty-three. I'm afraid she's scheduled to be terminated.

LUKE: Oh, no! We've got to do something.

HAN: What are you talking about?

LUKE: The droids belonged to her. She's the one in the message. We've got to help her.

HAN: Now, look, don't get any funny ideas. The old man wants us to wait right here.

LUKE: But he didn't know she was here. Look, will you just find a way back into that detention block?

HAN: I'm not going anywhere.

LUKE: They're going to execute her. Look, a few minutes ago you said you didn't want to just wait here to be captured. Now all you want to do is stay.

HAN: Marching into the detention area is not what I had in mind.

LUKE: But they're going to kill her!

HAN: Better her than me.

LUKE: She's rich.

Chewbacca growls.

HAN: Rich?

LUKE: Rich, powerful! Listen, if you were to rescue her, the reward would be …

HAN: What?

LUKE: Well, more wealth than you can imagine.

HAN: I don't know, I can imagine quite a bit!

LUKE: You'll get it!

HAN: I'd better!

LUKE: You will …

HAN: All right, kid. But you'd better be right about this!

LUKE: All right.

HAN: What's your plan?

LUKE: Uh … Threepio, hand me those binders there will you? Okay.

Luke moves toward Chewbacca with electronic cuffs.

LUKE: Now, I'm going to put these on you.

Chewie lets out a hideous growl. Luke sheepishly hands the binders to Han.

(CONT'D)

CONTINUED

LUKE: Okay, Han, you, you put those on.

HAN: Don't worry, Chewie. I think I know what he has in mind.

Han binds the Wookiee with electronic cuffs.

THREEPIO: Er, Master Luke, sir! Pardon me for asking ... but ... what should Artoo and I do if we're discovered here?

LUKE: Lock the door!

HAN: And hope they don't have blasters.

THREEPIO: That isn't very reassuring.

INT. DEATH STAR – DETENTION AREA

Luke and Han start off into the giant Imperial Death Star in their armored stormtrooper helmets. They try to look inconspicuous in their armored suits as they wait for a vacuum elevator to arrive. Troops, bureaucrats, and robots bustle about, ignoring the trio completely. Only a few give the giant Wookiee a curious glance.
Finally a small elevator arrives and the trio enters.

LUKE: I can't see a thing in this helmet.

A bureaucrat races to get aboard also, but is signaled away by Han. The door to the pod-like vehicle slides closed and the elevator car takes off through a vacuum tube.

INT. DEATH STAR – MAIN HALLWAY

Several stormtroopers walk through the wide main passageway. At the far end of the hallway, a passing flash of Ben Kenobi appears, then disappears down a small hallway. Darth Vader appears menacingly in the hallway but Ben seems to have escaped notice.

INT. DEATH STAR – INT. ELEVATOR – DETENTION SECURITY AREA

Han whispers to Luke under his breath.

HAN: This is not going to work.

LUKE: Why didn't you say so before?

HAN: I did say so before!

INT. DETENTION AREA

Elevator doors open. A tall, grim-looking officer approaches the trio.

OFFICER: Where are you taking this ... thing?

Chewie growls a bit at the remark but Han nudges him to shut up.

LUKE: Prisoner transfer from Cell Block one-one-three-eight.

OFFICER: I wasn't notified. I'll have to clear it.

The officer waves two troopers forward and goes back to his console to punch in the information. Han has unfastened one of Chewbacca's electronic cuffs.
Suddenly Chewbacca knocks one of the troopers aside and lets out with one of his ear-piercing howls. He grabs Han's laser rifle.

HAN: Look out! He's loose!

LUKE: He's going to pull us apart!

HAN: Go get him!

The startled guards are momentarily dumbfounded. Luke and Han have already pulled out their laser pistols and are blasting away at the camera eyes, laser gate controls, and the Imperial guards. Han rushes to the comlink system. He quickly checks the computer readout.

(CONT'D)

CONTINUED

HAN: We've got to find out which cell this princess of yours is in. Here it is ... twenty-one-eighty-seven. You go and get her. I'll hold them here.

Luke races down one of the cell corridors. Han speaks into the beeping comlink.

HAN: *(sounding official)* Everything's under control. Situation normal.

INTERCOM VOICE: What happened?

HAN: *(getting nervous)* Uh ... had a slight weapons malfunction. But, uh, everything's perfectly all right now. We're fine. We're all fine here, now, thank you. How are you?

INTERCOM VOICE: We're sending a squad up.

HAN: Uh, uh, negative, negative. We have a reactor leak here now. Give us a few minutes to lock it down. Large leak ... very dangerous.

INTERCOM VOICE: Who is this? What's your operating number?

Han blasts the comlink and it explodes.

HAN: Boring conversation anyway. *(yelling down the hallway)* Luke! We're going to have company.

INT. DEATH STAR – CELL ROW

Luke stops in front of one of the cells and opens the door. Inside, Luke sees the dazzling young princess-senator. She had been sleeping and is now looking at him with an uncomprehending look on her face. Luke is stunned by her incredible beauty and stands staring at her.

LEIA: *(finally)* Aren't you a little short for a stormtrooper?

LUKE: Huh? Oh ... the uniform. *(taking off his helmet)* I'm Luke Skywalker. I'm here to rescue you.

LEIA: You're who?

LUKE: I'm here to rescue you. I've got your R2 unit. I'm here with Ben Kenobi.

LEIA: Ben Kenobi! Where is he?

LUKE: Come on!

INT. DEATH STAR – CONFERENCE ROOM

Darth Vader stands addressing Governor Tarkin, who sits at the far end of the conference table.

VADER: He is here ...

TARKIN: Obi-Wan Kenobi! What makes you think so?

VADER: A tremor in the Force. The last time I felt it was in the presence of my old Master.

TARKIN: Surely he must be dead by now.

VADER: Don't underestimate the Force.

TARKIN: The Jedi are extinct, their fire has gone out of the universe. You, my friend, are all that's left of their religion.

There has been quiet buzz on the comlink.

TARKIN: Yes.

INTERCOM VOICE: We have an emergency alert in detention block AA-twenty-three.

TARKIN: The princess! Put all sections on alert!

VADER: Obi-Wan is here. The Force is with him.

TARKIN: If you're right, he must not be allowed to escape.

VADER: Escape is not his plan. I must face him alone.

(CONT'D)

CONTINUED

INT. DEATH STAR – MAIN HALLWAY

Ben Kenobi continues to evade detection.

INT. DEATH STAR – DETENTION AREA HALLWAY

An ominous buzzing sound is heard on the other side of the elevator door. Chewbacca responds with a growling noise.

HAN: Get behind me! Get behind me!

An explosion knocks a hole in the elevator door through which several Imperial troops begin to emerge.
   Han and Chewie fire their laser pistols at them through the smoke and flames. They turn and run down the cell hallway.

TROOPER: Off to your left. They went down in the cell bay.

Han and Chewie meet up with Luke and Leia.

HAN: Can't get out that way.

LEIA: Looks like you managed to cut off our only escape route.

HAN: *(sarcastically)* Maybe you'd like it back in your cell, Your Highness.

Luke takes a small comlink transmitter from his belt as they continue to exchange fire with stormtroopers making their way down the corridor.

LUKE: See-Threepio! See-Threepio!

THREEPIO: *(over comlink)* Yes sir?

LUKE: Are there any other ways out of the cell bay? ... We've been cut off! What was that? I didn't copy!

INT. DEATH STAR – MAIN BAY GANTRY – CONTROL TOWER

Threepio paces the control center in the company of little Artoo. Threepio talks into the small comlink transmitter.

THREEPIO: I said, all systems have been alerted to your presence, sir. The main entrance seems to be the only way in or out; all other information on your level is restricted.

Someone begins banging on the door.

TROOPER VOICE: Open up in there! Open up in there!

THREEPIO: Oh, no!

INT. DEATH STAR – DETENTION CORRIDOR

Luke and Leia crouch together in an alcove for protection as they continue to exchange fire with troops. Han and Chewbacca are barely able to keep the stormtroopers at bay at the far end of the hallway. The laserfire is very intense, and smoke fills the narrow cell corridor.

LUKE: There isn't any other way out.

HAN: I can't hold them off for ever! Now what?

LEIA: This is some rescue. When you came in here, didn't you have a plan for getting out?

HAN: *(indicating Luke)* He's the brains, sweetheart.

Luke looks sheepish and shrugs.

LUKE: Well, I didn't . . .

The princess grabs Luke's gun and fires at a small grate in the wall next to Han, almost frying him.

HAN: What the hell are you doing?

LEIA: Somebody has to save our skins. Into the garbage chute, fly boy.

(CONT'D)

CONTINUED

She tosses Luke's gun back to him and jumps through the narrow opening as Han and Chewbacca look on in amazement. Chewbacca sniffs the garbage chute and says something.

HAN: Get in there! Get in there you big furry oaf! I don't care what you smell! Get in there and don't worry about it.

Han gives him a big kick and the Wookiee disappears into the tiny opening. Luke and Han continue firing as they work their way toward the opening.

HAN: Wonderful girl! Either I'm going to kill her or I'm beginning to like her. Get in there!

Luke ducks laserfire as he jumps into the darkness. Han fires off a couple of quick blasts creating a smoky cover, then dives into the chute himself and is gone.

INT. DEATH STAR – GARBAGE ROOM

Han tumbles into a large room filled with garbage and muck. Chewbacca finds a small hatchway and struggles to get it open. It won't budge.

HAN: *(sarcastically)* The garbage chute was a really wonderful idea. What an incredible smell you've discovered! Let's get out of here! Get away from there . . .

LUKE: No! Wait!

Han draws his laser pistol and fires at the hatch. The laserbolt ricochets wildly around the small metal room. Everyone dives for cover in the garbage as the bolt explodes almost on top of them. Leia climbs out of the garbage with a rather grim look on her face.

LUKE: Will you forget it? It already tried it. It's magnetically sealed.

LEIA: Put that thing away! You're going to get us all killed.

HAN: Absolutely, Your Worship. Look, I had everything under control until you led us down here. You know, it's not going to take them long to figure out what happened to us.

LEIA: It could be worse.

A loud horrible, inhuman moan works its way up from the murky depths. Chewbacca begins to back away. Han and Luke stand fast with their laser pistols drawn. The Wookiee is cowering near one of the walls.

HAN: It's worse.

LUKE: There's something alive in here!

HAN: That's your imagination.

LUKE: Something just moved past my leg! Look! Did you see that?

HAN: What?

Suddenly Luke is yanked under the garbage.

HAN: Kid! Luke! Luke! Luke!

Solo tries to get to Luke. Luke surfaces with a gasp of air and thrashing of limbs. A membrane tentacle is wrapped around his throat.

LEIA: Luke!

Leia extends a long pipe toward him.

LEIA: Luke, Luke, grab hold of this.

LUKE: Blast it, will you! My gun's jammed.

HAN: Where?

LUKE: Anywhere! Oh!!

Solo fires his gun downward. Luke is pulled back into the muck by the slimy tentacle.

(CONT'D)

CONTINUED

HAN: Luke! Luke!

Suddenly the walls of the garbage receptacle shudder. Then everything is deathly quiet. Han and Leia give each other a worried look. With a rush of bubbles and muck Luke suddenly bobs to the surface.

LEIA: Help him!

Luke seems to be released by the thing.

LEIA: What happened?

LUKE: I don't know, it let go of me and disappeared . . .

HAN: I got a bad feeling about this.

Before anyone can say anything the walls begin to rumble and edge toward the Rebels.

LUKE: The walls are moving!

LEIA: Don't just stand there. Try and brace it with something. Help me!

They place poles and long metal beams between the closing walls, but they are simply snapped and bent as the giant trashmasher rumbles on. The situation doesn't look too good.

LUKE: Wait a minute!

Luke pulls out his comlink.

LUKE: Threepio, Come in, Threepio! Threepio! Where could he be?

INT. DEATH STAR – MAIN GANTRY – COMMAND OFFICE

The muted voice of Luke calling out to See-Threepio can be heard on Threepio's hand comlink, which is sitting on the deserted computer console. Artoo and Threepio are nowhere in sight. Suddenly there is a great explosion and the door of the control tower opens. Armed stormtroopers enter the chamber.

FIRST TROOPER: Take over! *(indicating a dead officer)* See to him! Look, there!

A trooper pushes a button and the supply cabinet slides open. See-Threepio and Artoo are inside. See-Threepio comes out into the office.

THREEPIO: They're madmen! They're heading for the prison level. If you hurry, you might catch them.

FIRST OFFICER: *(to his troops)* Follow me! You stand guard.

The troops hustle off down the hallway, leaving a guard to watch over the command office.

THREEPIO: *(to Artoo)* Come on!

The guard aims a blaster at them.

THREEPIO: Oh! All this excitement has overrun the circuits in my counterpart here. If you don't mind, I'd like to take him down to maintenance.

TROOPER: All right.

The guard nods and Threepio, with little Artoo in tow, hurries out the door.

INT. DEATH STAR – GARBAGE ROOM

As the walls rumble closer, the room gets smaller and smaller. Chewie is whining and trying to hold a wall back with his giant paws. Han and Leia are trying to brace the contracting walls with a pole. Leia begins to sink into the trash. Garbage is snapping and popping. Luke is trying to reach Threepio.

LUKE: Threepio! Come in, Threepio! Threepio!

HAN: Get to the top!

LEIA: I can't.

LUKE: Where could he be? Threepio! Threepio, will you come in?

(CONT'D)

CONTINUED

INT. DEATH STAR – MAIN FORWARD BAY – SERVICE PANEL

THREEPIO: They aren't here! Something must have happened to them. See if they've been captured.

Little Artoo carefully plugs his claw arm into a new wall socket and a complex array of electronic sounds spew from the tiny robot.

THREEPIO: Hurry!

INT. DEATH STAR – GARBAGE ROOM

The walls are only feet apart.

HAN: One thing's for sure. We're all going to be a lot thinner! *(to Leia)* Get on top of it!

LEIA: I'm trying!

INT. DEATH STAR – MAIN FORWARD BAY – SERVICE PANEL

THREEPIO: *(to Artoo)* Thank goodness, they haven't found them! Where could they be?

Artoo frantically beeps something to See-Threepio.

THREEPIO: Use the comlink? Oh, my! I forgot ... I turned it off!

Meanwhile, Luke is lying on his side, trying to keep his head above the rising ooze.

INT. DEATH STAR – MAIN FORWARD BAY – SERVICE PANEL

THREEPIO: Are you there, sir?

INT. DEATH STAR – GARBAGE ROOM

LUKE: Threepio!

INT. DEATH STAR – MAIN FORWARD BAY

THREEPIO: We've had some problems ...

LUKE: *(over comlink)* Will you shut up and listen to me. Shut down all the garbage mashers on the detention level, will you? Do you copy? Shut down all the garbage mashers on the detention level.

INT. DEATH STAR – MAIN FORWARD BAY – SERVICE PANEL

LUKE: *(over comlink)* Shut down all the garbage mashers on the detention level.

THREEPIO: *(to Artoo)* No. Shut them all down! Hurry!

Threepio hears the incredible screaming and hollering from Luke's comlink.

THREEPIO: Listen to them! They're dying, Artoo! Curse my metal body! I wasn't fast enough. It's all my fault! My poor master!

LUKE: *(over comlink, faintly)* Threepio, we're all right!

INT. DEATH STAR – GARBAGE ROOM

The screaming and hollering is the sound of joyous relief. The walls have stopped moving. Han and Leia embrace in the background.

LUKE: We're all right. You did great.

Luke moves to the pressure sensitive hatch, looking for a number.

LUKE: Hey ... hey, open the pressure maintenance hatch on unit number ... where are we?

INT. DEATH STAR – MAIN FORWARD BAY – SERVICE PANEL

Threepio looks at the computer panel as Han reads the number.

HAN: *(over comlink)* Three-two-six-three-eight-two-seven.

INT. DEATH STAR – TRACTOR BEAM – POWER GENERATOR TRENCH

(CONT'D)

CONTINUED

Ben enters a humming service trench that powers the huge tractor beam. The trench seems to be a hundred miles deep. The old Jedi edges his way along a narrow ledge leading to a control panel. He carefully makes several adjustments.

INT. DEATH STAR – UNUSED HALLWAY

The group exits the garbage room into a dusty, unused hallway. Han and Luke have removed the trooper suits and strapped on the blaster belts.

HAN: If we can just avoid any more female advice, we ought to be able to get out of here.

Luke smiles and scratches his head as he takes a blaster from Solo.

LUKE: Well, let's get moving!

Chewie begins growling and runs away from the hatch to the garbage room, where the dianoga evidently still lurks.

HAN: *(to Chewie)* Where are you going?

Han aims his pistol at the doorway.

LEIA: No, wait. They'll hear!

Han fires at the doorway. The noise of the blast echoes relentlessly throughout the empty passageway. Luke simply shakes his head in disgust.

HAN: *(to Chewie)* Come here, you big coward!

Chewie shakes his head no.

HAN: Chewie! Come here!

LEIA: Listen. I don't know who you are, or where you came from, but from now on, you do as I tell you. Okay?

Han is stunned at the command of the petite young girl.

HAN: Look, Your Worshipfulness, let's get one thing straight! I take orders from just one person! Me!

LEIA: It's a wonder you're still alive. *(looking at Chewie)* Will somebody get this big walking carpet out of my way?

Han watches her start away.

HAN: No reward is worth this.

They follow her, moving swiftly down the deserted corridor.

INT. DEATH STAR – POWER TRENCH

Suddenly behind Ben a detachment of stormtroopers marches to the power trench. Ben remains in the shadows as they move to within a few feet of him.

OFFICER: Give me regular reports, please.

FIRST TROOPER: Right.

All but two of the stormtroopers leave.

FIRST TROOPER: Do you know what's going on?

SECOND TROOPER: Maybe it's another drill.

Ben moves around the tractor beam, watching the stormtroopers as they turn their backs to him and chat. Ben gestures with his hand toward them, as the troops think they hear something in the other hallway. With the help of the Force, Ben deftly slips past the troopers and into the main hallway.

FIRST TROOPER: Have you seen that new BT-sixteen?

SECOND TROOPER: Yeah, some of the other guys were telling me about it. They say it's, it's quite a thing to ... What was that?

(CONT'D)

CONTINUED

FIRST TROOPER: That's nothing. Top-gassing. Don't worry about it.

INT. DEATH STAR — HALLWAY

Luke, Han, Chewbacca and Leia hurry down an empty hallway and stop before a bay window overlooking the pirateship. Troopers are milling around the ship. Luke takes out his pocket comlink.

HAN: *(looking at his ship)* There she is.

LUKE: See-Threepio, do you copy?

THREEPIO: *(voice)* Yes, sir.

LUKE: Are you safe?

THREEPIO: *(voice)* For the moment.

INT. DEATH STAR — MAIN FORWARD BAY

THREEPIO: We're in the main hangar across from the ship.

INT. DEATH STAR — HALLWAY

LUKE: We're right above you. Stand by.

Han has been watching the troops around the pirateship. Leia moves toward Han, touches his arm, and points out the window to the ship.

LEIA: You came in that thing? You're braver than I thought.

HAN: *(giving her a dirty look)* Nice! Come on!

They start off down the hallway. They round a corner and run right into Imperial stormtroopers heading toward them. Both groups are taken by surprise and stop in their tracks.

FIRST TROOPER: It's them! Blast them!

Before even thinking, Han fires his laser pistol. His blast knocks one of the stormtroopers into the air. Chewie follows his captain down the corridor, stepping past the fallen trooper on the floor.

HAN: *(to Luke and Leia)* Get back to the ship!

LUKE: Where are you going? Come back!

Han has already rounded a corner and does not hear.

LEIA: He certainly has courage.

LUKE: What good will it do us if he gets himself killed? Come on!

Luke is furious but doesn't have time to think about it. Luke and Leia start off toward the starship hangar.

INT. DEATH STAR — SUBHALLWAY

Han chases the stormtroopers down a long subhallway. He is yelling and brandishing his laser pistol. The troops reach a dead end and are forced to turn and fight. Han stops a few feet from them and assumes a defensive position. The troops begin to raise their laser guns. Soon the troopers are moving into an attack position in front of the lone starpirate. Han's determined look begins to fade as the troops begin to advance. Solo jumps back as they fire at him.

INT. DEATH STAR — SUBHALLWAY

Chewbacca runs down the subhallway in a last-ditch attempt to save his bold captain. Suddenly he hears the firing of laser guns and yelling. Around the corner shoots Han, pirate extraordinaire, running for his life, followed by a host of furious stormtroopers. Chewbacca turns and starts running the other way also.

INT. DEATH STAR — HALLWAY

Luke fires his laser pistol wildly as he and Leia rush down a narrow subhallway, chased by several stormtroopers. They quickly reach the end of the subhallway and race through an open hatchway.

(CONT'D)

CONTINUED

INT. DEATH STAR – CENTRAL CORE SHAFT

Luke and Leia race through the hatch on to a narrow bridge that spans a huge, deep shaft that seems to go into infinity. The bridge has been retracted into the wall of the shaft, and Luke almost rushed into the abyss. He loses his balance off the end of the bridge as Leia, behind him, takes hold of his arm and pulls him back.

LUKE: *(gasping)* I think we took a wrong turn.

Blasts from the stormtroopers' laser guns explode nearby reminding them of the oncoming danger. Luke fires back at the advancing troops. Leia reaches over and hits a switch that pops the hatch door shut with a resounding boom, leaving them precariously perched on a short piece of bridge overhang.

LEIA: There's no lock!

Luke blasts the controls with his laser pistol.

LUKE: That oughta hold them for a while.

LEIA: Quick, we've got to get across. Find the controls that extend the bridge.

LUKE: Oh, I think I just blasted it.

Luke looks at the blasted bridge control.

LEIA: They're coming through!

Luke notices something on his stormtrooper belt, when laserfire hits the wall behind him. Luke aims his laser pistol at a stormtrooper perched on a higher bridge overhang across the abyss from them. They exchange fire. Three more troopers appear on another overhang, also firing. A trooper is hit by Luke's laser fire, grabs at his chest, and plummets down the shaft. Troopers move back off the bridge; Luke hands his gun to Leia.

LUKE: Here, hold this.

Luke pulls a thin nylon cable from his trooper utility belt. It has a grappler hook on it.
    A trooper appears on a bridge overhang and fires at Luke and Leia. As Luke works with the rope, Leia returns the laser volley. Suddenly, the hatch door begins to open, revealing the feet of more troops.

LEIA: Here they come!

Leia hits one of the stormtroopers on the bridge above, and he falls. Luke tosses the rope across the gorge and it wraps itself around an outcropping pipe. He tugs on the tope to make sure it is secure, then grabs the princess in his arms. Leia looks at Luke, then kisses him quickly on the cheek. Luke is very surprised.

LEIA: For luck!

Luke pushes off and they swing across the treacherous abyss to the corresponding hatchway on the opposite side. Just as Luke and Leia reach the far side of the canyon, the stormtroopers break through the hatch and begin to fire at the escaping duo. Luke returns the fire before ducking into the tiny subhallway.

INT. DEATH STAR – NARROW PASSAGEWAY

Ben hides in the shadows of a narrow passageway as several stormtroopers rush past him in the main hallway. He checks to make sure they're gone, then moves down the hallway in the opposite direction.

TROOPER: We think they may be splitting up. They may be on levels five and six now, sir.

INT. DEATH STAR – MAIN FORWARD BAY

Threepio looks around at the troops milling about the pirateship entry ramp.

THREEPIO: Where could they be?

Artoo, plugged into the computer socket, swivels his dome, beeping a response.
    Han and Chewbacca run down a long corridor exchanging fire with several troopers hot on their trail.
    At the end of the hallway, blast doors begin to close in front of them. The young starpilot and his furry companion race through the huge doors as they are closing.

TROOPER: Open the blast doors! Open the blast doors!

(CONT'D)

CONTINUED

INT. DEATH STAR – HALLWAY LEADING TO MAIN FORWARD BAY

Ben moves along one of the tunnels leading to the hangar where the pirateship waits. Just before he reaches the hangar, Darth Vader comes into view at the end of the tunnel, his saber lit. Ben also ignites his and steps slowly forward.

VADER: I've been waiting for you. Obi-Wan. We meet again, at last. The circle is now complete.

Ben Kenobi moves with elegant ease into a classical offensive position.

VADER: When I left you, I was but the learner; now I am the master.

BEN: Only a master of evil, Darth.

Ben makes a sudden lunge at the huge warrior but is checked by a lightning movement of the Sith. A masterful slash stroke by Vader is blocked by the old Jedi. Another of the Jedi's blows is blocked, then countered. Ben moves around the Dark Lord and starts backing into the massive starship hangar. The two powerful warriors stand motionless for a few moments with laser swords crossed in mid-air, creating a low buzzing sound.

VADER: Your powers are weak, old man.

BEN: You can't win, Darth. If you strike me down I shall become more powerful than you can possibly imagine.

Their lightsabers continue to meet in combat.

VADER: You should not have come back.

INT. DEATH STAR – MAIN FORWARD BAY

Han Solo and Chewbacca, their weapons in hand, lean back against the wall surveying the forward bay, watching the Imperial stormtroopers make their rounds in the hangar.

HAN: Didn't we just leave this party?

Chewbacca growls a reply, as Luke and the princess join them.

HAN: What kept you?

LEIA: We ran into some old friends.

LUKE: Is the ship all right?

HAN: Seems okay, if we can get to it. Just hope the old man got the tractor beam out of commission.

INT. DEATH STAR – HALLWAY

Vader and Ben Kenobi continue their powerful duel.
    As they hit their lightsabers together, lightning flashes on impact. Troopers look on in interest as the old Jedi and Dark Lord of the Sith fight. Suddenly Luke spots the battle from his group's vantage point.

LUKE: Look!

Leia, Han and Chewie look up and see Ben and Vader on the far side of the docking bay.

INT. DEATH STAR – DOCKING BAY

Threepio and Artoo are in the center of the Death Star's Imperial docking bay.
    As the five stormtroopers who were guarding the starship rush past them heading toward Ben and the Sith Knight, Threepio beckons Artoo.

THREEPIO: Come on, Artoo, we're going!

INT. DEATH STAR – HALLWAY

Solo, Chewie, Luke and Leia tensely watch the duel. The troops have rushed toward the battling Knights.

HAN: Now's our chance! Go!

They start for Millennium Falcon.
    Ben has seen the troops charging toward him and realizes that he is trapped.

(CONT'D)

CONTINUED

    The old Jedi Knight looks over his shoulder at Luke, lifts his sword from Vader's, then watches his opponent with a serene look on his face.

LUKE: Ben?

Vader sweeps his sword round, cutting old Ben in half. Ben's cloak falls to the floor in two parts, but Ben is not in it. While the guards have been distracted, the adventurers and the robots have reached the starship.
    Luke sees Ben cut in two. Aghast, he yells out.

LUKE: No!

The stormtroopers turn toward Luke and begin firing at him. The robots are already moving up the ramp into the Millennium Falcon, while Luke, transfixed by anger and awe, returns their fire. Solo joins in the laserfire. Vader, who, puzzled at Ben's disappearance, has been poking at the empty cloak, looks up and advances toward them, as one of his troopers is struck down.

HAN: *(to Luke)* Come on!

LEIA: Come on! Come on! Luke, it's too late!

HAN: Blast the door! Kid!

Luke fires his laser pistol at the door control panel, and it explodes. The doors begin to slide shut. Three troopers charge forward firing laserbolts, as the door slides to a close behind them ... shutting Vader and the other troops out of the docking bay. A stormtrooper lies dead at the feet of his onrushing compatriots. Luke starts for the advancing troops, as Solo and Leia move up the ramp into the pirateship. He fires, hitting a stormtrooper, who crumples to the floor.

BEN'S VOICE: Run, Luke! Run!

Luke looks around to see where the voice came from. He turns towards the pirateship, ducking Imperial gunfire from the troopers and races into the ship.

INT. MILLENNIUM FALCON — COCKPIT

Han pulls back on the controls and the ship begins to move as Chewie adjusts his controls.

HAN: I hope the old man got that tractor beam out of commission, or this is going to be a real short trip. Okay, hit it!

Chewbacca growls in agreement.

EXT. MILLENNIUM FALCON

The Millennium Falcon powers away from the Death Star docking bay, makes a spectacular turn and disappears into the vastness of space.

INT. MILLENNIUM FALCON

Chewbacca congratulates Han on their escape.

EXT. MILLENNIUM FALCON

The Death Star recedes in the background.

INT. MILLENNIUM FALCON — CENTRAL HOLD AREA

Luke, saddened by the loss of Obi-Wan Kenobi, stares off blankly as the robots look on. Leia puts a blanket around him protectively, and Luke turns and looks at her. She sits down beside him.

INT. MILLENNIUM FALCON — COCKPIT

Solo spots approaching enemy ships.

HAN: *(to Chewie)* We're coming up on their sentry ships. Hold 'em off! Angle the deflector shields while I charge up the main guns!

EXT. MILLENNIUM FALCON

(CONT'D)

CONTINUED

The pirateship speeds through space.

INT. MILLENNIUM FALCON — CENTRAL HOLD AREA

Luke looks downward sadly, shaking his head back and forth, as the princess smiles comfortingly at him.

LUKE: I can't believe he's gone.

Artoo-Detoo beeps a reply.

LEIA: There wasn't anything you could have done.

Han rushes into the hold area where Luke is sitting with the princess.

HAN: *(to Luke)* Come on, buddy, we're not out of this yet!

INT. MILLENNIUM FALCON — GUNPORTS — COCKPIT

Solo climbs into his attack position in the topside gunport.

INT. MILLENNIUM FALCON — HOLD AREA

Luke gets up and moves out toward the gunports as Leia heads for the cockpit.

INT. MILLENNIUM FALCON — GUNPORTS — COCKPIT

Like climbs down the ladder into the gunport cockpit, settling into one of the two main laser cannons mounted in large rotating turrets on either side of the ship.

INT. MILLENNIUM FALCON — SOLO'S GUNPORT

Han adjusts his headset as he sits before the controls of his laser cannon, then speaks into the attached microphone.

HAN: *(to Luke)* You in, kid? Okay, stay sharp!

INT. MILLENNIUM FALCON — GUNPORTS — COCKPIT

Chewbacca and Princess Leia search the heavens for the attacking TIE fighters. The Wookiee adjusts the controls as the ship bounces slightly.

INT. MILLENNIUM FALCON — SOLO'S GUNPORT — COCKPIT

Computer graphic readouts form on Solo's target screen, as Han reaches for controls.

INT. MILLENNIUM FALCON — GUNPORT — COCKPIT

Luke sits in readiness for the attack, his hands on the laser cannon's control button.

INT. MILLENNIUM FALCON — COCKPIT

Chewbacca spots the enemy ships and barks.

LEIA: *(into intercom)* Here they come!

INT. COCKPIT POV SPACE

The Imperial TIE fighters move toward the Millennium Falcon, one each veering off to the left and right of the pirateship.

INT. TIE FIGHTER — COCKPIT

The stars whip past behind the Imperial pilot as he adjusts his maneuvering joy stick.

EXT. MILLENNIUM FALCON — IN SPACE

The TIE fighter races past the Falcon, firing laser beams as it passes.

INT. MILLENNIUM FALCON — HOLD AREA

Threepio is seated in the hold area, next to Artoo-Detoo. The pirateship bounces and vibrates as the power goes out in the room and then comes back on.

(CONT'D)

CONTINUED

INT. MILLENNIUM FALCON – COCKPIT – GUNPORTS

A TIE fighter maneuvers in front of Han, who follows it and fires at it with the laser cannon. Luke does likewise, as the fighter streaks into view. The ship has suffered a minor hit, and bounces slightly.

EXT. SPACE

Two TIE fighters dive down toward the pirateship.

INT. MILLENNIUM FALCON – GUNPORTS

Luke fires at an unseen fighter.

EXT. SPACE

The TIE fighter streaks past.

INT. MILLENNIUM FALCON – GUNPORTS

LUKE: They're coming in too fast!

INT. MILLENNIUM FALCON – MAIN PASSAGEWAY

A laserbolt streaks into the side of the pirateship. The ship lurches violently, throwing poor Threepio into a cabinet full of small computer chips.

THREEPIO: Oh!

INT. MILLENNIUM FALCON – COCKPIT GUNPORTS

Leia watches the computer readouts as Chewbacca manipulates the ship's controls.

LEIA: We've lost lateral controls.

HAN: Don't worry, she'll hold together.

An enemy laserbolt hits the pirateship's control panel, causing it to blow out in a shower of sparks.

HAN: *(to ship)* You hear me, baby? Hold together!

Artoo-Detoo advances toward the smoking, sparking control panel, beeping and dousing the inferno by spraying it with fire retardant.

INT. MILLENNIUM FALCON – GUNPORT

Luke swivels in his gun mount, following the TIE fighter with his laser cannon.

INT. MILLENNIUM FALCON – GUNPORT

Solo aims his laser cannon at the enemy fighters.

EXT. SPACE

A TIE fighter streaks in front of the starship.

INT. MILLENNIUM FALCON – COCKPIT

Leia watches the TIE ship fly over.

EXT. SPACE

A TIE fighter heads right for the pirateship, then zooms overhead.

INT. MILLENNIUM FALCON – GUNPORTS

Luke follows the TIE fighter across his field of view, firing laser beams from his cannon.

EXT. TIE FIGHTER

A TIE fighter dives past the pirateship.

INT. MILLENNIUM FALCON – COCKPIT – GUNPORTS

(CONT'D)

CONTINUED

Chewbacca and Leia watch anxiously as Luke fires at a TIE fighter. At his port, Han follows a fighter in his sights, releasing a blast of laserfire. He connects, and the fighter explodes into fiery dust. Han laughs victoriously.

EXT. SPACE

Two TIE fighters move toward and over the Millennium Falcon, unleashing a barrage of laserbolts at the ship.

INT. MILLENNIUM FALCON — GUNPORTS

Another TIE fighter moves in on the pirateship and Luke, smiling, fires the laser cannon at it, scoring a spectacular direct hit.

LUKE: Got him! I got him!

Han turns and gives Luke a victory wave which Luke gleefully returns.

HAN: Great kid! Don't get cocky.

Han turns back to his laser cannon.

EXT. SPACE

Two more TIE fighters cross in front of the pirateship.

INT. MILLENNIUM FALCON — COCKPIT

While Chewbacca manipulates the controls, Leia turns, looking over her shoulder out the ports.

LEIA: There are still two more of them out there!

EXT. SPACE

A TIE fighter moves up over the pirateship, firing laserblasts at it.

INT. MILLENNIUM FALCON — GUNPORTS

Luke and Han look into their respective projected target screens. An Imperial fighter crosses Solo's port, and Han swivels in his chair, following it with blasts from his laser cannon. Another fighter crosses Luke's port, and he reacts in a like manner.

EXT. SPACE

The TIE fighter zooms toward the pirateship, firing destructive blasts at it.

INT. MILLENNIUM FALCON — GUNPORTS — COCKPIT

Luke fires a laserblast at the approaching enemy fighter, and it bursts into spectacular explosion. Luke's projected screen gives a readout of the hit. The pirateship bounces slightly as it is struck by enemy fire.

EXT. SPACE — TIE FIGHTER

The last of the attacking Imperial TIE fighters looms in, firing upon the Falcon.

INT. MILLENNIUM FALCON — GUNPORT

Solo swivels behind his laser cannon, his aim describing the arc of the TIE fighter. The fighter comes closer, firing at the pirate ship, but a well-aimed blast from Solo's laser cannon hits the attacker, which blows up in a small atomic shower of burning fragments.

LUKE: *(laughing)* That's it! We did it!

LEIA: We did it!

The princess jumps up and gives Chewie a congratulatory hug.

INT. MILLENNIUM FALCON — PASSAGEWAY

Threepio lies on the floor of the ship, completely tangled in the smoking, sparking wires.

THREEPIO: Help! I think I'm melting! *(to Artoo)* This is all your fault.

(CONT'D)

CONTINUED

Artoo turns his dome from side to side, beeping in response.

EXT. SPACE — MILLENNIUM FALCON

The victorious Millennium Falcon moves off majestically through space.

INT. DEATH STAR — CONTROL ROOM

Darth Vader strides into the control room, where Tarkin is watching the huge view screen.

TARKIN: Are they away?

VADER: They have just made the jump into hyperspace.

TARKIN: You're sure the homing beacon is secure aboard their ship? I'm taking an awful risk, Vader. This had better work.

INT. MILLENNIUM FALCON — COCKPIT

Han, removing his gloves and smiling, is at the controls of the ship. Chewie moves into the aft section to check the damage. Leia is seated near Han.

HAN: Not a bad bit of rescuing, huh! You know, sometimes I amaze even myself.

LEIA: That doesn't sound too hard. They let us go. It's the only explanation for the ease of our escape.

HAN: Easy ... You call that easy?

LEIA: They're tracking us!

HAN: Not this ship, sister.

Frustrated, Leia shakes her head.

LEIA: At least the information in Artoo is still intact.

HAN: What's so important? What's he carrying?

LEIA: The technical readouts of that battle station. I only hope that when the data is analyzed, a weakness can be found. It's not over yet!

HAN: It is for me, sister! Look, I ain't in this for your revolution, and I'm not in it for you, Princess. I expect to be well paid. I'm in it for the money!

LEIA: You needn't worry about your reward. If money is all that you love, then that's what you'll receive.

She angrily turns, and as she starts out of the cockpit, passes Luke coming in.

LEIA: Your friend is quite a mercenary. I wonder if he really cares about anything ... or anybody.

LUKE: I care!

Luke, shaking his head, sits in the co-pilot seat. Han stares out at the vast blackness of space.

LUKE: So ... what do you think of her, Han?

HAN: I'm trying not to, kid!

LUKE: *(under his breath)* Good ...

HAN: Still, she's got a lot of spirit. I don't know, what do you think? Do you think a princess and a guy like me . . .

LUKE: No!

Luke says it with finality and looks away. Han smiles at young Luke's jealousy.

EXT. SPACE AROUND FOURTH MOON OF YAVIN

The battered pirateship drifts into orbit around the planet Yavin and proceeds to one of its tiny green moons.

EXT. FOURTH MOON OF YAVIN

(CONT'D)

CONTINUED

The pirateship soars over the dense jungle.

EXT. MASSASSI OUTPOST

An alert guard, his laser gun in hand, scans the countryside. He sets the gun down and looks toward the temple, barely visible in the foliage.

EXT. MASSASSI OUTPOST – JUNGLE TEMPLE

In a forest of gargantuan trees, lies an ancient temple. The air is heavy with the fantastic cries of unimaginable creatures. Han, Luke and the others are greeted by the Rebel troops.

INT. MASSASSI – MAIN HANGAR DECK

A military speeder stops in a huge spaceship hangar, set up in the interior of the crumbling temple.
     Willard, the commander of the Rebel forces, hurries up to the group and gives Leia a big hug.

WILLARD: *(holding Leia)* You're safe! When we heard about Alderaan we feared the worst.

LEIA: We have no time for sorrows, Commander. You must use the information in this R2 unit to help plan the attack. It's our only hope.

Artoo is debriefed.

EXT. SPACE

The surface of the Death Star ominously approaches the red planet Yavin.

INT. DEATH STAR – CONTROL ROOM

Grand Moff Tarkin and Lord Darth Vader are interrupted in their discussion by the buzz of the comlink. Tarkin moves to answer the call.

TARKIN: Yes.

DEATH STAR INTERCOM VOICE: We are approaching the planet Yavin. The Rebel base is on a moon on the far side. We are preparing to orbit the planet.

EXT. YAVIN – JUNGLE

A lone guard stands in a tower high above the Yavin landscape, surveying the countryside. A mist hangs over the jungle of twisted green.

INT. MASSASSI – WAR ROOM BRIEFING AREA

Dodonna stands before a large electronic wall display. Leia and several other senators are to one side of the giant readout. The low-ceilinged room is filled with starpilots, navigators, and a sprinkling of R2-type robots. Everyone is listening intently to what Dodonna is saying. Han and Chewbacca are standing near the back.

DODONNA: The battle station is heavily shielded and carries a firepower greater than half the starfleet. Its defences are designed around a direct large-scale assault. A small one-man fighter should be able to penetrate the outer defence.

Gold Leader, a rough-looking man in his early thirties, stands and addresses Dodonna.

GOLD LEADER: Pardon me for asking, sir, but what good are snub fighters going to be against that?

DODONNA: Well, the Empire doesn't consider a small one-man fighter to be any threat, or they'd have a tighter defence. An analysis of the plans provided by Princess Leia has demonstrated a weakness in the battle station.

Artoo-Detoo makes beeping sounds, and turns his head.

DODONNA: The approach will not be easy. You are required to maneuver straight down this trench and skim the surface to this point. The target area is only two meters wide. It's a small thermal exhaust port, right below the main port. The shaft leads directly to the reactor system. A precise hit will start a chain reaction which should destroy the station. Only a precise hit will set up a chain reaction. The shaft is ray-shielded, so you'll have to use proton torpedoes.

Luke is sitting next to Wedge Antilles, a hotshot pilot about sixteen years old.

(CONT'D)

CONTINUED

WEDGE: That's impossible, even for a computer.

LUKE: It's not impossible. I used to bull's-eye womp rats in my T-sixteen back home. They're not much bigger than two meters.

DODONNA: Then, man your ships! And may the Force be with you!

The group rises and begins to leave.

EXT. SPACE

The Death Star begins to move around the planet toward the tiny green moon.

INT. DEATH STAR

A circle of light intertwines around one another on the computer-projected screen showing the position of the Death Star in relation to Yavin and the fourth moon.

DEATH STAR INTERCOM VOICE: Orbiting the planet at maximum velocity. The moon with the Rebel base will be in range in thirty minutes.

Tarkin and Vader have been watching the screen with interest.

VADER: This will be a day long remembered. It has seen the end of Kenobi. It will soon see the end of the Rebellion.

INT. MASSASSI OUTPOST – MAIN HANGAR DECK

Luke and Threepio enter the huge spaceship hangar. Flight crews rush around loading last-minute armaments and unlocking power couplings. In an area isolated from this activity, Luke sees Han and Chewbacca loading small boxes on to an armored speeder.

MAN'S VOICE: *(over loudspeaker)* All flight troops, man your stations. All flight troops, man your stations.

Han is deliberately ignoring the activity of the fighter pilots' preparations. Luke is quite saddened at the sight of his friend's departure.

LUKE: So . . . you got your reward and you're just leaving then?

HAN: That's right, yeah! I got some old debts I got to pay off with this stuff. Even if I didn't, you don't think I'd be fool enough to stick around here, do you? Why don't you come with us? You're pretty good in a fight. I could use you.

LUKE: *(getting angry)* Come on! Why don't you take a look around? You know what's about to happen, what they're up against. They could use a good pilot like you. You're turning your back on them.

HAN: What good's a reward if you ain't around to use it? Besides, attacking the battle station ain't my idea of courage. It's more like suicide.

LUKE: All right. Well, take care of yourself, Han . . . I guess that's that you're best at, isn't it?

Luke goes off and Han hesitates, then calls to him.

HAN: Hey, Luke . . . may the Force be with you!

Chewie growls at his captain. Han turns to him.

HAN: What're you lookin' at? I know what I'm doing.

INT. MAIN HANGAR DECK – LUKE'S SHIP

MAN'S VOICE: *(over loudspeaker)* All pilots to your stations. All pilots to your stations.

Luke, Leia, and Dodonna meet under a huge spacefighter.

LEIA: What's wrong?

LUKE: Oh, it's Han! I don't know, I really thought he'd change his mind.

LEIA: He's got to follow his own path. No one can choose it for him.

(CONT'D)

CONTINUED

LUKE: I only wish Ben were here.

Leia gives Luke a little kiss, turns and goes off.
        As Luke begins to climb up the ladder into his sleek, deadly spaceship, the crew chief, who is working on the craft, points to little Artoo, who is being hoisted into a socket on the back of the fighter.

CHIEF: Hey, this R2 unit of yours seems a bit beat-up. Do you want a new one?

LUKE: Not on your life! That little droid and I have been through a lot together. *(to Artoo)* You okay, Artoo?

The crewmen are lowering Artoo-Detoo into the craft. Now becoming a part of the exterior shell of the starship, the little droid beeps that he is fine.

LUKE: Good.

Luke climbs up into the cockpit of his fighter and puts on his helmet. Threepio looks on from the floor of the massive hangar as the crewmen secure his little electronic partner into Luke's X-wing.

THREEPIO: Hang on tight, Artoo, you've got to come back.

It's an emotion-filled moment as Artoo beeps in agreement.

THREEPIO: You wouldn't want my life to get boring, would you?

Artoo whistles his reply.
        All final preparations are made for the approaching battle. The hangar is buzzing with the last minute activity as the pilots and crewmen alike make their final adjustments.
        Coupling hoses are disconnected from the ships as they are fueled. Cockpit shields lower smoothly into place over each pilot. A signalman, holding yellow guiding lights, directs the ships. Luke peers about through his goggles.

BEN'S VOICE: Luke, the Force will be with you.

Luke looks confused at the voice.

EXT. MASSASSI OUTPOST – JUNGLE

All that can be seen of the fortress is a lone guard standing on a small pedestal jutting out above the dense jungle. The muted gruesome crying sounds that naturally permeate this eerie purgatory are overwhelmed by the thundering din of ion rockets as a series of silver starships catapults from the foliage into a tight formation and disappears into the morning cloud cover.

INT. MASSASSI OUTPOST – WAR ROOM

The princess, Threepio, and a field commander stand quietly before a display showing the planet Yavin and its four moons.

MASSASSI INTERCOM VOICE: Stand-by alert. Death Star approaching. Estimated time to firing range, fifteen minutes.

EXT. SPACE

The Death Star slowly moves behind the massive yellow surface of Yavin in the foreground, as many X-wing fighters flying in formation zoom toward us and out of the frame.

INT. RED LEADER STARSHIP – COCKPIT

Red Leader to each side at his wingmen.

RED LEADER: All Wings report in.

INT. ANOTHER COCKPIT

One of the Rebel fighters checks in through his mike.

RED TEN: Red Ten standing by.

INT. BIGGS' COCKPIT

(CONT'D)

CONTINUED

Biggs checks his fighter's controls, alert and ready for combat.

RED SEVEN: *(over Biggs's headset)* Red Seven standing by.

BIGGS: Red Three standing by.

INT. PORKINS' COCKPIT

PORKINS: Red Six standing by.

RED NINE: *(over headset)* Red Nine standing by.

INT. WEDGE'S FIGHTER — COCKPIT

WEDGE: Red Two standing by.

INT. LUKE'S X-WING FIGHTER — COCKPIT

RED ELEVEN: *(over headset)* Red Eleven standing by.

LUKE: Red Five standing by.

EXT. LUKE'S X-WING FIGHTER

Artoo-Detoo, in position outside of the fighter, swivels his head and makes beeping sounds.

INT. RED LEADER'S FIGHTER — COCKPIT

RED LEADER: Lock S-foils in attack position.

EXT. SPACE

The group of X-wing fighters moves in formation toward the Death Star, unfolding the wings and locking them into the "X" position.

INT. PORKINS' COCKPIT

RED LEADER: *(over headset)* We're passing through their magnetic field.

INT. RED LEADER'S COCKPIT

RED LEADER: Hold tight!

INT. LUKE'S X-WING FIGHTER — COCKPIT

Luke adjusts his controls as he concentrates on the approaching Death Star. The ships begin to be buffeted slightly.

RED LEADER: *(over headset)* Switch your deflectors on.

INT. ANOTHER COCKPIT

RED LEADER: *(over headset)* Double front!

EXT. SPACE

The fighters, now X-shaped darts, move in formation. The Death Star now appears to be a small moon growing rapidly in size as the Rebel fighters approach. Complex patterns on the metallic surface begin to become visible.

INT. WEDGE'S COCKPIT

Wedge is amazed and slightly frightened at the awesome spectacle.

WEDGE: Look at the size of that thing!

INT. LUKE'S COCKPIT

RED LEADER: *(over headset)* Cut the chatter, Red Two.

INT. RED LEADER'S COCKPIT

RED LEADER: Accelerate to attack speed.

(CONT'D)

CONTINUED

EXT. SPACE

As the fighters move closer to the Death Star, the awesome size of the gargantuan Imperial fortress is revealed. Half of the deadly space station is in shadow and this area sparkles with thousands of small lights running in thin lines and occasionally grouped in large clusters; somewhat like a city at night as seen from a weather satellite.

INT. RED LEADER'S COCKPIT

RED LEADER: This is it, boys!

INT. GOLD LEADER'S COCKPIT

GOLD LEADER: Red Leader, this is Gold Leader.

INT. LUKE'S COCKPIT

RED LEADER: *(over headset)* I copy, Gold Leader.

INT. GOLD LEADER'S COCKPIT

GOLD LEADER: We're starting for the target shaft now.

RED LEADER: We're in position. I'm going to cut across the axis and try and draw their fire.

EXT. SPACE

Two squads of Rebel fighters peel off. The X-wings dive toward the Death Star surface. A thousand lights glow across the dark grey expanse of the huge station.

INT. DEATH STAR

In large turbo-powered laser gun emplacements, the huge guns rotate into position and begin firing.

EXT. SPACE AROUND THE DEATH STAR

Laserbolts streak through the star-filled night. The Rebel X-wing fighters move in toward the Imperial base, as the Death Star aims its massive laser guns at the Rebel forces and fires.

INT. MASSASSI OUTPOST – WAR ROOM

Princess Leia listens to the battle over the intercom. Threepio is at her side.

WEDGE: *(over war room speaker system)* Heavy fire, boss! Twenty-three degrees.

RED LEADER: *(over speaker)* I see it. Stay low.

EXT. SPACE

An X-wing zooms across the surface of the Death Star.

INT. DEATH STAR

A laser gun fires at the Rebel forces.

INT. WEDGE'S COCKPIT

Wedge maneuvers his fighter toward the menacing Death Star.

EXT. SPACE

X-wings continue in their attack course on the Death Star.

INT. LUKE'S X-WING FIGHTER – COCKPIT

Luke nosedives radically, starting his attack on the monstrous fortress.

LUKE: This is Red Five! I'm going in!

EXT. SPACE

(CONT'D)

CONTINUED

Luke's X-wing races toward the Death Star. Laserbolts streak from Luke's weapons, creating a huge fireball explosion on the dim surface.

INT. LUKE'S X-WING FIGHTER — COCKPIT

Terror crosses Luke's face as he realizes he won't be able to pull out in time to avoid the fireball.

BIGGS: *(over headset)* Luke, pull out!

EXT. SURFACE OF DEATH STAR

Luke's ship emerges from the fireball, with the leading edges of his wings slightly scorched.

INT. BIGGS' COCKPIT

BIGGS: Are you all right?

INT. LUKE'S X-WING FIGHTER — COCKPIT

Luke adjusts his controls and breathes a sigh of relief. Flak bursts outside the cockpit window.

LUKE: I got a little cooked, but I'm okay.

EXT. SURFACE OF THE DEATH STAR

Rebel fighters continue to strafe the Death Star's surface with laserbolts.

INT. DEATH STAR

The corridors are alive with activity. Alarms sound. Stormtroopers run in all directions. Walking in the middle of the chaos, a vision of calm and foreboding, is Darth Vader. One of his Astro-Officers rushes up to him.

ASTRO-OFFICER: We count thirty Rebel ships, Lord Vader. But they're so small they're evading our turbo-lasers!

VADER: We'll have to destroy them ship to ship. Get the crews to their fighters.

EXT. SPACE

Red Leader flies through a heavy hail of flak.

INT. RED LEADER'S X-WING — COCKPIT — TRAVELING

RED LEADER: Watch yourself! There's a lot of fire coming from the right side of that deflection tower.

INT. LUKE'S X-WING FIGHTER — COCKPIT — TRAVELING

LUKE: I'm on it.

INT. BIGGS' COCKPIT

BIGGS: I'm going in. Cover me, Porkins!

INT. PORKINS' COCKPIT

Porkins: I'm right with you, Red Three.

EXT. SURFACE OF THE DEATH STAR

Rebel fighters, firing laserbolts, streak towards the onrushing Death Star surface, causing a protruding tower to erupt in flames.

INT. DEATH STAR

Explosions reverberate through the massive structure. Many soldiers rush about in the chaos, silhouetted by the almost continual flash of explosions.

EXT. SPACE

A dense barrage of laserfire streaks by on all sides.

INT. PORKINS' COCKPIT

PORKINS: I've got a problem, here.

(CONT'D)

1:40

CONTINUED

EXT. SPACE

Laserfire continues to streak by on all sides.

INT. BIGGS' COCKPIT

BIGGS: Eject!

INT. PORKINS' COCKPIT

PORKINS: I can hold it.

INT. BIGGS' COCKPIT

BIGGS: Pull out!

INT. PORKINS' COCKPIT

PORKINS: No, I'm all right.

An explosion hits Porkins' ship and the cabin fills with smoke.

EXT. PORKINS' X-WING

Porkins' ship explodes.

INT. DEATH STAR

Tarkin stands in front of the computer-projected screen.

DEATH STAR INTERCOM VOICE: The Rebel base will be in firing range in seven minutes.

EXT. SPACE – LUKE'S X-WING

INT. LUKE'S COCKPIT

BEN'S VOICE: Luke, trust your feelings.

EXT. SURFACE OF THE DEATH STAR

Luke attacks the surface of the Death Star with laserfire.

DEATH STAR

Luke's attack wreaks its explosive effect inside the Death Star.

INT. LUKE'S COCKPIT

Luke peers out of hs cockpit at the surface of the Death Star.

EXT. SPACE

Luke's X-wing streaks past.

INT. MASSASSI – OUTPOST – WAR ROOM

On all sides technicians work in front of many lighted glass walls. Dodonna watches quietly from one corner. One of the officers speaks into his handset.

CONTROL OFFICER: Squad leaders, we've picked up a new group of signals. Enemy fighters coming your way.

INT. LUKE'S X-WING FIGHTER – COCKPIT – TRAVELING

Luke looks around to see if he can spot the approaching Imperial fighter.

LUKE: My scope's negative. I don't see anything.

INT. RED LEADER'S X-WING – COCKPIT – TRAVELING

RED LEADER: Pick up your visual scanning.

INT. BIGGS' COCKPIT – TRAVELING

RED LEADER: *(over headset)* Here they come.

(CONT'D)

CONTINUED

EXT. SPACE

Five ferocious Imperial TIE ships dive on the Rebel fighters.

INT. RED LEADER'S COCKPIT

RED LEADER: Watch it! You've got one on your tail.

EXT. SPACE

Imperial TIE fighter fires at Rebel X-wing.

INT. X-WING COCKPIT

Rebel pilot looks over his shoulder in panic.

INT. TIE FIGHTER'S COCKPIT

The TIE fighter pilot folows the X-wing, firing remorselessly.

EXT. SPACE (TIE FIGHTER'S POV)

Laserfire follows the X-wing.

INT. X-WING COCKPIT

The X-wing pilot is hit.

EXT. SPACE

The X-wing blows up.

INT. LUKE'S COCKPIT

RED LEADER: Biggs! You've picked one up ... Watch it!

INT. BIGGS'S COCKPIT

BIGGS: I can't see it!

EXT. SPACE AROUND THE DEATH STAR

Biggs zooms off the surface and into space, closely followed by an Imperial TIE fighter.

INT. BIGGS' COCKPIT – TRAVELING

Biggs sees the TIE ship behind him and swings around, trying to avoid him. The TIE ship fires several laserbolts at Biggs, but misses.

BIGGS: They're on me tight, I can't shake him ...

INT. LUKE'S COCKPIT

LUKE: I'll be right there.

EXT. SPACE

Luke pursues the TIE fighter which is pursuing Biggs.

INT. LUKE'S COCKPIT

Luke scans his computer.

EXT. SPACE

Luke continues to pursue the TIE ship.

INT. LUKE'S COCKPIT

Luke locks his target into his computer and fires.

EXT. SPACE

The TIE fighter explodes in a mass of flames.

(CONT'D)

CONTINUED

INT. DEATH STAR

Darth Vader strides purposefully down a Death Star corridor, and addresses two Imperial TIE fighter pilots.

VADER: Several fighters have broken off from the main group. Come with me!

INT. MASSASSI OUTPOST – WAR ROOM

A concerned Princess Leia, Threepio, Dodonna, and other officers of the Rebellion stand around the huge round readout screen, listening to the ship-to-ship communication on the room's loudspeaker.

BIGGS: *(over speaker)* Pull in! Luke . . . pull in!

WEDGE: *(over speaker)* Watch your back, Luke!

INT. LUKE'S X-WING FIGHTER – COCKPIT

WEDGE: *(over headset)* Watch your back! Fighters above you, coming in!

EXT. SPACE

Luke's ship soars away from the Death Star's surface as he spots the tailing TIE fighter.

INT. TIE FIGHTER'S COCKPIT

The TIE pilot takes aim at Luke's X-wing.

EXT. SPACE

The Imperial TIE fighter pilot scores a hit on Luke's ship. Fire breaks out on the right side of the X-wing.

INT. LUKE'S X-WING FIGHTER – COCKPIT

Luke looks out of his cockpit at the flames on his ship.

LUKE: I'm hit, but not bad.

EXT. LUKE'S X-WING FIGHTER

Smoke pours out from behind Artoo-Detoo.

LUKE'S VOICE: Artoo, see what you can do with it. Hang on back there.

Green laserfire moves past the beeping little robot as his head turns.

INT. LUKE'S X-WING FIGHTER – COCKPIT

Luke nervously works his controls.

RED LEADER: *(over headset)* Red Six . . .

INT. MASSASSI OUTPOST – WAR ROOM

In the war room, Leia stands frozen as she listens and worries about Luke.

RED LEADER: *(over speaker)* Can you see Red Five?

RED TEN: *(over speaker)* There's a heavy fire zone on this side. Red Five, where are you?

INT. LUKE'S X-WING FIGHTER – COCKPIT

Luke spots the TIE fighters behind him and soars away from the Death Star surface.

LUKE: I can't shake him!

EXT. SURFACE OF THE DEATH STAR

Luke's ship soars closer to the surface of the Death Star, an Imperial TIE fighter closing in on him in hot pursuit.

INT. WEDGE'S COCKPIT

The Death Star whips below Wedge.

(CONT'D)

CONTINUED

WEDGE: I'm on him, Luke!

INT. LUKE'S X-WING FIGHTER — COCKPIT

WEDGE: (over headset) Hold on!

EXT. SURFACE OF THE DEATH STAR

Wedge dives across the horizon toward Luke and the TIE fighter.

INT. WEDGE'S COCKPIT

Wedge moves his X-wing in rapidly.

INT. MASSASSI OUTPOST — WAR ROOM

Leia and Threepio follow the battle with concern.

INT. LUKE'S X-WING FIGHTER — COCKPIT

Luke reacts frantically.

LUKE: Blast it! Biggs, where are you?

INT. TIE FIGHTER — COCKPIT

The fighter pilot watches Wedge's X-wing approach. Another X-wing joins him, and both unleash a volley of laserfire on the Imperial fighter.

EXT. SPACE

The TIE fighter explodes, filling the screen with white light. Luke's ship can be seen far in the distance.

INT. LUKE'S X-WING FIGHTER — COCKPIT

Luke looks about in relief.

LUKE: Thanks, Wedge.

INT. MASSASSI OUTPOST — WAR ROOM

Leia, Threepio, Dodonna and other Rebel officers are listening to the Rebel fighters' radio transmissions over the war room intercom.

BIGGS: (over speaker) Good shooting, Wedge!

GOLD LEADER: (over speaker) Red Leader . . .

INT. GOLD LEADER'S Y-WING — COCKPIT

Gold Leader peels off and starts toward the long trenches at the Death Star surface pole.

GOLD LEADER: . . . This is Gold Leader. We're starting our attack run.

EXT. SPACE AROUND THE DEATH STAR

Three Y-wing fighters of the Gold group dive out of the stars toward the Death Star surface.

INT. MASSASSI OUTPOST — WAR ROOM

Leia and the others are grouped around the screen, as technicians move about attending to their duties.

RED LEADER: (over speaker) I copy, Gold Leader. Move into position.

EXT. SPACE AROUND THE DEATH STAR

Three Imperial TIE ships in precise formation dive toward the Death Star surface.

INT. DARTH VADER'S COCKPIT

Darth Vader calmly adjusts his control stick as the surface of the Death Star whips past in the window above his head.

(CONT'D)

CONTINUED

VADER: Stay in attack formation!

INT. MASSASSI OUTPOST — WAR ROOM

Technicians are seated at the computer readout table.

GOLD LEADER: *(over speaker)* The exhaust port is . . .

INT. GOLD LEADER'S Y-WING — COCKPIT

GOLD LEADER: . . . marked and locked in!

EXT. SPACE AROUND THE DEATH STAR

Gold Leader approaches the surface and pulls out to skim the surface of the huge station. The ship moves into a deep trench, firing laserbolts. The surface streaks past as laserfire is returned by the Death Star.

INT. GOLD FIVE'S Y-WING — COCKPIT — TRAVELING

Gold Five is a pilot in his early fifties with a very battered helmet that looks like it's been through many battles. His fighter is buffeted by Imperial flak.

GOLD LEADER: *(over headset)* Switch all power to front deflector screens.

INT. GOLD LEADER'S Y-WING — COCKPIT

Gold Leader races down the enormous trench that leads to the exhaust port. Laserbolts blast toward him in increasing numbers, occasionally exploding near the ship, causing it to bounce about.

GOLD LEADER: Switch all . . .

INT. GOLD TWO'S Y-WING

Gold Two is a younger pilot, about Luke's age.

GOLD LEADER: *(over headset)* . . . power to front deflector screens.

EXT. SURFACE OF THE DEATH STAR

Three Y-wings skim the Death Star surface deep in the trench, as laserbolts streak past on all sides.

EXT. DEATH STAR SURFACE — GUN EMPLACEMENT

An exterior surface gun blazes away at the oncoming Rebel fighters.

INT. GOLD LEADER'S Y-WING — COCKPIT

GOLD LEADER: How many guns to you think, Gold Five?

INT. MASSASSI OUTPOST — WAR ROOM

GOLD FIVE: *(over speaker)* Say about twenty guns. Some on the surface, some on the towers.

Leia, Threepio, and the technicians view the projected target screen, as target lights glow. The red target near the center blinks on and off.

MASSASSI INTERCOM VOICE: *(over speaker)* Death Star will be in range in five minutes.

EXT. SURFACE OF THE DEATH STAR

The three Y-wing fighters race toward camera and zoom past through a hail of laserfire.

INT. GOLD LEADER'S Y-WING — COCKPIT

Gold Leader pulls his computer targeting device down in front of his eyes. Laserbolts continue to batter the Rebel craft.

GOLD LEADER: Switch to targeting computer.

INT. GOLD LEADER'S Y-WING — COCKPIT

Gold Two's ship shudders under intense laser barrage.

(CONT'D)

CONTINUED

GOLD TWO: Computer's locked. Getting a signal.

As the fighters begin to approach the target area, suddenly all the laserfire stops. An eerie calm clings over the trench as the surface whips past in a blur.

GOLD TWO: The guns ... they've stopped!

EXT. SURFACE OF THE DEATH STAR

Two Y-wings zoom down the Death Star trench.

INT. GOLD FIVE'S COCKPIT

Gold Five looks behind him.

GOLD FIVE: Stabilize your rear deflectors. Watch for enemy fighters.

INT. GOLD LEADER'S Y-WING – COCKPIT

GOLD LEADER: They're coming in! Three marks at two ten.

EXT. SPACE AROUND THE DEATH STAR

Three Imperial TIE ships, Darth Vader in the center flanked by two wingmen, dive in precise formation almost vertically toward the Death Star surface.

INT. DARTH VADER'S COCKPIT

Darth Vader calmly adjusts his control stick as the stars zoom by.

VADER: I'll take them myself! Cover me!

INT. THE WINGMAN'S COCKPIT

WINGMAN: Yes, sir.

EXT. SPACE AROUND THE DEATH STAR

Three TIE fighters zoom across the surface of the Death Star.

INT. DARTH VADER'S COCKPIT

Vader lines up Gold Two in his targeting computer. Vader's hands grip the control stick as he presses the button.

INT. GOLD TWO'S Y-WING – COCKPIT

The cockpit explodes around Gold Two. His head falls forward.

EXT. SPACE AROUND THE DEATH STAR

As Gold Two's ship explodes, debris is flung out into space.

INT. GOLD LEADER'S Y-WING – COCKPIT

Gold Leader looks over his shoulder at the scene.

EXT. DEATH STAR TRENCH

The three TIE fighters race along in the trench in a tight formation.

INT. GOLD LEADER'S Y-WING – COCKPIT

Gold Leader begins to panic.

EXT. DEATH STAR TRENCH

The three TIE fighters are closing.

INT. GOLD LEADER'S Y-WING – COCKPIT

GOLD LEADER: *(into mike)* It's no good, I can't maneuver!

INT. GOLD FIVE'S Y-WING – COCKPIT

(CONT'D)

CONTINUED

Gold Five, the old veteran, tries to calm Gold Leader.

GOLD FIVE: Stay on target.

INT. GOLD LEADER'S Y-WING – COCKPIT

The Death Star races by outside the cockpit window as he adjusts his targeting device.

GOLD LEADER: We're too close.

INT. GOLD FIVE'S Y-WING – COCKPIT

The older pilot remains calm.

GOLD FIVE: Stay on target!

EXT. DEATH STAR TRENCH

The TIE fighters close in.

INT. GOLD LEADER'S Y-WING – COCKPIT

Now he's really panicked.

GOLD LEADER: Loosen up!

INT. DARTH VADER'S COCKPIT

Vader calmly adjusts his targeting computer and pushes the fire button.

INT. GOLD LEADER'S Y-WING – COCKPIT

Gold Leader's ship is hit by Vader's lasers.

EXT. SURFACE OF THE DEATH STAR

Gold Leader explodes in a ball of flames, throwing debris in all directions.

INT. GOLD FIVE'S Y-WING – COCKPIT

Gold Five moves in on the exhaust port.

GOLD FIVE: Gold Five to Red Leader . . .

INT. LUKE'S X-WING FIGHTER – COCKPIT

Luke looks over his shoulder at the action outside of his cockpit.

GOLD FIVE: *(over headset)* Lost Tiree, lost Hutch.

INT. RED LEADER'S COCKPIT

RED LEADER: I copy, Gold Leader.

INT. GOLD FIVE'S Y-WING – COCKPIT

GOLD FIVE: They came from behind . . .

EXT. SURFACE OF THE DEATH STAR

One of the engines explodes on Gold Five's Y-wing fighter, blazing out of control. He dives past the horizon toward the Death Star's surface. Gold Five, a veteran of countless campaigns, spins toward his death.

INT. LUKE'S X-WING FIGHTER – COCKPIT

Luke looks nervously about him at the explosive battle.

INT. DEATH STAR – CONTROL ROOM

OFFICER: We've analyzed their attack, sir, and there is a danger. Should I have your ship standing by?

TARKIN: Evacuate? In our moment of triumph? I think you overestimate their chances!

(CONT'D)

CONTINUED

Tarkin turns to the computer readout screen. Flames move around the green disk at the center of the screen; numbers read across the bottom.

VOICE: *(over speaker)* Rebel base, three minutes and closing.

INT. RED LEADER'S COCKPIT

Red Leader looks over at his wingmen.

RED LEADER: Red boys, this is Red Leader.

INT. MASSASSI OUTPOST – WAR ROOM

RED LEADER: *(over speaker)* Rendezvous at mark six point one.

WEDGE: *(over speaker)* This is Red Two. Flying towards you.

BIGGS: *(over speaker)* Red Three, standing by.

Dodonna moves to the intercom.

INT. RED LEADER'S COCKPIT

DODONNA: *(over headset)* Red Leader, this is Base One. Keep half your group out of range for the next run.

INT. BIGGS' COCKPIT

Biggs listens in.

INT. LUKE'S X-WING FIGHTER – COCKPIT

RED LEADER'S VOICE: *(over headset)* Copy, Base One. Luke, take Red Two and Three.

INT. RED LEADER'S COCKPIT

RED LEADER: Hold up here and wait for my signal . . .

INT. LUKE'S X-WING FIGHTER – COCKPIT

RED LEADER'S VOICE: *(over headset)* . . . to start your run.

Luke nods his head.

EXT. SPACE AROUND THE DEATH STAR

The X-wing fighters of Luke, Biggs, and Wedge fly in formation high above the Death Star's surface.

INT. LUKE'S X-WING FIGHTER – COCKPIT

Luke peers out from his cockpit.

EXT. SURFACE OF THE DEATH STAR

Two X-wings move across the surface of the Death Star. Red Leader's X-wing drops down to the surface leading to the exhaust port.

INT. RED LEADER'S COCKPIT

Red Leader looks around to watch for the TIE fighters. He begins to perspire.

RED LEADER: This is it!

EXT. SPACE

Red Leader roams down the trench of the Death Star as lasers streak across the black heavens.

EXT. DEATH STAR SURFACE – GUN EMPLACEMENT

A huge remote-control laser cannon fires at the approaching Rebel fighters.

EXT. DEATH STAR TRENCH

The Rebel fighters evade the Imperial laserblasts.

(CONT'D)

CONTINUED

INT. RED TEN'S COCKPIT

RED TEN: We should be able to see it by now.

EXT. DEATH STAR TRENCH

From the cockpits of the Rebel pilots, the surface of the Death Star streaks by, with Imperial laserfire shooting toward them.

INT. RED LEADER'S COCKPIT

RED LEADER: Keep your eyes open for those fighters!

EXT. DEATH STAR TRENCH

The Rebel fighters fly in formation.

INT. RED TEN'S COCKPIT.

RED TEN: There's too much interference!

EXT. SPACE – ABOVE DEATH STAR TRENCH

Three X-wing fighters move in formation above the Death Star trench.

RED TEN'S VOICE: Red Five, can you see them from where you are?

INT. LUKE'S X-WING FIGHTER – COCKPIT

Luke looks down at the Death Star surface below.

LUKE: No sign of any ... Wait!

LUKE: *(over headset)* Coming in point three five.

Red Ten looks up and sees the Imperial fighters.

RED TEN: I see them.

EXT. SURFACE OF THE DEATH STAR

Three TIE fighters, Vader flanked by two wingmen, dive in a tight formation. The sun reflects off their dominant solar fins as they loop toward the Death Star's surface.

INT. RED LEADER'S COCKPIT

RED LEADER: I'm in range.

Red Leader moves his targeting device in front of his eyes.

EXT. SURFACE OF THE DEATH STAR

Red Leader's X-wing moves up the Death Star trench.

INT. RED LEADER'S COCKPIT

RED LEADER: Target's coming up!

Red Leader looks into his targeting device at his computer target readout screen.

RED LEADER: Just hold them off for a few seconds.

INT. DARTH VADER'S COCKPIT

Vader adjusts his control lever and dives on the X-wing fighters.

VADER: Close up formation.

The three TIE fighters move in formation across the Death Star surface.

INT. RED LEADER'S COCKPIT

RED LEADER: Almost there!

(CONT'D)

CONTINUED

Red Leader lines up his target on the targeting device cross hairs.

EXT. SURFACE OF THE DEATH STAR

Vader and his wingmen zoom down the trench.

INT. DARTH VADER'S COCKPIT

Vader rapidly approaches the two X-wings of Red Ten and Red Twelve. The X-wings show in the center of Vader's computer screen. Vader's laser cannon flashes below the view of the front porthole.

EXT. SPACE

Red Twelve's X-wing fighter is hit by Vader's laserfire, and it explodes into flames against the trench.

INT. RED TEN'S COCKPIT

Red Ten works at his controls furiously, trying to avoid Vader's fighter behind him.

RED TEN: You'd better let her loose.

INT. RED LEADER'S COCKPIT

Red Leader is concentrating on his targeting device.

RED TEN: *(over headset)* They're right behind me.

RED LEADER: Almost there!

INT. RED TEN'S COCKPIT

Red Ten panics.

RED TEN: I can't hold them!

EXT. SURFACE OF THE DEATH STAR

Vader and his wingmen whip through the trench in pursuit of the Rebel fighters.

INT. RED TEN'S COCKPIT

Red Ten looks over his shoulder.

INT. DARTH VADER'S COCKPIT

Vader coolly pushes the fire button on his control stick.

INT. RED TEN'S COCKPIT

Darth Vader's well-aimed laserfire proves to be unavoidable, and strikes Red Ten's ship. Red Ten screams in anguish and pain.

EXT. SPACE AROUND THE DEATH STAR

Red Ten's ship explodes and bursts into flames.

INT. RED LEADER'S COCKPIT

Grimly, Red Leader takes careful aim and watches his computer targeting device, which shows the target lined up in the cross hairs, and fires.

EXT. DEATH STAR TRENCH

Red Leader's missiles zoom down the trench.

RED LEADER: It's away!

EXT. DEATH STAR SURFACE

Red Leader's X-wing pulls up just before a huge explosion billows out of the trench.
    An armed Imperial stormtrooper is knocked to the floor by the attack explosion. Other troopers scurrying about the corridors are knocked against the wall and lose their balance.

(CONT'D)

CONTINUED

INT. MASSASSI OUTPOST — WAR ROOM

Leia and the others stare at the computer screen.

RED NINE'S VOICE: *(over speaker)* It's a hit!

RED LEADER: *(over speaker)* Negative.

INT. RED LEADER'S COCKPIT

Tiny explosions are visible in the distance.

RED LEADER: Negative! It didn't go in, just impacted on the surface.

INT. MASSASSI OUTPOST — WAR ROOM

Leia shows her disappointment.

EXT. SPACE AROUND THE DEATH STAR — TIE FIGHTER

Darth Vader peels off in pursuit as Red Leader's X-wing passes the Death Star horizon.

INT. DARTH VADER'S COCKPIT

Vader swings his ship around for his next kill.

INT. RED LEADER'S COCKPIT

LUKE: *(over headset)* Red Leader, we're right above you. Turn to point .

INT. LUKE'S X-WING FIGHTER — COCKPIT

Luke tries to spot Red Leader. He looks down at the Death Star surface.

LUKE: . . . oh-five; we'll cover for you.

RED LEADER: *(over headset)* Stay there . . .

INT. RED LEADER'S COCKPIT

A wary Red Leader looks about nervously.

RED LEADER: . . . I just lost my starboard engine.

INT. WEDGE'S COCKPIT

Wedge looks down out of his cockpit.

INT. LUKE'S X-WING FIGHTER — COCKPIT

RED LEADER: *(over headset)* Get set up . . .

INT. RED LEADER'S COCKPIT

RED LEADER: . . . for your attack run.

INT. DARTH VADER'S COCKPIT

Vader's gloved hand makes contact with the control sticks, and he presses their firing buttons.

EXT. SPACE AROUND THE DEATH STAR

Laserbolts are firing from Vader's TIE fighter, connecting with Red Leader's Rebel X-wing fighter.

INT. RED LEADER'S COCKPIT

Red Leader screams.

Luke looks out the window of his X-wing at the explosion of Red Leader's fighter far below. For the first time, he feels the helplessness of his situation.

INT. DEATH STAR

DEATH STAR INTERCOM VOICE: Rebel base, one minute and closing.

(CONT'D)

CONTINUED

Grand Moff Tarkin casts a sinister eye at the computer screen.

INT. MASSASSI OUTPOST — WAR ROOM

Dodonna and Princess Leia, with Threepio beside them, listen intently to the talk between the pilots. The room is grim after Red Leader's death. Princess Leia nervously paces the room.

LUKE: *(over speaker)* Biggs, Wedge, let's close it up. We're going in. We're going in full throttle.

INT. LUKE'S COCKPIT

LUKE: That ought to keep those fighters off our back.

INT. WEDGE'S COCKPIT

WEDGE: Right with you, boss.

EXT. SPACE AROUND THE DEATH STAR

The two X-wings peel off against a background of stars and dive toward the Death Star.

INT. BIGGS' COCKPIT

BIGGS: Luke, at that speed will you be able to pull out in time?

LUKE: It'll be just like Beggar's Canyon back home.

EXT. SPACE AROUND THE DEATH STAR

The three X-wings move in towards the trench unleashing a barrage of laserfire. Laserbolts are returned from the Death Star.

INT. BIGGS' COCKPIT

Biggs struggles with his controls.

BIGGS: We'll stay back far enough to cover you.

INT. LUKE'S COCKPIT

WEDGE: *(over headset)* My scope shows the tower, but I can't see the exhaust port!

INT. WEDGE'S COCKPIT

WEDGE: Are you sure the computer can hit it?

EXT. DEATH STAR TRENCH

The two covering X-wings fly down the trench, dodging laserbolts.

EXT. DEATH STAR — GUN EMPLACEMENT

The Death Star laser cannon slowly rotates as it shoots laserbolts.

INT. LUKE'S X-WING FIGHTER — COCKPIT

LUKE: Watch yourself! Increase speed full throttle!

WEDGE: What about that tower?

INT. LUKE'S X-WING FIGHTER — COCKPIT

LUKE: You worry about those fighters! I'll worry about the tower!

EXT. DEATH STAR SURFACE

Luke's X-wing streaks through the trench, firing lasers.

INT. LUKE'S X-WING FIGHTER — COCKPIT

Luke breaks into a nervous sweat as the laserfire is returned, nicking one of his wings close to the engine.

LUKE: *(to Artoo)* Artoo ... that, that stabilizer's broken loose again. See if you can't lock it down!

(CONT'D)

CONTINUED

EXT. LUKE'S X-WING FIGHTER

Artoo works to repair the damages. The canyon wall rushes by in the background, making his delicate task seem more precarious.

EXT. DEATH STAR

Two laser cannons are firing on the Rebel fighters.

INT. BIGGS' COCKPIT

Biggs looks around nervously for the TIE fighters.

INT. WEDGE'S COCKPIT

Wedge looks up and sees the TIE ships.

EXT. DEATH STAR TRENCH

Vader and his wingmen are closing in.

INT. WEDGE'S COCKPIT

WEDGE: Fighters. Coming in, point three.

Luke's targeting device marks off the distance to the target.

EXT. SPACE AROUND THE DEATH STAR

Vader and his wingmen zoom closer.

INT. WEDGE'S COCKPIT

Wedge looks over his shoulder at the closing TIE fighters.

INT. DARTH VADER'S COCKPIT

Vader adjusts his controls and fires laserbolts at the two X-wings flying down the trench. He scores a direct hit on Wedge.

INT. MASSASSI OUTPOST – WAR ROOM

Leia and the others are grouped around the computer board.

WEDGE: *(over headset)* I'm hit!

INT. WEDGE'S COCKPIT

WEDGE: I can't stay with you.

LUKE: *(over headset)* Get clear, Wedge.

INT. LUKE'S X-WING FIGHTER – COCKPIT

LUKE: You can't do any more good back there!

INT. WEDGE'S COCKPIT

WEDGE: Sorry!

EXT. SPACE AROUND THE DEATH STAR

Wedge pulls his crippled X-wing back away from the battle.

Vader watches the escape but issues a command to his wingmen.

VADER: Let him go! Stay on the leader!

EXT. SPACE AROUND THE DEATH STAR

Luke's X-wing speeds down the trench; the three TIE fighters, still in perfect unbroken formation, tail close behind.

(CONT'D)

CONTINUED

INT. BIGGS' COCKPIT

Biggs looks around at the TIE fighters. He is worried.

BIGGS: Hurry, Luke, they're coming in much faster this time.

INT. LUKE'S COCKPIT

BIGGS: *(over headset)* We can't hold them!

EXT. SPACE AROUND THE DEATH STAR

The three TIE fighters move ever closer, closing in on Luke and Biggs.

INT. LUKE'S X-WING FIGHTER — COCKPIT

Luke looks back anxiously at little Artoo.

LUKE: Artoo, try and increase the power!

EXT. LUKE'S X-WING FIGHTER

Ignoring the bumpy ride, a beeping Artoo-Detoo struggles to increase the power, his dome swiveling.

EXT. SPACE AROUND THE DEATH STAR

Stealthily, the TIE formation creeps closer.

INT. DARTH VADER'S COCKPIT

Vader adjusts his control stick.

INT. BIGGS' COCKPIT

Biggs looks around at the TIE fighters.

INT. LUKE'S X-WING FIGHTER — COCKPIT

Luke looks into his targeting device.

BIGGS: *(over headset)* Hurry up, Luke! Wait!

EXT. SPACE AROUND THE DEATH STAR

Vader and his wingmen race through the Death Star trench. Biggs moves in to cover for Luke, but Vader gains on him.

INT. BIGGS' COCKPIT

Biggs sees the TIE fighters aiming at him.

INT. DARTH VADER'S COCKPIT

Vader squeezes the fire button on his controls.

INT. BIGGS' COCKPIT

Biggs' cockpit explodes around him, lighting him in red.

EXT. SURFACE OF THE DEATH STAR

Biggs' ship bursts into a million flaming bits and scatters across the surface.

INT. MASSASSI OUTPOST — WAR ROOM

Leia and the others stare at the computer board

INT. LUKE'S X-WING FIGHTER — COCKPIT

Luke is stunned by Biggs' death, but his anger is also growing.

INT. DEATH STAR — CONTROL ROOM

Grand Moff Tarkin watches the projected target screen with satisfaction.

(CONT'D)

CONTINUED

DEATH STAR INTERCOM VOICE: Rebel base, thirty seconds and closing.

INT. DARTH VADER'S COCKPIT

Vader takes aim on Luke and talks to his wingmen.

VADER: I'm on the leader.

EXT. SURFACE OF THE DEATH STAR – LUKE'S SHIP

Luke's ship streaks through the trench of the Death Star.

INT. MASSASSI OUTPOST – WAR ROOM

Princess Leia glances at Threepio with a solid, grim determination. Threepio seems nervous.

THREEPIO: Hang on, Artoo!

INT. LUKE'S X-WING FIGHTER – COCKPIT

Luke concentrates on his targeting device.

EXT. SURFACE OF THE DEATH STAR

Three TIE fighters charge away down the trench toward Luke. Vader's fingers curl around the control stick.

INT. LUKE'S X-WING FIGHTER – COCKPIT

Luke adjusts the lens of his targeting device.

EXT. SURFACE OF THE DEATH STAR

Luke's ship charges down the trench.

INT. LUKE'S X-WING FIGHTER – COCKPIT

Luke lines up the yellow cross-hair lines of the targeting device's screen. He looks into the targeting device, then starts at a voice he hears.

BEN'S VOICE: Use the Force, Luke.

EXT. SURFACE OF THE DEATH STAR

The Death Star trench zooms by.

INT. LUKE'S X-WING FIGHTER – COCKPIT

Luke looks up, then starts to look back into the targeting device. He has second thoughts.

BEN'S VOICE: Let go, Luke.

EXT. SURFACE OF THE DEATH STAR

Luke's fighter streaks through the trench.

INT. DARTH VADER'S COCKPIT

VADER: The Force is strong with this one!

Vader follows Luke's X-wing down the trench.

INT. LUKE'S X-WING FIGHTER – COCKPIT

Luke looks to the targeting device, then away as he hears Ben's voice.

BEN'S VOICE: Luke, trust me.

Luke's hand reaches for the control panel and presses the button. The targeting device moves away.

INT. MASSASSI OUTPOST – WAR ROOM

Leia and the others stand watching the projected screen.

BASE VOICE: (*over speaker*) His computer's off. Luke, you switched off your targeting computer. What's wrong?

(CONT'D)

CONTINUED

LUKE'S VOICE: (*over speaker*) Nothing. I'm all right.

EXT. SURFACE OF THE DEATH STAR

Luke's ship streaks ever close to the exhaust port.

INT. LUKE'S X-WING FIGHTER – COCKPIT

Luke looks at the Death Star surface streaking by.

INT. LUKE'S X-WING FIGHTER

Artoo-Detoo turns his head from side to side, beeping in anticipation.

EXT. SURFACE OF THE DEATH STAR

The three TIE fighters, manned by Vader and his two wingmen, follow Luke's X-wing down the trench.
Vader maneuvers his controls as he looks at his doomed target. He presses the fire buttons on his control sticks. Laserfire shoots toward Luke's X-wing fighter.

LUKE'S X-WING FIGHTER

A large burst of Vader's laserfire engulfs Artoo. The arms go limp on the smoking little droid as he makes a high-pitched sound.

INT. LUKE'S X-WING FIGHTER – COCKPIT

Luke looks frantically back over his shoulder at Artoo.

EXT. LUKE'S X-WING FIGHTER

Smoke billows out around little Artoo and sparks begin to fly.

LUKE: I've lost Artoo!

Artoo's beeping sound dies out.

INT. MASSASSI OUTPOST – WAR ROOM

Leia and the others stare intently at the projected screen, while Threepio watches the princess.

MASSASSI INTERCOM VOICE: The Death Star has cleared the planet. The Death Star has cleared the planet.

Lights representing the Death Star and targets glow brightly.

INT. DEATH STAR – CONTROL ROOM

DEATH STAR INTERCOM VOICE: Rebel base, in range.

Lights representing the Death Star and targets glow brightly.

TARKIN: You may fire when ready.

DEATH STAR INTERCOM VOICE: Commence primary ignition.

An officer reaches up and pushes buttons on the control panel.

EXT. SURFACE OF THE DEATH STAR

The three TIE fighters zoom down the Death Star's trench in pursuit of Luke, never breaking formation.

INT. LUKE'S COCKPIT

Luke's looks anxiously at the exhaust port.

INT. DARTH VADER'S COCKPIT

Vader adjusts his control sticks, checking his projected targeting screen.

EXT. SURFACE OF THE DEATH STAR

Luke's ship barrels down the trench.

(CONT'D)

CONTINUED

INT. LUKE'S COCKPIT

Luke continues determinedly down the trench.

INT. DARTH VADER'S COCKPIT

Vader's targeting computer swings around into position. Vader takes careful aim on Luke's X-wing fighter.

VADER: I have you now.

He pushes the fire buttons.

EXT. SURFACE OF THE DEATH STAR

The three TIE fighters move in on Luke. As Vader's center fighter unleashes a volley of laserfire, one of the TIE ships at his side is hit and explodes into flame. The two remaining ships continue to move on.

INT. LUKE'S X-WING FIGHTER – COCKPIT

Luke looks about, wondering whose laserfire destroyed Vader's wingman.

INT. DARTH VADER'S COCKPIT

Vader is taken by surprise, and looks out from his cockpit.

VADER: What?

INT. DARTH VADER'S WINGMAN – COCKPIT

Vader's wingman searches around him trying to locate the unknown attacker.

INT. MILLENNIUM FALCON – COCKPIT

Han grins from ear to ear.

HAN: *(yelling)* Yahoo!

EXT. SPACE AROUND THE DEATH STAR

The Millennium Falcon heads right at the two TIE fighters. It's a collision course.

INT. WINGMAN'S COCKPIT

The wingman spots the pirateship coming at him and warns the Dark Lord.

WINGMAN: Look out!

EXT. DEATH STAR TRENCH

Vader's wingman panics at the sight of the oncoming pirate starship and veers radically to one side, colliding with Vader's TIE fighter in the process. Vader's wingman crashes into the side wall of the trench and explodes.

EXT. SPACE AROUND THE DEATH STAR

Vader's damaged ship has spun out of the trench with a damaged wing and continues to spin out of control with a bent solar fin, heading for deep space.

INT. DARTH VADER'S COCKPIT

Vader turns round and round in circles as his ship spins into space.

EXT. SURFACE OF THE DEATH STAR

Solo's ship moves in toward the Death Star trench.

INT. MILLENNIUM FALCON – COCKPIT

Solo, smiling, speaks to Luke over his headset mike.

HAN: *(into mike)* You're all clear, kid. Now let's . . .

INT. MASSASSI OUTPOST – WAR ROOM

(CONT'D)

1:49

CONTINUED

Leia and the others listen to Solo's transmission.

HAN: *(over speaker)* . . . blow this thing and go home!

INT. LUKE'S X-WING FIGHTER — COCKPIT

Luke looks up and smiles. He concentrates on the exhaust port, then fires his laser torpedoes.

EXT. SURFACE OF THE DEATH STAR

Luke's torpedo shoots towards the port and seems to simply disappear into the surface and not explode. But the shots do find their mark and have gone into the exhaust port and are heading for the main reactor.

INT. LUKE'S X-WING FIGHTER — COCKPIT

Luke throws his head back in relief.

INT. DEATH STAR

An Imperial soldier runs to the control panel board and pulls the attack lever as the board behind him lights up.

INTERCOM VOICE: Stand by.

EXT. SPACE AROUND THE DEATH STAR

Two X-wings, a Y-wing, and the pirateship race toward Yavin in the distance.

INT. DEATH STAR

Several Imperial soldiers, flanking a pensive Grant Moff Tarkin, busily push control levers and buttons.

INTERCOM VOICE: Stand by.

EXT. SPACE AROUND THE DEATH STAR

The Rebel ships have raced out of sight, leaving the moon-like Death Star alone against a blanket of stars. The Death Star bursts into a supernova, creating a spectacular heavenly display.

INT. MILLENNIUM FALCON — COCKPIT

HAN: Great shot, kid. That was one in a million.

INT. LUKE'S X-WING FIGHTER — COCKPIT

Luke is at last at ease, and his eyes are closed.

BEN'S VOICE: Remember, the Force will be with you . . . always.

The ship rocks back and forth.

EXT. DARTH VADER'S TIE FIGHTER

Vader's ship spins off into space.

INT. DARTH VADER'S TIE FIGHTER

Vader rights his ship.

EXT. SPACE

Vader's TIE fighter heads off into space.

EXT. SPACE

The Rebel ships race toward the fourth moon of Yavin.

INT. MASSASSI OUTPOST — MAIN HANGAR

Luke climbs out of his starship fighter and is cheered by a throng of ground crew and pilots. Luke climbs down the ladder as they all welcome him with laughter, cheers, and shouting.
    Princess Leia rushes toward him.

LEIA: Luke!

(CONT'D)

CONTINUED

She throws her arms around Luke and hugs him as they dance around a circle. Solo runs in toward Luke.

HAN: *(laughing)* Hey! Hey!

Han and Luke embrace one another.

LUKE: *(laughing)* I knew you'd come back! I just knew it!

HAN: Well, I wasn't gonna let you get all the credit and take all the reward.

Luke and Han look at one another, as Solo playfully shoves at Luke's face. Leia moves in between them.

LEIA: *(laughing)* Hey, I knew there was more to you than money.

Luke looks toward the ship.

LUKE: Oh no!

The fried little Artoo-Detoo is lifted off the back of the fighter and carried off under the worried eyes of Threepio.

THREEPIO: Oh, my! Artoo! Can you hear me? Say something! *(to mechanic)* You can repair him, can't you?

TECHNICIAN: We'll get to work on him right away.

THREEPIO: You must repair him! Sir, if any of my circuits or gears will help, I'll gladly donate them.

LUKE: He'll be all right.

EXT. MASSASSI OUTPOST

Trumpets are heard over the jungle setting.

INT. MASSASSI – MAIN THRONE ROOM

Luke, Han, and Chewbacca enter the huge ruins of the main temple. Hundreds of troops are lined up in neat rows. At the far end stands a vision in white, the beautiful young Senator Leia. Luke and the others solemnly march up the long aisle and kneel before Senator Leia.

Chewbacca is confused. Dodonna and several other dignitaries stand behind the Princess Leia. Leia is dressed in a long white dress and is staggeringly beautiful. She places a gold medallion around Han's neck. He winks at her. To one side a pristine Threepio stands, awestruck by the whole event. She then repeats the ceremony with Luke, who is moved by the event. They turn and face the assembled troops, who all applaud them. Chewbacca growls and a shined-up and fully repaired Artoo beeps with happiness.

FADE OUT

END CREDITS OVER STARS

THE END

(CONT'D)

STAR WARS

Episode V

THE EMPIRE STRIKES BACK

CONTINUED

A long time ago in a galaxy far,
far away....

A vast sea of stars serves as the backdrop for the main title. War drums echo through the heavens as a roll-up slowly crawls into infinity.

STAR WARS

Episode V

THE EMPIRE STRIKES BACK

It is a dark time for the
Rebellion. Although the Death
Star has been destroyed,
Imperial troops have driven the
Rebel forces from their hidden
base and pursued them across
the galaxy.

Evading the dreaded Imperial
Starfleet, a group of freedom
fighters led by Luke Skywalker
has established a new secret
base on the remote ice world
of Hoth.

The evil lord Darth Vader
obsessed with finding young
Skywalker, has dispatched
thousands of remote probes into
the far reaches of space....

EXT. GALAXY – PLANET HOTH

A Star Destroyer moves through space. It releases Imperial probe robots from its underside.
    One of these probes zooms towards the planet Hoth and lands on its ice-covered surface. An explosion marks the point of impact.

EXT. HOTH – METEORITE CRATER – SNOW PLAIN – DAY

A weird mechanical sound rises above the whining of the wind. A strange probe robot, with several extended sensors, emerges from the smoke-shrouded crater. The ominous mechanical probe floats across the snow plain and disappears.

EXT. PLAIN OF HOTH – DAY

A small figure gallops across the windswept ice slope. The bundled rider is mounted on a large gray two-legged snow lizard, a tauntaun.
    The rider gallops up a slope and reins his lizard to a stop. Pulling off his protective goggles, Luke Skywalker notices something in the sky. He takes a pair of electrobinoculars from his utility belt and through them sees smoke rising from where the probe robot has crashed.
    The wind whips at Luke's fur-lined cap and he activates a comlink transmitter. His tauntaun shifts nervously beneath him.

LUKE: *(into comlink)* Echo Three to Echo Seven. Han, old buddy, do you read me?

After a little static a familiar voice is heard.

HAN: *(over comlink)* Loud and clear, kid. What's up?

LUKE: *(into comlink)* Well, I finished my circle. I don't pick up any life readings.

(CONT'D)

CONTINUED

HAN: *(over comlink)* There isn't enough life on this ice cube to fill a space cruiser. The sensors are placed, I'm going back.

LUKE: *(into comlink)* Right. I'll see you shortly. There's a meteorite that hit the ground near here. I want to check it out. It won't take long.

Luke clicks off his transmitter and reins back on his nervous lizard. He pats the beast on the head to calm it.

LUKE: Hey, steady girl. Hey, what's the matter? You smell something?

Suddenly he hears a monstrous howl and turns to see an eleven-foot-tall shape towering over him. It is a Wampa Ice Creature, lunging at him ferociously.
 Luke is hit by a huge white claw. He falls unconscious into the snow and in a moment the terrified screams of the tauntaun are cut short by the horrible snap of a neck being broken.
 The Wampa Ice Creature grabs Luke by one ankle and drags him away across the frozen plain.

EXT. HOTH – REBEL BASE ENTRANCE – DAY

A stalwart figure rides his tauntaun up to the entrance of an enormous ice cave.

INT. HOTH – REBEL BASE – MAIN HANGAR DECK

Rebel troopers rush about unloading supplies and otherwise securing their new base. The rider, Han Solo, swings off his lizard and pulls off his goggles.
 He walks into the main hangar deck toward the Millennium Falcon, which is parked among several fighters. Mechanics, R2 units, and various other droids hurry about. Han stops at the Millennium Falcon where his Wookiee copilot, Chewbacca, is welding on a central lifter.

HAN: Chewie! Chewie! Chewie!

Chewie stops his work and lifts his face shield, growling an irritated greeting to his boss.

HAN: All right, don't lose your temper. I'll come right back and give you a hand.

Chewbacca puts his mask back on and returns to his welding as Han leaves.

INT. HOTH – REBEL BASE – COMMAND CENTER

A makeshift command center has been set up in a blasted area of thick ice. The low-ceilinged room is a beehive of activity. Controllers, troopers, and droids move about setting up electronic equipment and monitoring radar signals.
 General Rieekan looks up from a console at Han's approach.

RIEEKAN: Solo?

HAN: No sign of life out there, General. The sensors are in place. You'll know if anything comes around.

RIEEKAN: Commander Skywalker reported in yet?

HAN: No. He's checking out a meteorite that hit near him.

RIEEKAN: With all the meteor activity in this system, it's going to be difficult to spot approaching ships.

Han blurts out what is on his mind.

HAN: General, I got to leave. I can't stay anymore.

Princess Leia, standing at a console nearby, is dressed in a short white combat jacket and pants. Her hair is braided and tied across her head in a Nordic fashion. She overhears their conversation and seems somewhat distressed.

RIEEKAN: I'm sorry to hear that.

HAN: Well, there's a price on my head. If I don't pay off Jabba the Hutt, I'm a dead man.

RIEEKAN: A death mark's not an easy thing to live with. You're a good fighter, Solo. I hate to lose you.

HAN: Thank you, General.

(CONT'D)

CONTINUED

He turns to Leia as Rieekan moves away.

HAN: *(with feeling)* Well, Your Highness, I guess this is it.

LEIA: That's right.

Leia is angry. Han sees she has no warmth to offer him. He shakes his head and adopts a sarcastic tone.

HAN: *(coolly)* Well, don't get all mushy on me. So long, Princess.

Han walks away into the quiet corridor adjoining the command center. Leia stews a moment, then hurries after him.

INT. HOTH – REBEL BASE – ICE CORRIDOR

LEIA: Han!

Han stops in the corridor and turns to face Leia.

HAN: Yes, Your Highnessness?

LEIA: I thought you had decided to stay.

HAN: Well, the bounty hunter we ran into on Ord Mantell changed my mind.

LEIA: Han, we need you!

HAN: We need?

LEIA: Yes.

HAN: Oh, what about you need?

LEIA: *(mystified)* I need? I don't know what you're talking about.

HAN: *(shakes his head, fed up)* You probably don't.

LEIA: And what precisely am I supposed to know?

HAN: Come on! You want me to stay because of the way you feel about me.

LEIA: Yes. You're a great help to us. You're a natural leader ...

HAN: No! That's not it. Come on. Aahhh – uh huh! Come on.

Leia stares at him, then understands.

LEIA: You're imagining things.

HAN: Am I? Then why are you following me? Afraid I was going to leave without giving you a goodbye kiss?

LEIA: I'd just as soon kiss a Wookiee.

HAN: I can arrange that. You could use a good kiss!

Angrily, Han strides down the corridor as Leia stares after him.

INT. HOTH – REBEL BASE – ANOTHER ICE CORRIDOR

A familiar stream of beeps and whistles heralds the approach of Artoo-Detoo and See-Threepio, who appear around a corner and move along an ice wall towards the main hangar.

THREEPIO: Don't try to blame me. I didn't ask you to turn on the thermal heater. I merely commented that it was freezing in the princess' chamber.

Artoo beeps a response.

THREEPIO: But it's supposed to be freezing. How are we going to dry out all her clothes? I really don't know.

Artoo beeps a stream of protesting whistles.

THREEPIO: Oh, switch off.

(CONT'D)

CONTINUED

INT. HOTH – REBEL BASE – MAIN HANGAR DECK

The two robots stop at Han Solo's space freighter. Han and Chewie are still struggling with their central lifters.

HAN: *(to Chewie)* Why did you take this apart now? I'm trying to get us out of there and you pull both of these –

THREEPIO: Excuse me, sir.

HAN: *(to Chewie)* Put them back together right now.

THREEPIO: Might I have a word with you, please?

HAN: What do you want?

THREEPIO: Well, it's Princess Leia, sir. She's been trying to get you on the communicator.

HAN: I turned it off. I don't want to talk to her.

THREEPIO: Oh. Well, Princess Leia is wondering about Master Luke. He hasn't come back yet. She doesn't know where he is.

HAN: I don't know where he is.

THREEPIO: Nobody knows where he is.

HAN: What do you mean, 'nobody knows'?

THREEPIO: Well, uh, you see . . .

Han walks off, as Threepio follows him.

HAN: Deck Officer! Deck Officer!

THREEPIO: Excuse me, sir. Might I inqu –

Han abruptly puts his hand over Threepio's mouth as the deck officer approaches.

DECK OFFICER: Yes, sir?

HAN: Do you know where Commander Skywalker is?

DECK OFFICER: I haven't seen him. It's possible he came in through the south entrance.

HAN: It's possible? Why don't you go find out? It's getting dark out there.

DECK OFFICER: Yes, sir.

The deck officer leaves hurriedly, as Han takes his hand off Threepio's mouth.

THREEPIO: Excuse me, sir. Might I inquire what's going on?

HAN: Why not?

THREEPIO: Impossible man. Come along, Artoo, let's find Princess Leia. Between ourselves, I think Master Luke is in considerable danger.

INT. HOTH – REBEL BASE – MAIN ICE TUNNEL

Deck officer and his assistant hurry toward Han as he enters the tunnel.

DECK OFFICER: Sir. Commander Skywalker hasn't come in the south entrance. He might have forgotten to check in.

HAN: Not likely. Are the speeders ready?

DECK OFFICER: Er, not yet. We're having some trouble adapting them to the cold.

HAN: Then we'll have to go out on tauntauns.

DECK OFFICER: Sir, the temperature's dropping too rapidly.

HAN: That's right. And my friend's out in it.

(CONT'D)

CONTINUED

ASSISTANT OFFICER: I'll cover sector twelve. Have com-control set to screen alpha.

Han pushes through the troops and mounts a tauntaun.

DECK OFFICER: Your tauntaun'll freeze before you reach the first marker.

HAN: Then I'll see you in hell!

Han maneuvers his mount out of the cave and races into the dark and bitter night.

EXT. HOTH — ICE GORGE — DUSK

The jagged face of a huge ice wall sits gloomily in the dim twilight of a Hoth day. Luke hangs upside-down, ankles frozen into icy stalactites, his extended arms within a foot of the snow floor. He opens his eyes as a chilling moan of the hideous ice creature echoes off the gorge walls. Luke pulls himself up, grabs hold of his ankles, and futilely tries to unfasten the thongs.

Exhausted, he drops back into his hanging position. As he hangs there, he spies his lightsaber lying about three feet out of reach.

He focuses on the saber and, as his hand strains toward the weapon, he squeezes his eyes tight in concentration.

Just as the ice creature looms over Luke, the lightsaber jumps into Luke's hand.

The young warrior instantly ignites his sword, swings up, and cuts himself loose from the ice. He flops to the snow in a heap. Luke scrambles to his feet. He swings his lightsaber and the beast screams in pain.

EXT. HOTH — ENTRANCE TO ICE GORGE — DUSK

Luke scrabbles out of the gorge into the dark and snowy twilight. Weak and exhausted, he tumbles down a snow bank.

EXT. HOTH — SNOW PLAIN — DUSK

A small, lone figure riding a tauntaun races through the hostile vastness of snow and cold. As it runs, the tauntaun's legs kick up large clouds of snow and ice into the snowy air.

EXT. HOTH — OUTSIDE ICE HANGAR — DUSK

Artoo stands in the falling snow, beeping worriedly. Threepio moves stiffly over to him.

THREEPIO: You must come along now, Artoo. There's really nothing more we can do. And my joints are freezing up.

Artoo beeps, long and low.

THREEPIO: Don't say things like that! Of course we'll see Master Luke again. And he'll be quite all right, you'll see. *(to himself)* Stupid little short-circuit. He'll be quite all right.

Threepio has turned to go back inside the main hangar as Artoo mournfully keeps his vigil.

EXT. HOTH — SNOWDRIFT — DUSK

The wind is blowing quite strong now. Luke gets up and struggles to stay upright, but falls over again. Meanwhile, the searching Han dismounts from his tauntaun.

INT. REBEL BASE — MAIN HANGAR DECK — ENTRANCE — NIGHT

A Rebel lieutenant moves to Major Derlin, an officer keeping watch.

LIEUTENANT: Sir, all the patrols are in. Still no ... still no contact from Skywalker or Solo.

Princess Leia stands waiting for a sign of the two Rebel heroes. Threepio and Artoo approach.

THREEPIO: Mistress Leia, Artoo says he's been quite unable to pick up any signals, although he does admit that his own range is far too weak to abandon all hope.

DERLIN: Your Highness, there's nothing more we can do tonight. The shield doors must be closed.

Leia nods an acknowledgement, but she is lost in thought.

DERLIN: Close the doors.

(CONT'D)

CONTINUED

LIEUTENANT: Yes, sir.

Chewie lets out a short moan. At the same moment, Artoo begins a complex series of efficient beeps.

THREEPIO: Artoo says the changes of survival are seven hundred and twenty-five ... to one.

Leia stands praying to herself as the huge metal doors slam across the entrance of the ice cave. The loud booms echo throughout the huge cavern. Chewie lets out another suffering howl.

THREEPIO: Actually, Artoo has been known to make mistakes ... from time to time. Oh, dear, oh, dear. Don't worry about Master Luke, I'm sure he'll be all right. He's quite clever, you know ... for a human being.

EXT. HOTH – SNOWDRIFT – DUSK

Luke lies face down in the snow, nearly unconscious.

BEN: Luke ... Luke.

Slowly Luke looks up and sees Ben Kenobi, barely visible through the blowing snow. It is hard to tell if Kenobi is real or a hallucination.

LUKE: *(weakly)* Ben?

BEN: You will go to the Dagobah system.

LUKE: Dagobah system?

BEN: There you will learn from Yoda, the Jedi Master who instructed me.

LUKE: *(groaning faintly)* Ben ... Ben.

The image of Ben fades, revealing a lone tauntaun rider approaching from the windswept horizon.
    Luke drops into unconsciousness.
    Han hurries to his snow-covered friend. Han's tauntaun lets out a low, pitiful bellow. But Han's concern is with Luke, and he holds him urgently.

HAN: Luke! Luke! Don't do this, Luke. Come on, give me a sign here.

Luke doesn't respond. Han hears a rasping sound behind him. He turns, just in time to see his tauntaun stagger and then fall over into the snow.
    Han drags Luke to the beast.

HAN: Not much time.

He pushes Luke's inert form against the belly of the now dead beast.

LUKE: *(moaning)* Ben ... Ben ...

Han ignites Luke's saber and cuts the beast from head to toe.

HAN: Hang on, kid.

LUKE: *(mumbling)* Dagobah system ... You ... Dagobah ...

HAN: This may smell bad, kid ...

LUKE: *(moaning)* Yoda ...

HAN: *(struggling to get Luke inside the carcass)* ... but it will keep you warm ... till I can get the shelter built. Agh! Agh ... I thought they smelled bad on the outside! Agh!

The wind has picked up considerably, making it difficult to move. Han removes a pack from the dead creature's back, taking out a shelter container. He begins to set up what can only be a pitiful protection against a bitter Hoth night.

EXT. HOTH – SNOWDRIFT – DAWN

Four snub-nosed armored snowspeeders race across the white landscape.

INT. SNOWSPEEDER – COCKPIT

(CONT'D)

CONTINUED

There is only one pilot, Zev, in the enclosed two-man craft. He concentrates on the scopes which ring his cockpit. He hears a low beep from one of his monitors.

ZEV: *(into transmitter)* Echo Base ... I've got something! Not much, but it could be a life form ...

EXT. HOTH — SNOWDRIFT

The small craft banks and makes a slow arc, then races off in a new direction.

INT. SNOWSPEEDER — COCKPIT

The pilot switches over to a new transmitter.

ZEV: *(into transmitter)* Commander Skywalker, do you copy? This is Rogue Two. This is Rogue Two. Captain Solo, do you copy?

EXT. HOTH — SNOWDRIFT

The snowspeeder races across the white landscape.

INT. SNOWSPEEDER — COCKPIT

ZEV: Commander Skywalker, do you copy? This is Rogue Two.

There is a sharp crackle of static, then a faint voice.

HAN: *(filtered over Zev's receiver)* Good morning. Nice of you guys to drop by.

ZEV: *(switching transmitters)* Echo Base ... this is Rogue Two. I found them. Repeat, I found them.

EXT. HOTH — SNOWDRIFT — DAY

Standing outside the small shelter he has set up, Han spots Zev's snowspeeder approaching in the distance, and waves at the tiny craft.

INT. REBEL BASE — MAIN HANGAR DECK

The snowspeeder returns.

INT. REBEL BASE — MEDICAL CENTER

Strange robot surgeons adjust a mass of electronic equipment. Luke is submerged in a bacta tank, thrashing about in his delirium.

INT. REBEL BASE — MEDICAL CENTER — RECOVERY ROOM

Luke sits up in a recovery-room bed, weak but smiling. His face shows terrible wounds from the Wampa's attack.

THREEPIO: Master Luke, sir, it's so good to see you fully functional again.

Artoo beeps his good wishes.

THREEPIO: Artoo expresses his relief, also.

Han and Chewie make their entrance, the Wookiee growling his greetings.

HAN: How you feeling, kid? You don't look so bad to me. In fact, you look strong enough to pull the ears off a gundark.

LUKE: Thanks to you.

HAN: That's two you owe me, junior.

Han turns as Leia enters the room. He looks at her with a big, devilish grin.

HAN: Well, Your Worship, looks like you managed to keep me around for a little while longer.

LEIA: *(haughtily)* I had nothing to do with it. General Rieekan thinks it's dangerous for any ships to leave the system until we've activated the energy shield.

HAN: That's a good story. I think you just can't bear to let a gorgeous guy like me out of your sight.

(CONT'D)

CONTINUED

LEIA: I don't know where you get your delusions, laser-brain.

Chewie is amused; he laughs in his manner. Han, enjoying himself, regards Chewie good-humoredly.

HAN: Laugh it up, fuzzball. But you didn't see us alone in the south passage. *(looking pointedly at Luke)* She expressed her true feelings for me.

Leia is flushed, eyes darting between Luke and Han.

LEIA: My ... ! Why, you stuck-up ... half-witted ... scruffy-looking ... nerf-herder!

HAN: Who's scruffy-looking? *(to Luke)* I must have hit pretty close to the mark to get her all riled up like that, huh, kid?

Leia looks vulnerable for a moment, then the mask falls again, and she focuses on Luke.

LEIA: Why, I guess you don't know everything about women yet.

With that she leans over and kisses Luke on the lips. Then she turns on her heel and walks out, leaving everyone in the room slightly dumbstruck. With some smugness, Luke puts his hand behind his head and grins.
    Meanwhile, in the distance, the muffled sound of an alarm has been heard.

ANNOUNCER: *(over loudspeaker)* Headquarters personnel, report to command center.

The voice repeats the order and Han, Chewie, Artoo and Threepio hurry out of the room, bidding farewell to Luke.

HAN: Take it easy.

THREEPIO: Excuse us, please.

INT. HOTH – REBEL BASE – COMMAND CENTER

Rieekan looks up grimly from a console screen. He calls over to Leia and Han.

RIEEKAN: Princess ... we have a visitor.

The group hurries over to Rieekan.

RIEEKAN: We've picked up something outside the base of zone twelve, moving east.

SENIOR CONTROLLER: It's metal.

LEIA: Then it couldn't be one of those creatures.

HAN: It could be a speeder, one of ours.

SENIOR CONTROLLER: No. Wait – there's something very weak coming through.

Threepio has stepped up to the control panel and listens intently to the strange signal.

THREEPIO: Sir, I am fluent in six million forms of communication. This signal is not used by the Alliance. It could be an Imperial code.

The transmission ends in static.

HAN: It isn't friendly, whatever it is. Come on, Chewie, let's check it out.

RIEEKAN: Send Rogues Ten and Eleven to station three-eight.

EXT. HOTH – SNOW PLAIN – DAY

The dark probe robot lowers its large antennae from the top of its head and moves away from the smouldering ruins of station three-eight and down a ridge towards the Rebel base.
    The probe droid spots Chewbacca who, not thirty feet away has popped his head over a snow bank. Instantly, the probe robot swings around, firing its deadly ray. But before it can get a shot off, it is hit from behind by a laserbolt from Han Solo's blaster, and explodes in a million pieces.

INT. HOTH – REBEL BASE – COMMAND CENTER

Leia and Rieekan listen to Han on the comlink.

(CONT'D)

CONTINUED

HAN: *(over comlink)* Fraid there's not much left.

LEIA: *(into comlink)* What was it?

HAN: *(over comlink)* Droid of some kind. I didn't hit it that hard. It must have had a self-destruct.

LEIA: *(into comlink)* An Imperial probe droid.

HAN: *(over comlink)* It's a good bet the Empire knows we're here.

RIEEKAN: We'd better start the evacuation.

EXT. SPACE — IMPERIAL FLEET

Darth Vader's Star Destroyer, larger and more awesome than the five Imperial Star Destroyers that surround it, sits in the vastness of space. The six huge ships are surrounded by a convoy of smaller spacecraft. TIE fighters dart to and fro.

INT. DARTH VADER'S STAR DESTROYER — BRIDGE — MAIN CONTROL DECK

Darth Vader, Lord of the Sith, surveys his fleet from the bridge. As the squat, evil-looking Admiral Ozzel and the younger, powerfully built General Veers approach him, Captain Piett hurries up to Ozzel.

PIETT: Admiral.

OZZEL: Yes Captain?

PIETT: I think we've got something, sir. The report is only a fragment from a probe droid in the Hoth system, but it's the best lead we've had.

OZZEL: *(irritated)* We have thousands of probe droids searching the galaxy. I want proof, not leads!

PIETT: The visuals indicate life readings.

OZZEL: It could mean anything. If we followed up every lead ...

PIETT: But, sir, the Hoth system is supposed to be devoid of human forms.

Controllers working the vast complex of electronic controls hear ominous approaching footsteps and look up from their controls. Darth Vader moves across the wide bridge like a chill wind.

VADER: You found something?

PIETT: Yes, my lord.

Vader moves to a large screen showing an image of the Rebel snow base. Rebel speeders can be seen approaching the base in the distance.

VADER: *(studying the image on the console screen)* That's it. The Rebels are there.

OZZEL: My lord, there are so many uncharted settlements. It could be smugglers, it could be ...

VADER: That is the system. And I'm sure Skywalker is with them. Set your course for the Hoth system. General Veers, prepare your men.

VEERS: Admiral?

Ozzel nods.

INT. HOTH — REBEL BASE — TRANSPORT BAY

A captain issues instructions to two of his men at the entrance to the main transport bay. The Rebels are moving to evacuate quickly, but not in panic.

REBEL CAPTAIN: Groups seven and ten will stay behind to fly the speeders. As soon as each transport is loaded, evacuation control will give clearance for immediate launch.

REBEL FIGHTER: Right, sir.

INT. HOTH — REBEL BASE — MAIN HANGAR DECK

(CONT'D)

CONTINUED

Han is welding on the lifters of the Millennium Falcon.
He finishes his work and stands up straight.

HAN: *(shouting to Chewie)* All right, that's it. Try it ...

Smoke rises from a minor explosion of the lifter.

HAN: Off! Turn it off! Turn it off! Off!

INT. REBEL BASE – MEDICAL CENTER

Luke dresses in readiness for the evacuation as his attending medical droid stands by.

MEDICAL DROID: Sir, it will take quite a while to evacuate the T-forty-sevens.

LUKE: Well, forget the heavy equipment. There's plenty of time to get the smaller modules on the transports.

MEDICAL DROID: Take care, sir.

LUKE: Thanks.

INT. REBEL BASE – MAIN HANGAR DECK

Pilots and gunners scurry about. Luke is headed toward a row of armored speeders. He stops at the rear of the Millennium Falcon, where Han and Chewie are still trying to repair the right lifter.

LUKE: Chewie, take care of yourself, okay?

As Luke pats Chewie on the arm, Chewie puts his arms around Luke and gives him a tight hug. Han is discussing the lifter with a repair droid when he sees Luke.

HAN: Hi, kid. *(to droid)* There's got to be a reason for it. Check it at the other end. Wait a second. *(to Luke)* You all right?

LUKE: Yeah.

Luke nods, smiles, then walks on. He and Han have exchanged a silent communication, each wishing the other safety, happiness – many things, all difficult to verbalize.

HAN: Be careful.

LUKE: You, too.

INT. REBEL BASE – CONTROL ROOM

In the control room, a controller urgently gestures for general Rieekan to check a computer scan.

CONTROLLER: General, there's a fleet of Star Destroyers coming out of hyperspace in sector four.

RIEEKAN: Reroute all power to the energy shield. We've got to hold them till all transports are away. Prepare for ground assault.

EXT. SPACE – IMPERIAL FLEET

Six huge Star Destroyers move through space into the Hoth system.

INT. VADER'S STAR DESTROYER – VADER'S CHAMBER – MEDITATION CUBICLE

In the cubicle the brooding Dark Lord sits in meditation. General Veers has come to see Vader. Although seemingly very sure of himself, Veers is still not bold enough to interrupt the meditating lord. The young general stands quietly at attention until the evil presence speaks.

VADER: What is it, General?

VEERS: My lord, the fleet has moved out of light-speed. Com-Scan has detected an energy field protecting an area of the sixth planet of the Hoth system. The field is strong enough to deflect any bombardment.

VADER: *(angrily)* The Rebels are alerted to our presence. Admiral Ozzel came out of light-speed too close to the system.

VEERS: He felt surprise was wiser ...

(CONT'D)

CONTINUED

VADER: He is as clumsy as he is stupid. General, prepare your troops for a surface attack.

VEERS: Yes, my lord.

Veers turns smartly and leaves as Vader activates a large viewscreen showing the bridge of his mighty ship. Admiral Ozzel appears on the viewscreen, standing slightly in front of Captain Piett.

OZZEL: Lord Vader, the fleet has moved out of light-speed, and we're preparing to ... Aaagh!

VADER: You have failed me for the last time, Admiral. Captain Piett.

Piett steps forward, as the admiral moves away, slightly confused, gasping and touching his throat as it begins to constrict painfully.

PIETT: Yes, my lord.

VADER: Make ready to land our troops beyond their energy field and deploy the fleet so that nothing gets off the system. You are in command now, Admiral Piett.

PIETT: Thank you, Lord Vader.

Piett's pleasure about his unexpected promotion is not an unmixed emotion. He glances warily at the struggling Admiral Ozzel who, with a final choke, has stumbled and fallen in a lifeless heap before him.

INT. REBEL BASE – MAIN HANGAR DECK

With a sense of urgency, Leia quickly briefs a group of pilots gathered in the center of the hangar.

LEIA: All troop carriers will assemble at the north entrance. The heavy transport ships will leave as soon as they're loaded. Only two fighter escorts per ship. The energy shield can only be opened for a short time, so you'll have to stay very close to your transports.

HOBBIE: Two fighters against a Star Destroyer?

LEIA: The ion cannon will fire several shots to make sure that any enemy ships will be out of your flight path. When you've gotten past the energy shield, proceed directly to the rendezvous point. Understood?

PILOTS: *(in unison)* Right. Yeah.

LEIA: Good luck.

DERLIN: Okay. Everybody to your stations. Let's go!

The pilots hurry away.

EXT. HOTH – ICE PLAIN – SNOW TRENCH – DAY

Rebel troops carry heavy bazooka-type weapons and position them along a snow trench. Men hurriedly respond to their officers' yelled orders.
    Other troops swing a gun turret into position.

INT. REBEL BASE – COMMAND CENTER

Princess Leia and General Rieekan are tense but trying very hard not to show any fear.

RIEEKAN: Their primary target will be the power generators. Prepare to open shield.

EXT. ICE PLAIN

The Rebel transport and two escort fighters begin their departure from the ice planet.

EXT. SPACE – IMPERIAL STAR DESTROYER

A huge Imperial Star Destroyer rests against a sea of stars far above the white surface of the planet Hoth.

INT. IMPERIAL STAR DESTROYER – BRIDGE

An Imperial controller approaches his commander.

CONTROLLER: Sir. Rebel ships are coming into our sector.

(CONT'D)

CONTINUED

CAPTAIN: Good. Our first catch of the day.

INT. REBEL BASE – COMMAND CENTER

WOMAN CONTROLLER: Stand by, ion control ... Fire!

EXT. REBEL BASE – ICE CAVE – ION CANNON

The giant ball-shaped ion cannon blasts two red energy beams skyward.

EXT. SPACE – HOTH – REBEL TRANSPORT

The Rebel transport and its escorts race away from the white planet, closely followed by the two red energy beams.

As the Rebel transport races toward the waiting Imperial Star Destroyer, it is overtaken by the two scarlet energy bolts. The Imperial Star Destroyer is hit in the conning tower by the powerful bolts, which set up fiery explosions on its metal hull.

The big Destroyer veers out of control. As the Imperial ship careens into deep space, the Rebel transport races away to safety.

INT. REBEL BASE – MAIN HANGAR DECK

Pilots, gunners and troopers hurry to their stations and their vehicles.

ANNOUNCER: *(over loudspeaker)* The first transport is away.

Everyone cheers at the announcement, which echoes through the hangar. Luke runs toward his snowspeeder. His gunner, Dack, a fresh-faced, eager kid, is already aboard and glad to see him. Luke climbs in.

DACK: Feeling all right, sir?

LUKE: Just like new, Dack. How about you?

DACK: Right now I feel like I could take on the whole Empire myself.

LUKE: *(quietly, strapping in)* I know what you mean.

EXT. HOTH – ICE PLAIN

A thin horizon line cuts across the bleak landscape. Small dot-size objects begin to appear on the horizon, moving in the direction of the Rebel base.

EXT. HOTH – ICE PLAIN – SNOW TRENCH

A Rebel officer lifts a pair of electrobinoculars to his eyes. Through the lens he sees a very close view of a giant Imperial snow walker. He adjusts the view, which then zooms back to reveal two more of the ominous lumbering battle machines.

The officer lowers his binoculars as the regular rhythmic pounding begins to make the ground vibrate. The pounding grows louder and is accompanied by a high-pitched, metallic rattling. The officer speaks into his comlink.

TRENCH OFFICER: Echo Station Three-T-Eight.

INT. REBEL BASE – CORRIDOR

Pilots and gunners race to their waiting snowspeeders.

TRENCH OFFICER: *(over comlink)* We have spotted Imperial walkers!

Ice and snow begin falling from the walls of the corridor, shaken by the pounding Imperial snow walkers as they draw ever nearer.

CONTROLLER: Imperial walkers on the north ridge.

EXT. HOTH – ICE PLAIN – SNOW TRENCH

The Rebel troops aim their weapons at the horizon as explosions erupt all around them. They are nervous and their grip on their weapons tightens from the cold and from fear.

(CONT'D)

CONTINUED

INT. LUKE'S SNOWSPEEDER, ROGUE LEADER — COCKPIT

LUKE: (into comlink) Echo Station Five-seven. We're on our way.

EXT. HOTH — ICE PLAIN — BATTLEFIELD

The fleet of snowspeeders races above the ice field at full throttle. They accelerate away from the base and head toward the distant walkers.

INT. LUKE'S SNOWSPEEDER, ROGUE LEADER — COCKPIT

LUKE: (into comlink) All right, boys, keep tight now.

DACK: Luke, I have no approach vector. I'm not set.

LUKE: Steady, Dack. Attack pattern delta. Go now'

EXT. HOTH — ICE PLAIN — BATTLEFIELD

Four speeders race away past an enormous walker and bank to the right.

INT. LUKE'S SNOWSPEEDER, ROGUE LEADER — COCKPIT

LUKE: All right, I'm coming in.

He turns his speeder and heads directly at one of the walkers, flying toward its towering legs. The horizon twists as the speeder banks between the legs.

LUKE: (into comlink) Hobbie, you still with me?

EXT. HOTH — ICE PLAIN — BATTLEFIELD

Two speeders race directly at a walker, then split and fly past it.
    Three other walkers march onward, firing all cannons.

EXT. HOTH — ICE PLAIN — SNOW TRENCH

Rebel troops fire on the approaching walkers, as snow and ice explode all around them.

EXT. HOTH — ICE PLAIN — BATTLEFIELD

A speeder banks through and away from the legs of a walker. Two other speeders pass the first speeder from the opposite direction.
    A giant walker head swivels and fires, striking a snowspeeder and sending it crashing in a ball of flames.

INT. IMPERIAL SNOW WALKER — COCKPIT

General Veers and two walker pilots keep a careful eye on the racing Rebel speeders as they maneuver their lumbering war machine forward.
    Luke's speeder banks in from the side of Veers' walker and heads straight for its viewport, blasting away. An explosion hits the walker window, but dissipates, doing no harm. The speeder roars up and over the impregnable war machine.

INT. LUKE'S SNOWSPEEDER, ROGUE LEADER — COCKPIT

LUKE: That armor's too strong for blasters.

EXT. HOTH — ICE PLAIN — BATTLEFIELD

Another walker lumbers on as two snowspeeders bank past it.

INT. LUKE'S SNOWSPEEDER, ROGUE LEADER — COCKPIT

LUKE: (into comlink) Rogue Group, use your harpoons and tow cables. Go for the legs. It might be our only chance of stopping them.

EXT. HOTH — ICE PLAIN — BATTLEFIELD

Two snowspeeders streak by.

INT. LUKE'S SNOWSPEEDER, ROGUE LEADER — COCKPIT

(CONT'D)

CONTINUED

LUKE: *(to Dack)* All right, stand by, Dack.

Dack is at the gunner's controls.

DACK: Oh Luke, we've got a malfunction in fire control. I'll have to cut in the auxiliary.

LUKE: Just hang on. Hang on, Dack. Get ready to fire that tow cable.

Dack, sitting behind his harpoon gun, is hit by a volley of fire.

EXT. HOTH — ICE PLAIN BATTLEFIELD

Rogue Leader flies under the walker.

INT. LUKE'S SNOWSPEEDER, ROGUE LEADER — COCKPIT

Luke turns around to see if Dack is all right.

LUKE: Dack? Dack!

Dack is lost. His forehead rests on his smoldering controls.

EXT. HOTH — ICE PLAIN — SNOW TRENCH AREA

Rebel troops fire the dishlike ray gun while explosions erupt around them.

EXT. HOTH — ICE PLAIN — BATTLEFIELD

Two walkers lumber toward the Rebel base as a speeder flies behind them emitting a plume of smoke.

INT. IMPERIAL SNOW WALKER — COCKPIT

Through the cockpit window, Veers watches the approach to the Rebel power generators in the distance.

EXT. HOTH — ICE PLAIN — SNOW TRENCH

The dishlike ray gun is hit by a laserbolt and instantly explodes.

INT. IMPERIAL SNOW WALKER — COCKPIT

A hologram of Darth Vader appears on a control panel screen.

VEERS: Yes, Lord Vader. I've reached the main power generators. The shield will be down in moments. You may start your landing.

EXT. HOTH — ICE PLAIN — BATTLEFIELD

Two snowspeeders bank sharply.

INT. LUKE'S SNOWSPEEDER, ROGUE LEADER — COCKPIT

LUKE: *(into comlink)* Rogue Three.

INT. WEDGE'S SNOWSPEEDER, ROGUE THREE — COCKPIT

WEDGE: *(into comlink)* Copy, Rogue Leader.

LUKE: *(over comlink)* Wedge, I've lost my gunner. You'll have to make this shot. I'll cover for you.

INT. LUKE'S SNOWSPEEDER, ROGUE LEADER — COCKPIT

LUKE: Set your harpoon. Follow me on the next pass.

EXT. HOTH — ICE PLAIN — BATTLEFIELD

Two snowspeeders bank sharply.

INT. WEDGE'S SNOWSPEEDER, ROGUE THREE — COCKPIT

WEDGE: *(into comlink)* Coming around, Rogue Leader.

Wedge's young gunner, Janson, grimaces behind his harpoon.

INT. LUKE'S SNOWSPEEDER, ROGUE LEADER — COCKPIT

(CONT'D)

CONTINUED

LUKE: *(into comlink)* Steady, Rogue Two.

EXT. HOTH — BATTLEFIELD

Wedge's speeder races through the legs of one of the monstrous walkers.

INT. WEDGE'S SNOWSPEEDER, ROGUE THREE — COCKPIT

WEDGE: *(to gunner)* Activate harpoon.

Wedge's gunner reaches for a firing switch to activate the harpoon. The harpoon flashes out, and speeds toward the receding legs of the walker.

EXT. HOTH — BATTLEFIELD

The harpoon hurtles toward the walker. In an instant it is embedded in one of the walker's legs.

INT. WEDGE'S SNOWSPEEDER, ROGUE THREE — COCKPIT

WEDGE: *(to gunner)* Good shot, Janson.

EXT. HOTH — BATTLEFIELD

The speeder Rogue Three races around one of the giant walker's feet, trailing the cable behind it. Continuing around the back foot, Rogue Three then circles the walker around the tail end.

INT. WEDGE'S SNOWSPEEDER, ROGUE THREE — COCKPIT

Janson grimaces.

EXT. HOTH — ICE PLAIN — BATTLEFIELD

Wedge's snowspeeder continues to circle the giant walker.

INT. WEDGE'S SNOWSPEEDER, ROGUE LEADER — COCKPIT

Wedge checks his controls and banks around the front of the walker.

WEDGE: One more pass.

JANSON: Coming around. Once more.

EXT. HOTH — BATTLEFIELD

The speeder sweeps left to right in front of the giant legs, towing the cable behind it.

INT. WEDGE'S SNOWSPEEDER, ROGUE THREE — COCKPIT

Wedge has swung the speeder between the legs of the giant walker.

JANSON: Cable out! Let her go!

WEDGE: Detach cable.

EXT. WEDGE'S SNOWSPEEDER, ROGUE THREE

The cable release on the back of the speeder snaps loose and the cable drops away.

INT. WEDGE'S SNOWSPEEDER, ROGUE THREE — COCKPIT

JANSON: Cable detached.

EXT. HOTH — BATTLEFIELD

The speeder zooms away into the distance. The tangled legs of the enormous war machine attempt a step, but as they do the giant Imperial walker begins to topple. It teeters for a moment, and then crashes on to the ice ground, sending snow flying.

EXT. HOTH — ICE PLAIN — SNOW TRENCH

The troops in the trenches cheer at the sight of the crashing walker.
An officer gives a signal to his men.

(CONT'D)

CONTINUED

TRENCH OFFICER: Come on!

The Rebel troops charge toward the doomed walker, followed by two Rebel speeders flying overhead, which fire at it; it explodes, showing lumps of metal on to the frozen ground.

INT. WEDGE'S SNOWSPEEDER, ROGUE THREE – COCKPIT

Wedge lets out a triumphant yell, banking his speeder away from the fallen walker.

WEDGE: *(into comlink)* Whooha! That got him!

INT. LUKE'S SNOWSPEEDER, ROGUE LEADER – COCKPIT

LUKE: *(into comlink)* I see it, Wedge. Good work.

INT. REBEL BASE – COMMAND CENTER

Leia and General Rieekan monitor computer screens as the command center is shaken by the continuing battle.

RIEEKAN: I don't think we can protect two transports at a time.

LEIA: It's risky, but we can't hold out much longer. We have no choice.

RIEEKAN: Launch patrols.

LEIA: *(to an aide)* Evacuate remaining ground staff.

INT. REBEL BASE – MAIN HANGAR

Muffled distant explosions are creating widening cracks in the ice roof of the hangar. Trying to ignore the noise and falling bits of snow, Han works on one of the Falcon's lifters while Chewie works on one of the wings. Noticing Chewie attach a wrong part, Han grows impatient.

HAN: No, no! No! This one goes there, that one goes there. Right?

In another area of the hangar, Threepio watches as Artoo is raised up into Luke's X-wing fighter.

THREEPIO: Artoo, you take good care of Master Luke now, understand? And ... do take good care of yourself. Oh, dear, oh, dear.

EXT. HOTH – BATTLEFIELD

The fierce battle on the vast snow plains of Hoth rages on. The Imperial walkers continue their slow, steady assault on the Rebel base, firing lasers as they lumber ever onward. In the snow trench, Rebel troops fire large bazooka-like guns and dishlike ray guns as explosions erupt around them. A gun tower is hit by a laserbolt and instantly explodes. Another blast destroys a ray gun.

INT. IMPERIAL SNOW WALKER – COCKPIT

General Veers is surveying the battlefield.

VEERS: All troops will debark for ground assault. Prepare to target the main generator.

EXT. HOTH – BATTLEFIELD

Luke's speeder and Rogue Two fly in formation, banking and flying above the erupting battlefield.

INT. LUKE'S SNOWSPEEDER, ROGUE LEADER – COCKPIT

Luke, glancing over, sees Rogue Two on his left.'

LUKE: *(into comlink)* Rogue Two, are you all right?

ZEV: *(over comlink)* Yeah.

INT. ZEV'S SNOWSPEEDER, ROGUE TWO – COCKPIT

ZEV: *(into comlink)* I'm with you, Rogue Leader.

INT. LUKE'S SNOWSPEEDER, ROGUE LEADER -- COCKPIT

LUKE: *(into comlink)* We'll set harpoon. I'll cover for you.

(CONT'D)

Luke Skywalker

Illustration by Howard Chaykin

This was the first poster produced to promote *Star Wars*. It was printed by 20th Century-Fox for the 1976 World Science Fiction Convention in Kansas City.

Star Wars Style 'A' Poster

Illustration by Tom Jung

With the release of *Star Wars* came the style 'A' one-sheet. There are at least four printing variations on this poster.

Star Wars Style 'A' Half-sheet poster

Illustration by Tom Jung

This poster has different artwork than the other style 'A' poster; it
appears in the half-sheet size only.

***Star Wars* Style 'C' Poster**
Illustration by Tom Cantrell

This poster was produced for British release and was never used in U.S. theatres.

Star Wars Style 'D' poster

Illustration by Drew Struzan and Charles White III

With the rerelease of *Star Wars* in 1978 came the style 'D' one-sheet.
The original artwork hangs in George Lucas' home.

Star Wars Happy Birthday Poster
Photography by Weldon Anderson
Design by Tony Seiniger and Associates

At the end of the first year of *Star Wars* distribution, a special birthday
poster was released to theatres still playing the movie.

Star Wars **1979 Reissue Poster**
Illustration by Tom Jung

A detail from the poster featuring a cropped version of the Tom Jung
style 'A' artwork.

Star Wars Is Back Poster (1982 Reissue)
Illustration by Tom Jung

1982 saw Star Wars again released to theatres. This time the poster
featured a unique banner across the lower right hand side advertising the
future release of Return of the Jedi, making this poster especially
collectible.

The Empire Strikes Back Style 'A' Poster
Illustration by Rodger Kastel

This poster was quickly dubbed the 'love story' poster due to the *Gone with the Wind* style artwork.

The Empire Strikes Back Style 'B' Poster

Illustration by Tom Jung

This poster was released to replace the style 'A' after it was pulled due to
a contract dispute with Billy Dee Williams.

The Empire Strikes Back 1981 Summer Rerelease Poster
Illustration by Tom Jung

This poster was issued for the 1981 rerelease of *The Empire Strikes Back*.

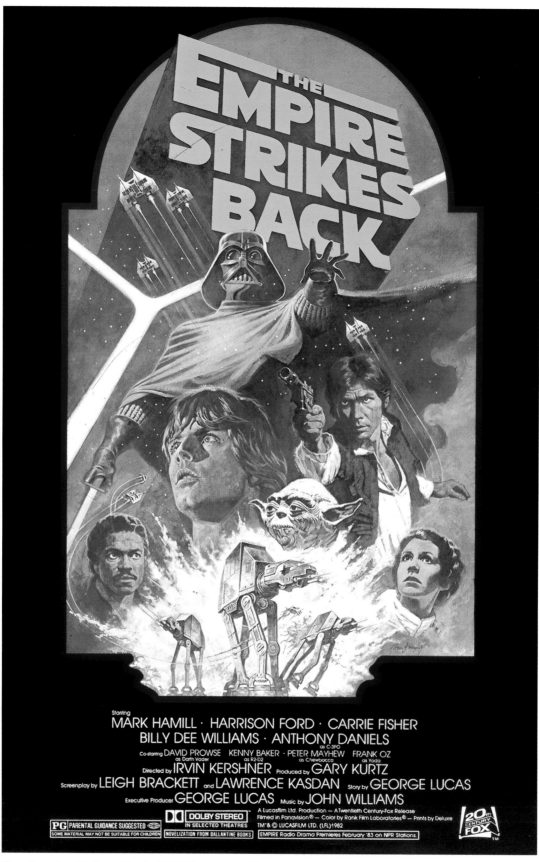

The Empire Strikes Back 1982 Rerelease Poster
Illustration by Tom Jung

This poster has a small note at the bottom of the poster for fans to listen
for the radio drama of *The Empire Strikes Back* on National Public Radio.

***Revenge of the Jedi* Advance Second Version**
Illustration by Drew Struzan

This is the second version of this poster to be released; it differs from the
first in that it has the release date added at the bottom of the poster.
Both versions of this poster were pulled.

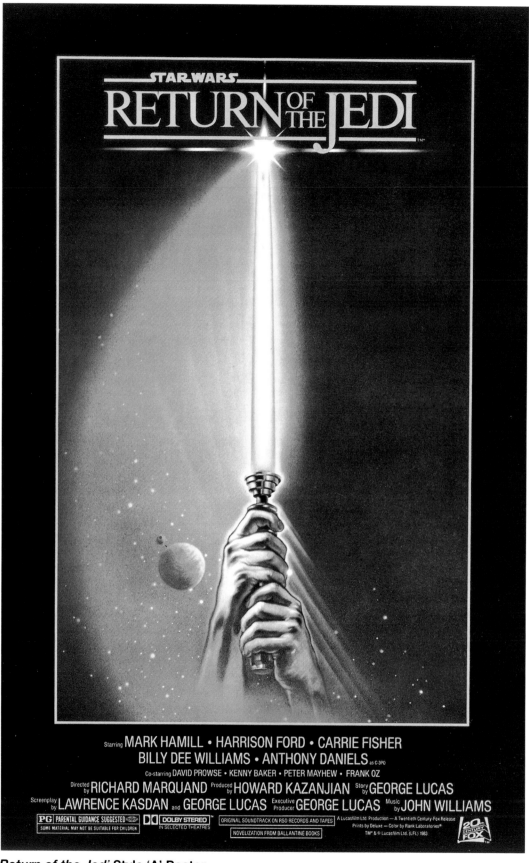

Return of the Jedi Style 'A' Poster
Illustration by Tim Reamer
Design by Paykos Phior

When *Return of the Jedi* came to theatres in May of 1983, the style 'A'
one-sheet was released.

***Return of the Jedi* Style 'B' Poster**

Illustration by Kazuhiko Sano

Three printing variations of this style 'B' poster exist.

Return of the Jedi 1985 Reissue Poster

Illustration by Tom Jung

This poster was distributed free to the first 50 viewers of the *Star Wars* Saga Triple Bill showing on March 28, 1985, at each of the nine theatres (in the U.S.) housing the one-day-only event.

CONTINUED

EXT. HOTH — BATTLEFIELD

The two speeders race across the horizon toward the giant walkers.

INT. ZEV'S SNOWSPEEDER, ROGUE TWO — COCKPIT

ZEV: *(into comlink)* Coming around.

INT. LUKE'S SNOWSPEEDER, ROGUE LEADER — COCKPIT

LUKE: *(into comlink)* Watch that cross fire, boys.

INT. ZEV'S SNOWSPEEDER, ROGUE TWO — COCKPIT

ZEV: *(into comlink)* Set for position three. *(to gunner)* Steady.

INT. LUKE'S SNOWSPEEDER, ROGUE LEADER — COCKPIT

LUKE: *(into comlink)* Stay tight and low.

INT. ZEV'S SNOWSPEEDER, ROGUE TWO — COCKPIT

Zev is hit.

EXT. ZEV'S SNOWSPEEDER, ROGUE TWO

Suddenly Zev's speeder is hit by a laserbolt and the cockpit explodes in a ball of flame.

INT. LUKE'S SNOWSPEEDER, ROGUE LEADER — COCKPIT

Desperately, Luke works the controls of his flak-buffeted ship. Suddenly, the speeder is rocked by a explosion. Luke struggles with the controls with a look of terror on his face. Electrical sparks jump about the cockpit.

LUKE: *(into comlink)* Hobbie, I've been hit!

INT. LUKE'S SNOWSPEEDER, ROGUE LEADER

Luke's snowspeeder crash-dives towards the legs of the giant walker.

INT. LUKE'S SNOWSPEEDER, ROGUE LEADER — COCKPIT

Luke's snowspeeder crash-lands.

INT. LUKE'S SNOWSPEEDER, ROGUE LEADER

Luke struggles to escape from the cockpit as a walker bears down on him, and just throws himself clear in time.

INT. REBEL BASE — COMMAND CENTER

Laserblasts can be heard thundering above. Han appears, running. Cracks have appeared in some of the walls and some pipes have broken, sending hot steam billowing into the underground hallways. Han hurries into the command center. It is a shambles — a gigantic cave-in has almost obliterated the room, but some people are still at their posts. He finds Leia and Threepio near one of the control boards.

HAN: You all right?

Leia is surprised to see him.

LEIA: Why are you still here?

HAN: I heard the command center had been hit.

LEIA: You got your clearance to leave.

HAN: Don't worry, I'll leave. First I'm going to get you to your ship.

THREEPIO: Your Highness, we must take this last transport. It's our only hope.

LEIA: *(to controller)* Send all troops in sector twelve to the south slope to protect the fighters.

A blast rocks the command center, throwing Threepio backward into Han's arms.

ANNOUNCER: *(over loudspeaker)* Imperial troops have entered the base. Imperial troops have entered . . .

(CONT'D)

CONTINUED

HAN: Come on ... that's it.

LEIA: *(to head controller)* Give the evacuation code signal. And get to your transports!

Leia looks exhausted. Han has grabbed her arm and starts to lead her out.
 As Han, Leia and Threepio run out of the command center, the code signal can be heard echoing off the corridor walls.

HEAD CONTROLLER: K-one-zero ... all troops disengage.

THREEPIO: *(to Han and Leia)* Oh! Wait for me!

EXT. BATTLEFIELD – SNOW TRENCH

Rebel troops retreat under the awesome Imperial onslaught.

OFFICER: Begin retreat!

SECOND OFFICER: Fall back! Fall back!

Troops flee from the battle, the ground exploding around them.

EXT. HOTH – BATTLEFIELD

The giant walkers, firing lasers, advance toward the Rebel headquarters.

EXT. HOTH – SNOW TRENCH

Continuing their retreat, the Rebels see the walkers looming ever nearer.

EXT. HOTH – BATTLEFIELD – ICE PLAIN

On the battlefield, Luke is running, too. He looks up at the underbelly of a huge walker, passing by overhead.
 Luke fires his harpoon gun at the walker's underside. A thin cable follows the projectile from the gun. The magnetic head and cable attach firmly to the metal hull.
 Soon he is pulled up the cable and hangs dangling underneath the walker.
 The walker's giant feet continue to pound onward across the frozen snow. Stray laserbolts whistle by Luke as he reaches a small hatch. Hanging precariously, Luke cuts the solid metal hatch with his laser sword.
 He takes a land mine from around his belt and throws it inside the Imperial machine. Quickly, Luke starts down the cable and crashes on to the icy ground far below.
 The giant walker stops in mid-step. A muffled explosion comes from within – followed by several more. The machine topples over, smoking thickly.

EXT. HOTH – BATTLEFIELD

Veers' walker continues to advance toward the Rebel base.

INT. IMPERIAL SNOW WALKER – COCKPIT

Inside his walker, General Veers prepares to fire on the Rebel power generators.

VEERS: Distance to power generators?

PILOT: One-seven, decimal two-eight.

EXT. HOTH – BATTLEFIELD

The walker shoots down a snowspeeder.

INT. IMPERIAL SNOW WALKER – COCKPIT

Veers reaches for the electro-rangefinder and lines up the main generator.

VEERS: Target. Maximum fire power.

EXT. HOTH – BATTLEFIELD

The Rebel troops continue their desperate retreat, pushed back by the relentless Imperial assault.

INT. IMPERIAL SNOW WALKER – COCKPIT

(CONT'D)

CONTINUED

From the cockpit of Veers' snow walker the Rebel main generator can be seen exploding in a ball of flame.

INT. HOTH — REBEL BASE — ICE CORRIDORS

With Threepio lagging behind, Han and Leia race through the crumbling ice corridors. Suddenly, there is an explosion. Han turns, grabs the princess, and shields her with his body as a tremendous cave-in blocks their path.
    He takes the comlink from his pocket.

HAN: *(into comlink)* Transport, this is Solo. Better take off — I can't get to you. I'll get her out on the Falcon.

Han and Leia turn and race down the corridor.

THREEPIO: But ... but ... but ... where are you going? Oh ... come back!!

INT. HOTH — REBEL BASE — COMMAND CENTER

Imperial troops have reached the base. As they push through the blocked passageway, Darth Vader strides behind them.

INT. HOTH — REBEL BASE — ICE CORRIDOR

Han and Leia run toward the entrance of the main hangar where the Millennium Falcon is docked. Threepio still lags behind.

THREEPIO: Wait! Wait for me! Wait! Stop!

The door to the hangar closes in his face.

THREEPIO: *(exasperated)* How typical.

Quickly, the door re-opens as Han reaches out and pulls the golden droid through.

HAN: Come on.

INT. HOTH — REBEL BASE — MAIN HANGAR

Chewie has been pacing under the shelter of the Millennium Falcon's landing gear. The giant Wookiee lets out a relieved grunt at seeing Han and Leia running toward the ship.

HAN: Hurry up, goldenrod, or you're going to be a permanent resident!

THREEPIO: Wait! Wait!

Han and Leia run up the ramp after Chewie, closely followed by Threepio.

INT. HOTH — REBEL BASE — ICE CORRIDOR

Vader strides through the base corridors, surveying the place.

INT. REBEL BASE — MAIN HANGAR — MILLENNIUM FALCON

On the hangar deck, the Millennium Falcon struggles to start up.

INT. MAIN HANGAR — MILLENNIUM FALCON — MAIN HOLD

A worried Leia observes as Chewie watches a troublesome gauge and Han, standing before a control panel, is busy flipping switches.

HAN: *(to Chewie)* How's this?

The Wookiee barks a negative reply.

LEIA: Would it help if I got out and pushed?

Threepio hurries into the hold.

THREEPIO: Captain Solo, Captain Solo ...

HAN: It might.

THREEPIO: Sir, might I suggest that you ...

(CONT'D)

CONTINUED

Han gives the gold robot a devastating look.

THREEPIO: It can wait.

INT. MAIN HANGAR — MILLENNIUM FALCON — COCKPIT

They move to the cockpit where Han flips some more switches. Leia, impatient, is disbelieving.

LEIA: This bucket of bolts is never going to get us past that blockade.

HAN: This baby's got a few surprises left in her, sweetheart.

INT. HOTH — REBEL BASE — MAIN HANGAR

A squad of stormtroopers rushes into the far side of the hangar.

INT. MAIN HANGAR — MILLENNIUM FALCON

A laser gun appears on the Falcon and swings around to fire at the Imperial troops.

INT. HOTH — REBEL BASE — MAIN HANGAR

The stormtroopers are hit by the Falcon's fire and are thrown about in all directions.

INT. MAIN HANGAR — MILLENNIUM FALCON — COCKPIT

Chewie rushes into the cockpit.

HAN: Come on! Come on! Switch over. Let's hope we don't have a burnout.

Chewie settles into his chair.

INT. HOTH — REBEL BASE — MAIN HANGAR

The stormtroopers hurriedly set up a large bazooka-like weapon.

INT. MAIN HANGAR — MILLENNIUM FALCON — COCKPIT

Han gets the engine to fire.

HAN: See?

LEIA: Someday you're going to be wrong, and I just hope I'm there to see it.

INT. — REBEL BASE — MAIN HANGAR

The Falcon's laser gun continues to exchange fire with Imperial stormtroopers.

INT. MAIN HANGAR — MILLENNIUM FALCON — COCKPIT

Han looks at Chewie.

HAN: Punch it!

The roar of the Falcon's main engines blasts out everything as the ice-cave wall rushes by outside the cockpit window.

INT. REBEL BASE — MAIN HANGAR

Vader enters the hangar, closely followed by more stormtroopers. Hearing the loud roar of the Millennium Falcon's engines, Vader looks toward the main hangar doors just in time to see the Falcon lift up and disappear outside the cave.

EXT. HOTH — ICE SLOPE — DAY

Luke looks up as the Millennium Falcon races above him, flying very close to the ground.
    He and two other pilots trudge toward their X-wing fighters. Luke waves to fighters overhead, then heads toward his own fighter.

LUKE: Artoo!

Artoo, seated in his cubbyhole, chirps an excited greeting.

(CONT'D)

CONTINUED

LUKE: Get her ready for takeoff.

WEDGE: Good luck, Luke. See you at the rendezvous.

Luke lowers himself into the cockpit of his X-wing while Artoo waits in the cubbyhole, beeping impatiently.

LUKE: Don't worry, Artoo. We're going, we're going.

The canopy over the X-wing lowers and snaps shut.

EXT. SPACE – LUKE'S X-WING

Luke's fighter, its wings closed, speeds away from the icy planet. Then it banks sharply.

INT. LUKE'S X-WING – COCKPIT

The monitor screen on Luke's control panel prints out a question from the concerned Artoo.

LUKE: *(into comlink)* There's nothing wrong, Artoo. Just setting a new course.

EXT. LUKE'S X-WING

Artoo beeps once again.

INT. LUKE'S X-WING – COCKPIT

LUKE: *(into comlink)* We're not going to regroup with the others.

Artoo begins a protest, whistling an unbelieving, What?!

LUKE: *(into comlink)* We're going to the Dagobah system.

EXT. LUKE'S X-WING

Artoo chirps up again.

LUKE: *(into comlink)* Yes, Artoo?

INT. LUKE'S X-WING – COCKPIT

Artoo utters a soft, carefully phrased stream of whistles.
    Luke reads Artoo's exclamation on his control panel.

LUKE: *(into comlink, chuckling)* That's all right. I'd like to keep it on manual control for a while.

EXT. LUKE'S X-WING

The little droid lets out a defeated whimper. Luke continues on his course.

EXT. SPACE – MILLENNIUM FALCON

The Millennium Falcon speeds away from Hoth, closely followed by one huge Star Destroyer and four tiny TIE fighters.

INT. MILLENNIUM FALCON – COCKPIT

Inside the cockpit, Chewie lets out a loud howl. Han checks the deflectors as the ship is buffeted by exploding flak. He appears to be doing six things at once.

HAN: *(harried)* I saw 'em! I saw 'em!

LEIA: Saw what?

HAN: Star Destroyers. Two of them, coming right at us.

Threepio bumps and bangs his way into the cockpit.

THREEPIO: Sir, Sir! Might I suggest . . .

HAN: *(to Leia)* Shut him up or shut him down! *(to Chewie)* Check the deflector shields!

Chewie barks a reply as he readjusts an overhead switch.

(CONT'D)

CONTINUED

HAN: Oh, great. Well, we can still outmaneuver them.

EXT. SPACE – MILLENNIUM FALCON – STAR DESTROYERS

The Millennium Falcon has been racing toward one of the huge oncoming Star Destroyers. Suddenly, the Falcon starts into a steep dive straight down, closely followed by TIE fighters. The underside of the Star Destroyer continues on a collision course with the two oncoming Star Destroyers.

INT. STAR DESTROYER – BRIDGE

Out of the front window, the two approaching Star Destroyers can be seen veering to the left.

IMPERIAL OFFICER: Take evasive action!

Alarms sound all over the huge ship. The two other Star Destroyers get closer, one of them moving over the bridge so close that it makes brushing contact with it.

EXT. SPACE – MILLENNIUM FALCON – TIE FIGHTERS

The Millennium Falcon races away from the colliding Star Destroyers, still followed by four TIE fighters. Laserbolts spark the pitch-black skies.
     Things have calmed down a bit, but the race isn't over yet.

HAN: Prepare to make the jump to light-speed!

Chewie barks at Han. The ship is buffeted by laserblasts.

THREEPIO: But, sir!

LEIA: They're getting closer!

The buffeting of the lasers becomes louder and stronger.

HAN: *(with a gleam in his eye)* Oh, yeah? Watch this.

Expectantly, they look out the cockpit window as stars do not go into hyperspace, but just sit there.

LEIA: Watch what?

HAN: I think we're in trouble.

THREEPIO: If I may say so, sir, I noticed earlier, the hyperdrive motivator has been damaged. It's impossible to go to light-speed!

HAN: We're in trouble!

The explosions become heavier.

EXT. SPACE – MILLENNIUM FALCON – TIE FIGHTERS – STAR DESTROYER

The Falcon races into the starry vastness, followed by the four Imperial TIE fighters and an Imperial Star Destroyer.

INT. MILLENNIUM FALCON – HOLD

Han works furiously at some control panels while giving various orders to Chewie.

HAN: Horizontal boosters . . . ! *(Chewie barks)* Alluvial dampers . . . ! *(Chewie barks)* Now? That's not it. Bring me the hydrospanners! *(Chewie barks)*

Chewie hurries over to the pit and places the tools on the edge.

HAN: I don't know how we're going to get out of this one.

Suddenly, a loud thump hits the side of the Falcon, causing it to lurch radically. Chewie barks. The tools fall into the pit on top of Han.

HAN: Oww! Chewie!

More turbulence rocks the ship.

(CONT'D)

CONTINUED

HAN: Those were no laserblasts! Something hit us.

INT. MILLENNIUM FALCON – COCKPIT

LEIA: *(into comlink)* Han, get up here!

INT. MILLENNIUM FALCON – HOLD

HAN: Come on, Chewie!

Han climbs out of the hold like a shot. Both he and Chewie run out of the hold and toward the cockpit.

INT. MILLENNIUM FALCON – COCKPIT

Out of the front cockpit window, they see hundreds of asteroids.

LEIA: Asteroids!

Han changes places with Leia who has been at the controls. Han works his controls.

HAN: Oh, no! Chewie, set two-seven-one.

A chunk of rock crosses in front of the ship.

LEIA: What are you doing? You're not actually going into an asteroid field?

Another asteroid bumps against the ship.

HAN: They'd be crazy to follow us, wouldn't they?

EXT. MILLENNIUM FALCON

The Millennium Falcon weaves through the asteroid field.

INT. MILLENNIUM FALCON – COCKPIT

LEIA: You don't have to do this to impress me.

THREEPIO: Sir, the possibility of successfully navigating an asteroid field is approximately three thousand, seven hundred and twenty to one.

HAN: Never tell me the odds!

EXT. ASTEROID BELT – MILLENNIUM FALCON

A large asteroid tumbles away from the Falcon's path. Other asteroids of all sizes pass by in every direction. The tiny Millennium Falcon veers around the big asteroid and races past it through the rain of rocks, followed by four TIE fighters, which bob and weave around the asteroids.
   One of the pursuing TIE fighters connects with an asteroid and explodes. Another fighter is pelted and explodes.

INT. MILLENNIUM FALCON – COCKPIT

Asteroids race by the cockpit window as Han pilots his trusty craft through the dangerous field.
   Looking out the cockpit window, the Falcon crew sees a big asteroid drop past the window, narrowly missing their ship.
   Chewie moans in terror as a slightly smaller asteroid comes especially close – too close – and bounces off the Falcon with a loud crunch. Princes Leia sits stone-faced, staring at the action. Threepio cries out in alarm, and covers his eyes with his hands.

HAN: *(to Leia)* You said you wanted to be around when I made a mistake; well, this could be it, sweetheart.

LEIA: I take it back. We're going to get pulverized if we stay out here much longer.

HAN: I'm not going to argue with that.

The group watches as more asteroids race by outside the window.

THREEPIO: Pulverized?

HAN: I'm going in closer to one of those big ones.

(CONT'D)

CONTINUED

LEIA: Closer?

THREEPIO: Closer?!

Chewbacca barks the same word, only louder.

EXT. MILLENNIUM FALCON – ASTEROID BELT

The Millennium Falcon dives toward the surface of one of the moon-size asteroids. The two remaining TIE fighters follow the Falcon to the large asteroid, firing laserbolts. The Falcon skims the surface of the giant asteroid as, all the while, small asteroids explode on the surface of the ship.
The TIE fighters follow the Falcon, down the canyons of the moon-sized asteroid until they crash into the canyon walls and explode.

INT. MILLENNIUM FALCON – COCKPIT

Rattled by the violent rocking of the starship, Threepio is nearly in hysterics.

THREEPIO: Oh, this is suicide!

Han notices something on his main scope and nudges his faithful Wookiee, pointing.

HAN: There. That looks pretty good.

LEIA: What looks pretty good?

HAN: Yeah. That'll do nicely.

THREEPIO: *(to Leia)* Excuse me, ma'am, but where are we going?

Out of the cockpit windows, they see that they are skimming the surface of the enormous asteroid and nearing a large crater.

EXT. MILLENNIUM FALCON – GIANT ASTEROID CRATER

The Millennium Falcon dives into the huge crater.

INT. MILLENNIUM FALCON – COCKPIT

LEIA: I hope you know what you're doing.

HAN: Yeah, me too.

INT. GIANT ASTEROID CRATER

The walls are barely visible as the Falcon speeds through the tunnellike opening.

EXT. SPACE – LUKE'S X-WING

The tiny X-wing speeds toward the planet Dagobah.

INT. LUKE'S X-WING – COCKPIT

Artoo whistles. His words are translated and screened on the computer scope.

LUKE: *(into comlink)* Yes, that's it. Dagobah.

EXT. LUKE'S X-WING

Artoo beeps a hopeful inquiry.

INT. LUKE'S X-WING – COCKPIT

LUKE: *(into comlink)* No, I'm not going to change my mind about this.

EXT. LUKE'S X-WING

Artoo listens as Luke, getting a little nervous, continues.

LUKE: *(over comlink)* I'm not picking up any cities or technology.

INT. LUKE'S X-WING – COCKPIT

(CONT'D)

CONTINUED

LUKE: Massive life-form readings, though. There's something alive down there ...

EXT. LUKE'S X-WING

Again, Artoo beeps, this time a slightly worried question.

INT. LUKE'S X-WING – COCKPIT

LUKE: *(into comlink)* Yes, I'm sure it's perfectly safe for droids.

EXT. SPACE – DAGOBAH – LUKE'S X-WING

The X-wing continues its flight down through the twilight above the cloud-covered planet.

EXT. LUKE'S X-WING

Artoo beeps and whistles frantically as clouds race by.

INT. LUKE'S X-WING – COCKPIT

Luke must operate his controls carefully since the cloud cover has completely obscured his vision.

LUKE: *(into comlink)* I know, I know! All the scopes are dead. I can't see a thing! Just hang on. I'm going to start the landing cycle ...

EXT. LUKE'S X-WING

Artoo continues to squeal electronically.

INT. LUKE'S X-WING – COCKPIT

The blast of the retrorockets is deafening, drowning out Artoo's electronic squeals. Suddenly, there is a cracking sound as if limbs were being broken off trees and then a tremendous jolt as the spacecraft stops. Luke looks out of the cockpit.

EXT. DAGOBAH – DUSK

The mist-shrouded X-wing fighter is almost invisible in the thick fog. Luke climbs out on to the long nose of the spacecraft as Artoo pops out of his cubbyhole on the back. The young warrior surveys the fog, which is barely pierced by the ship's landing lights. About all he came make out are some giant, twisted trees nearby. Artoo whistles anxiously.

LUKE: No, Artoo, you stay put. I'll have a look around.

Artoo lets out a short beep. As Luke moves along the nose, Artoo loses his balance and disappears with a splash into the boggy lake.

LUKE: Artoo?

Luke kneels and leans over the plane looking for Artoo, but the water is still and reveals no sign of the little droid.

LUKE: Artoo! Where are you? Artoo!

A small periscope breaks the surface of the water and a gurgly beep is heard. The periscope starts to move to shore. Luke is relieved.

LUKE: You be more careful. Artoo – that way!

Luke jumps off the plane into the water. The periscope still steadily moves toward shore.
Suddenly, through the thick fog layer, a dark shape appears, moving toward the little droid. The droid disappears from sight, uttering a pathetic electronic scream as Luke scrambles ashore. The dark, sinuous bog beast dives beneath the swampy water.

LUKE: Artoo!

The black surface is still as death itself ... until PHHEEWAAT!! The runt-size robot is spat out of the water, makes a graceful arc, and comes crashing down into a patch of soft gray moss.

(CONT'D)

CONTINUED

LUKE: Oh, no! Are you all right? Come on. *(helping Artoo to his feet)* You're lucky you don't taste very good. Anything broken?

Artoo responds with feeble, soggy beeps.

LUKE: If you're saying coming here was a bad idea, I'm beginning to agree with you. Artoo, what are we doing here? It's like ... something out of a dream, or, I don't know. *(wiping the mud and roots from Artoo's round metal body)* Maybe I'm just going crazy.

As Luke glances around at the spooky swamp jungle that surrounds him, Artoo ejects a stream of muddy water from one of his cranial ports.

EXT. SPACE

The Imperial Starfleet moves through space, seeking its prey.

INT. VADER'S STAR DESTROYER – VADER'S CHAMBER

Admiral Piett hesitates in the entryway to Vader's private chamber.
      After a moment, he steps into the room and pauses at the surprising sight before him.
      Darth Vader, his back turned, is on the far side of the chamber. A droid attends him. Among the various apparatuses surrounding them, a respirator tube now retracts from Vader's uncovered head. The head is bald with a mass of ugly scar tissue covering it. The droid lowers the mask and helmet on to Vader's head. When it is in place, the Dark Lord turns to face Piett.

VADER: Yes, Admiral?

PIETT: Our ships have sighted the Millennium Falcon, lord. But ... it has entered an asteroid field and we cannot risk –

VADER: *(interrupting)* Asteroids do not concern me, Admiral. I want that ship, not excuses.

PIETT: Yes, Lord.

EXT. ASTEROID CAVE – MILLENNIUM FALCON

The pirate starship rests in a dark, dripping asteroid cave. It is so dark that the cave's exact dimensions are impossible to determine.

INT. MILLENNIUM FALCON – COCKPIT

HAN: I'm going to shut down everything but the emergency power systems.

Han and Chewie busily shut down the engine and all electronic systems. Threepio and Leia watch worriedly.

THREEPIO: Sir, I'm almost afraid to ask, but ... does that include shutting me down, too?

HAN: No. I need you to talk to the Falcon, find out what's wrong with the hyperdrive.

Suddenly, the ship lurches, causing all the loose items in the cockpit to go flying. Chewie howls.

THREEPIO: Sir, it's quite possible this asteroid is not entirely stable.

HAN: Not entirely stable? I'm glad you're here to tell us these things. Chewie, take the professor in the back and plug him into the hyperdrive.

THREEPIO: Oh! Sometimes I just don't understand human behaviour. After all, I'm only trying to do my job in the most ...

The sliding door closes behind the indignant Threepio as Chewie and he move back to the hold. Suddenly, the ship lurches again, throwing Leia across the cabin into Han's arms. Then, abruptly, the motion stops as suddenly as it started. With some surprise, Leia realizes she is in Han's arms.

LEIA: Let go.

HAN: Sshh!

LEIA: Let go, please.

(CONT'D)

CONTINUED

Leia flushes, averting her eyes. She's not exactly fighting to get free. But, of course, Han blows it ...

HAN: Don't get excited.

The anger rises in Leia.

LEIA: Captain, being held by you isn't quite enough to get me excited.

HAN: Sorry, sweetheart. We haven't got time for anything else.

Han grins wickedly at Leia as he turns and exits through the door. Leia's confused emotions show clearly on her lovely face.

EXT. DAGOBAH – BOG CLEARING – DUSK

The mist has dispersed a bit, but it is still a very gloomy-looking swamp.
 Luke carries an equipment box from the shore to the clearing.

LUKE: What? Ready for some power? Okay. Let's see now. Put that in there. *(taking a power cable, he plugs it into Artoo's noselike socket)* There you go.

The droid whistles his appreciation.

LUKE: *(sighs)* Now all I got to do is find this Yoda ... *(nervously, he looks around at the foreboding jungle)* if he even exists. It's really a strange place to find a Jedi Master.

Luke then opens a container of processed food and sits before the thermal heater.

LUKE: This place gives me the creeps.

Artoo beeps in agreement with that sentiment.

LUKE: Still ... there's something familiar about this place. I don't know ... I feel like ...

STRANGE VOICE: Feel like what?

Luke jumps out of his skin. Artoo beeps in terror. The young warrior grabs for his blaster as he spins around, looking for the speaker. Mysteriously standing right in front of Luke is a strange, bluish creature, not more than two feet tall. The wizened little thing is dressed in rags. It covers its face.

LUKE: *(looking at the creature)* Like we're being watched!

CREATURE: Away put your weapon! I mean you no harm. I am wondering, why are you here?

After some hesitation, Luke puts away his weapon, although he really doesn't understand why.

LUKE: I'm looking for someone.

CREATURE: Looking? Found someone, you have, I would say, hmmm?

The little creature laughs.

LUKE: *(trying to keep from smiling)* Right.

CREATURE: Help you I can. Yes, mmmm.

LUKE: I don't think so. I'm looking for a great warrior.

CREATURE: Ahhh! A great warrior. *(laughs and shakes his head)* Wars not make one great.

With the aid of a walking stick, the tiny stranger moves over to one of the cases of supplies. He begins to rummage around.
 Their tiny visitor picks up the container of food Luke was eating from and takes a bite.

LUKE: Put that down! Now ... Hey! That's my dinner!

The creature spits out the bite he has taken. He makes a face.

CREATURE: How you get so big, eating food of this kind?

(CONT'D)

CONTINUED

LUKE: Listen, friend, we didn't mean to land in that puddle, and if we could get our ship out, we would, but we can't so why don't you just...

CREATURE: *(teasing)* Aww, can't you get your ship out?

The creature starts rummaging through one of Luke's supply cases.

LUKE: Hey, get out of there!

CREATURE: Ahhh! *(as Luke rescues an item from his clasp)* No! Oh!

LUKE: Hey, you could have broken this.

The creature begins to throw the contents of the case out behind him, finally spotting something of interest — a tiny power lamp — and examines it with delight.

LUKE: Don't do that. Ohhh ... you're making a mess. Hey, give me that!

CREATURE: *(retreating with the lamp)* Mine! Or I will help you not.

Clutching its treasure, the creature backs away from Luke, drawing closer to Artoo. As Luke and the creature argue, one of Artoo's little arms slowly moves out toward the power lamp, completely unnoticed by the creature.

LUKE: I don't want your help. I want my lamp back. I'm gonna need it to get out of this slimy mudhole.

CREATURE: Mudhole? Slimy? My home this is.

Artoo grabs hold of the lamp and the two little figures are immediately engaged in a tug-of-war over it.
    Artoo beeps a few angry 'Give me thats'.

CREATURE: Ah, ah, ah!

LUKE: Oh, Artoo, let him have it!

CREATURE: Mine! Mine!

LUKE: Artoo!

CREATURE: Mine!

Artoo lets go. The creature pokes Artoo lightly with his stick.

LUKE: *(fed up)* Now will you move along, little fella? We've got a lot of work to do.

CREATURE: No! No, no! Stay and help you, I will. *(laughs)* Find your friend.

LUKE: I'm not looking for a friend. I'm looking for a Jedi Master.

CREATURE: Oohhh, Jedi Master. Yoda. You seek Yoda.

LUKE: You know him?

CREATURE: Mmm. Take you to him, I will. *(laughs)* Yes, yes. But now, we must eat. Come. Good food. Come.

With that, the creature scurries out of the clearing, laughing merrily. Luke stares after him.

CREATURE: *(in the distance)* Come, come.

Luke makes his decision.

LUKE: Artoo, stay and watch after the camp.

Luke starts after the creature. Artoo, very upset, whistles a blue streak of protests.
    Artoo beeps even more frantically. But as Luke disappears from view, the worried little droid grows quieter, and utters a soft electronic sigh.

INT. MILLENNIUM FALCON — MAIN HOLD AREA

Threepio is at the control panel, which emits a few mystifying beeps.

THREEPIO: Oh, where is Artoo when I need him?

(CONT'D)

CONTINUED

Han enters the hold area and kneels on the floor near the control box.

THREEPIO: Sir, I don't know where your ship learned to communicate, but it has the most peculiar dialect. I believe, sir, it says that the power coupling on the negative axis has been polarized. I'm afraid you'll have to replace it.

HAN: Well, of course I'll have to replace it.

He hands a wire coil up to Chewie who is working near the ceiling.

HAN: Here! And Chewie ...

Chewie brings his head back through the trap door in the ceiling and whines. Han glances back at Threepio, then speaks quietly to Chewie so only he can hear.

HAN: *(continuing)* ... I think we'd better replace the negative power coupling.

Leia finishes welding the valve she has been working on and attempts to re-engage the system by pulling a lever attached to the valve. It doesn't budge. Han notices her struggle, and moves to help her. She rebuffs him.

HAN: Hey, Your Worship, I'm only trying to help.

LEIA: *(still struggling)* Would you please stop calling me that?

Han hears a new tone in her voice. He watches her pull on the lever.

HAN: Sure, Leia.

LEIA: Oh, you make it so difficult sometimes.

HAN: I do, I really do. You could be a little nicer, though. *(he watches her reaction)* Come on, admit it. Sometimes you think I'm all right.

She lets go of the lever and licks her sore hand.

LEIA: Occasionally ... maybe ... *(a little smile, haltingly)* ... when you aren't acting like a scoundrel.

HAN: Scoundrel? Scoundrel? I like the sound of that.

Han has taken her hand and starts to massage it.

LEIA: Stop that.

HAN: Stop what?

Leia is flushed, confused.

LEIA: Stop that! My hands are dirty.

HAN: My hands are dirty too. What are you afraid of?

LEIA: *(looking right into his eyes)* Afraid?

Han looks at her with a piercing look. He's never looked more handsome, more dashing, more confident.

HAN: You're trembling.

LEIA: I'm not trembling.

Then with an irresistible combination of physical strength and emotional power, the space pirate begins to draw Leia toward him ... very slowly.

HAN: You like me because I'm a scoundrel. There aren't enough scoundrels in your life.

Leia is now very close to Han and as she speaks, her voice becomes an excited whisper, a tone completely in opposition to her words.

LEIA: I happen to like nice men.

HAN: I'm a nice man.

LEIA: No, you're not. You're ...

(CONT'D)

CONTINUED

He kisses her now, with slow, hot lips. He takes his time, as though he had forever, bending her body backward. She has never been kissed like this before.

Suddenly, Threepio appears in the doorway, speaking excitedly.

THREEPIO: Sir, sir! I've isolated the reverse power flux coupling.

Han turns slowly, icily, from their embrace.

HAN: Thank you. Thank you very much.

THREEPIO: Oh, you're perfectly welcome, sir.

The moment is spoiled.

EXT. SPACE — ASTEROID FIELD

The Imperial fleet moves through the asteroid-filled void, intently seeking its prey.

INT. VADER'S STAR DESTROYER — BRIDGE

Before Darth Vader are the hologram images of battleship commanders. One of these images, the commander of a ship that has just exploded, is fading quickly away. Another image is faded and continually disrupted by static. It is the image of Captain Needa, commander of the Star Destroyer most hotly on the tail of the Millennium Falcon. Admiral Piett and an aide stand behind the Dark Lord.

NEEDA: *(in hologram)* . . . and that, Lord Vader, was the last time they appeared in any of our scopes. Considering the amount of damage we've sustained, they must have been destroyed.

VADER: No, Captain, they're alive. I want every ship available to sweep the asteroid field until they are found.

The Imperial star captain fades out as Admiral Piett approaches Vader.

PIETT: Lord Vader.

VADER: Yes, Admiral, what is it?

The admiral is scared, his face white as a sheet.

PIETT: The Emperor commands you to make contact with him.

VADER: Move the ship out of the asteroid field so that we can send a clear transmission.

PIETT: Yes, my lord.

EXT. ASTEROID FIELD — VADER'S STAR DESTROYER

Vader's Imperial Star Destroyer moves against the vast sea of stars away from the rest of the fleet.

INT. VADER'S STAR DESTROYER — VADER'S CHAMBER

The Dark Lord, Darth Vader, is alone in his chamber. Vader kneels as a strange sound enters the room.

VADER: What is thy bidding, my Master?

A twelve-foot hologram of the Galactic Emperor materializes before Vader. The Emperor's dark robes and monk's hood are reminiscent of the cloak worn by Ben Kenobi. His voice is even deeper and more frightening than Vader's.

EMPEROR: There is a great disturbance in the Force.

VADER: I have felt it.

EMPEROR: We have a new enemy — Luke Skywalker.

VADER: Yes, my Master.

EMPEROR: He could destroy us.

VADER: He's just a boy. Obi-Wan can no longer help him.

EMPEROR: The Force is strong with him. The son of Skywalker must not become a Jedi.

(CONT'D)

CONTINUED

VADER: If he could be turned, he would become a powerful ally.

EMPEROR: Yes. Yes. He would be a great asset. Can it be done?

VADER: He will join us or die, Master.

Vader bows.

EXT. DAGOBAH – CREATURE'S HOUSE – NIGHT

A heavy downpour of rain pounds through the gnarled trees. A strange baroque mud house sits on a moss-covered knoll on the edge of a small lagoon. The small, gnomish structure radiates a warm glow from its thick glass windows. As the rain tap-dances a merry tune on Artoo's head, the stubby little droid rises up on his tiptoes to peek into one of the glowing portals.

INT. CREATURE'S HOUSE

Artoo, peeking in the window, sees the inside the house – a very plain, but cozy dwelling. Everything is in the same scale as the creature. The only thing out of place in the miniature room is Luke, whose height makes the four-foot ceiling seem even lower.
The creature is in an adjoining area – his little kitchen – cooking up an incredible meal. Luke watches impatiently.

LUKE: Look, I'm sure it's delicious. I just don't understand why we can't see Yoda now.

CREATURE: Patience! For the Jedi it is time to eat as well. Eat, eat. Hot.

Moving with some difficulty in the cramped quarters, Luke sits down near the fire and serves himself from the pot. Tasting the unfamiliar concoction, he is pleasantly surprised.

CREATURE: Good food, hm? Good, hmmm?

LUKE: How far away is Yoda? Will it take us long to get there?

CREATURE: Not far. Yoda not far. Patience. Soon you will be with him. Rootleaf, I cook. Why wish you become Jedi? Hm?

LUKE: Mostly because of my father, I guess.

CREATURE: Ah, father. Powerful Jedi was he, mmm, powerful Jedi, mmm.

LUKE: *(a little angry)* Oh, come on. How could you know my father? You don't even know who I am. *(fed up)* Oh, I don't know what I'm doing here. We're wasting our time.

The creature is turned away from Luke and speaks to a third party.

CREATURE: *(irritated)* I cannot teach him. The boy has no patience.

Luke's head turns in the direction the creature faces. But there is no one there. The boy is bewildered, but it gradually dawns on him that the little creature is Yoda, the Jedi Master, and that he is speaking with Ben.

BEN'S VOICE: He will learn patience.

YODA: Hmmm. Much anger in him, like his father.

BEN'S VOICE: Was I any different when you taught me?

YODA: Hah. He is not ready.

LUKE: Yoda! I am ready. I . . . Ben! I, I can be a Jedi. Ben, tell him I'm ready.

Trying to see Ben, Luke starts to get up but hits his head on the low ceiling.

YODA: Ready, are you? What know you of ready? For eight hundred years have I trained Jedi. My own counsel will I keep on who is to be trained! A Jedi must have the deepest commitment, the most serious mind. *(to the invisible Ben, about Luke)* This one a long time have I watched. All his life has he looked away . . . to the future, to the horizon. Never his mind on where he was. Hmm? What he was doing. Hmph. Adventure. Heh! Excitement. Heh! A Jedi craves not these things. *(turning to Luke)* You are reckless!

(CONT'D)

CONTINUED

Luke knows it is true.

BEN'S VOICE: So was I, if you remember.

YODA: He is too old. Yes, too old to begin the training.

Luke thinks he detects a subtle softening in Yoda's voice.

LUKE: But I've learned so much.

Yoda turns his piercing gaze on Luke, as though the Jedi Master's huge eyes could somehow determine how much the boy has learned. After a long moment, the little Jedi turns toward where he alone sees Ben.

YODA: *(sighs)* Will he finish what he begins?

LUKE: I won't fail you *(as Yoda turns back toward him)* I'm not afraid.

YODA: Yeah. You will be. You will be.

EXT. SPACE – STAR DESTROYERS – ASTEROID FIELD

The Imperial fleet around Vader's ship is surrounded by the asteroid storm. Smaller Imperial vessels search for their prey.

EXT. ASTEROID CAVE – MILLENNIUM FALCON

The Millennium Falcon continues to lie low.

INT. ASTEROID CAVE – MILLENNIUM FALCON – COCKPIT

The cockpit is quiet and lit only by the indicator lights on the control panel. Princess Leia sits in the pilot's seat, thinking of Han and the confusion he has created within her. Suddenly, something outside the cockpit window catches her eye. The reflection of the panel lights obscures her vision until a soft suctionlike cup attaches itself to the windscreen and large, yellow eyes flash open and stare back at her. Startled, the young princess races from the cockpit.

INT. ASTEROID CAVE – MILLENNIUM FALCON – HOLD AREA

The lights go bright for a second, then go out again. Threepio and Chewbacca watch as Han finishes with some wires.

THREEPIO: Sir, if I may venture an opinion –

HAN: I'm not really interested in your opinion, Threepio.

Leia rushes into the cabin just as Han drops the final floor panel into place.

LEIA: *(out of breath)* There's something out there.

HAN: Where?

LEIA: Outside, in the cave.

As she speaks, there comes a sharp banging on the hull.

THREEPIO: There it is! Listen! Listen!

Chewie looks up and moans anxiously.

HAN: I'm going out there.

LEIA: Are you crazy?

HAN: I just got this bucket back together. I'm not going to let something tear it apart.

He grabs his breath mask off a rack and hurries out.

LEIA: Oh, then I'm going with you.

Chewie and Leia follow suit.

(CONT'D)

CONTINUED

THREEPIO: I think it might be better if I stay behind and guard the ship. *(hears another mysterious noise)* Oh, no.

EXT. ASTEROID CAVE — MILLENNIUM FALCON

It is very dark and dank inside the huge asteroid cave, too dark to see what is attacking the ship.

LEIA: This ground sure feels strange. It doesn't feel like rock.

Han kneels and studies the ground, then attempts to study the outline of the cave.

HAN: There's an awful lot of moisture in here.

LEIA: I don't know. I have a bad feeling about this.

HAN: Yeah.

HAN: *(to Leia)* Watch out!

Han has seen a five-foot-long shape moving across the top of the Falcon. The leathery creature lets out a screech as Han blasts it with a laserbolt. Chewie barks through his face mask.
    The black shape tumbles off the spaceship and on to the ground.

HAN: *(to Chewie)* It's all right. It's all right.

Han looks down to investigate the dead creature.

HAN: Yeah, what I thought. Mynock. Chewie, check the rest of the ship, make sure there are no more attached. They're chewing on the power cables.

LEIA: Mynocks?

HAN: Go on inside. We'll clean them off if there are any more.

Just then, a swarm of the ugly creatures swoops through the air. Leia puts her arms over her head to protect herself as she runs toward the ship. Several of the batlike creatures flap their wings loudly against the cockpit window of the Falcon. Inside, Threepio shudders at their presence.

THREEPIO: Ohhh! Go away! Go away! Beastly thing. Shoo! Shoo!

As Chewie shoos a mynock away with his blaster, the cave rocks. Han looks around the strange cave.

HAN: Wait a minute . . .

He unholsters his blaster and fires at the far side of the huge cave. The cavern begins to shake and the ground starts to buckle.
    Leia and Han move for the ship, followed closely by a barking Chewie.

INT. ASTEROID CAVE — MILLENNIUM FALCON — ENTRY AREA

The ship continues to shake and heave.

HAN: Pull her up, Chewie, let's get out of here!

The Wookiee heads for the cockpit as Han, followed by Threepio, rushes to the hold area and checks the scopes on the control panel. Leia hurries after.

LEIA: The Empire is still out there. I don't think it's wise to . . .

Han rushes past her and heads for the cockpit.

HAN: *(interrupting)* No time to discuss this in committee.

And with that he is gone. The main engines of the Falcon begin to whine. Leia races after him, bouncing around in the shaking ship.

LEIA: *(angry)* I am not a committee!

INT. ASTEROID CAVE — MILLENNIUM FALCON — COCKPIT

Han reaches the pilot's seat and pulls back on the throttle.

(CONT'D)

CONTINUED

LEIA: You can't make the jump to light-speed in this asteroid field . . .

HAN: Sit down, sweetheart. We're taking off!

As the ship begins to move forward, Chewie barks. He notices something outside the window ahead. Threepio sees it, too.

THREEPIO: Look!

HAN: I see it, I see it.

Suddenly a row of jagged white stalagmites and stalactites can be seen surrounding the entrance. And as the Falcon moves forward, the entrance to the cave grows ever smaller. Han pulls hard on the throttle, sending his ship surging forward.

THREEPIO: We're doomed!

LEIA: The cave is collapsing!

HAN: This is no cave.

LEIA: What?

Leia sees that the rocks of the cave entrance are not rocks at all, but giant teeth, quickly closing around the tiny ship.

INT. SPACE SLUG MOUTH

The Millennium Falcon, zooming through the monster's mouth, rolls on its side and barely makes it between two of the gigantic white teeth before the huge jaw slams closed.

EXT. CAVE ENTRANCE – GIANT ASTEROID

The enormous space slug moves its head out of the cave as the Falcon flies out of its mouth. The monster tilts its head, watching the starship fly away.

EXT. MILLENNIUM FALCON – GIANT ASTEROID

The Falcon races out of the asteroid crater and into the deadly rain of the asteroid storm.

EXT. CAVE ENTRANCE – GIANT ASTEROID

The monstrous slug withdraws its head back into its crater.

EXT. DAGOBAH – DAY

With Yoda strapped to his back, Luke climbs up one of the many thick vines that grow in the swamp. Panting heavily, he continues his course – climbing, flipping through the air, jumping over roots, and racing in and out of the heavy ground fog.

YODA: Run! Yes. A Jedi's strength flows from the Force. But beware of the dark side. Anger . . . fear . . . aggression. The dark side of the Force are they. Easily they flow, quick to join you in a fight. If once you start down the dark path, forever will it dominate your destiny, consume you it will, as it did Obi-Wan's apprentice.

LUKE: Vader. Is the dark side stronger?

YODA: No . . . no . . . no. Quicker, easier, more seductive.

LUKE: But how am I to know the good side from the bad?

YODA: You will know. When you are calm, at peace. Passive. A Jedi uses the Force for knowledge and defense, never for attack.

LUKE: But tell me why I can't . . .

YODA: *(interrupting)* No, no, there is no why. Nothing more will I teach you today. Clear your mind of questions. Mmm. Mmmmmmm.

Artoo beeps in the distance as Luke lets Yoda down to the ground. Breathing heavily, he takes his shirt from a nearby tree branch and pulls it on.

(CONT'D)

CONTINUED

> Yoda sits on a large root, poking his Gimer Stick into the dirt.
>
> Luke turns to see a huge, dead, black tree, its base surrounded by a few feet of water. Giant, twisted roots form a dark and sinister cave on one side. Luke stares at the tree, trembling.

LUKE: There's something not right here. I feel cold, death.

YODA: That place ... is strong with the dark side of the Force. A domain of evil it is. In you must go.

LUKE: What's in there?

YODA: Only what you take with you.

> Luke looks warily between the tree and Yoda. He starts to strap on his weapon belt.

YODA: Your weapons ... you will not need them.

> Luke gives the tree a long look, then shakes his head no. Luke reaches up to brush aside some hanging vines and enters the tree.

INT. DAGOBAH — TREE CAVE

> Luke moves into the almost total darkness of the wet and slimy cave. The youth can barely make out the edge of the passage. He sees a lizard crawling up the side of the cave and a snake wrapped around the branches of a tree. Luke draws a deep breath, then pushes deeper into the cave.
>
> The space widens around him, but he feels that rather than sees it. It is very quiet here.
>
> Then, Darth Vader appears across the blackness. They cross lightsabers, but Luke parries perfectly and slashes at Vader with his sword.
>
> Vader is decapitated. His helmet-encased head flies from his shoulders as his body disappears into the darkness. The helmet containing Vader's head spins and bounces and finally stops. For an instant it rests on the floor, then it explodes. The black helmet and breath mask fall away to reveal ... Luke's head.
>
> Across the space, the standing Luke stares at the sight, wide-eyed in terror.

EXT. SPACE — VADER'S STAR DESTROYER

> Vader's Imperial Star Destroyer moves through space, guarded by its convoy of TIE fighters.

INT. VADER'S STAR DESTROYER — BRIDGE — CONTROL DECK

> Vader stands in the back control area of his ship's bridge with a motley group of men and creatures. Admiral Piett and two controllers stand at the front of the bridge and watch the group with scorn.

PIETT: Bounty hunters. We don't need that scum.

FIRST CONTROLLER: Yes, sir.

PIETT: Those Rebels won't escape us.

> A second controller interrupts.

SECOND CONTROLLER: Sir, we have a priority signal from the Star Destroyer Avenger.

PIETT: Right.

> The group standing before Vader is a bizarre array of galactic fortune hunters: There is Bossk, a slimy, tentacled monster with two huge, bloodshot eyes in a soft baggy face; Zuckuss and Dengar, two battle-scarred, mangy human types; IG-88, a battered, tarnished chrome war droid; 4-Lom, a bounty hunter droid; and Boba Fett, a man in a weapon-covered armored spacesuit.

VADER: There will be a substantial reward for the one who finds the Millennium Falcon. You are free to use any methods necessary, but I want them alive. No disintegrations.

BOBA FETT: As you wish.

> At that moment, Admiral Piett approaches Vader in a rush of excitement.

PIETT: Lord Vader! My lord, we have them.

EXT. IMPERIAL STAR DESTROYER, AVENGER — ASTEROID BELT

(CONT'D)

CONTINUED

The Millennium Falcon speeds through deep space, closely followed by a firing Imperial Star Destroyer.

INT. MILLENNIUM FALCON — COCKPIT

The ship shudders as flak explodes near the cockpit window. Threepio checks a tracking scope on the side control panel while Leia watches tensely out the window.

THREEPIO: Oh, thank goodness we're coming out of the asteroid field.

EXT. MILLENNIUM FALCON — STAR DESTROYER, AVENGER — ASTEROID FIELD

The Falcon is hit hard by a bolt from the Star Destroyer which creates a huge explosion near the cockpit of the smaller ship. The Falcon tilts steeply, then rights itself.

INT. MILLENNIUM FALCON — COCKPIT

Han corrects the angle of his ship.

HAN: Let's get out of here. Ready for light-speed? One ... two ... three!

Han pulls back on the hyperspace throttle and — nothing happens.

HAN: *(frantic)* It's not fair!

Chewie is very angry and starts to growl and bark at his friend and captain. Again, Han desperately pulls back on the throttle as flak bursts continue to rock the ship.

HAN: The transfer circuits are all working. It's not my fault!

Chewie puts his head in his hands, whining.

LEIA: *(almost expecting it)* No light-speed?

HAN: It's not my fault.

EXT. MILLENNIUM FALCON — STAR DESTROYER, AVENGER — ASTEROID FIELD

The Millennium Falcon is closely pursued by the firing Star Destroyer.

INT. MILLENNIUM FALCON — COCKPIT

THREEPIO: Sir, we just lost the main rear deflector shield. One more direct hit on the back quarter and we're done for.

Han makes a decision.

HAN: Turn her around.

Chewie barks in puzzlement.

HAN: I said turn her around! I'm going to put all power in the front shield.

LEIA: You're going to attack them?!

THREEPIO: Sir, the odds of surviving a direct assault on an Imperial Star Destroyer —

LEIA: Shut up!

EXT. SPACE — MILLENNIUM FALCON — ASTEROID FIELD

The Falcon banks, making a steep, twisting turn.

INT. STAR DESTROYER, AVENGER — BRIDGE

The Imperials stationed on the Avenger's bridge are stunned to see the small spaceship headed directly at them. The Destroyer's commander, Captain Needa, can scarcely believe his eyes.

NEEDA: They're moving to attack position!

EXT. SPACE — MILLENNIUM FALCON — ASTEROID FIELD

The Millennium Falcon is racing toward the Star Destroyer, looking very small against the massive surface of the

(CONT'D)

CONTINUED

Imperial ship. As it moves across the surface of the Star Destroyer, the Falcon weaves to avoid the numerous flak bursts.

INT. STAR DESTROYER, AVENGER — BRIDGE

NEEDA: Shields up!

EXT. SPACE — MILLENNIUM FALCON — ASTEROID FIELD

The Falcon sweeps past.

INT. STAR DESTROYER, AVENGER — BRIDGE

Needa and his men duck as the Falcon nears the bridge window. At the last minute, the Falcon veers off and out of sight. All is quiet.

NEEDA: Track them. They may come round for another pass.

TRACKING OFFICER: Captain Needa, the ship no longer appears on our scopes.

NEEDA: They can't have disappeared. No ship that small has a cloaking device.

TRACKING OFFICER: Well, there's no trace of them, sir.

COMMUNICATIONS OFFICER: Captain, Lord Vader demands an update on the pursuit.

NEEDA: *(drawing a breath)* Get a shuttle ready. I shall assume full responsibility for losing them, and apologize to Lord Vader. Meanwhile, continue to scan the area.

COMMUNICATIONS OFFICER: Yes, Captain Needa.

EXT. DAGOBAH — BOG — DAY

Luke's face is upside-down and showing enormous strain. He stands on his hands, with Yoda perched on one of his feet. Luke lifts one hand from the ground. His body wavers, but he maintains his balance.
    Artoo, standing nearby, is whistling and beeping frantically.

YODA: Use the Force, yes. Now ... the stone.

Near Luke and Yoda are two rocks the size of bowling balls. Luke stares at the rocks and concentrates. One of the rocks lifts from the ground and floats up to rest on the other.

YODA: Feel it.

But, distracted by Artoo's frantic beeping, Luke loses his balance.

YODA: Concentrate!

Luke finally collapses. Yoda jumps clear. Annoyed by the disturbance, Luke looks over at Artoo, who is rocking urgently back and forth in front of him.
    Catching on, Luke moves to the swamp's edge. The X-wing fighter has sunk, and only the tip of its nose shows above the lake's surface.

LUKE: Oh, no. We'll never get it out now.

YODA: So certain are you. Always with you it cannot be done. Hear you nothing that I say?

Luke looks uncertainly out at the ship.

LUKE: Master, moving stones around is one thing. This is totally different.

YODA: No! No different! Only different in your mind. You must unlearn what you have learned.

LUKE: *(focusing, quietly)* All right. I'll give it a try.

YODA: No! Try not. Do. Or do not. There is no try.

Luke closes his eyes and concentrates on thinking the ship out.
    Slowly, the X-wing's nose begins to rise above the water. It hovers for a moment and then slides back, disappearing once again.

(CONT'D)

CONTINUED

LUKE: *(panting heavily)* I can't. It's too big.

YODA: Size matters not. Look at me. Judge me by my size, do you? Mm? Mmmm.

Luke shakes his head.

YODA: And well you should not. For my ally is the Force. And a powerful ally it is. Life creates it, makes it grow. Its energy surrounds us and binds us. Luminous beings are we ... *(Yoda pinches Luke's shoulder)* ... not this crude matter. You must feel the Force around you. *(gesturing)* Here, between you ... me ... the tree ... the rock ... everywhere! Yes, even between the land and the ship!

LUKE: *(discouraged)* You want the impossible.

Quietly, Yoda turns toward the sunken X-wing fighter. With his eyes closed and his head bowed, he raises his arm and points at the ship.
Soon, the fighter rises above the water and moves forward as Artoo beeps in terror and scoots away.
The entire X-wing moves majestically, surely, toward the shore. Yoda, perched on a tree root, guides the fighter carefully down toward the beach.
Luke stares in astonishment as the fighter settles gently on to the shore. He walks toward Yoda.

LUKE: I don't ... I don't believe it.

YODA: That is why you fail.

EXT. SPACE – IMPERIAL FLEET

The fleet around Vader's Star Destroyer now includes Needa's Star Destroyer, the Avenger. Needa's shuttle departs for Vader's Star Destroyer.

INT. VADER'S STAR DESTROYER – BRIDGE

Clutching desperately at his throat, Captain Needa slumps down, then falls over on his back, at the feet of Darth Vader.

VADER: Apology accepted, Captain Needa.

Two stormtroopers pick up the lifeless body and carry it quickly away as Admiral Piett and two of his captains hurry up to the Dark Lord.

PIETT: Lord Vader, our ships have completed their scan of the area and found nothing. If the Millennium Falcon went into light-speed, it'll be on the other side of the galaxy by now.

VADER: Alert all commands. Calculate every possible destination along their last known trajectory.

PIETT: Yes, my lord. We'll find them.

VADER: Don't fail me again, Admiral.

Vader exits as the admiral turns to an aide, a little more uneasy than when he arrived.

PIETT: Alert all commands. Deploy the fleet.

EXT. SPACE – IMPERIAL FLEET

Vader's ship moves away, flanked by its fleet of smaller ships. The Avenger glides off into space in the opposite direction. No one on that ship or on Vader's is aware that, clinging to the side of the Avenger, is the pirateship, the Millennium Falcon.

INT. MILLENNIUM FALCON – COCKPIT

THREEPIO: Captain Solo, this time you have gone too far. *(Chewie growls)* No, I will not be quiet, Chewbacca. Why doesn't anyone listen to me?

HAN: *(to Chewie)* The fleet is beginning to break up. Go back and stand by the manual release for the landing claw.

Chewie barks, struggles from his seat, and climbs out of the cabin.

(CONT'D)

CONTINUED

THREEPIO: I really don't see how that is going to help. Surrender is a perfectly acceptable alternative in extreme circumstances. The Empire may be gracious enough —

Leia reaches over and shuts off Threepio, mid-sentence.

HAN: Thank you.

Leia slips out of her chair and moves next to the handsome pilot.

LEIA: What did you have in mind for your next move?

HAN: Well, if they follow standard Imperial procedure, they'll dump their garbage before they go to light-speed, and then we just float away.

LEIA: With the rest of the garbage. Then what?

HAN: Then we've got to find a safe port somewhere around here. Got any ideas?

LEIA: No. Where are we?

HAN: The Anoat system.

LEIA: Anoat system. There's not much there.

HAN: No. Well, wait. This is interesting. Lando.

He points to a computer mapscreen on the control panel.

LEIA: Lando system?

HAN: Lando's not a system, he's a man. Lando Calrissian. He's a card player, gambler, scoundrel. You'd like him.

LEIA: Thanks.

HAN: Bespin. It's pretty far, but I think we can make it.

LEIA: *(reading from the computer)* A mining colony?

HAN: Yeah, a Tibanna gas mine. Lando conned somebody out of it. We go back a long way, Lando and me.

LEIA: Can you trust him?

HAN: No. But he has got no love for the Empire, I can tell you that.

Chewie barks over the intercom. Han quickly changes his readouts and stretches to look out the cockpit window.

HAN: *(into intercom)* Here we go, Chewie. Stand by. Detach!

Leia thinks for a moment; a grin creeps across her face.

LEIA: You do have your moments. Not many of them, but you do have them.

Leia gives Han a quick kiss.

EXT. SPACE — IMPERIAL STAR DESTROYER

As the Avenger Star Destroyer moves slowly into space, the hatch on its underbelly opens, sending a trail of junk floating behind it. Hidden among the refuse, the Falcon tumbles away. In the next moment, the Avenger roars off into hyperspace. The Falcon's engines are ignited, and it races off into the distance. Amidst the slowly drifting junk, Boba Fett's ship appears and moves after the Falcon.

INT. BOBA FETT'S SHIP — COCKPIT

Boba Fett is tailing the Millennium Falcon.

EXT. DAGOBAH — BOG — CLEARING — DAY

In the clearing behind Yoda's house, Luke again stands upside-down, but his face shows less strain and more concentration than before. Yoda stands beside the young warrior.

YODA: Concentrate.

(CONT'D)

CONTINUED

An equipment case slowly rises into the air.

YODA: Feel the Force flow. Yes.

Nearby Artoo watches, humming to himself, when suddenly he, too, rises into the air. His head turns frantically, looking for help.

YODA: Good. Calm, yes. Through the Force, things you will see. Other places. The future ... the past. Old friends long gone.

Luke suddenly becomes distressed.

LUKE: Han! Leia!

The packing box and Artoo fall to the ground with a crash, then Luke himself tumbles over.

YODA: *(shaking his head)* Hmm. Control, control. You must learn control.

LUKE: I saw ... I saw a city in the clouds.

YODA: Mmm. Friends you have there.

LUKE: They were in pain.

YODA: It is the future you see.

LUKE: Future? Will they die?

Yoda closes his eyes and lowers his head.

YODA: Difficult to see. *(looking up)* Always in motion is the future.

LUKE: I've got to go to them.

YODA: Decide you must how to serve them best. If you leave now, help them you could. But you would destroy all for which they have fought and suffered.

Luke is stopped cold by Yoda's words. Glooms shrouds him as he nods his head sadly.

EXT. BESPIN SURFACE – MILLENNIUM FALCON

It is dawn on the soft pink gaseous planet of Bespin. Huge billowing clouds form a canyon as the ship banks around them, headed toward the system's Cloud City.
    Suddenly, two twin-pod cars appear and move toward the Falcon.

INT. MILLENNIUM FALCON – COCKPIT

HAN: No, I don't have a landing permit. I'm trying to reach Lando Calrissian.

One of the cloud cars opens fire on the Falcon, its flak rocking the ship.

HAN: *(into transmitter)* Whoa! Wait a minute! Let me explain.

INTERCOM VOICE: You will not deviate from your present course.

THREEPIO: Rather touchy, aren't they?

LEIA: I thought you knew this person.

Chewie barks and growls at his boss.

HAN: *(to Chewie)* Well, that was a long time ago. I'm sure he's forgotten about that.

INTERCOM VOICE: Permission granted to land on Platform Three-two-seven.

HAN: *(into transmitter)* Thank you.

Angry, Han snaps off the intercom.

HAN: *(to the worried princess and her droid)* There's nothing to worry about. We go way back, Lando and me.

Leia doesn't look convinced.

(CONT'D)

CONTINUED

LEIA: Who's worried?

EXT. CLOUD CITY – MILLENNIUM FALCON – CLOUD CARS

The clouds part to reveal a full view of the city as it bobs in and out of the cloud surface. The cloud cars and the Falcon head for the gleaming white metropolis.

EXT. CLOUD CITY – LANDING PLATFORM – MILLENNIUM FALCON

With the cloud cars still guarding it, the Falcon lands on one of the Cloud City's platforms.

EXT. LANDING PLATFORM – DOOR OF MILLENNIUM FALCON

Han and Chewie stand at the open door, armed, surveying the scene warily. Leia follows behind them.

THREEPIO: Oh. No one to meet us.

LEIA: I don't like this.

HAN: Well, what would you like?

THREEPIO: Well, they did let us land.

HAN: Look, don't worry. Everything's going to be fine. Trust me.

A small group appears in the doorway to the landing platform.

HAN: See? My friend. *(to Chewie)* Keep your eyes open, huh?

Chewie growls as Han walks down the ramp. Lando and his men head across the bridge to meet the space pirate.

HAN: Hey?

Lando Calrissian, a suave, dashing black man in his thirties, leads a group of aides and some Cloud City guards toward the landing platform.
    The group, like the other citizens of the city, is a motley collection of aliens, droids and humans of all descriptions.
    Lando stops ten feet from Han. The two men eye each other carefully. Lando shakes his head. He has a grim expression on his face.

LANDO: Why, you slimy, double-crossing, no-good swindler! You've got a lot of guts coming here, after what you pulled.

Han points to himself innocently, mouthing Me?
    Lando moves threateningly toward Han. Suddenly, he throws his arms around his startled, long-lost friend and embraces him.

LANDO: *(laughs)* How you doing, you old pirate? So good to see you! I never thought I'd catch up with you again. Where you been?

EXT. LANDING PLATFORM – DOOR OF MILLENNIUM FALCON

THREEPIO: Well, he seems very friendly.

LEIA: *(wary)* Yes … very friendly.

The two old friends embrace, laughing and chuckling.

LANDO: What are you doing here?

HAN: *(gestures toward the Falcon)* Ahh … repairs. I thought you could help me out.

LANDO: *(in mock panic)* What have you done to my ship?

HAN: Your ship? Hey, remember, you lost her to me fair and square.

Chewie, Leia, and Threepio have made their way down the ramp.

LANDO: And how are you doing, Chewbacca? You still hanging around with this loser?

Chewie growls a reserved greeting. Lando suddenly notices the princess and smiles admiringly.

(CONT'D)

CONTINUED

LANDO: Hello. What have we here? Welcome. I'm Lando Calrissian. I'm the administrator of this facility. And who might you be?

LEIA: Leia.

LANDO: Welcome, Leia.

Lando kisses her hand.

HAN: All right, all right, you old smoothie.

Han takes Leia by the hand and steers her away from Lando.

THREEPIO: Hello, sir. I am See-Threepio, human-cyborg relations. My facilities are at your . . .

Before Threepio can finish his self-introduction, Lando has turned to follow Han and Leia, who are walking toward the city.

THREEPIO: Well, really!

Lando, his aide, Lobot, and Han lead the way across the bridge, followed by Threepio, Chewie, and Leia.

LANDO: What's wrong with the Falcon?

HAN: Hyperdrive.

LANDO: I'll get my people to work on it.

HAN: Good.

Lando turns to Leia.

LANDO: You know, that ship saved my life quite a few times. She's the fastest hunk of junk in the galaxy.

HAN: How's the gas mine? Is it still paying off for you?

INT. CLOUD CITY – CORRIDOR

The group has crossed the narrow bridge and entered the city. They walk down the lovely Art Deco passageway, rounding several corners and passing many small plazas as they go. Threepio lags a bit behind.

LANDO: Oh, not as well as I'd like. We're a small outpost and not very self-sufficient. And I've had supply problems of every kind. I've had labor difficulties . . . *(Han laughs)* What's so funny?

HAN: You. Listen to you — you sound like a businessman, a responsible leader. Who'd have thought that, huh?

LANDO: You know, seeing you sure brings back a few things.

Lando is reflective. He stops and looks at Han a moment.

HAN: Yeah.

LANDO: *(shakes his head)* Yeah. I'm responsible these days. It's the price you pay for being successful.

The group moves on through the corridor.
  The lagging Threepio passes a Threepio-type silver droid who is coming out of a door.

THREEPIO: Oh! Nice to see a familiar face.

SECOND THREEPIO: *(mumbles)* E chu ta!

THREEPIO: How rude!

Threepio stops, watching the silver droid move away. Then he hears the muffled beeping and whistling of an R2 unit coming from within the room.

THREEPIO: That sounds like an R2 unit in there.

INT. CLOUD CITY – ANTEROOM

Curious, Threepio enters the room.

(CONT'D)

CONTINUED

THREEPIO: I wonder if . . .

Threepio walks through the doorway to the main room. He looks in.

THREEPIO: Hello? Hello? How interesting.

MAN'S VOICE: *(from within)* Who are you?

THREEPIO: Who am I? Oh, I'm terribly sorry. I . . . I didn't mean to intrude. No, no, please don't get up. No!

A laserbolt to Threepio's chest sends him flying in twenty directions. Smoldering mechanical arms and legs bounce off the walls as the door whooshes closed behind him.

INT. CLOUD CITY — CORRIDOR

Lando, Han, and Leia have continued down the corridor unaware of Threepio's dreadful accident. Chewbacca glances around, sniffs the air, but shrugs his shoulders and follows the group.

EXT. DAGOBAH — BOG — DUSK

In the bright lights of the fighter, Luke inspects the cockpit of the ship. Artoo sits on top of the X-wing, settling down into his cubbyhole. Yoda perches nearby on a log.

YODA: Luke! You must complete the training.

LUKE: I can't keep the vision out of my head. They're my friends. I've got to help them.

YODA: You must not go!

LUKE: But Han and Leia will die if I don't.

BEN'S VOICE: You don't know that.

Luke looks toward the voice in amazement. Ben has materialized as a real, slightly shimmering image near Yoda. The power of his presence stops Luke.

BEN: Even Yoda cannot see their fate.

LUKE: But I can help them! I feel the Force!

BEN: But you cannot control it. This is a dangerous time for you, when you will be tempted by the dark side of the Force.

YODA: Yes, yes. To Obi-Wan you listen. The cave. Remember your failure at the cave!

LUKE: But I've learned so much since then, Master Yoda. I promise to return and finish what I've begun. You have my word.

BEN: It is you and your abilities the Emperor wants. That is why your friends are made to suffer.

LUKE: That's why I have to go.

BEN: Luke, I don't want to lose you to the Emperor the way I lost Vader.

LUKE: You won't.

YODA: Stopped they must be. On this all depends. Only a fully-trained Jedi Knight with the Force as his ally will conquer Vader and his Emperor. If you end your training now, if you choose the quick and easy path, as Vader did, you will become an agent of evil.

BEN: Patience.

LUKE: And sacrifice Han and Leia?

YODA: If you honor what they fight for . . . yes!

BEN: If you choose to face Vader, you will do it alone. I cannot interfere.

Luke is in great anguish. He struggles with the dilemma, a battle raging in his mind.

LUKE: I understand. *(he climbs up his X-wing)* Artoo, fire up the convertors.

(CONT'D)

CONTINUED

Artoo whistles a happy reply. Luke climbs into his ship.

BEN: Luke, don't give in to hate — that leads to the dark side.

YODA: Strong is Vader. Mind what you have learned. Save you it can.

LUKE: I will. And I'll return. I promise.

Artoo closes the cockpit.

YODA: *(sighs)* Told you, I did. Reckless is he. Now matters are worse.

BEN: That boy is our last hope.

YODA: *(looks up)* No. There is another.

The roar of the engines and the wind engulfs Ben and Yoda.

EXT. SPACE — PLANET DAGOBAH

Luke's tiny X-wing rockets away from the green planet of Dagobah and off into space.

EXT. BESPIN — CLOUD CITY

Within the quarters assigned her on Cloud City, Leia paces in agitation.

INT. CLOUD CITY — LIVING QUARTERS — DAY

Leia has changed from her cold-weather pants and jacket to a lovely dress. Her hair is down, tied back with ribbons. She moves from a large, open window and turns to see Han entering through the doorway.

HAN: The ship's almost finished. Two or three more things and we're in great shape.

LEIA: The sooner the better. Something's wrong here. No one has seen or knows anything about Threepio. He's been gone too long to have gotten lost.

Han takes Leia by the shoulders and gently kisses her forehead.

HAN: Relax. I'll talk to Lando. See what I can find out.

LEIA: I don't trust Lando.

HAN: Well, I don't trust him, either. But he is my friend. Besides, we'll soon be gone.

LEIA: And then you're as good as gone, aren't you?

Not speaking, Han considers her words and gazes at her troubled face.

INT. CLOUD CITY — JUNK ROOM

The room is piled high with broken and discarded machine parts. Ugnaughts, small hoglike creatures, separate the junk and throw some pieces onto a conveyor belt which moves briskly toward a pit of molten metal. Pieces of Threepio's golden body move down the belt. Chewie enters the room and spots an Ugnaught picking up and inspecting Threepio's head. The Wookiee barks a command, startling the Ugnaught, then reaches to grab the head. But the Ugnaught tosses it away from him to another Ugnaught. This game of keep-away goes on until Threepio's head falls from their grip and bounces with a clang on to the ground.

INT. CLOUD CITY — LIVING QUARTERS — DAY

The door zaps open. Chewbacca walks in, carrying a packing case of Threepio, arms and legs hanging over the edges.

LEIA: What happened?

Chewie sets the case on a table, grunting and groaning an explanation.

HAN: Where? Found him in a junk pile?

LEIA: Oh, what a mess. Chewie, do you think you can repair him?

The giant Wookiee studies the array of robot parts. He looks at the princess and moans sadly.

(CONT'D)

CONTINUED

HAN: Lando's got people who can fix him.

LEIA: No, thanks.

Lando enters

LANDO: I'm sorry. Am I interrupting anything?

LEIA: Not really.

LANDO: You look absolutely beautiful. You truly belong here with us among the clouds.

LEIA: *(coolly)* Thank you.

LANDO: Will you join me for a little refreshment?

Chewie barks at the mention of food and licks his lips.

LANDO: Everyone's invited, of course.

Leia takes Lando's preferred arm, and the group turns to go. Lando spots Threepio's remains.

LANDO: Having trouble with your droid?

HAN: No.

Han and Leia exchange a quick glance.

HAN: No problem. Why?

Han and Leia move arm-in-arm through the door, followed by Lando and Chewie.

INT. CLOUD CITY – CORRIDOR – DAY

Leia walks between Han and Lando as Chewie follows a short distance behind. Long shafts of light pour across a corridor between tall, pure-white columns.

LANDO: So, you see, since we're a small operation, we don't fall into the ... uh ... jurisdiction of the Empire.

LEIA: So you're part of the mining guild then?

LANDO: No, not actually. Our operation is small enough not to be noticed ... which is advantageous for everybody since our customers are anxious to avoid attracting attention to themselves.

The group walks into another corridor and heads for a huge doorway at the far end.

HAN: Aren't you afraid the Empire's going to find out about this little operation and shut you down?

LANDO: It's always been a danger but it looms like a shadow over everything we've built here. But things have developed that will ensure security. I've just made a deal that will keep the Empire out of here for ever.

INT. CLOUD CITY – DINING ROOM

The mighty doors to the dining room slide open and the group enters the dining room. At the far end of a huge banquet table sits Darth Vader.
Faster than the wink of an eye, Han draws his blaster and pops off a few shots directly at Vader. The Dark Lord quickly raises his hand, deflecting the bolts into one of the side walls, where they explode harmlessly. Just as quickly, Han's weapon zips into Vader's hand.

VADER: We would be honored if you would join us.

Boba Fett, the bounty hunter, steps out from behind Vader. Imperial stormtroopers cut off the adventurers' escape.

LANDO: I had no choice. They arrived right before you did. I'm sorry.

HAN: I'm sorry, too.

EXT. LUKE'S X-WING – BESPIN SYSTEM

Luke's X-wing races through thick clouds toward Cloud City.

(CONT'D)

CONTINUED

INT. LUKE'S X-WING — COCKPIT

Luke is grim-faced as he pilots his course toward Bespin's shining city. Artoo's beeps and whistles are transmitted on to the scope.

LUKE: *(into comlink)* No. Threepio's with them.

EXT. LUKE'S X-WING

Artoo whistles another worried inquiry.

INT. LUKE'S X-WING — COCKPIT

LUKE: *(into comlink)* Just hang on. We're almost there.

EXT. LUKE'S X-WING — BESPIN SYSTEM

Luke X-wing closes on Cloud City.

INT. CLOUD CITY — LARGE CELL

Chewbacca is in a Cloud City prison cell. The stark room is flooded with hot light. To add to Chewie's misery, a high-pitched whistle screeches loudly. Chewie is going mad. He paces across the floor and shakes the bars of his cell. The whistle stops abruptly. Moaning to himself, the prisoner moves to a platform where the disassembled pieces of Threepio lie. He picks up the golden droid's head and meditates on it for a moment, barking a few philosophical remarks. Chewie sticks the robot's head on its torso and starts adjusting wires and circuits.

    Suddenly, the lights in Threepio's eyes spark to life as Chewie touches two connectors together. Threepio immediately begins to speak, but his voice is so uneven as to be nearly unintelligible.

THREEPIO: Mmm. Oh, my. Uh, I, uh — Take this off! I, uh, don't mean to intrude here. I, don't, no, no, no ... Please don't get up. No!

Chewie looks at Threepio in bewilderment. He gets an idea and adjusts some connections, whereupon Threepio immediately begins speaking normally.

THREEPIO: Stormtroopers? Here? We're in danger. I must tell the others. Oh, no! I've been shot!

INT. CLOUD CITY — PRISON ENTRY AREA

Darth Vader strides through the room as two stormtroopers prepare an elaborate torture mechanism. Han is strapped to a rack which tilts forward onto the torture device. Vader activates the mechanism, creating two bursts of sparks, which strike Han.

INT. CLOUD CITY — HOLDING CHAMBER

The door opens, and Vader leaves the torture room just as Han screams a sharp, piercing cry of agony. In the holding chamber, Lando and Boba Fett await Vader.

LANDO: Lord Vader.

VADER: *(to Fett)* You may take Captain Solo to Jabba the Hutt after I have Skywalker.

Han's screams filter through the torture room door.

BOBA FETT: He's no good to me dead.

VADER: He will not be permanently damaged.

LANDO: Lord Vader, what about Leia and the Wookiee?

VADER: They must never again leave this city.

LANDO: That was never a condition of our agreement, nor was giving Han to this bounty hunter!

VADER: Perhaps you think you're being treated unfairly.

LANDO: No.

VADER: Good. It would be unfortunate if I had to leave a garrison here.

(CONT'D)

CONTINUED

The doors of the elevator close on Vader. Lando walks swiftly down another corridor, muttering to himself.

LANDO: This deal is getting worse all the time.

INT. CLOUD CITY – LARGE CELL

Chewie now has a little more of Threepio back together. One arm is connected, but the legs are yet to be attached. There is one small problem, however: it seems the Wookiee has managed to put the droid's head on backward.

THREEPIO: Oh, yes, that's very good. I like that. Oh! Something's not right because now I can't see. Oh. Oh, that's much better. Wait. Wait! Oh, my! What have you done? I'm backwards, you fleabitten furball. Only an overgrown mophead like you would be stupid enough –

Threepio is cut off in mid-sentence as Chewie angrily deactivates a circuit and the droid shuts down. The door to the chamber slides open and a ragged Han Solo is shoved into the room by two stormtroopers. Barking his concern, the huge Wookiee picks Han up. Han is very pale, with dark circles under his eyes.

HAN: I feel terrible.

Chewie helps Han to a platform and then turns as the door slides open revealing Leia. She, too, looks a little the worse for wear. The troopers push her into the cell, and the door slides closed. She moves to Han, who is lying on the platform, and kneels next to him, gently stroking his head.

LEIA: Why are they doing this?

HAN: They never even asked me any questions.

The cell door slides open. Lando and two of his guards enter.

LEIA: Lando.

HAN: Get out of here, Lando!

LANDO: Shut up and listen! Now, Vader has agreed to turn Leia and Chewie over to me.

HAN: Over to you?

LANDO: They'll have to stay here, but at least they'll be safe.

LEIA: What about Han?

LANDO: Vader's giving him to the bounty hunter.

LEIA: Vader wants us all dead.

LANDO: He doesn't want you at all. He's after somebody called Skywalker.

HAN: Luke?

LANDO: Lord Vader has set a trap for him.

Leia's mind is racing.

LEIA: And we're the bait.

LANDO: Yeah, well, he's on his way.

Han's rage peaks.

HAN: Perfect. You fixed us all real good, didn't you? *(spits it out)* My friend!

Han has hauled himself up and punches Lando. One of the guards hits Han with his rifle butt and he falls to the floor. Chewie growls and starts for the other guard. He points his laser weapon at the giant Wookiee, but Lando stops him.

LANDO: Stop! I've done all I can. I'm sorry I couldn't do better, but I got my own problems.

HAN: Yeah, you're a real hero.

Lando and his guards leave. Leia and Chewie help Han sit up.

(CONT'D)

CONTINUED

LEIA: You certainly have a way with people.

INT. CLOUD CITY – CARBON-FREEZING CHAMBER

Armor-suited stormtroopers stand at the ready in the large chamber, which is filled with pipes and chemical tanks. In the middle of the room is a round pit housing a hydraulic platform. Darth Vader and Lando stand near the platform.

VADER: This facility is crude, but it should be adequate to freeze Skywalker for his journey to the Emperor.

An Imperial soldier appears.

IMPERIAL SOLDIER: Lord Vader, ship approaching, X-wing class.

VADER: Good. Monitor Skywalker and allow him to land.

The soldier bows and leaves the chamber.

LANDO: Lord Vader, we only use this facility for carbon freezing. You put him in there … it might kill him.

VADER: I do not want the Emperor's prize damaged. We will test it … on Captain Solo.

Lando's face registers dismay.

EXT. SPACE – BESPIN SYSTEM – LUKE'S X-WING

Luke's X-wing moves through the clouds as it nears the city.

INT. LUKE'S X-WING – COCKPIT

Encountering no city guards, Luke scans his display panels with concern.

EXT. CLOUD CITY

Luke's X-wing approaches the city.

INT. CLOUD CITY – CARBON-FREEZING CHAMBER

There has been great activity on the carbon-freezing platform. Six Ugnaughts have frantically prepared the chamber for use. A special coffinlike container has been put in place. With Boba Fett in the lead, a squad of six stormtroopers brings in Han, Leia, and Chewie. Strapped to Chewie's back, with only his head, torso, and one arm assembled, is Threepio. Threepio's head faces the opposite direction from Chewie's. The remaining pieces of his body are randomly bundled to the Wookiee's back so that his legs and other arm stick out at odd angles from the pack.

THREEPIO: If only you had attached my legs, I wouldn't be in this ridiculous position. Now, remember, Chewbacca, you have a responsibility to me, so don't do anything foolish.

HAN: *(to Lando)* What's going on … buddy?

LANDO: You're being put into carbon freeze.

Boba Fett moves away from the group to Darth Vader.

BOBA FETT: What if he doesn't survive? He's worth a lot to me.

VADER: The Empire will compensate you if he dies. Put him in!

Realizing what is about to happen, Chewie lets out a wild howl and attacks the stormtroopers surrounding Han. From the instant of Chewie's first move, Threepio begins to scream in panic while he tries to protect himself with his one arm.

THREEPIO: Oh, no! No, no, no! Stop

HAN: Stop, Chewie, stop! Stop!

THREEPIO: Yes, stop, please! I'm not ready to die.

Han breaks away from his captors. Vader has evidently nodded to the guards to let him go and the pirate breaks up the fight.

(CONT'D)

CONTINUED

HAN: Hey, hey! Listen to me. Chewie! Chewie, this won't help me. Hey! Save your strength. There'll be another time. The princess — you have to take care of her. You hear me? Huh?

The Wookiee wails a doleful farewell.
    Han turns to Princess Leia. They look sorrowfully at one another, then Han moves toward her and gives her a final, passionate kiss.

LEIA: I love you!

HAN: I know.

Helpless, Leia watches the dashing pirate on the hydraulic platform. Han looks one final time at his friends — and then, suddenly, the platform drops. Chewie howls. Leia turns away in agony.
    Lando winces in sorrow; it makes a life-changing impression on him.
    Instantly, smoke begins to pour forth. Holding Leia, Chewie half-turns away from the sight, giving Threepio a view of the procedure.

THREEPIO: What … what's going on? Turn round. Chewbacca, I can't see.

Chewie howls.
    A huge mechanical tong lifts the steaming metal-encased space pirate out of the vat and stands him on the platform. Some Ugnaughts rush over and push the block over on to the platform.
    Lando kneels and adjusts some knobs, measuring the heat. He shakes his head in relief.

THREEPIO: Oh … they've encased him in carbonite. He should be quite well protected — if he survived the freezing process, that is.

VADER: Well, Calrissian, did he survive?

LANDO: Yes, he's alive. And in perfect hibernation.

Vader turns to Boba Fett.

VADER: He's all yours, bounty hunter. Reset the chamber for Skywalker.

IMPERIAL OFFICER: Skywalker has just landed, my lord.

VADER: Good. See to it that he finds his way in here. Calrissian, take the princess and the Wookiee to my ship.

LANDO: You said they'd be left in the city under my supervision.

VADER: I am altering the deal. Pray I don't alter it any further.

Lando's hand instinctively goes to his throat as he turns to Leia, Chewie and Threepio.

INT. CLOUD CITY — CORRIDOR — DAY

As Luke and Artoo move carefully down a deserted corridor, they hear a group of people coming down a side hallway.
    Boba Fett enters from a side hallway followed by two guards pushing the floating, encased body of Han Solo. Two stormtroopers follow. The two guards whisk Han into another hallway as Artoo lets out an excited series of beeps and whistles. Luke glares at the tiny droid, who stops in his tracks with a feeble squeak. But the noise has drawn the attention of Fett, who fires a deadly laser at Luke, which explodes to one side and tears up a huge chunk of wall.
    Leia, Chewie, Threepio, and Lando are herded down a second hallway by several other stormtroopers. Leia turns just in time to see Luke. Surreptitiously, Lando sends a signal to his aide, Lobot.

LEIA: Luke! Luke, don't — it's a trap! It's a trap!

Before she can finish, she is pulled through a doorway and disappears from sight. Luke races after the group, leaving little Artoo trailing behind.

INT. CLOUD CITY — ANTEROOM

Luke runs into an anteroom and stops to get his bearings. Leia and the others are nowhere to be seen. Behind Luke, Artoo scoots down the corridor toward the anteroom when suddenly a giant metal door comes slamming down, cutting off Luke's exit.

(CONT'D)

CONTINUED

INT. CLOUD CITY — CARBON-FREEZING CHAMBER

Luke rises into the chamber, borne by the platform. The room is deathly quiet. Very little steam escapes the pipes and no one else seems to be in the large room. Warily, Luke walks toward the stairway.

Steam begins to build up in the chamber. Looking up through the steam, Luke sees a dark figure standing on a walkway above him.

VADER: The Force is with you, young Skywalker. But you are not a Jedi yet.

Luke moves up the stairs to face Vader. He feels confident, eager to engage his enemy.

Luke ignites his sword in answer. In an instant, Vader's own sword is lit. Luke lunges, but Vader repels the blow. Again Luke attacks, and the swords of the two combatants clash in battle.

INT. CLOUD CITY — CORRIDOR

Leia, Lando and Chewie, with Threepio on his back, march along, guarded by stormtroopers. The group reaches an intersection where Lobot and a dozen of Lando's guards stand at attention.

The guards immediately aim their weapons at the startled stormtroopers. Taking the stormtroopers' weapons from them, Lando hands one to Leia.

LANDO: *(to Lobot)* Well done. Hold them in the security tower — and keep it quiet. Move.

As Lando's guards quickly march the stormtroopers away, Lando begins to undo Chewie's binding.

LEIA: What do you think you're doing?

LANDO: We're getting out of here.

THREEPIO: I knew all along it had to be a mistake.

Chewie turns on Lando and starts to choke him.

LEIA: Do you think that after what you did to Han that we're going to trust you?

Lando tries to free himself from Chewie.

LANDO: *(choking)* I had no choice . . .

Chewie barks ferociously.

THREEPIO: *(to Chewie)* What are you doing? Trust him, trust him!

LEIA: Oh, so we understand, don't we, Chewie? He had no choice.

LANDO: I'm just trying to help . . .

LEIA: We don't need any of your help.

LANDO: *(choking)* H-a-a-a . . .

LEIA: What?

THREEPIO: It sounds like Han.

LANDO: There's still a chance to save Han . . . At the East Platform . . .

LEIA: Chewie.

Chewie finally releases Lando, who fights to get his breath back.

THREEPIO: *(to Lando)* I'm terribly sorry about all this. After all, he's only a Wookiee.

EXT. CLOUD CITY — EAST LANDING PLATFORM — BOBA FETT'S SHIP

BOBA FETT: Put Captain Solo in the cargo hold.

The two guards slide Han's enclosed body into an opening in the side of the bounty hunter's ship. Boba Fett climbs aboard on a ladder next to the side opening.

INT. CLOUD CITY — CORRIDOR

(CONT'D)

CONTINUED

Lando, Leia and Chewie run down a Cloud City corridor. Artoo rushes after them, beeping wildly.

THREEPIO: Artoo! Artoo! Where have you been?

Chewie turns around to see the stubby droid, causing Threepio to be spun out of sight of his friend.

THREEPIO: Wait, turn round, you woolly ...! *(to Artoo)* Hurry, hurry! We're trying to save Han from the bounty hunter!

Whistling frantically to Threepio, Artoo scoots along with the racing group.

THREEPIO: Well, at least you're still in one piece! Look what happened to me!

EXT. EAST LANDING PLATFORM – SIDE BAY

An elevator door slides open and Leia, Chewbacca and Lando race for a large bay overlooking the East Landing Platform.
    Just as they arrive, Boba Fett's ship takes off against the cloudy sunset sky.
    In wild anguish, Chewie howls and starts firing at the ship.

THREEPIO: Oh, no! Chewie, they're behind you!

A laserbolt explodes near the princess. Everyone turns to see what Threepio has already spotted coming from the other direction: stormtroopers.
    Laserbolts continue to explode around the princess and the Wookiee, but they barely notice. They seem possessed, transported, as all the frustration of captivity and anger of loss pour out through their death-dealing weapons.
    After a few moments, the group begins to move through the rain of laserfire.

INT. CLOUD CITY – CARBON-FREEZING CHAMBER

Luke and Vader are locked in combat on the platform overlooking the chamber. Their swords clash, the platform sways.

VADER: You have learned much, young one.

LUKE: You'll find I'm full of surprises.

Vader makes two quick moves, hooking Luke's sword out of his hands and sending it flying. Another lightning move at Luke's feet forces the youth to jump back to protect himself. Losing his balance, Luke rolls down the stars to the circular carbon-freezing platform. There he sprawls on the floor, surprised and shaken. Just in time he looks up to see Vader, like a giant black bird, flying right at him. Luke rolls away as Vader lands. Crouching, Luke keeps his gaze steadily on his enemy.

VADER: Your destiny lies with me, Skywalker. Obi-Wan knew this to be true.

LUKE: No!

Behind Luke the hydraulic elevator cover has opened noisily. All the while, Luke slowly, cautiously moves back, away from the Dark Lord.
    Suddenly, Luke loses his balance and falls back into the opening.

VADER: All too easy. Perhaps you are not as strong as the Emperor thought.

There is a rumble, and in an instant freezing steam rises to obscure Vader's vision. Vader turns aside and deactivates his sword.
    Through the steam behind Vader something blurs upward.
    Vader turns around – and then looks up. He sees Luke, who has leaped fifteen feet straight up and who now hangs from some hoses on the carbonite outlet.

VADER: Impressive ... most impressive.

Luke jumps down to the platform where he is separated from Vader by the steaming carbonite pit. He raises his hand. His sword, which had fallen on another part of the platform, swiftly jumps into his outstretched hand and is instantly ignited. Vader and he clash swords.

(CONT'D)

CONTINUED

VADER: Obi-Wan has taught you well. You have controlled your fear ... now release your anger. Only your hatred can destroy me.

Luke is more cautious, controlling his anger. He begins to retreat as Vader goads him on. As Luke takes a defensive position, he realizes he has been foolhardy.

   Breathing hard, Luke jumps in the air, turning a somersault over Vader. He lands on the floor and slashes at Vader as the room continues to fill up the screen. A quick sword exchange and Luke forces Vader back. Another exchange and Vader retreats. Luke presses forward.

   Vader retreats before Luke's skillful sword. Vader blocks the sword, but loses his balance and falls into the outer rim of pipes. The energy Luke has used to stop Vader has brought him to the point of collapse. Luke moves to the edge and looks down, but sees no sign of Vader. He then deactivates his sword, hooks it on his belt, and moves down into the pit.

INT. CLOUD CITY – TUNNEL AND REACTOR CONTROL ROOM

Moving through a tunnellike entrance, Luke cautiously approaches the reactor room. He ignites his sword and moves into the room and toward a large window as Vader enters.

   Luke raises his sword and moves forward to attack.

   Behind Luke a large pipe detaches itself from the wall and comes smashing forward toward his back. Luke turns and cuts it in half.

   As Luke and Vader cross swords, another piece of equipment detaches and comes flying at Luke. Small tools and equipment come flying at him. Bombarded from all sides, Luke does his best to deflect everything, but soon he is bloodied and bruised. Finally, one machine glances off him and goes flying out the large window. A fierce wind blows into the room, whipping everything about and creating a horrendous noise. In the center of the room, unmoving, stands the dark, rocklike figure of Vader.

   A piece of machinery hits Luke and he is sucked out the window.

INT. GANTRY – OUTSIDE CONTROL ROOM – REACTOR SHAFT

Luke has fallen on to the gantry, and hangs over the edge. He begins to scramble up.

INT. CLOUD CITY – CORRIDOR LEADING TO LANDING PLATFORM

Leia, Lando, Chewie and the droids are fighting a running battle with stormtroopers. They come round a corner and head for the door to the landing platform. Lando punches desperately at the door's control panel.

LANDO: The security code has been changed!

THREEPIO: Artoo, you can tell the computer to override the security system. Artoo, hurry!

Threepio has pointed to a computer socket on the control panel. Artoo beeps and scoots toward it. Lando meanwhile has connected up to the panel's intercom.

LANDO: Attention! This is Lando Calrissian. The Empire has taken control of the city. I advise everyone to leave before more Imperial troops arrive.

Artoo takes off a connector cover and sticks his computer arm into the socket. Suddenly, a short beep turns into a wild scream. Artoo's circuits light up, his head spins wildly, and smoke begins to seep out underneath him. Quickly, Chewie pulls him away.

LANDO: This way.

Lando, Leia, Artoo and Chewie flee down the corridor. As he scoots along with them, Artoo sends some angry beeps Threepio's way.

THREEPIO: Well, don't blame me. I'm an interpreter. I'm not supposed to know a power socket from a computer terminal.

INT. CLOUD CITY – CORRIDOR

In a panic, Cloud City residents are trying to get out of the city. Some carry boxes, others packages. They run, then change direction.

   Stormtroopers pursue Lando, Leia and Chewie, who are firing back at them. Artoo works on another door to the landing platform while Threepio berates him for his seeming ineptitude.

(CONT'D)

CONTINUED

THREEPIO: Ah. We're not interested in the hyperdrive on the Millennium Falcon. Its fixed! Just open the door, you stupid lump.

A triumphant beep from Artoo — and the door snaps open.

THREEPIO: *(to Artoo)* I never doubted you for a second. Wonderful!

Chewie, Leia and Lando retreat along the corridor.
 Artoo lays down a cloud of fog, obscuring everything, as the group dashes outside.

EXT. LANDING PLATFORM — CLOUD CITY — DUSK

They race for the Millennium Falcon as a battalion of stormtroopers reaches the main door. Lando and Leia hold off the troops as the droids get on board with Chewie. As Chewie bounds to the ship with Threepio on his back, Threepio hits his head on the top of the ramp.

THREEPIO: Ouch! Oh! Ah! That hurt. Bend down, you thoughtless ... Ow!

LANDO: Leia! Go!

Lando and Leia race up the ramp under a hail of laserfire as Chewie starts up the ship.

INT. MILLENNIUM FALCON — CORRIDOR

Artoo drags the partially assembled Threepio down the corridor of the Falcon.

THREEPIO: I thought that hairy beast would be the end of me. Of course I've looked better.

Artoo beeps understandingly.

EXT. CLOUD CITY — LANDING PLATFORM — DUSK

Troops fire after it as the Millennium Falcon lifts gracefully into the twilight sky and roars away from the city.

INT. GANTRY — OUTSIDE CONTROL ROOM — REACTOR SHAFT

Luke moves along the railing and up to the control room. Vader lunges at him and Luke immediately raises his lit sword to meet Vader's. Sparks fly as they duel, Vader gradually forcing Luke backward toward the gantry.

VADER: You are beaten. It is useless to resist. Don't let yourself be destroyed as Obi-Wan did.

Luke answers by rolling sideways and thrusting his sword at Vader so viciously that he nicks Vader on the shoulder. The black armor sparks and smokes and Vader seems to be hurt, but immediately recovers.
 Luke has backed off along the narrow end of the gantry as Vader comes at him, slashing at the young Jedi with his sword. Luke makes a quick move around the instrument complex attached to the end of the gantry. Vader's sword comes slashing down, cutting the complex loose; it begins to fall.
 Then Vader's sword comes down across Luke's right forearm, cutting off his hand and sending his sword flying. In great pain, Luke squeezes his forearm under his left armpit and moves back along the gantry to its extreme end. Vader follows. The wind subsides. Luke holds on. There is nowhere else to go.

VADER: There is no escape. Don't make me destroy you, Luke, you do not yet realize your importance. You have only begun to discover your power. Join me and I will complete your training. With our combined strength, we can end this destructive conflict and bring order to the galaxy.

LUKE: I'll never join you!

VADER: If you only knew the power of the dark side. Obi-Wan never told you what happened to your father.

LUKE: He told me enough! He told me you killed him.

VADER: No. I am your father.

Shocked, Luke looks at Vader in utter disbelief.

LUKE: No. No. That's not true! That's impossible!

VADER: Search your feelings. You know it to be true.

LUKE: No! No!

(CONT'D)

CONTINUED

VADER: Luke. You can destroy the Emperor. He has foreseen this. It is your destiny. Join me, and together we can rule the galaxy as father and son.

Vader has put away his sword and holds his hand out to Luke.

VADER: Come with me. It is the only way.

A calm comes over Luke, and he makes a decision. In the next instant he steps off the gantry platform into space. The Dark Lord looks over the platform and sees Luke falling far below. The wounded Jedi begins to drop fast, unable to grab on to anything to break his fall.

INT. REACTOR SHAFT

Suddenly, Luke is sucked into an exhaust pipe in the side of the shaft.

INT. EXHAUST PIPE

Luke tumbles through the exhaust pipe.
   He slides to the end of the slickly polished pipe and stops, then falls through a circular grill.

EXT. BOTTOM OF CLOUD CITY – WEATHER VANE – DUSK

Luke tumbles out, emerging at the undermost part of Cloud City. Reaching out desperately, he manages to grab on to an electronic weather vane.

LUKE: Ben ... Ben, please!

Luke tries to pull himself up on the weather vane but slips back down. He hooks one of this legs around the fragile instrument. All the while, a powerful current of air rushes out at him from the exhaust pipe.

LUKE: Ben. Leia!

EXT. CLOUD CITY – MILLENNIUM FALCON – DUSK

The Millennium Falcon is leaving Cloud City.

INT. MILLENNIUM FALCON – COCKPIT

Leia seems to be lost in a fog, her expression troubled.

EXT. BOTTOM OF CLOUD CITY – WEATHER VANE – DUSK

LUKE: Hear me! Leia!

INT. MILLENNIUM FALCON – COCKPIT

LEIA: Luke ... We've got to go back.

Chewie is busy operating the ship. Lando stands next to the Wookiee, watching a readout on the control panel.
   Chewie growls in surprise.

LANDO: What?

LEIA: I know where Luke is.

LANDO: But what about those fighters?

Chewie barks in agreement with Lando.

LEIA: Chewie, just do it.

LANDO: But what about Vader?

Chewie turns on Lando, the newcomer, with an ominous growl.

LANDO: All right, all right, all right.

EXT. CLOUD CITY – MILLENNIUM FALCON – DUSK

The Falcon makes a graceful banking turn back toward Cloud City.

EXT. CLOUD CITY – CORRIDOR

(CONT'D)

CONTINUED

Vader strides toward the landing platform, followed by an aide and stormtroopers.

VADER: Bring my shuttle.

EXT. BOTTOM OF CLOUD CITY – WEATHER VANE

Nearly unconscious, Luke hangs upside-down on the weather vane.

EXT. MILLENNIUM FALCON – BOTTOM OF CLOUD CITY

The Falcon dives to the underside of the floating city.

INT. MILLENNIUM FALCON – COCKPIT

Leia tries to remain calm.

LANDO: *(pointing out the cockpit window)* Look, someone's up there.

LEIA: It's Luke. Chewie, slow down. Slow down and we'll get under him. Lando, open the top hatch.

Lando rushes out of the cockpit.

EXT. BOTTOM OF CLOUD CITY – WEATHER VANE

Luke hangs by one arm from the crossbar of the weather vane. He slips from the bar and grabs on to the pole of the vane as the Falcon banks toward him.
　　The Falcon positions itself under Luke as Lando moves up through the opening of the hatch. Luke begins to slide and finally falls from the vane into space.

INT. MILLENNIUM FALCON – COCKPIT

Out of the cockpit window, Leia sees Luke.

LEIA: Okay. Easy, Chewie.

The Falcon closes in on Luke.

EXT. BOTTOM OF CLOUD CITY

The Falcon positions itself under Luke.

INT. MILLENNIUM FALCON – HATCH

The hatch pops open with a hiss of pressure. Lando has gone up to help the battered warrior inside the ship.

EXT. BOTTOM OF CLOUD CITY

As Lando appears in the hatchway, Luke falls toward the Falcon and TIE fighters appear.

INT. MILLENNIUM FALCON – COCKPIT

Flak bursts all around it as the Falcon banks away from the city. Leia and Chewie struggle with the controls.

LEIA: *(into intercom)* Lando?

LANDO: *(over intercom)* Okay, let's go.

EXT. BOTTOM OF CLOUD CITY

The Falcon races away.

INT. MILLENNIUM FALCON – HOLD

Lando helps Luke into the Falcon.

EXT. BOTTOM OF CLOUD CITY

The Falcon is closely followed by the three TIE fighters, all of which keep up a heavy laser assault on the fleeing starship.

INT. MILLENNIUM FALCON – COCKPIT

(CONT'D)

CONTINUED

Explosions erupt all around the cockpit, buffeting the ship wildly. Chewie howls as he frantically tries to control the ship.

 Luke, bloody and battered, enters the cockpit supported by Lando. Leia jumps up and hugs him while Chewie barks in joyous relief.

LUKE: Oh, Leia.

LANDO: All right, Chewie. Let's go.

Leia helps Luke from the cockpit as another huge blast rocks the ship.

EXT. SPACE – CLOUD CITY – DAY

The Falcon, still followed by the three TIE fighters, races away from the cloud-covered city.

INT. MILLENNIUM FALCON – SLEEPING QUARTERS

Luke rests on a cot, his injured arm wrapped in a protective cuff. Leia gently wipes his face. The ship lurches again. She kisses him. Then Leia leaves the quarters.

LEIA: I'll be back.

EXT. SPACE

The Millennium Falcon is relentlessly pursued by TIE fighters.

INT. MILLENNIUM FALCON – COCKPIT

Lando anxiously watches the flashing lights on the control panel and hurriedly adjusts some switches. Seated next to him, Chewie has pointed out a new blip appearing on the panel. Leia, watching over their shoulder, recognizes the shape.

LEIA: Star Destroyer.

EXT. SPACE

The TIE fighters continue to chase the Millennium Falcon, still shooting lasers.

INT. MILLENNIUM FALCON – COCKPIT

LANDO: All right, Chewie. Ready for light-speed.

LEIA: If your people fixed the hyperdrive. All the coordinates are set. It's now or never.

LANDO: Punch it!

Chewie barks in agreement and pulls back on the light-speed throttle. The sound of the ion engine changes ... it is winding up. Faces are tense, expectant. But nothing happens, and the engine goes off. Chewie lets out a frustrated howl. Flak violently rocks the ship.

LANDO: They told me they fixed it. I trusted them to fix it. It's not my fault!

Chewie gets up from his chair and starts out of the cockpit. He gives Lando an angry shove as he storms past him.

EXT. SPACE

Vader's Star Destroyer determinedly follows the Falcon.

INT. VADER'S STAR DESTROYER – BRIDGE

Vader strides across the bridge to look out the window as Admiral Piett approaches him.

PIETT: They'll be in range of our tractor beam in moments, my lord.

VADER: Did your men deactivate the hyperdrive on the Millennium Falcon?

PIETT: Yes, my lord.

VADER: Good. Prepare the boarding party and set your weapons for stun.

(CONT'D)

CONTINUED

PIETT: Yes, my lord. Lieutenant.

LIEUTENANT: Yes, sir.

INT. MILLENNIUM FALCON — HOLD

Chewie enters through the doorway, grunting to himself.
Beeping while he works, Artoo is busy connecting some wires to Threepio who now has one leg attached.

THREEPIO: Noisy brute. Why don't we just go into light-speed?

Artoo beeps in response.

THREEPIO: We can't? How would you know the hyperdrive is deactivated?

Artoo whistles knowingly.

THREEPIO: The city's central computer told you? Artoo-Detoo, you know better than to trust a strange computer. Ouch! Pay attention to what you're doing!

Chewie is in the pit. He is trying to loosen something with an enormous wrench.

INT. MILLENNIUM FALCON — COCKPIT

Leia is seated in front of the control panel. Lando is working on some other controls. Sparks fly.

EXT. SPACE

The Millennium Falcon is pursued around the Star Destroyer by the three firing TIE fighters.

INT. VADER'S STAR DESTROYER — BRIDGE

Vader stands on the bridge, watching as the Millennium Falcon is chased by the TIE fighters. As the Falcon draws nearer, Vader's breathing gets slightly faster.

VADER: Luke.

INT. MILLENNIUM FALCON — SLEEPING QUARTERS

Luke realizes that Vader's ship is very near. He feels resigned to his fate. He senses that he is beaten, more emotionally than physically.

LUKE: Father.

INT. VADER'S STAR DESTROYER — BRIDGE

VADER: Son, come with me.

INT. MILLENNIUM FALCON — SLEEPING QUARTERS

LUKE: *(moaning)* Ben, why didn't you tell me?

INT. MILLENNIUM FALCON — COCKPIT

Lando and Leia are at the controls of the Falcon. Meanwhile, in the ship's hold, Chewie continues to work frantically on the hyperdrive mechanism.

LANDO: *(into intercom)* Chewie!

Frustrated, Chewie uses his wrench like a club and hits the panel . . .

EXT. SPACE

The Falcon races past the huge Imperial Star Destroyer followed very closely by the TIE fighters.

INT. MILLENNIUM FALCON — COCKPIT

Luke enters the cockpit and looks out the window. He is almost unconscious with pain and depression.

LUKE: It's Vader.

INT. VADER'S STAR DESTROYER — BRIDGE

(CONT'D)

CONTINUED

VADER: Luke ... it is your destiny.

INT. MILLENNIUM FALCON — COCKPIT

LUKE: Ben, why didn't you tell me?

EXT. SPACE

TIE fighters pursue the Millennium Falcon.

INT. VADER'S STAR DESTROYER — BRIDGE

PIETT: Alert all commands. Ready for the tractor beam.

INT. MILLENNIUM FALCON — HOLD

Artoo races to a control panel and starts working on a circuit board. Furious, Threepio stands on one leg, yelling.

THREEPIO: Artoo, come back at once! You haven't finished with me yet! You don't know how to fix the hyperdrive. Chewbacca can do it. I'm standing here in pieces, and you're having delusions of grandeur!

Artoo moves a circuit on a control panel. Suddenly, the control panel lights up.

INT. MILLENNIUM FALCON — COCKPIT

Leia and Lando are thrown back into their seats as the Millennium Falcon unexpectedly shoots into hyperdrive.

INT. MILLENNIUM FALCON — HOLD

The ship tilts up and Artoo topples into the pit on top of Chewie.

THREEPIO: You did it!

INT. MILLENNIUM FALCON — COCKPIT

Stars stream past as the Millennium Falcon shoots into light-speed.

EXT. SPACE

The Falcon soars into infinity and away from the huge Star Destroyer.

INT. VADER'S STAR DESTROYER — BRIDGE

Admiral Piett looks at Vader in terror. Vader turns slowly and walks off the bridge, his hands held behind his back in a contemplative gesture.

EXT. SPACE — REBEL STAR CRUISER

The Millennium Falcon is attached to a huge Rebel cruiser by a docking tube. Rebel fighters move about the giant cruiser, and a Rebel transport ship hovers near the fleet.

INT. MILLENNIUM FALCON — COCKPIT

Lando sits in the pilot's seat as he talks into the comlink.

LANDO: *(into comlink)* Luke, we're ready for takeoff.

Chewie enters, barking.

LUKE: *(over comlink)* Good luck, Lando.

EXT. SPACE — REBEL STAR CRUISER

LANDO: *(into comlink)* When we find Jabba the Hutt and that bounty hunter, we'll contact you.

INT. STAR CRUISER — MEDICAL CENTER

Luke speaks into the comlink as a medical droid works on his hand. Leia stands near him.

LUKE: *(into comlink)* I'll meet you at the rendezvous point on Tatooine.

(CONT'D)

CONTINUED

INT. MILLENNIUM FALCON — COCKPIT

LANDO: (into comlink) Princess, we'll find Han. I promise.

INT. STAR CRUISER — MEDICAL CENTER

LUKE: (into comlink) Chewie, I'll be waiting for your signal.

Chewie's wail comes over the comlink.

LUKE: (into comlink) Take care, you two.

INT. MILLENNIUM FALCON — COCKPIT

LUKE: (over comlink) May the Force be with you.

Chewie wails.

INT. STAR CRUISER — MEDICAL CENTER

Chewie's wail comes over the comlink.
    Luke looks down at his hand. A metalized type of bandage has been wrapped around his wrist. The medical droid makes some adjustments in a tiny electronic unit, then pricks each one of Luke's fingers.

LUKE: Ow!

Luke wriggles his fingers, makes a fist, and relaxes it. His hand is completely functional.
    He gets up and walks over to Leia. There is a new bond between them, a new understanding. Leia is thinking about Han; Luke is thinking about his uncertain and newly complicated future. Together they stand at the large window of the medical center looking out on the Rebel Star Cruiser and a dense, luminous galaxy swirling in space.
    Luke puts his arm around Leia. The droids stand next to them, and Threepio moves closer to Artoo, putting his arm on him.

INT. MILLENNIUM FALCON — COCKPIT

Lando and Chewie are at the controls.

EXT. SPACE

The Millennium Falcon turns away from the Rebel cruiser and blasts into space.

INT. STAR CRUISER — MEDICAL CENTER

Luke, Leia, Threepio and Artoo watch as the Millennium Falcon moves into view, and zooms away into space.

EXT. SPACE

The Millennium Falcon recedes into space.

INT. STAR CRUISER — MEDICAL CENTER

Threepio looks emotional. Artoo beeps.

EXT. SPACE — REBEL STAR CRUISER

While Luke, Leia, and the droids stand, looking out the window of the star cruiser, slowly, the cruiser moves away into space.

DISSOLVE TO:

EXT. GALAXY — SPACE

END CREDITS FADE IN AND OUT OVER BACKGROUND.

THE END

(CONT'D)

STAR WARS

Episode VI

RETURN OF THE JEDI

CONTINUED

A long time ago in a galaxy far,
far away. . . .

The boundless heavens serve as a backdrop for the main title, followed by a roll-up, which crawls into infinity.

STAR WARS

Episode VI

RETURN OF THE JEDI

Luke Skywalker has returned to
his home planet of Tatooine in
an attempt to rescue his
friend Han Solo from the
clutches of the vile gangster
Jabba the Hutt.

Little does Luke know that the
GALACTIC EMPIRE has secretly
begun construction on a new
armored space station even
more powerful than the first
dreaded Death Star.

When completed, this ultimate
weapon will spell certain doom
for the small band of rebels
struggling to restore freedom
to the galaxy . . .

PAN DOWN to reveal a monstrous half-completed Death Star, its massive superstructure curling away beyond the completed section like the arms of a giant octopus.

An Imperial Star Destroyer moves overhead toward the massive armored space station, followed by two zipping TIE fighters. A small Imperial shuttle rockets from the main bay of the ship and hustles toward to Death Star.

INT. IMPERIAL SHUTTLE — COCKPIT

The shuttle captain makes contact with the Death Star.

SHUTTLE CAPTAIN: Command station, this is ST Three-Twenty-One. Code Clearance Blue. We're starting our approach. Deactivate the security shield.

INT. DEATH STAR CONTROL ROOM

DEATH STAR CONTROLLER: The security deflector shield will be deactivated when we have confirmation of your code transmission. Stand by. You are clear to proceed.

INT. IMPERIAL SHUTTLE — COCKPIT

SHUTTLE CAPTAIN: We're starting our approach.

EXT. SPACE.

The shuttle and its two escorting TIE fighters approach, and the shuttle enters the Death Star.

INT. DEATH STAR CONTROL ROOM

Operators move about among the control panels.
A control officer addresses a shield operator.

OFFICER: Inform the commander that Lord Vader's shuttle has arrived.

OPERATOR: Yes, sir.

(CONT'D)

CONTINUED

The Imperial shuttle has landed in the massive docking bay. A squad of Imperial stormtroopers moves into formation before the craft.

INT. DEATH STAR — MAIN DOCKING BAY

The Death Star Commander, Moff Jerjerrod, a tall, confident technocrat, strides through the assembled troops to the base of the shuttle ramp. The troops stand to attention; many are uneasy about the new arrival. Even the arrogant Death Star Commander swallows nervously.

The exit hatch of the shuttle opens with a whoosh, revealing only darkness. Then, heavy footsteps and mechanical breathing. From this black void appears Darth Vader, Lord of the Sith. Vader looks over the assemblage as he walks down the ramp.

JERJERROD: Lord Vader, this is an unexpected pleasure. We're honored by your presence.

VADER: You may dispense with the pleasantries, Commander. I'm here to put you back on schedule.

The commander turns ashen and begins to tremble.

JERJERROD: I assure you, Lord Vader, my men are working as fast as they can.

VADER: Perhaps I can find new ways to motivate them.

JERJERROD: I tell you, this station will be operational as planned.

VADER: The Emperor does not share your optimistic appraisal of the situation.

JERJERROD: But he asks the impossible. I need more men.

VADER: Then perhaps you can tell him when he arrives.

JERJERROD: *(aghast)* The Emperor's coming here?

VADER: That is correct, Commander. And he is most displeased with your apparent lack of progress.

JERJERROD: We shall double our efforts.

VADER: I hope so, Commander, for your sake. The Emperor is not as forgiving as I am.

EXT. ROAD TO JABBA'S PALACE — TATOOINE

A lonely, windswept road meanders through the desolate Tatooine terrain. Artoo-Detoo and See-Threepio are making their way along the road toward the ominous palace of Jabba the Hutt. Artoo beeps.

THREEPIO: Of course I'm worried. And you should be, too. Lando Calrissian and poor Chewbacca never returned from this awful place.

Artoo whistles timidly.

THREEPIO: Don't be so sure. If I told you half the things I've heard about this Jabba the Hutt, you'd probably short-circuit.

The two droids fearfully approach the massive gate to the palace.

EXT. JABBA'S PALACE — GATE

THREEPIO: Artoo, are you sure this is the right place?

Threepio looks around for some kind of signalling device.

THREEPIO: I'd better knock, I suppose.

He timidly knocks on the iron door.

THREEPIO: *(instantly)* There doesn't seem to be anyone here. Let's go back and tell Master Luke.

A small hatch in the middle of the door opens and a spidery mechanical arm, with a large electronic eyeball on the end, pops out and inspects the two droids.

STRANGE VOICE: Tee chuta hhat yudd!

THREEPIO: Goodness gracious me!

(CONT'D)

CONTINUED

The eye continues to jabber in its strange language.
Threepio points to Artoo, then to himself.

THREEPIO: Artoo Detoowha bo Seethreepiowha ey toota odd mishka Jabba du Hutt.

The eye pokes forward towards Threepio, there is a laugh, then the eye zips back into the door. The hatch slams shut.

THREEPIO: I don't think they're going to let us in, Artoo. We'd better go.

Artoo bleeps his reluctance as Threepio turns to leave. Suddenly, the massive door starts to rise with a horrific metallic screech. The robots turn back and face an endless black cavity.
Artoo starts forward into the gloom.

THREEPIO: Artoo, wait. Oh, dear! Artoo, Artoo, I really don't think we should rush into all this.

Threepio rushes after his stubby companion. Artoo continues down the corridor, with Threepio following.

THREEPIO: Oh, Artoo! Artoo, wait for me!

INT. JABBA'S PALACE – HALLWAY

The frightened robots are met by two giant, green Gamorrean guards. One guard grunts an order. Artoo beeps nervously.

THREEPIO: Just you deliver Master Luke's message and get us out of here. Oh, my!

The door slams shut with a loud crash that echoes throughout dark passageway.

THREEPIO: Oh, no.

Walking toward them out of the darkness is Bib Fortuna, a humanlike alien with long tentacles protruding from his skull.

BIB: Die Wanna Wanga!

THREEPIO: Oh, my! Die Wanna Wauaga We – we bring a message to your master, Jabba the Hutt.

Artoo lets out a series of quick beeps.

THREEPIO: *(continuing)* ... and a gift. *(thinks for a moment, then to Artoo)* Gift, what gift?

Bib shakes his head negatively.

BIB: Nee labba no badda. Me chaade su goodie.

Bib holds out his hands toward Artoo and the tiny droid backs up a bit, letting out a protesting array of squeaks. Threepio turns to the strange-looking alien.

THREEPIO: He says that our instructions are to give it only to Jabba himself!

Bib thinks about this for a moment.

THREEPIO: I'm terribly sorry. I'm afraid he's ever so stubborn about these sort of things.

Bib gestures for the droids to follow.

BIB: Nudd Chaa.

The droids follow the tall, tentacled alien into the darkness, trailed by the two guards.

THREEPIO: Artoo, I have a bad feeling about this.

INT. JABBA'S THRONE ROOM

The throne room is filled with the vilest, most grotesque creatures ever conceived in the universe. Artoo and Threepio seem very small as they pause in the doorway to the dimly lit chamber.
Light shafts partially illuminate the drunken courtiers as Bib Fortuna crosses the room to the platform upon which rests the leader of this nauseating crowd: Jabba the Hutt. The monarch of the galactic underworld is a repulsive blob of bloated fat with a maniacal grin. Chained to the horrible creature is the beautiful alien dancer

(CONT'D)

CONTINUED

named Oola. At the foot of the dais sits an obnoxious birdlike creature, Salacious Crumb. Bib whispers something in the slobbering degenerate's ear. Jabba laughs, horribly, at the two terrified droids before him. Threepio bows politely.

THREEPIO: Good morning. The message, Artoo, the message.

JABBA: Bo Shuda!

Artoo whistles, and a beam of light projects from his domed head, creating a hologram of Luke on the floor.
    The image grows to over ten feet tall, and the young Jedi towers over the space gangsters.

LUKE: Greetings, Exalted One. Allow me to introduce myself. I am Luke Skywalker, Jedi Knight and friend to Captain Solo. I know that you are powerful, mighty Jabba, and that your anger with Solo must be equally powerful. I seek an audience with your Greatness to bargain for Solo's life.
(Jabba's crowd laughs) With your wisdom, I'm sure that we can work out an arrangement which will be mutually beneficial and enable us to avoid any unpleasant confrontation. As a token of my goodwill, I present to you a gift: these two droids.

Threepio is startled by this announcement.

THREEPIO: What did he say?

LUKE: *(continuing)* Both are hardworking and will serve you well.

THREEPIO: This can't be! Artoo, you're playing the wrong message.

Luke's hologram disappears.
    Bib speaks to Jabba in Huttese.

JABBA: *(in Huttese subtitled)* There will be no bargain.

THREEPIO: We're doomed.

JABBA: *(in Huttese subtitled)* I will not give up my favorite decoration. I like Captain Solo where he is.

Jabba looks toward an alcove beside the throne. Hanging high, flat against the wall, exactly as we saw him last, is a carbonized Han Solo.

THREEPIO: Artoo, look! Captain Solo. And he's still frozen in carbonite.

INT. DUNGEON CORRIDOR

One of Jabba's Gamorrean guards marches Artoo and Threepio down a dank, shadowy passageway lined with holding cells. The cries of unspeakable creatures bounce off the cold stone walls. Occasionally a repulsive arm or tentacle grabs through the bars at the hapless droids.

THREEPIO: What could possibly have come over Master Luke. Is it something I did? He never expressed any unhappiness with my work. Oh! Oh! How horrid!

A large tentacle wraps around Threepio's neck.

THREEPIO: Ohh!

He manages to break free. Artoo beeps pitifully and they move on to a door at the end of the corridor.

INT. BOILER ROOM

The door slides open, revealing a room filled with steam and noisy machinery. The guard has motioned them into the boiler room, where a power droid is upside down. As smoking brands are pressed into his feet, the stubby robot lets out an agonized electronic scream. Threepio cringes. They are met by a tall, thin humanlike robot named EV-9D9 (Eve-Ninedenine).

NINEDENINE: Ah, good. New acquisitions. You are a protocol droid, are you not?

THREEPIO: I am See-Threepio, human-cy-

NINEDENINE: Yes or no will do.

THREEPIO: Oh. Well, yes.

(CONT'D)

CONTINUED

NINEDENINE: How many languages do you speak?

THREEPIO: I am fluent in over six million forms of communication and can readily —

NINEDENINE: Splendid! We have been without an interpreter since our master got angry with our last protocol droid and disintegrated him.

THREEPIO: Disintegrated?

NINEDENINE: *(to a Gamorrean guard)* Guard! This protocol droid might be useful. Fit him with a restraining bolt and take him back up to His Excellency's main audience chamber.

The guard shoves Threepio toward the door.

THREEPIO: *(disappearing)* Artoo, don't leave me! Ohhh!

Artoo lets out a plantive cry as the door closes. Then he beeps angrily.

NINEDENINE: You're a feisty little one, but you'll soon learn some respect. I have need for you on the master's sail barge. And I think you'll fill in nicely.

The poor work droid in the background lets out another tortured electronic scream.

INT. JABBA'S THRONE ROOM

The court of Jabba the Hutt is in the midst of a drunken, raucous party. Sloppy, smelly monsters cheer and make rude noises as Oola and a fat female dancer perform in front of Jabba's throne.
     Jabba leers at the dancers and with a lustful gleam in his eye beckons Oola to come and sit with him. She stops dancing and backs away, shaking her head. Jabba gets angry and points to a spot next to him.

JABBA: Da Eitha!

The lovely alien shakes her head again and screams.

OOLA: Na Chuba negtorie Na! Na! Natoota . . .

Jabba is furious and pulls her toward him, tugging on the chain.

JABBA: Boscka!

He pushes a button and, before the dancer can flee, a trap door in the floor springs open and swallows her up. As the door snaps shut, a muffled growl is followed by a hideous scream. Jabba and his monstrous friends laugh hysterically and several revelers hurry over to watch her fate through a grate.
     Threepio cringes and glances wistfully at the carbonite form of Han Solo, but is distracted by a gunshot offscreen. An unnatural quiet sweeps the boisterous gathering.
     On the far side of the room, the crush of debauchers moves aside to allow the approach of Boushh, an oddly cloaked bounty hunter, leading his captive, Han Solo's co-pilot, Chewbacca the Wookiee.
     The bounty hunter bows before the gangster and speaks a greeting in a strange, electronically processed tongue (Ubese).

BOUSHH: *(in Ubese subtitled)* I have come for the bounty on this Wookiee.

THREEPIO: Oh, no! Chewbacca!

JABBA: *(in Huttese subtitled)* At last we have the mighty Chewbacca.

Jabba calls for Threepio. The reluctant droid obeys.

THREEPIO: Oh, uh, yes, uh, I am here, Your Worshipfulness. Uh . . . yes!

Jabba continues speaking, as Threepio nervously translates.

THREEPIO: Oh. The illustrious Jabba bids you welcome and will gladly pay you the reward of twenty-five thousand.

BOUSHH: *(in Ubese subtitled)* I want fifty thousand. No less.

THREEPIO: Fifty thousand. No less.

(CONT'D)

CONTINUED

Jabba immediately flies into a rage, knocking the golden droid off the raised throne into a clattering heap on the floor.

Boushh adjusts his weapon as Jabba raves in Huttese and Threepio struggles back on to the throne. The disheveled droid tries to compose himself.

THREEPIO: Oh, oh ... but what, what did I say? *(to Boushh)* Uh, the mighty Jabba asks why he must pay fifty thousand.

The bounty hunter holds up a small silver ball in his hand.

THREEPIO: Because he's holding a thermal detonator.

Threepio is very nervous. The guards instantly back away, as do most of the other monsters in the room. But Boba Fett raises his gun. The room has fallen into a tense hush. Jabba begins to laugh.

JABBA: *(in Huttese subtitled)* This bounty hunter is my kind of scum, fearless and inventive.

Jabba continues.

THREEPIO: Jabba offers the sum of thirty-five. And I do suggest you take it.

Bib and the other monsters study the bounty hunter and wait for his reaction.

BOUSHH: Zeebuss.

Boushh releases a switch on the thermal detonator and it goes dead.

THREEPIO: He agrees!

The raucous crowd of monsters erupts in a symphony of cheers and applause as the party returns to its full noisy pitch. Chewbacca growls and is led away. The band starts up and dancing girls take the center of the floor, to the hoots of the loudly appreciative creatures.

Boushh leans against a column with gunfighter cool and surveys the scene, his gaze stopping only when it connects with a glare from across the room: Boba Fett is watching him.

INT. DUNGEON CORRIDOR AND CELL

Gamorrean guards lead Chewie down the same hallway we saw before. As he is led away we spot Lando Calrissian, disguised as a skiff guard in a partial face mask. When a tentacle reaches out at the Wookiee, Chewie's ferocious roar echoes against the walls and the tentacle snaps back into its cell in terror. It takes both the guards to hurl Chewie roughly into a cell, slamming the door behind him.

EXT. JABBA'S PALACE

The palace is sitting in the light of the double sunset. On the road in front, a large toadlike creature flicks its tongue out for a desert rodent, and burps in satisfaction.

JABBA'S THRONE ROOM — NIGHT

Silence. The room is deserted, only the awful debris of the alien celebration giving mute witness to the activity here before. Several drunk creatures lie unconscious around the room, snoring loudly.

A shadowy figure moves stealthily among the columns at the perimeter of the room and is revealed to be Boushh, the bounty hunter. He picks his way carefully through the snoring, drunken monsters.

Han Solo, the frozen space pirate, hangs spotlighted on the wall, his coffinlike case suspended by a force field. The bounty hunter deactivates the force field by flipping a control switch to one side of the coffin.

The heavy case slowly lowers to the floor of the alcove.

Boushh steps up to the case, studying Han, then turns to the controls on the side of the coffin. He activates a series of switches and slides the decarbonization lever. The case begins to emit a sound as the hard shell covering the contours of Han's face begins to melt away. The bounty hunter watches as Han's body is freed of its metallic coat and his forearms and hands, previously raised in reflexive protest, drop slackly to his side. His face muscles relax from their mask of horror. He appears quite dead.

Boushh's ugly helmet leans close to Han's face listening for the breath of life. Nothing. He waits. Han's eyes pop open with a start and he beings shaking. The bounty hunter steadies the staggering newborn.

BOUSHH: Just relax for a moment. You're free of the carbonite.

(CONT'D)

CONTINUED

Han touches his face with his hand.

BOUSHH: Shhh. You have hibernation sickness.

HAN: I can't see.

BOUSHH: Your eyesight will return in time.

HAN: Where am I?

BOUSHH: Jabba's palace.

HAN: Who are you?

The bounty hunter reaches up and lifts the helmet from his head, revealing the beautiful face of Princess Leia.

LEIA: Someone who loves you.

HAN: Leia!

LEIA: I gotta get you out of here.

As Leia helps her weakened lover to stand up, the relative quiet is pierced by an obscene Huttese cackle from the other side of the alcove.

HAN: What's that? I know that laugh.

The curtain on the far side of the alcove opens, revealing Jabba the Hutt, surrounded by Bib and other aliens. He laughs again, and his gross cronies join in a cacophony of alien glee.

HAN: Hey, Jabba. Look, Jabba. I was just on my way to pay you back but I got a little sidetracked. It's not my fault.

Jabba laughs.

JABBA: *(in Huttese subtitled)* It's too late for that, Solo. You may have been a good smuggler, but now you're Bantha fodder.

HAN: Look —

JABBA: *(continuing; in Huttese subtitled)* Take him away.

The guards grab Han and start to lead him away.

HAN: Jabba . . . I'll pay you triple! You're throwing away a fortune here. Don't be a fool!

Han is dragged off.

JABBA: *(in Huttese subtitled)* Bring her to me.

Jabba chuckles as Lando and a second guard lead the beautiful young princess toward him.

LEIA: We have powerful friends. You're gonna regret this.

JABBA: *(in Huttese subtitled)* I'm sure.

Inexorably her lovely face moves to within a few inches of Jabba's ugly blob of a head.

LEIA: *(turning away in disgust)* Ugh!

THREEPIO: Ohhh, *(quickly turning away in disgust)* I can't bear to watch.

INT. DUNGEON CELL

The blinded star captain is thrown into the dungeon and the door slams behind him, leaving only a thin sliver of light from a crack in the ceiling. Han is trying to collect himself when suddenly a growl is heard from the far side of the cell. He listens.

HAN: Chewie? Chewie, is that you?

The shadowy figure of Chewie lets out a crazy yell and races toward Han, hugging him.

(CONT'D)

CONTINUED

HAN: Chew — Chewie!

The giant Wookiee barks with glee.

HAN: Wait, I can't see pal. What's goin' on?

Chewie barks an excited blue streak.

HAN: Luke? Luke's crazy. He can't even take care of himself, much less rescue anybody.

Chewie barks a reply.

HAN: A — a Jedi Knight? I'm out of it for a little while, everybody gets delusions of grandeur.

Chewie growls insistently. He holds Han to his chest and pets his head.

HAN: I'm all right, pal. I'm all right.

INT. MAIN GATE AND HALL — JABBA'S PALACE

Noisily, the main gate lifts to flood the blackness with blinding light and reveal the silhouetted figure of Luke Skywalker. He is clad in a robe similar to Ben's and wears neither pistol nor laser sword. Luke strides purposefully into the hallway. Two giant guards move to block Luke's path. Luke halts.

Luke raises his hand and points at the puzzled guards, who immediately lower their spears and fall back. The young Jedi lowers his hand and moves on down the hallway.

INT. JABBA'S THRONE ROOM

Jabba is asleep on his throne, with Leia lying in front of him. Salacious sits by Jabba's tail, watching it wriggle. Leia is now dressed in the skimpy costume of a dancing girl, a chain runs from a manacle/necklace at her throat to her new master, Jabba the Hutt. Threepio stands behind Jabba.

Bib Fortuna appears out of the gloom. He speaks to Luke as they approach each other.

LUKE: I must speak with Jabba.

Bib answers in Huttese, shaking his head in denial.

INT. JABBA'S THRONE ROOM

Leia looks up in recognition of Luke's voice.

INT. MAIN GATE AND HALL — JABBA'S PALACE

Luke stops and stares at Bib; he raises his hand slightly.

LUKE: You will take me to Jabba now!

Bib turns in hynotic response to Luke's command, and Luke follows him into the gloom.

LUKE: You serve your master well.

Bib responds.

LUKE: And you will be rewarded.

INT. JABBA'S THRONE ROOM

Bib comes up to the gangster slug.

THREEPIO: At last! Master Luke's come to rescue me!

BIB: Master.

Jabba awakens with a start and Bib continues, in Huttese.

BIB: Luke Skywalker, Jedi Knight.

JABBA: *(in Huttese subtitled)* I told you not to admit him.

LUKE: I must be allowed to speak.

BIB: *(in Huttese subtitled)* He must be allowed to speak.

(CONT'D)

CONTINUED

Jabba, furious, shoves Bib away. Luke stares hard at Jabba.

JABBA: *(in Huttese subtitled)* You weak-minded fool! *(turning)* He's using an old Jedi mind trick.

LUKE: You will bring me Captain Solo and the Wookiee to me.

JABBA: *(laughing)* *(in Huttese subtitled)* Your mind powers will not work on me, boy.

LUKE: Nevertheless, I'm taking Captain Solo and his friends. You can either profit by this ... or be destroyed! It's your choice. But I warn you not to underestimate my powers.

Jabba smiles. Threepio attempts to warn Luke about the pit.

THREEPIO: Master Luke, you're standing on ...

JABBA: *(in Huttese subtitled)* There will be no bargain, young Jedi. I shall enjoy watching you die.

Luke reaches out, and a pistol jumps out of the guard's holster and flies into Luke's hand. The bewildered guard grabs for it as Jabba raises his hand.

JABBA: Boscka!

The floor suddenly drops away, sending Luke and the hapless guard into the pit. The pistol goes off, blasting a hole in the ceiling.

INT. RANCOR PIT

Luke and the guard have dropped twenty-five feet from a chute into the dungeonlike cage. Luke gets to his feet as the guard yells hysterically for help.

INT. JABBA'S THRONE ROOM

Jabba laughs and his courtiers join him. Leia starts forward but is comforted by a human guard – Lando, recognizable behind his mask.

INT. RANCOR PIT

A crowd has gathered up around the edge of the pit as a door in the side of the pit starts to rumble open.

THREEPIO: Oh, no! The rancor!

At the side of the pit, an iron door rumbles upward and a giant, fanged rancor emeges. The guard runs to the side of the pit and tries futilely to scramble to the top. The hideous beast closes in on him.

INT. JABBA'S THRONE ROOM

The spectators look on.

INT. RANCOR PIT

The rancor moves past Luke, and as the guard continues to scramble, the rancor picks him up and pops him into its slavering jaws. A few screams, and the guard is swallowed with a gulp.

INT. JABBA'S THRONE ROOM

The audience cheers and laughs at the guard's fate.

INT. RANCOR PIT

The monster turns and starts for Luke.

INT. JABBA'S THRONE ROOM

Jabba smiles.

INT. RANCOR PIT

The young Jedi dashes away just ahead of the monster's swipe at him, and picks up the long arm bone of an earlier victim. The monster grabs Luke.

INT. JABBA'S THRONE ROOM

(CONT'D)

CONTINUED

The audience cheers.

INT. RANCOR PIT

The monster brings him up to his salivating mouth.

INT. JABBA'S THRONE ROOM

Leia can hardly bear to watch.

INT. RANCOR PIT

At the last moment, Luke wedges the bone in the monster's mouth and is dropped to the floor. The monster bellows in rage and flails about.

The monster crunches the bone in its jaws and sees Luke, who squeezes into a crevice in the pit wall. Luke looks past the monster to the holding cave beyond. On the far side of the holding cave is a utility door — if only he can get to it. The rancor spots Luke and reaches into the crevice for him. Luke grabs a large rock and raises it, smashing it down on the rancor's finger.

INT. HOLDING TUNNEL — RANCOR PIT

The rancor lets out a howl as Luke makes a run for the holding cave. He reaches the door and pushes a button to open it. When he succeeds, he sees a heavy barred gate between him and safety. Beyond the gate two guards have looked up from their dinner. Luke turns to see the monster heading for him, and pulls with all his might on the gate. The guards move to the gate and start poking at the young Jedi with spears, laughing.

INT. JABBA'S THRONE ROOM

The audience is mad with excitement.

INT. HOLDING TUNNEL — RANCOR PIT

Luke crouches (against the wall) as the monster starts to reach for him. Suddenly he notices a main door control panel halfway up the wall. As the rancor moves in for the kill, Luke picks up a skull from the cave floor and hurls it at the panel. A split second before the rancor reaches Luke, the panel explodes. The giant overhead door comes crashing down on the beast's head, squashing it.

INT. THRONE ROOM

A startled gasp is heard from the stunned court. There's consternation at this turn of events. Heads look to Jabba, who is actually turning red with anger.

INT. HOLDING TUNNEL — RANCOR PIT

The beast breathes its last.

INT. THRONE ROOM

Leia cannot suppress her joy.

INT. RANCOR PIT

The rancor keepers have come into the cage and are examining their dead beast. One of them breaks down and weeps. The other glares menacingly at Luke, who is unworried. Several guards rush into the holding tunnel and take Luke away.

INT. THRONE ROOM

Jabba utters harsh commands to his guards and they hurry off.

JABBA: *(in Huttese subtitled)* Bring me Solo and the Wookiee. They will all suffer for this outrage.

INT. RANCOR PIT

The weeping rancor keeper is consoled and led away.

INT. THRONE ROOM

(CONT'D)

CONTINUED

The crowd of creepy courtiers parts as Han and Chewie are brought into the throne room, and other guards, including Lando, drag Luke up the steps.

LUKE: Han!

HAN: Luke!

LUKE: Are you all right?

HAN: Fine. Together again, huh?

LUKE: Wouldn't miss it.

HAN: How are we doing?

LUKE: The same as always.

HAN: That bad, huh? Where's Leia?

LEIA: I'm here.

Threepio is standing behind the grotesque gangster as he strokes Leia like a pet cat.
Threepio steps forward and translates for the captives.

THREEPIO: Oh, dear. His High Exaltedness, the great Jabba the Hutt, has decreed that you are to be terminated immediately.

HAN: Good. I hate long waits.

THREEPIO: You will therefore be taken to the Dune Sea and cast into the Pit of Carkoon, the nesting place of the all-powerful Sarlacc.

HAN: *(to Luke)* Doesn't sound so bad.

THREEPIO: In his belly you will find a new definition of pain and suffering, as you are slowly digested over a thousand years.

Chewie barks.

HAN: On second thought, let's pass on that, huh?

LUKE: You should have bargained Jabba. That's the last mistake you'll ever make.

Jabba cackles evilly at this.
As the guards drag the prisoners from the throne room, Leia looks concerned, but Luke Skywalker, Jedi warrior, cannot suppress a smile.

EXT. TATOOINE DUNE SEA

Jabba's huge sail barge moves above the desert surface accompanied by two smaller skiffs.

INT. BARGE OBSERVATION DECK

Jabba's entire retinue is travelling with him, drinking, eating and having a good time.

EXT. TATOOINE DUNE SEA

The sail barge and skiffs continue their journey.

INT. BARGE OBSERVATION DECK

Jabba the Hutt rides like a sultan in the massive antigravity ship. Leia is watching her friends in one of the skiffs.

EXT. TATOOINE DUNE SEA – SKIFF

The skiff glides close, revealing Luke, Han, and Chewie – all in bonds – surrounded by guards, one of whom is Lando in disguise.

HAN: I think my eyes are getting better. Instead of a big dark blur, I see a big light blur.

(CONT'D)

CONTINUED

LUKE: There's nothing to see. I used to live here, you know.

HAN: You're gonna die here, you know. Convenient.

LUKE: Just stick close to Chewie and Lando. I've taken care of everything.

HAN: Oh ... great!

INT. BARGE OBSERVATION DECK

The chain attached to Leia'a neck is pulled tight and Jabba tugs the scantily clad princess to him.

JABBA: *(in Huttese subtitled)* Soon you will learn to appreciate me.

Threepio wanders among the sail barge aliens, bumping into a smaller droid serving drinks, spilling them all over the place. The stubby droid lets out an angry series of beeps and whistles.

THREEPIO: Oh, I'm terribly sor ... Artoo! What are you doing here?

Artoo beeps a quick reply.

THREEPIO: Well, I can see you're serving drinks, but this place is dangerous. They're going to execute Master Luke and, if we're not careful, us too!

Artoo whistles a singsong response.

THREEPIO: Hmm. I wish I had your confidence.

EXT. SARLACC PIT

The convoy moves up over a huge sand pit. The sail barge stops to one side of the depression, as does the escort skiff. But the prisoners' skiff moves out directly over the center and hovers. A plank is extended from the edge of the prisoners' skiff. At the bottom of the deep cone of sand is a repulsive, mucous-lined hole, surrounded by thousands of needle-sharp teeth. This is the Sarlacc. Guards release Luke's bonds and shove him out on to the plank above the Sarlacc's mouth.

INT. SAIL BARGE OBSERVATION DECK

Jabba and Leia are now by the rail, watching.

EXT. SAIL BARGE

Threepio's voice is amplified across loudspeakers.

THREEPIO: Victims of the almighty Sarlacc: His Excellency hopes that you will die honorably. But should any of you wish to beg for mercy ...

INT. SAIL BARGE OBSERVATION DECK

Bib listens gleefully.

EXT. SAIL BARGE

THREEPIO: ... the great Jabba the Hutt will now listen to your pleas.

INT. SAIL BARGE OBSERVATION DECK

Jabba waits as Artoo zips unnoticed up the ramp to the upper deck.

EXT. SKIFF

Han steps forward arrogantly and begins to speak.

HAN: Threepio, you tell that slimy piece of worm-ridden filth he'll get no such pleasure from us. Right?

Chewie growls his agreement. Artoo appears on the upper deck of the sail barge.

LUKE: Jabba! This is your last chance. Free us or die.

INT. SAIL BARGE OBSERVATION DECK

The assembled monsters rock with mocking laughter. Jabba's laughter subsides as he speaks into the comlink.

(CONT'D)

CONTINUED

JABBA: (*in Huttese subtitled*) Move him into position.

EXT. SKIFF — PLANK

Luke is prodded by a guard to the edge of the plank over the gaping Sarlacc! He exchanges nods with Lando.

EXT. BARGE — UPPER DECK

Artoo is at the rail facing the pit.

EXT. SKIFF — PLANK

Han looks around for a way out of their plight.

INT. SAIL BARGE OBSERVATION DECK

Leia looks worried.

EXT. SKIFF PLANK

Luke looks up at Artoo, then gives a jaunty salute: the signal the little droid has been waiting for.

EXT. BARGE — UPPER DECK

A flap opens in Artoo's domed head.

INT. SAIL BARGE OBSERVATION DECK

JABBA: (*in Huttese subtitled*) Put him in.

EXT. SKIFF — PLANK

Luke is prodded and jumps off the plank to the cheers of the bloodthirsty spectators. But, before anyone can even perceive what is happening, he spins around and grabs the end of the plank by his fingertips. The plank bends wildly from his weight and catapults him skyward.

EXT. BARGE — UPPER DECK

Artoo sends Luke's light saber arcing toward him.

EXT. SKIFF

In midair he does a complete flip and drops down into the skiff. He casually extends an open palm — and his lightsaber drops into his hand.
    With samurai speed, Luke ignites it and attacks the guards. The other guards swarm toward Luke. He wades into them, lightsaber flashing.

EXT. SARLACC PIT

A guard falls overboard and lands in the soft, sandy slope of the pit, and begins sliding into the pit.

INT. SAIL BARGE

Jabba watches this and explodes in rage. He barks commands, and the guards around him rush off to do his bidding. The scuzzy creatures watching the action from the window are in an uproar.

EXT. SKIFF

Luke knocks another guard off the skiff and into the waiting mouth of the Sarlacc. He starts to untie Chewie's bonds.

LUKE: Easy, Chewie.

EXT. UPPER DECK — SAIL BARGE

The deck gunmen on the barge set up a cannon on the upper deck.

EXT. SKIFF

Lando struggles with a guard at the back of the skiff.

EXT. UPPER DECK — SAIL BARGE

(CONT'D)

CONTINUED

At that moment, a deck gunman unleashes a blast from his cannon.

EXT. SKIFF

Lando is tossed from the deck of the rocking skiff. He manages to grap a rope and dangles desperately above the Sarlacc pit.

LANDO: Whoa! Whoa! Help!

EXT. UPPER DECK — SAIL BARGE

With two swift strides, the dangerous Boba Fett ignites his rocket pack, leaps into the air, and flies from the barge down to the skiff.

EXT. SKIFF

Boba lands on the skiff and starts to aim his laser gun at Luke, who has freed Han and Chewie from their bonds. But before Boba can fire, the young Jedi spins on him, lightsaber sweeping, and hacks the bounty hunter's gun in half.

    Immediately, the skiff takes another direct hit from the barge's deck gun. Shards of skiff deck fly. Chewie and Han are thrown against the rail.

HAN: Chewie, you okay. Where is he?

The Wookiee is wounded and he howls in pain. For a moment, Luke is distracted, and in that moment, Boba fires a cable out of his armored sleeve. Instantly, Luke is wrapped in a strong cable, his arms pinned against his side.

EXT. UPPER DECK — SAIL BARGE

The deck gunman continues to blast the skiff with his cannon.

EXT. SKIFF

Luke's sword arm is free only from the wrist down. He bends his wrist so the lightsaber points straight up to reach the wire lasso and cuts through. Luke shrugs away the cable and stands free.

    Another blast from the barge's deck gun hits near Boba and he is knocked unconscious to the deck, next to where Lando is hanging.

LANDO: Han! Chewie?

HAN: Lando!

Luke is a little shaken but remains standing as a fusillade brackets him. The second skiff, loaded with guards firing their weapons, moves in on Luke fast. Luke leaps toward the incoming second skiff. The young Jedi leaps into the middle of the second skiff and begins decimating the guards from their midst.

    Chewie, wounded, has barked directions to Han, guiding him toward a spear which has been dropped by one of the guards. Finally, Han grabs hold of the spear.

    Boba Fett, badly shaken, rises from the deck. He looks over at the other skiff, where Luke is whipping a mass of guards. Boba raises his arm and aims his lethal appendage.

    Chewie barks desperately to Han.

HAN: Boba Fett?! Where?

The space pirate turns around blindly, and the long spear in his hand whacks squarely in the middle of Boba's rocket pack.

    The impact of the swing causes the rocket pack to ignite. Boba blasts off, flying over the second skiff like a missile, smashing against the side of the huge sail barge and sliding away into the air. He screams as his armored body makes its last flight past Lando and directly into the mucous mouth of the Sarlacc. The Sarlacc burps.

INT. SAIL BARGE

Leia wrecks the power supply, throwing the observation deck into darkness, then leaps on to Jabba's throne, and throws the chain that enslaves her over his head around his bulbous neck. Then she dives off the other side of the throne, pulling the chain violently in her grasp. Jabba's flaccid neck contracts beneath the tightening chain. His huge eyes bulge from the sockets and his scum-coated tongue flops out.

(CONT'D)

CONTINUED

EXT. SKIFF

Luke continues to destroy the aliens on the guards' skiff, as Han extends his spear downward to Lando, who is still dangling precariously from a rope on the prisoners' skiff.

HAN: Lando, grab it!

LANDO: Lower it!

HAN: I'm trying!

INT. SAIL BARGE

The Exalted Hutt's huge tail spasms through its death throes and then slams down into final stillness.

EXT. SKIFF

A major hit from the barge deck gun knocks the skiff on its side. Han and almost everything else on board slides overboard. The rope breaks, and Lando falls to the side of the Sarlacc pit. Luckily, Han's foot catches on the skiff railing and he dangles above Lando and the pit. The wounded Wookiee holds on to the skiff for dear life.

HAN: Whoa! Whoa! Whoa! Grab me, Chewie! I'm slipping.

Chewie grabs hold of Han's feet, holding him upside down, as Han extends the spear toward Lando, who is clutching to the side of the pit.
    Luke has finished off the last guard on the second skiff. He sees the deck gun blasting away at his helpless companions.

EXT. UPPER DECK – SAIL BARGE

The deck gunner continues to blast away.

EXT. SKIFF

Luke leaps from the skiff, across the chasm of air, to the sheer metallic side of the sail barge.
Barely able to get a fingerhold, he is about to begin a painful climb up the hull, when suddenly an alien comes through a hatch inches from his head. With Jedi agility, Luke grasps the wrist holding the gun and yanks the helpless guard through the hatch and into the deadly pit.
    The injured Chewie is still reaching over the rail for the dangling Han, who is, in turn, still blindly reaching down toward the desperate Lando. The Baron has stopped his slippage down the sandy slope of the Sarlacc pit by lying very still.

HAN: Grab it! Almost . . . You almost got it!

EXT. UPPER DECK – SAIL BARGE

The deck gunner fires again.

EXT. SKIFF

The blast hits the front of the tilted skiff, causing Lando to let go of the spear.

LANDO: Hold it! Whoa!

EXT. UPPER DECK

The deck gunners have Chewie and the desperate dangling human chain in the gun sights when something up on deck commands their attention. Luke, standing before them like a pirate king, ignites his lightsaber. The deck gunners have barely reached for their pistols before the young Jedi has demolished them.

EXT. SKIFF

Again Han extends the spear toward Lando.

HAN: Gently now. All . . . all right. Easy. Hold me, Chewie.

Lando screams. One of the Sarlacc's tentacles has wrapped tightly around his ankle, dragging him down the side of the pit.

(CONT'D)

CONTINUED

HAN: Chewie!

EXT. UPPER DECK – SAIL BARGE

Luke continues to hold the upper deck against all comers.

EXT. SKIFF

HAN: Chewie, give me the gun. Don't move, Lando.

LANDO: No, wait! I thought you were blind!

HAN: It's all right. Trust me. Don't move.

LANDO: A little higher! Just a little higher!

Han adjusts his aim as Lando lowers his head, and the fuzzy-eyed pirate fires at the tentacle. Direct hit. The tentacle releases Lando.

HAN: Chewie, pull us up! All right . . . up, Chewie, up!

Chewie starts to pull them on board the skiff.

INT. SAIL BARGE – OBSERVATION DECK

Artoo extends a small laser gun and blasts Leia's chain apart.

LEIA: Come on. We gotta get out of here.

Artoo and Leia race for the exit, passing Threepio, who is kicking and screaming as Salacious Crumb, the reptilian monkey-monster, picks out one of the golden droid's eyes.

THREEPIO: Not my eye! Artoo, help! Quickly, Artoo. Oh! Ohhh!

Artoo zips over and zaps Salacious, sending him skyward with a scream, into the rafters.

THREEPIO: Beast!

EXT. SKIFF

On board the skiff, Chewie and Lando are helping Han up.

EXT. UPPER DECK – SAIL BARGE

Luke is warding off laser blasts with his lightsaber, surrounded by guards and fighting like a demon. Leia emerges on to the deck as Luke turns to face another guard.

LUKE: *(to Leia)* Get the gun! Point it at the deck!

Leia turns toward the barge cannon, climbs on the platform, and swivels the gun around.

LUKE: Point it at the deck!

A laser blast hits Luke's mechanical hand and he bends over in pain, but manages to swing his lightsaber upward and take out the last of the guards.
Near the rail of the upper deck, Artoo and Threepio steady themselves as Threepio gets ready to jump. Artoo beeps wildly.

THREEPIO: Artoo, where are we going? I couldn't possibly jump . . .

Artoo butts the golden droid over the edge and steps off himself, tumbling toward the sand.
Luke runs along the empty deck toward Leia and the barge gun, which she has brought around to point down at the deck.

LUKE: Come on!

Luke has hold of one of the rigging ropes from the mast. He gathers Leia in his other arm and kicks the trigger of the deck gun. The gun explodes into the deck as Luke and Leia swing out toward the skiff.

EXT. SKIFF

(CONT'D)

CONTINUED

Han is tending to the wounded Chewie as Luke and Leia land on the skiff with flair.

LUKE: Let's go! And don't forget the droids.

LANDO: We're on our way.

The sail barge is exploding in stages in the distance. Half of the huge craft is on fire.

EXT. SAND DUNE

Artoo's periscope sticks up from the dune where he landed. Next to it, Threepio's legs are the only things above sand. As the skiff floats above them, two large electromagnets dangle down on a wire. Both droids are pulled from the sand.

EXT. SAND DUNE

The burning sail barge continues its chain of explosions. As the skiff sails off across the desert, the barge settles to the sand and disappears in one final conflagration.

EXT. SPACE ABOVE TATOOINE

The desolate yellow planet fills the screen. The Falcon appears and grows huge, to roar directly over camera, followed by Luke's X-wing, which peels off to the left.

INT. X-WING COCKPIT

Luke is at the controls. He speaks into his comlink to the others, in the Millennium Falcon.

LUKE: Meet you back at the fleet.

LEIA: *(over comlink)* Hurry. The Alliance should be assembled by now.

LUKE: I will.

HAN: *(over comlink)* Hey, Luke, thanks. Thanks for comin' after me. Now I owe you one.

EXT. X-WING

Artoo, who is attached to Luke's X-wing outside the canopy, beeps a message.

INT. X-WING — COCKPIT

The message from Artoo appears on the small monitor screen in front of Luke. He smiles at the monitor and speaks to Artoo, as he pulls a black glove on to cover his wounded mechanical hand.

LUKE: That's right, Artoo. We're going to the Dagobah system. I have a promise to keep ... to an old friend.

EXT. SPACE

Luke's X-wing soars off.

EXT. DEATH STAR

Squads of TIE fighters escort an Imperial shuttle toward the half-completed Death Star.

INT. DOCKING BAY — DEATH STAR

Thousands of Imperial troops in tight formation fill the mammoth docking bay. Vader and the Death Star commander wait at the landing platform, where the shuttle has come to rest.

The Emperor's Royal Guards come down the shuttle's ramp and create a lethal perimeter. Then, in the huge silence which follows, the Emperor appears. He is a rather small, shriveled old man. His bent frame slowly makes its way down the ramp with the aid of a gnarled cane. He wears a hooded cloak similar to the one Ben wears, except that it is black. The Emperor's face is shrouded and difficult to see. Commander Jerjerrod and Darth Vader are kneeling to him.

EMPEROR: *(to Vader)* Rise, my friend.

The Supreme Ruler of the galaxy beckons to the Dark Lord. Vader rises, and falls in next to the Emperor as he slowly makes his way along the rows of troops. Jerjerrod and the other commanders will stay kneeling until the

(CONT'D)

CONTINUED

Supreme Ruler and Vader, followed by several Imperial dignitaries, pass by; only then do they join in the procession.

VADER: The Death Star will be completed on schedule.

EMPEROR: You have done well, Lord Vader. And now I sense you wish to continue your search for young Skywalker.

VADER: Yes, my master.

EMPEROR: Patience, my friend. In time he will seek you out. And when he does, you must bring him before me. He has grown strong. Only together can we turn him to the dark side of the Force.

VADER: As you wish.

EMPEROR: Everything is proceeding as I have foreseen.

He laughs to himself as they pass along the vast line of Imperial troops.

EXT. YODA'S HOUSE – DAGOBAH

Once again, Artoo finds himself waiting around in the damp environs of the swamp planet, and he's none too happy about it. He beeps disconsolately to himself and turns to look at Yoda's cottage. Warm yellow light escapes the oddly shaped windows to fight the gloom.

INT. YODA'S HOUSE

A walking stick taps hesitantly across the earthen floor of the cottage. The small green hand that clutches it is followed by the familiar face of Yoda, the Jedi Master. His manner is frail, and his voice, though cheerful, seems weaker.

YODA: Hmm. That face you make? Look I so old to young eyes?

Luke is sitting in a corner of the cramped space and, indeed, his look has been woeful. Caught, he tries to hide it.

LUKE: No ... of course not.

YODA: *(tickled, chuckles)* I do, yes, I do! Sick have I become. Old and weak. *(points a crooked finger)* When nine hundred years old you reach, look as good you will not. Hmm?

Yoda chuckles at this, coughs, and hobbles over toward his bed.

YODA: Soon will I rest. Yes, for ever sleep. Earned it, I have.

Yoda sits himself on his bed, with great effort.

LUKE: Master Yoda, you can't die.

YODA: Strong am I with the Force ... but not that strong! Twilight is upon me and soon night must fall. That is the way of things ... the way of the Force.

LUKE: But I need your help. I've come back to complete the training.

YODA: No more training do you require. Already know you that which you need.

Yoda sighs, lying back on his bed.

LUKE: Then I am a Jedi.

YODA: *(shakes his head)* Ohhh. Not yet. One thing remains: Vader. You must confront Vader. Then, only then, a Jedi will you be. And confront him you will.

Luke is in agony. He is silent for a moment, screwing up his courage. Finally he is able to ask.

LUKE: Master Yoda ... is Darth Vader my father?

Yoda's eyes are full of weariness and compassion. An odd, sad smile creases his face. He turns painfully on his side, away from Luke.

YODA: Mmm ... rest I need. Yes ... rest.

(CONT'D)

CONTINUED

Luke watches him, each moment an eternity.

LUKE: Yoda, I must know.

YODA: Your father he is. Told you, did he?

LUKE: Yes.

A new look of concern crosses Yoda's face. He closes his eyes.

YODA: Unexpected this is, and unfortunate ...

LUKE: Unfortunate that I know the truth?

YODA: No.

Yoda opens his eyes again and studies the youth.

YODA: *(gathering all his strength)* Unfortunate that you rushed to face him ... that incomplete was your training. That not ready for the burden were you.

LUKE: I'm sorry.

YODA: Remember, a Jedi's strength flows from the Force. But beware. Anger, fear, aggression. The dark side are they. Once you start down the dark path, forever will it dominate your destiny. *(faintly)* Luke ... Luke ...

The young Jedi moves closer to him.

YODA: Do not ... Do not underestimate the powers of the Emperor, or suffer your father's fate, you will. Luke, when gone am I ... the last of the Jedi will you be. Luke, the Force runs strong in your family. Pass on what you have learned, Luke ... *(with great effort)* There is ... another ... Sky ... walker.

The ancient green creature catches his breath and dies. Luke stares at his dead master as he disappears in front of his eyes.

EXT. DAGOBAH SWAMP – X-WING

Luke wanders back to where his ship is sitting. Artoo beeps a greeting, but is ignored by his depressed master. Luke kneels down, begins to help Artoo with the ship, then stops and shakes his head rejectedly.

LUKE: I can't do it, Artoo. I can't go on alone.

BEN: *(offscreen)* Yoda will always be with you.

Luke looks up to see the shimmering image of Ben Kenobi.

LUKE: Obi-Wan!

The ghost of Ben Kenobi approaches him through the swamp.

LUKE: Why didn't you tell me? You told me Vader betrayed and murdered my father.

BEN: Your father was seduced by the dark side of the Force. He ceased to be Anakin Skywalker and became Darth Vader. When that happened, the good man who was your father was destroyed. So what I told you was true ... from a certain point of view.

LUKE: (derisive) A certain point of view!

BEN: Luke, you're going to find that many of the truths we cling to depend greatly on our own point of view.

Luke is unresponsive. Ben studies him in silence for a moment.

BEN: Anakin was a good friend.

As Ben speaks, Luke settles on a stump, mesmerized.

BEN: When I first knew him, your father was already a great pilot. But I was amazed how strongly the Force was with him. I took it upon myself to train him as a Jedi. I thought that I could instruct him just as well as Yoda. I was wrong.

Luke is entranced.

(CONT'D)

CONTINUED

LUKE: There is still good in him.

BEN: He's more machine now than man. Twisted and evil.

LUKE: I can't do it, Ben.

BEN: You cannot escape your destiny. You must face Darth Vader again.

LUKE: I can't kill my own father.

BEN: Then the Emperor has already won. You were our only hope.

LUKE: Yoda spoke of another.

BEN: The other he spoke of is your twin sister.

LUKE: But I have no sister.

BEN: Hmm. To protect you both from the Emperor, you were hidden from your father when you were born. The Emperor knew, as I did, if Anakin were to have any offspring, they would be a threat to him. That is the reason why your sister remains safely anonymous.

LUKE: Leia! Leia's my sister.

BEN: Your insight serves you well. Bury your feelings deep down, Luke. They do you credit. But they could be made to serve the Emperor.

Luke looks into the distance, trying to comprehend all this.

EXT. SPACE – REBEL FLEET

The vast Rebel Fleet stretches as far as the eye can see. Overhead a dozen small Corellian battleships fly in formation. Fighters and battlecruisers surround the largest of the Rebel Star Cruisers, the Headquarters Frigate.

INT. HEADQUARTERS FRIGATE – MAIN BRIEFING ROOM

Hundreds of Rebel commanders of all races and forms are assembling in the War Room. Wedge is among them. In the center of the room is a holographic model depicting the half-completed Imperial Death Star, the nearby moon of Endor, and the protecting deflector shield.
    Moving through the crowd, Han finds Lando. He peers at Lando's new insignia on his chest, and is amused.

HAN: Well, look at you, a general, huh?

LANDO: Someone must have told them about my little maneuver at the battle of Taanab.

HAN: *(sarcastic)* Well, don't look at me, pal. I just said you were a fair pilot. I didn't know they were lookin' for somebody to lead this crazy attack.

LANDO: *(smiling)* I'm surprised they didn't ask you to do it.

HAN: Well, who says they didn't. But I ain't crazy. You're the respectable one, remember?

Mon Mothma, the leader of the Alliance, has entered the room. She is a stern but beautiful woman in her fifties. Mon Mothma signals for attention, and the room falls silent.

MON MOTHMA: The Emperor has made a critical error and the time for our attack has come.

This causes a stir. Mon Mothma turns to a holographic model of the Death Star, the nearby Endor moon and the protecting deflector shield in the center of the room.

MON MOTHMA: The data brought to us by the Bothan spies pinpoints the exact location of the Emperor's new battle station. We also know that the weapon systems of this Death Star are not yet operational. With the Imperial fleet spread throughout the galaxy in a vain effort to engage us, it is relatively unprotected. But most important of all, we've learned that the Emperor himself is personally overseeing the final stages of the construction of this Death Star. Many Bothans died to bring us this information. Admiral Ackbar, please.

Admiral Ackbar (a salmon-colored Mon Calamari) steps forward, indicating the Death Star's force field and the Moon of Endor.

(CONT'D)

CONTINUED

ACKBAR: You can see here the Death Star orbiting the forest Moon of Endor. Although the weapon systems on this Death Star are not yet operational, the Death Star does have a strong defence mechanism. It is protected by an energy shield which is generated from the nearby forest Moon of Endor. The shield must be deactivated if any attack is to be attempted. Once the shield is down, our cruisers will create a perimeter, while the fighters fly into the superstructure and attempt to knock out the main reactor. General Calrissian has volunteered to lead the fighter attack.

Han turns to Lando with a look of respect.

HAN: Good luck.

Lando returns his look.

HAN: You're gonna need it.

ACKBAR: General Madine.

Madine moves center stage.

GENERAL MADINE: We have stolen a small Imperial shuttle. Disguised as a cargo ship, and using a secret Imperial code, a strike team will land on the moon and deactivate the shield generator.

The assembly begins to mumble among themselves.

THREEPIO: Sounds dangerous.

LEIA: *(to Han)* I wonder who they found to pull that off.

GENERAL MADINE: General Solo, is your strike team assembled?

Leia, startled, looks up at Han, surprise changing to admiration.

HAN: Uh, my team's ready. I don't have a command crew for the shuttle.

Chewbacca raises his hairy paw and volunteers. Han looks up at him.

HAN: Well, it's gonna be rough, pal. I didn't want to speak for you.

Chewie waves that off with a huge growl.

HAN: *(smiles)* That's one.

LEIA: Uh, General ... count me in.

VOICE: *(offscreen)* I'm with you, too!

They turn in that direction and peer into the crowd, which parts to admit Luke. Han and Leia are surprised and delighted.
Leia moves to Luke and embraces him warmly. She senses a change in him and looks into his eyes questioningly.

LEIA: What is it?

LUKE: *(hesitant)* Ask me again sometime.

Han, Chewie and Lando crowd around Luke as the assembly breaks up.

HAN: Luke.

LUKE: Hi, Han ... Chewie.

Artoo beeps a singsong observation to a worried Threepio.

THREEPIO: 'Exciting' is hardly the word I would choose.

INT. HEADQUARTERS FRIGATE – MAIN DOCKING BAY

The Millennium Falcon rests beyond the stolen Imperial Shuttle, which looks anomalous among all the Rebel ships in the vast docking bay crowded now with the Rebel strike team loading weapons and supplies. Lando turns to face Han.

(CONT'D)

CONTINUED

HAN: Look: I want you to take her. I mean it. Take her. You need all the help you can get. She's the fastest ship in the fleet.

LANDO: All right, old buddy. You know, I know what she means to you. I'll take good care of her. She — She won't get a scratch. All right?

HAN: Right. I got your promise. Not a scratch.

LANDO: Look, would you get going, you pirate.

Han and Lando pause, then exchange salutes.

LANDO: Good luck.

HAN: You too.

Han goes up the ramp. Lando watches him go and then slowly turns away.

INT. IMPERIAL SHUTTLE — COCKPIT

Luke is working on a back control panel as Han comes in and takes the pilot's seat. Chewie, in the seat next to him, is trying to figure out all the Imperial controls.

HAN: You got her warmed?

LUKE: Yeah, she's comin' up.

Chewie growls a complaint.

HAN: I don't think the Empire had Wookiees in mind when they designed her, Chewie.

INT. HEADQUARTERS FRIGATE — MAIN DOCKING BAY

The shuttle warms up.

INT. IMPERIAL SHUTTLE COCKPIT

Leia comes in from the hold and puts a hand on Han's shoulder.
     Han's glance has stuck on something out the window: the Millennium Falcon. Leia nudges him gently.

LEIA: Hey, are you awake?

HAN: Yeah. I just got a funny feeling. Like I'm not gonna see her again.

Chewie, on hearing this, stops his activity and looks longingly out at the Falcon, too.

LEIA: *(softly)* Come on, General, let's move.

Han snaps back to life.

HAN: Right. Chewie, let's see what this piece of junk can do. Ready, everybody?

LUKE: All set.

THREEPIO: Here we go again.

EXT. SPACE — THE REBEL FLEET

The stolen Imperial shuttle leaves the main docking bay of the Headquarters Frigate, and lowers its wings into flight position.

INT. IMPERIAL SHUTTLE — COCKPIT

HAN: All right, hang on.

EXT. SPACE — THE REBEL FLEET

The Imperial shuttle zooms off into space.

EXT. SPACE — DEATH STAR

TIE fighters patrol the surface of the Death Star.

(CONT'D)

CONTINUED

INT. EMPEROR'S THRONE ROOM

The converted control room is dimly lit. The Emperor stands before a large window which looks out across the half-completed Death Star to the giant green Moon of Endor.
Darth Vader stands with other members of the Imperial council. The ruler's back is to Vader.

VADER: What is thy bidding, my master?

EMPEROR: *(turning)* Send the fleet to the far side of Endor. There it will stay until called for.

VADER: What of the reports of the Rebel fleet massing near Sullust?

EMPEROR: It is of no concern. Soon the Rebellion will be crushed and young Skywalker will be one of us! Your work here is finished, my friend. Go out to the command ship and await my orders.

VADER: Yes, my master.

Vader bows, then turns and exits the throne room as the Emperor walks toward the waiting council members.

EXT. SPACE — DEATH STAR — MOON

The Imperial shuttle approaches the Death Star.

INT. STOLEN IMPERIAL SHUTTLE — COCKPIT

There is a great deal of Imperial traffic in the area as the construction proceeds on the Death Star. TIE fighters, and a few Star Destroyers move about.
As Chewie flips switches, through the viewscreen, the Death Star and the huge Super Star Destroyer can be seen.

HAN: If they don't go for this, we're gonna have to get outta here pretty quick, Chewie.

Chewie growls his agreement.

CONTROLLER: *(over radio)* We have you on our screen now. Please identify.

HAN: Shuttle Tydirium requesting deactivation of the deflector shield.

EXT. SPACE — DEATH STAR — MOON

The shuttle approaches the Super Star Destroyer.

INT. SUPER STAR DESTROYER — BRIDGE

CONTROLLER: *(into radio)* Shuttle Tydirium, transmit the clearance code for shield passage.

INT. STOLEN IMPERIAL SHUTTLE — COCKPIT

HAN: Transmission commencing.

LEIA: Now we find out if that code is worth the price we paid.

HAN: It'll work. It'll work.

Chewie whines nervously. They listen tensely as the sound of a high speed transmission begins. Luke stares at the huge Super Star Destroyer that looms ever larger before them.

LUKE: Vader's on that ship.

HAN: Now don't get jittery, Luke. There are a lot of command ships. Keep your distance though, Chewie, but don't look like you're trying to keep your distance.

Chewie barks a question.

HAN: I don't know. Fly casual.

Chewie barks his worries as the Super Star Destroyer grows larger out the window.

INT. VADER'S STAR DESTROYER — BRIDGE

(CONT'D)

CONTINUED

Lord Vader walks down the row of controllers to where Admiral Piett is looking over the tracking screen of the controller we've seen earlier. Piett looks round at Vader's approach.

VADER: Where is that shuttle going?

PIETT: *(into comlink)* Shuttle Tydirium, what is your cargo and destination?

PILOT VOICE (HAN) : *(filtered)* Parts and technical crew for the forest moon.

The Bridge Commander looks to Vader for a reaction.

VADER: Do they have code clearance?

PIETT: It's an older code, sir, but it checks out. I was about to clear them.

Vader looks upward, as he senses Luke's presence.

INT. STOLEN IMPERIAL SHUTTLE – COCKPIT

LUKE: I'm endangering the mission. I shouldn't have come.

HAN: It's your imagination, kid. Come on. Let's keep a little optimism here.

EXT. SPACE – STOLEN IMPERIAL SHUTTLE – DEATH STAR

The shuttle continues on its way.

INT. VADER'S STAR DESTROYER – BRIDGE

PIETT: Shall I hold them?

VADER: No. Leave them to me. I will deal with them myself.

PIETT: *(surprised)* As you wish, my lord. *(to controller)* Carry on.

INT. STOLEN IMPERIAL SHUTTLE – COCKPIT

The group waits tensely.

HAN: They're not goin' for it, Chewie.

CONTROLLER: *(filtered)* Shuttle Tydirium, deactivation of the shield will commence immediately. Follow your present course.

Everyone breathes a sigh of relief. Everyone but Luke, who looks worried.

HAN: Okay! I told you it was gonna work. No problem.

EXT. SPACE – STOLEN IMPERIAL SHUTTLE – ENDOR

The stolen Imperial shuttle moves off toward the green Sanctuary Moon.

INT. VADER'S STAR DESTROYER – BRIDGE

Vader watches from the bridge.

EXT. ENDOR – FOREST CANOPY

The shuttle comes in to land.

EXT. FOREST LANDING SITE – ENDOR

In the moon's dark primeval forest, dwarfed by the ancient, towering trees, the helmeted Rebel contingent makes its way up the steep trail. Leia and Han are slightly ahead of Luke and Chewie. The troops of the strike-team squad follow, with Artoo and Threepio bringing up the rear.

Up ahead, Han and Leia reach a crest in the hill and drop suddenly to the ground, signaling the rest of the group to stop.

THREEPIO: Oh, I told you it was dangerous here.

Their P.O.V.: not far below them, two Imperial scouts are wandering through bushes in the valley below. Their two rocket bikes are parked nearby.

(CONT'D)

CONTINUED

LEIA: Should we try and go around?

HAN: It'll take time. This whole party'll be for nothing if they see us. Chewie and I will take care of this. You stay here.

LUKE: Quietly, there might be more of them out there.

HAN: *(grins)* Hey ... it's me.

Han and Chewie turn and start through the bushes toward the scouts. Luke and Leia exchange smiles.

Han sneaks up behind one of the scouts, steps on a twig and the scout whirls, knocking Han into a tree. The scout shouts for his companion.

SCOUT #1: Go for help! Go!

LUKE: *(sarcastic)* Great! Come on.

The second scout jumps on his speeder bike and takes off, but Chewie gets off a shot on his crossbow laser weapon, causing the scout to crash into a tree. Han and Scout #1 are in a rousing fistfight.

Luke starts for the scuffle, followed by Leia. As they run through the bushes, Leia stops and points to where two more scouts are sitting on their speeder bikes, with an unoccupied bike parked nearby.

LEIA: Over there! Two more of them!

LUKE: I see them. Wait, Leia.

But Leia doesn't hear him and races for the remaining speeder bike. She starts it up and takes off as Luke jumps on the bike behind her.

Luke and Leia speed into the dense foliage in hot pursuit, barely avoiding two huge trees.

HAN: Hey, wait! Ahhh!

He flips the remaining scout to the ground.

LUKE: *(pointing to the controls)* Quick! Jam their comlink. Center switch!

EXT. FOREST – THE BIKE CHASE

The two fleeing Imperial scouts have a good lead as Luke and Leia pursue through the giant trees at 200 miles an hour.

LUKE: Move closer!

Leia guns it, closing the gap, as the two scouts recklessly veer through a narrow gap in the trees.

LUKE: Get alongside that one!

Leia pulls her speeder bike up so close to the scout's bike that they scrape noisily. Luke leaps from his bike to the back of the scout's, grabs the Imperial warrior around the neck, and flips him off the bike, into a thick tree trunk. Luke gains control of the bike and follows Leia, who has pulled ahead. They tear off after the remaining scout.

The speeding chase passes two more Imperial scouts. These two swing into pursuit, chasing Luke and Leia, firing away with their laser cannon. The two Rebels look behind them just as Luke's bike takes a glancing hit.

LUKE: *(indicating the one ahead)* Keep on that one! I'll take these two!

With Leia shooting ahead, Luke suddenly slams into braking mode. Luke's bike is a blur to the two pursuing scouts as they zip by him on either side. Luke slams his bike into forward and starts firing away, having switched places with his pursuers in a matter of seconds. Luke's aim is good and one scout's bike is blasted out of control. It explodes against a tree trunk.

The scout's cohort takes one glance back at the flash and shifts into turbo drive, going even faster. Luke keeps on his tail.

Far ahead, Leia and the first scout are doing a high-speed slalom through the death-dealing trunks. Now Leia aims her bike skyward and rises out of sight.

The scout turns in confusion, unable to see his pursuer. Suddenly, Leia dives down upon him from above, cannon blasting.

(CONT'D)

CONTINUED

Leia moves in alongside him. The scout eyes her beside him, reaches down, and pulls out a handgun. Before Leia can react, the scout has blasted her bike, sending it out of control. The happy scout looks back at the explosion. But when he turns forward again, he is on a collision course with a giant fallen tree. He hits his brakes to no avail and disappears in a conflagration.

ANOTHER PART OF THE FOREST: Luke and the last remaining scout continue their weaving chase through the trees. Now Luke moves up close. The scout responds by slamming his bike into Luke's.

Both riders look ahead — a wide trunk looms directly in Luke's path, but the scout's bike beside him makes it almost impossible for him to avoid it. Luke reacts instinctively and dives off the bike. It explodes against the tree. The scout sweeps out and circles back to find Luke.

Luke rises from the undergrowth as the scout bears down on him and opens fire with his laser cannon. Luke ignites his laser sword and begins deflecting the bolts. The scout's bike keeps coming and it appears that in a second it will cut Luke in half. At the last instant, Luke steps aside and chops off the bike's control vanes with one mighty slash. The scout's bike begins to pitch and roll, then slams directly into a tree in a giant ball of fire.

EXT. SCOUT CAMPSITE — FOREST

Han, Chewie and the droids, along with the rest of the squad, wait anxiously in the clearing. Artoo's radar screen sticks out of his domed head and revolves, scanning the forest. He beeps.

THREEPIO1 Oh, General Solo, somebody's coming.

Han, Chewie, and the rest of the squad raise their weapons.

THREEPIO: Oh!

Luke runs out of the foliage.

HAN: Luke! Where's Leia?

LUKE: *(concerned)* What? She didn't come back?

HAN: I thought she was with you.

LUKE: We got separated.

Luke and Han exchange a silent, grim look.

LUKE: Hey, we better go look for her.

Han signals to a Rebel officer.

HAN: Take the squad ahead. We'll meet at the shield generator at 0300.

LUKE: Come on, Artoo. We'll need your scanners.

Luke, Chewie, Han and the droids move off in one direction as the squad proceeds in another.

THREEPIO: Don't worry, Master Luke. We know what to do.

They move off into the woods.

THREEPIO: *(to Artoo)* And you said it was pretty here. Ugh!

EXT. FOREST CLEARING — LEIA'S CRASH SITE

A strange little furry creatre with huge black eyes come slowly into view. The creature is an Ewok, by the name of Wicket. He seems somewhat puzzled, and prods Leia with a spear. The stubby ball of fuzz jumps back and prods her again.

LEIA: Cut it out!

Leia sits up and stares at the three-foot high Ewok. She tries to figure out where she is and what has happened. Her clothes are torn, she's bruised and disheveled.

The Ewok holds his four-foot-long spear in a defensive position. Leia stands up, and the Ewok backs away.

LEIA: I'm not gonna hurt you.

Leia looks around at the dense forest, then sits down, with a sigh, on a fallen log.

(CONT'D)

CONTINUED

LEIA: Well, looks like I'm stuck here. Trouble is, I don't know where here is. Maybe you can help me.

She looks over at the watchful little Ewok and pats the log beside her.

LEIA: Come on, sit down.

Wicket holds his spear up warily and growls at her like a puppy.

LEIA: I promise I won't hurt you. Now come here.

Leia pats the log again, causing more growls and squeaks from the little bear creature.

LEIA: All right. You want something to eat?

She takes a scrap of food out of her pocket and offers it to him. Wicket takes a step backward, then cocks his head and moves cautiously toward Leia, chattering in his squeaky Ewok language.

LEIA: That's right. Come on. Hmmm?

Sniffing the food cautiously, the Ewok comes forward toward Leia and sits on the log beside her. She takes off her helmet, and the little creature jumps back, startled again. He runs along the log, pointing his spear at her and chattering a blue streak. Leia holds out the helmet to him.

LEIA: Look, it's a hat. It's not gonna hurt you. Look.

Reassured, Wicket lowers his spear and climbs back on the log, coming to investigate the helmet.

LEIA: You're a jittery little thing, aren't you?

Suddenly Wicket's ears perk up and he begins to sniff the air. He looks around warily, whispering some Ewokese warning to Leia.

LEIA: What is it?

Suddenly a laser bolt comes out of the foliage and explodes on the log next to Leia. Leia and Wicket both roll backwards off the log, hiding behind it. Leia holds her own laser gun ready.

Another shot, and still no sight of anyone in the forest. Wicket disappears underneath the log. Suddenly a large Imperial scout is standing over her with his weapon pointed at her head. He reaches out his hand for her weapon.

SCOUT #1: Freeze! Come on, get up!

A second scout emerges from the foliage in front of the log.

SCOUT #1: Go get your ride and take her back to base.

SCOUT #2: Yes, sir.

The second scout starts toward his bike, as Wicket, crouched under the log, extends his spear and hits the first scout on the leg. The scout jumps and lets out an exclamation and looks down at Wicket, puzzled. Leia grabs a branch and knocks him out. She dives for his laser pistol, and the second scout, now on his bike, takes off. Leia fires away and hits the escaping bike, causing it to crash into the first scout's bike, which flies end over end and explodes. The forest is quiet once more. Wicket pokes his fuzzy head up from behind the log and regards Leia with new respect. He mumbles his awe. Leia hurries over, looking around all the time, and motions the chubby little creature into the dense foliage.

LEIA: Come on, let's get out of here.

As they move into the foliage, Wicket shrieks and tugs at Leia to follow him.

EXT. DEATH STAR SURFACE

TIE fighters patrol.

INT. EMPEROR'S TOWER — THRONE ROOM

Two red Imperial Guards stand watch at the elevator as the door opens to reveal Vader. Vader enters the eerie, foreboding throne room. It appears to be empty. His footsteps echo as he approaches the throne. He waits, absolutely still. The Emperor sits with his back to the Dark Lord.

(CONT'D)

CONTINUED

EMPEROR: I told you to remain on the command ship.

VADER: A small Rebel force has penetrated the shield and landed on Endor.

EMPEROR: *(no surprise)* Yes, I know.

VADER: *(after a beat)* My son is with them.

EMPEROR: *(very cool)* Are you sure?

VADER: I have felt him, my master.

EMPEROR: Strange, that I have not. I wonder if your feelings on this matter are clear, Lord Vader.

Vader knows what is being asked.

VADER: They are clear, my master.

EMPEROR: Then you must go to the Sanctuary Moon and wait for him.

VADER: *(skeptical)* He will come to me?

EMPEROR: I have foreseen it. His compassion for you will be his undoing. He will come to you and then you will bring him before me.

VADER: *(bows)* As you wish.

The Dark Lord strides out of the throne room.

EXT. FOREST CLEARING – LEIA'S CRASH SITE

Moving through the heavy foliage near the clearing where we last saw Leia, Luke finds Leia's helmet, and picks it up with an expression of concern.

HAN: *(offscreen)* Luke! Luke!

Luke runs with the helmet to where Han has found the charred wreckage of a speeder bike in the grass.

THREEPIO: Oh, Master Luke.

LUKE: There's two more wrecked speeders back there. And I found this.

He tosses the helmet to Han.

THREEPIO: I'm afraid that Artoo's sensors can find no trace of Princess Leia.

HAN: *(gravely)* I hope she's all right.

Chewbacca growls, sniffing the air, then, with a bark, pushes off through the foliage.

HAN: What, Chewie? What, Chewie?

The others rush to keep up with the giant Wookiee.

EXT. FOREST – DENSE FOLIAGE

The group has reached a break in the undergrowth. Chewie walks up to a tall stake planted in the ground. There is a dead animal hanging from it.

HAN: Hey, I don't get it.

The rest of the group joins the Wookiee around the stake.

HAN: *(continuing)* Nah. It's just a dead animal, Chewie.

Chewie can't resist. He reaches toward the meat.

LUKE: Chewie, wa-wait! Don't!

Too late. The Wookiee has already pulled the animal from the stake. Sprooing! The group finds itself hanging in an Ewok net, suspended high above the clearing. Chewie howls his regret. Their bodies are a jumble in the net.

HAN: Nice work. Great, Chewie! Great! Always thinking with your stomach.

(CONT'D)

CONTINUED

LUKE: Will you take it easy. Let's just figure out a way to get out of this thing. (*trying to free an arm*) Han, can you reach my lightsaber?

HAN: Yeah, sure.

Meanwhile, Artoo is at the bottommost point in the net. He extends his cutting appendage and begins slicing at the net. The net continues to spin.

THREEPIO: Artoo, I'm not sure that's such a good idea. It's a very long dro-o-p.

Artoo has cut through and the entire group tumbles out of the net, crashing to the ground. As they regain their senses and sit up, they realize they are surrounded by dozens of Ewoks, each brandishing a long spear.

HAN: Wait . . . ? Hey! Point that thing someplace else.

Han pushes the spear wielded by Teebo out of his face and a second Ewok warrior comes up to argue with Teebo. The spear returns to Han's face.

HAN: Hey!

Han grabs the spear angrily and starts to go for his laser pistol.

LUKE: Han, don't. It'll be all right.

The Ewoks swarm through them and confiscate their weapons. Luke gives them his lightsaber.

LUKE: Chewie, give 'em your crossbow.

Chewie growls at the furry critters. Threepio gets free of the net and sits up, rattled.

THREEPIO: Oh, my head. Oh, my goodness!

When the Ewoks see Threepio, they let out a gasp and chatter among themselves. The Ewoks begin to chant at Threepio, and bow down before him. Chewie lets out a puzzled bark. Han and Luke regard the bowed creatures in wonder. Threepio speaks to them in their native tongue.

LUKE: Do you understand anything they're saying?

THREEPIO: Oh, yes, Master Luke! Remember that I am fluent in over six million forms of communication.

HAN: What are you telling them?

THREEPIO: Hello, I think . . . I could be mistaken. They're using a very primitive dialect. But I do believe they think I am some sort of god.

The others think that's very funny.

HAN: Well, why don't you use your divine influence and get us out of this?

THREEPIO: I beg your pardon, General Solo, but that just wouldn't be proper.

HAN: Proper!?

THREEPIO: It's against my programming to impersonate a deity.

Han moves toward Threepio threateningly.

HAN: Why, you . . .

The Ewoks move in to protect their god and Han is surrounded by a menacing circle of spears, all aimed at him. He holds up his hands placatingly.

HAN: My mistake. He's an old friend of mine.

EXT. FOREST

A procession of Ewoks winds through the ever-darkening forest. Their prisoners – Han, Luke, Chewie and Artoo – are tied to long poles.
     Each pole is carried on the shoulders of several Ewoks.

EXT. FOREST WALKWAY – MOON FOREST

(CONT'D)

CONTINUED

Behind the captives, Threepio is carried on a litter, like a king, by the remaining creatures.

The procession moves along a shaky, narrow, wooden walkway, high in the giant trees. It stops at the end of the walkway, which drops off into nothingness. On the other side of the abyss is a village of mud huts and rickety walkways attached to the giant trees. The lead Ewok takes hold of a long vine and swings across to the village square; the other Ewoks follow suite.

EXT. EWOK VILLAGE SQUARE

The procession winds its way into the village square. The group stops before the largest hut.

Han, Luke, Chewie and Artoo are still bound to their poles. Han is placed on a spit above what looks like a barbecue pit. Threepio's litter/throne is gently placed near the pit. He watches with rapt fascination. Han, Luke and Chewie are less fascinated. Chewie growls his concern.

HAN: I have a really bad feeling about this.

Suddenly all activity stops as Logray, the tribal Medicine Man, comes out of the big hut. He goes to Threepio, whose throne has been placed on an elevated platform. He is holding Luke's lightsaber.
Logray speaks to Threepio and the assemblage of fuzzy Ewoks, pointing to the prisoners.

HAN: What did he say?

THREEPIO: I'm rather embarrased, General Solo, but it appears you are to be the main course at a banquet in my honor.

The Ewoks begin filling the pit under Han with firewood.
The drums start beating, and all the furryheads turn to the large hut. Leia emerges, wearing an animal-skin dress. She sees what's happening at the same moment the prisoners see her.

LUKE: Leia?

HAN: Leia!

As she moves toward them, the Ewoks block her way with raised spears.

LEIA: Oh!

THREEPIO: Your Royal Highness.

Leia looks around at the assembled Ewoks and sighs.

LEIA: But these are my friends. Threepio, tell them they must be set free.

Threepio talks to Logray, who listens and shakes his head negatively. The Medicine Man gestures toward the prisoners and barks some orders. Several Ewoks jump up and pile more wood on the barbecue with vigor.

HAN: Somehow, I got the feeling that didn't help us very much.

LUKE: Threepio, tell them if they don't do as you wish, you'll become angry and use your magic.

THREEPIO: But Master Luke, what magic? I couldn't possibly — ''

LUKE: Just tell them.

Threepio speaks to the Ewoks. The Ewoks are disturbed. Logray calls Threepio's bluff.

THREEPIO: You see, Master Luke, they didn't believe me. Just as I said they wouldn't.

Luke closes his eyes and begins to concentrate.
Now the litter/throne, with Threepio sitting upon it, rises from the ground. As first Threepio doesn't notice and keeps talking.

THREEPIO: What-wha-what's happening! Oh, dear! Oh!

The Ewoks fall back in terror from the floating throne. Now Threepio begins to spin as though he were on a revolving stool, with Threepio calling out in total panic at his situation.

THREEPIO: Put me down! He-e-elp! Somebody help! Master Luke! Artoo! Somebody, somebody, help! Master Luke, Artoo, Artoo, quickly! Do something, somebody! Oh! Ohhh!

(CONT'D)

CONTINUED

Logray yells orders to the cowering Ewoks. They rush up and release the bound prisoners. Artoo crashes to the ground. When the Ewoks set him upright, the little droid is fighting mad. Artoo beeps a blue streak at the nearest Ewok and begins pursuing him, finally getting close enough to zap him with an electric charge. The Ewok jumps two feet in the air and runs away, screaming. Han enfolds Leia in an embrace. Luke slowly lowers Threepio and the throne to the ground.

THREEPIO: Oh, oh, oh, oh! Thank goodness.

LUKE: Thanks Threepio.

THREEPIO *(still shaken)* : I . . . never knew I had it in me.

EXT. FOREST WALKWAY

The sounds of a council can be heard.

EXT. CHIEF'S HUT

Younger Ewoks cram the doorway.

INT. CHIEF'S HUT – COUNCIL OF ELDERS

A glowing fire dances in the center of the spartan, low-ceilinged room, creating a kaleidoscope of shadows on the walls. Along one side, a group of ten Ewok elders flanks a larger gray-haired Ewok, Chief Chirpa, who sits on his throne. The Rebels sit along the walls of the hut, with Threepio between the two groups and Wicket and Teebo off to one side.

Threepio is in the midst of a long, animated speech in the Ewoks' squeaky native tongue. The Ewoks listen carefully and occasionally murmur comments to each other.

Threepio points several times at the Rebel group and pantomimes a short history of the Galactic Civil War, mimicking the explosion and rocket sounds, imitating Imperial walkers. Throughout the long account, certain familiar names are distinguishable in English: Princess Leia, Artoo, Darth Vader, Death Star, Jedi, Obi-Wan Kenobi. Artoo begins beeping excitedly at Threepio.

THREEPIO: Yes, Artoo, I was just coming to that.

Threepio continues with: Millennium Falcon, Cloud City, Vader, Han Solo, carbonite, Sarlacc, bringing the history up to the present time.

At the end of it, the Chief, Logray, and the elders confer, then nod in agreement.

HAN: What's going on?

LEIA: I don't know.

Luke has been sharing the joy with smiling visage, but now something passes like a dark cloud through his consciousness. The others do not notice.

Logray makes a pronouncement.

The drums begin to sound, and the Ewoks gesticulate wildly.

THREEPIO: Wonderful! We are now a part of the tribe.

Several of the little teddy bears run up and hug the Rebels.

HAN: Just what I always wanted.

Luke wanders outside into the moonlight. Leia notices and follows.

Chewbacca is being enthusiastically embraced by an Ewok, while Wicket clings to Han's leg.

HAN: *(chuckles)* Well, short help is better than no help at all, Chewie. *(to Wicket)* Thank you.

THREEPIO: He says the scouts are going to show us the quickest way to the shield generator.

HAN: Good. How far is it? Ask him. We need some fresh supplies, too. And try and get our weapons back.

Han pulls Threepio back as he keeps trying to translate.

HAN: *(continuing)* And hurry up, will ya? I haven't got all day.

EXT. EWOK VILLAGE

(CONT'D)

CONTINUED

The walkway is deserted now. The windows of the little huts glow and flicker from the fires inside. The sounds of the forest fill the soft night air. Luke has wandered away from the Chief's hut and stands staring up at the Death Star. Leia finds him like that.

LEIA: Luke, what's wrong?

Luke turns and looks at her a long moment.

LEIA: Leia ... do you remember your mother? Your real mother?

LEIA: Just a little bit. She died when I was very young.

LUKE: What do your remember?

LEIA: Just ... images, really. Feelings.

LUKE: Tell me.

LEIA: *(a little surprised at his insistence)* She was very beautiful. Kind, but ... *(looks up)* sad. Why are you asking me this?

He is looking away.

LUKE: I have no memory of my mother. I never knew her.

LEIA: Luke, tell me. What's troubling you?

LUKE: Vader is here ... now, on this moon.

LEIA: *(alarmed)* How do you know?'

LUKE: I felt his presence. He's come for me. He can feel when I'm near. That's why I have to go. *(facing her)* As long as I stay, I'm endangering the group and our mission here. I have to face him.

Leia is confused.

LEIA: Why?

LUKE: He's my father.

LEIA: Your father?!

LUKE: There's more. It won't be easy for you to hear it, but you must. If I don't make it back, you're the only hope for the Alliance.

Leia is very disturbed by this.

LEIA: Luke, don't talk that way. You have a power I ... I don't understand and could never have.

LUKE: You're wrong, Leia. You have that power, too. In time, you'll learn to use it as I have. The Force is strong in my family. My father has it ... I have it ... and my sister has it.

Leia stares into his eyes. What she sees frightens her. But she doesn't draw away. She begins to understand.

LUKE: Yes. It's you Leia.

LEIA: I know. Somehow ... I've always known.

LUKE: Then you know why I have to face him.

LEIA: No! Luke, run away, far away. If he can feel your presence, then leave this place. I wish I could go with you.

LUKE: No, you don't. You've always been strong.

LEIA: But why must you confront him?

LUKE: Because ... there is good in him. I've felt it. He won't turn me over to the Emperor. I can save him. I can turn him back to the good side. I have to try.

They hold each other and look at each other, brother and sister.

(CONT'D)

CONTINUED

Leia holds back her tears as Luke slowly lets her go and moves away. He disappears on to the walkway that leads out of the village. Leia, bathed in moonlight, watches him go as Han comes out of the Chief's hut and comes over to her.

HAN: Hey, what's goin' on?

LEIA: Nothing – I just want to be alone for a little while.

HAN: *(angry)* Nothing? Come on, tell me. What's goin on?

She looks up at him, struggling to control herself.

LEIA: I ... I can't tell you.

HAN: *(loses his temper)* Could you tell Luke? Is that who you could tell?

LEIA: I ...

HAN: Ahhh ...

He starts to walk away, exasperated, then stops and walks back to her.

HAN: I'm sorry.

LEIA: Hold me.

Han gathers her tightly in his protective embrace.

EXT. FOREST – IMPERIAL LANDING PLATFORM

An Imperial shuttle floats down from the Death Star and lands gracefully on the huge platform.
   Now, an Imperial walker approaches the platform from the darkness of the forest. The whole outpost – platform, walkers, military – looks particularly offensive in the midst of this verdant beauty.

EXT. IMPERIAL LANDING PLATFORM – LOWER DECK

Darth Vader walks down the ramp of the shuttle on to the platform. Coming out of an elevator, he appears on a ramp on a lower level. He walks toward another ramp exit and is met by three troopers and a commander with Luke, in binders, at their center. The young Jedi gazes at Vader with complete calm.

COMMANDER: This is a Rebel that surrendered to us. Although he denies it, I believe there may be more of them, and I request permission to conduct a further search of the area.

Vader looks at Luke, turns away and faces the commander.

COMMANDER: He was armed only with this.

The commander places Luke's lightsaber in Vader's hands.

VADER: Good work, Commander. Leave us. Conduct your search and bring his companions to me.

COMMANDER: Yes, my lord.

The officer and troops withdraw. Vader and Luke are left alone on the ramp.

VADER: The Emperor has been expecting you.

LUKE: I know, Father.

VADER: So, you have accepted the truth.

LUKE: I've accepted the truth that you were once Anakin Skywalker, my father.

VADER: *(turning to face him)* That name no longer has any meaning for me.

LUKE: It is the name of your true self. You've only forgotten. I know there is good in you. The Emperor hasn't driven it from you fully. That was why you couldn't destroy me. That's why you won't bring me to your Emperor now.

Vader looks down from Luke to the lightsaber in his own black-gloved hand. He seems to ponder Luke's words.
   Vader ignites the lightsaber and holds it to examine its humming, brilliant blade.

(CONT'D)

CONTINUED

VADER: I see you have constructed a new lightsaber. Your skills are complete. *(extinguishing the lightsaber)* Indeed, you are powerful, as the Emperor has foreseen.

LUKE: Come with me.

VADER: Obi-Wan once thought as you do. You don't know the power of the dark side. I must obey my master.

LUKE: I will not turn ... and you'll be forced to kill me.

VADER: If that is your destiny ...

LUKE: Search your feelings, Father. You can't do this. I feel the conflict within you. Let go of your hate.

VADER: It is too late for me, Son. *(signaling to some distant stormtroopers)* The Emperor will show you the true nature of the Force. He is your master now.

Vader and Luke stand staring at one another for a long moment.

LUKE: Then my father is truly dead.

EXT. ENDOR – RIDGE OVERLOOKING SHIELD GENERATOR

Han, Leia, Chewbacca, the droids, Wicket and another Ewok scout, Paploo, hide on a ridge overlooking the massive Imperial shield generator.
At the base of the generator is an Imperial landing platform. Leia studies the installation.

LEIA: The main entrance to the control bunker's on the far side of that landing platform. This isn't going to be easy.

HAN: Hey, don't worry. Chewie and me got into a lot of places more heavily guarded than this.

Wicket and Paploo are chattering away in Ewok language. They speak to Threepio.

LEIA: What's he saying?

THREEPIO: He says there's a secret entrance on the other side of the ridge.

EXT. SPACE – REBEL FLEET

The vast fleet hangs in space. A giant Rebel Star Cruiser is up at the front, but now the Millennium Falcon roars up to a spot ahead of it, tiny in comparison.

INT. MILLENNIUM FALCON – COCKPIT

Lando is in the pilot seat.

LANDO: Admiral, we're in position. All fighters accounted for.

INT. REBEL STAR CRUISER – BRIDGE

ACKBAR: Proceed with the countdown. All groups assume attack coordinates.

INT. MILLENNIUM FALCON – COCKPIT

Lando's alien copilot, Nein Nunb, takes some getting used to in the familiar environs of the Falcon's cockpit. Lando turns to his weird copilot.

LANDO: Don't worry, my friend's down there. He'll have that shield down on time ...

The copilot flips some switches and grunts an alien comment.

LANDO: *(to himself)* ... or this'll be the shortest offensive of all time.

INT. REBEL STAR CRUISER – BRIDGE

ACKBAR: All craft, prepare to jump into hyperspace on my mark.

INT. MILLENNIUM FALCON – COCKPIT

LANDO: All right. Stand by.

He pulls a lever, and the stars outside begin to streak.

(CONT'D)

CONTINUED

EXT. SPACE — REBEL FLEET

We are treated to an awesome sight: first the Millennium Falcon, then Ackbar's Star Cruiser, then, in large segments, the huge fleet roars into hyperspace.

INT. ACKBAR'S STAR CRUISER — BRIDGE

The stars streak by Ackbar on his bridge.

EXT. SPACE — REBEL FLEET

The remainder of the Rebel fleet roars into hyperspace. And disappears.

EXT. ENDOR — RIDGE OVERLOOKING CONTROL BUNKER

Han, Leia, Chewie, the droids and their two Ewok guides, Wicket and Paploo, have reunited with the Rebel strike squad. The entire group is spread through the thick undergrowth. Beneath them is the bunker that leads into the generator. Four Imperial scouts, their speeder bikes parked near by, keep watch over the bunker entrance. Paploo chatters away to Han in Ewok language.

HAN: Back door, huh? Good idea.

Wicket and Paploo continue their Ewok conversation.

HAN: *(continuing)* It's only a few guards. This shouldn't be too much trouble.

LEIA: Well, it only takes one to sound the alarm.

HAN: *(with self-confident grin)* Then we'll do it real quiet-like.

Paploo has scampered into the underbrush. Threepio asks Wicket where Paploo went and is given a short reply.

THREEPIO: Oh! Oh, my. Uh, Princess Leia!

Leia quiets him.

THREEPIO: I'm afraid our furry companion has gone and done something rather rash.

Chewie barks. Han, Leia and company watch in distress.

LEIA: Oh, no.

EXT. THE BUNKER ENTRANCE

Paploo has slipped out of the undergrowth near where the Imperial scouts are lounging.

HAN: *(sighs)* There goes our surprise attack.

Paploo silently swings his furry ball of a body on to one of the scouts' speeder bikes and begins flipping switches at random. Suddenly, the bike's engine fires up with a tremendous roar.

EXT. RIDGE

Han, Leia and company watch in distress.

SCOUT: Look! Over there! Stop him!

The Imperial scouts race toward Paploo just as his speeder bike comes into motion. Paploo hangs on by his paws and shoots away into the forest.
Three of the Imperial scouts jump on their rocket bikes and speed away in pursuit. The fourth watches them go.

EXT. RIDGE

Han, Leia, and Chewie exchange delighted looks.

HAN: Not bad for a little furball. There's only one left. *(to Wicket)* You stay here. We'll take care of this.

Threepio moves to stand next to Wicket and Artoo.

THREEPIO: I have decided that we shall stay here.

(CONT'D)

CONTINUED

EXT. FOREST

Paploo sails through the trees, more lucky than in control. It's scary, but he loves it. When the Imperial scouts pull within sight behind him and begin firing laser bolts, he decides he's had enough. As he rounds a tree, out of their sight, Paploo grabs a vine and swings up into the trees. A moment later, the scouts tear under him in pursuit of the still-flying, unoccupied bike.

EXT. BUNKER

Han sneaks up behind the remaining Imperial scout, taps him on the shoulder and lets the scout chase him behind the bunker into the arms of the waiting Rebel strike team.

INT. BUNKER

The group enters the bunker silently.

EXT. SPACE – DEATH STAR

The half-completed Death Star hangs in space over the Moon of Endor.

INT. DEATH STAR – EMPEROR'S THRONE ROOM

The elevator opens. Vader and Luke enter the room alone. They walk across the dark space to stand before the throne, father and son, side by side beneath the gaze of the Emperor. Vader bows to his master.

EMPEROR: Welcome, young Skywalker. I have been expecting you.

Luke peers at the hooded figure defiantly. The Emperor smiles, then looks down at Luke's binders.

EMPEROR: You no longer need those.

The Emperor motions ever so slightly with his finger and Luke's binders fall away, clattering noisily to the floor. Luke looks down at his own hands, free now to reach out and grab the Emperor's neck. He does nothing.

EMPEROR: Guards, leave us.

The red-cloaked guards turn and disappear behind the elevator.

EMPEROR: *(to Luke)* I'm looking forward to completing your training. In time you will call me Master.

LUKE: You're gravely mistaken. You won't convert me as you did my father.

The Emperor gets down from his throne and walks up very close to Luke. The Emperor looks into his eyes and, for the first time, Luke can perceive the evil visage within the hood.

EMPEROR: Oh, no, my young Jedi. You will find that it is you who are mistaken ... about a great many things.

VADER: His lightsaber.

Vader extends a gloved hand toward the Emperor, revealing Luke's lightsaber. The Emperor takes it.

EMPEROR: Ah, yes, a Jedi's weapon. Much like your father's. By now you must know your father can never be turned from the dark side. So will it be with you.

LUKE: You're wrong. Soon I'll be dead ... and you with me.

The Emperor laughs.

EMPEROR: Perhaps you refer to the imminent attack of your Rebel fleet.

Luke looks down momentarily.

EMPEROR: Yes ... I assure you we are quite safe from your friends here.

LUKE: Your overconfidence is your weakness.

Vader looks at Luke.

EMPEROR: Your faith in your friends is yours.

VADER: It is pointless to resist, my son.

(CONT'D)

CONTINUED

The Emperor has returned to his throne and now turns to face Luke.

EMPEROR: *(angry)* Everything that has transpired has done so according to my design. Your friends *(indicates Endor)* up there on the Sanctuary Moon ...

Luke reacts.

EMPEROR: *(continuing)* ... are walking into a trap. As is your Rebel fleet! It was I who allowed the Alliance to know the location of the shield generator. It is quite safe from your pitiful little band. An entire legion of my best troops awaits them.

Luke's look darts from the Emperor to the sword in the Emperor's hand.

EMPEROR: Oh ... I'm afraid the deflector shield will be quite operational when your friends arrive.

INT. BUNKER – MAIN CONTROL ROOM

Han, Leia, Chewie and the Rebel strike team storm through a door and enter the main control room, taking all of the personnel prisoner.

HAN: All right! Up! Move! Come on! Quickly! Quickly! Chewie!

The Rebel troops herd the generator controllers away from their panels. Leia glances at one of screens on the control panel.

LEIA: Han! Hurry! The fleet will be here any moment.

HAN: Charges! Come on, come on!

EXT. BUNKER

Several more controllers and stormtroopers run into the bunker, leaving guards at the door. Threepio watches nervously in the bushes.

THREEPIO: Oh, my! They'll be captured!

Wicket chatters in Ewok language, and then takes off full steam into the forest.

THREEPIO: Wa-ait! Wait, come back! Artoo, stay with me.

INT. BUNKER.

IMPERIAL OFFICER: Freeze!

Han looks up from setting charges as an Imperial officer enters. He deals with him, but he and Leia spin to find dozens of Imperial weapons trained on them and their cohorts.

COMMANDER: You Rebel scum.

A poised force of Imperial troops surround them. Even more pour into the room, roughly disarming the Rebel contingent. Han, Leia, and Chewie exchange looks. They're helpless.

INT. MILLENNIUM FALCON – COCKPIT

Lando operates the controls to come out of hyperspace.

EXT. SPACE – ENDOR, DEATH STAR, REBEL FLEET

The Rebel fleets comes out of hyperspace with an awesome roar. The Millennium Falcon and several Rebel fighters are at the front as the space armada bears down on its target, the Death Star and its Sanctuary Moon.

INT. REBEL STAR CRUISER – BRIDGE

Ackbar surveys his Rebel fleet from the bridge.

INT. MILLENNIUM FALCON – COCKPIT

Lando flips switches, checks his screen, and speaks into the radio.

LANDO: All wings report in.

(CONT'D)

CONTINUED

INT. WEDGE'S X-FIGHTER — COCKPIT

WEDGE: Red Leader standing by.

INT. GRAY LEADER'S — COCKPIT

GRAY LEADER: Gray Leader standing by.

INT. GREEN LEADER'S — COCKPIT

GREEN LEADER: Green Leader standing by.

INT. WEDGE'S X-FIGHTER — COCKPIT

WEDGE: Lock S-foils in attack positions.

EXT. SPACE — REBEL FLEET

The Rebel fleet converges on the Death Star.

INT. REBEL STAR CRUISER

From the bridge of the Rebel Headquarters Frigate, Admiral Ackbar watches the fighters massing outside his viewscreen.

ACKBAR: May the Force be with us.

INT. MILLENNIUM FALCON — COCKPIT

Lando looks worriedly at his alien copilot, Nien Nunb, who points to the control panel and talks to Lando.

LANDO: We've got to be able to get some kind of a reading on that shield, up or down. Well, how could they be jamming us if they don't know ... we're coming?

Lando shoots a concerned look out at the approaching Death Star as the implications of what he's just said sink in. He hits a switch on his comlink.

LANDO: Break off the attack! The shield is still up.

INT. WEDGE'S X-FIGHTER — COCKPIT

WEDGE: I get no reading. Are you sure?

LANDO: *(voiceover)* Pull up!

INT. MILLENNIUM FALCON — COCKPIT

LANDO: All craft pull up!

EXT. SPACE — DEATH STAR SHIELD

The Falcon and the fighters of Red Squad veer off desperately to avoid the unseen wall.

INT. REBEL STAR CRUISER — BRIDGE

Alarms are screaming and lights flashing as the huge ship changes course abruptly. Other ships in the fleet shoot by outside as the armada tries to halt its forward momentum.

ACKBAR: Take evasive action! Green Group, stick close to holding sector MV-7.

EXT. SPACE — DEATH STAR SHIELD

The Rebel fleet takes evasive action.

INT. REBEL STAR CRUISER — BRIDGE

A Mon Calamari controller turns away from his screen and calls out to Ackbar, quite excited.

CONTROLLER: Admiral, we have enemy ships in sector 47.

The Admiral turns to the controller.

ACKBAR: It's a trap!

(CONT'D)

CONTINUED

EXT. SPACE – REBEL FLEET

The Millennium Falcon flies into the Imperial trap.

INT. MILLENNIUM FALCON – COCKPIT

LANDO: *(over comlink)* Fighters coming in.

EXT. SPACE

The Millennium Falcon and several squads of Rebel fighters head into an armada of TIE fighters. The sky explodes as a fierce dogfight ensues in and around the giant Rebel cruisers.

INT. REBEL COCKPIT

REBEL PILOT: There's too many of them!

EXT. SPACE

The Millennium Falcon flies through the dogfight.

INT. MILLENNIUM FALCON – COCKPIT

LANDO: Accelerate to attack speed! Draw their fire away from the cruisers.

INT. WEDGE'S X-FIGHTER – COCKPIT

WEDGE: Copy, Gold Leader.

EXT. SPACE – REBEL CRUISER

The battle continues around the giant cruisers.

INT. DEATH STAR – EMPEROR'S THRONE ROOM

Through the round window behind the Emperor's throne can be seen the distant flashes of the space battle in progress.

EMPEROR: Come, boy. See for yourself.

The Emperor is sitting in his throne. Luke moves to look through a small section of the window. Vader also moves forward.

EMPEROR: From here you will witness the final destruction of the Alliance, and the end of your insignificant Rebellion.

Luke is in torment. He glances at this lightsaber sitting on the armrest of the throne. The Emperor watches him and smiles, touches his lightsaber.

EMPEROR: You want this, don't you? The hate is swelling in your now. Take your Jedi weapon. Use it. I am unarmed. Strike me down with it. Give in to your anger. With each passing moment, you make yourself more my servant.

Vader watches Luke in his agony.

LUKE: No!

EMPEROR: It is unavoidable. It is your destiny. You, like your father, are now mine!

EXT. FOREST – GENERATOR BUNKER

Han, Leia, Chewie and the rest of the strike team are led out of the bunker by their captors. The surrounding area, deserted before, is now crowded with two-legged Imperial walkers and hundred of Imperial troops. The situation looks hopeless.

STORMTROOPER: All right, move it! I said move it! Go on!

From the undergrowth beyond the clearing comes Threepio.

THREEPIO: Hello! I say, over there! Were you looking for me?

(CONT'D)

CONTINUED

BUNKER COMMANDER: Bring those two down here.

STORMTROOPER: Let's go.

Artoo and Threepio are standing near one of the big trees. As six Imperial stormtroopers rush over to take them captive, the two droids duck out of sight behind the tree.

THREEPIO: Well, they're on their way. Artoo, are you sure this was good idea?

STORMTROOPER: Freeze! Don't move!

THREEPIO: We surrender.

The stormtroopers come around the tree and find the two droids waiting quietly to be taken. As the Imperial troops move to do that, however, a band of Ewoks drops down from above and overpowers them.

THREEPIO: Ohhh! Stand back, Artoo.

In a nearby tree, an Ewok raises a horn to his lips and sounds the Ewok attack call. All hell breaks loose as hundreds of Ewoks throw their fuzzy bodies into the fray against the assembled stormtroopers and their awesome two-legged walkers.
    Stormtroopers fire on Ewoks with sophisticated weapons while their furry little adversaries sneak up behind the Imperial troopers and bash them over the head with large clubs.
    Ewoks in handmade, primitive hanggliders drop rocks on to the stormtroopers, dive-bombing their deadly adversaries. One is hit in the wing with laser fire and crashes.
    A line of Ewoks hangs desperately to a vine that is hooked to a walker's foot. As the walker moves along, the fuzzy creatures are dragged behind.
    In the confusion of the battle, Han and Leia break away and dive for the cover of the bunker door as explosions erupt around them. Han goes to the bunker door control panel.

LEIA: The code's changed. We need Artoo!

HAN: Here's the terminal.

LEIA: *(into comlink)* Artoo, where are you? We need you at the bunker right away.

Artoo and Threepio are hiding behind a log as the battle rages around them. Suddenly the stubby little astrodroid lets out a series of whistles and shoots off across the battlefield. Threepio, panicked, runs after him.

THREEPIO: Going? What do you mean, you're going? But – but going where, Artoo? No, wait! Artoo! Oh, this is no time for heroics. Come back!

A group of Ewoks has moved a primitive catapult into position. They fire off a large boulder that hits one of the walkers. The walker turns and heads for the catapult, blasting away with both guns. The Ewoks abandon their weapons and flee in all directions.

EXT. OUTER SPACE

The Falcon and other Rebel fighters are engaged in a ferocious combat with Imperial TIE fighters, the battle raging around the cruisers of the Rebel armada.

INT. MILLENNIUM FALCON – COCKPIT

Lando is in radio communication with the pilots of the other Rebel squads.

LANDO: Watch yourself, Wedge! Three from above!

INT. WEDGE'S X-FIGHTER – COCKPIT

WEDGE: Red Three, Red Two, pull in!

INT. RED TWO'S – COCKPIT

RED TWO: Got it!

EXT. SPACE

The dogfight between Rebel X-wings and Imperial TIE fighters rages.

(CONT'D)

CONTINUED

INT. RED THREE'S — COCKPIT

RED THREE: Three of them coming in, twenty degrees!

INT. WEDGE'S X-FIGHTER — COCKPIT

WEDGE: Cut to the left! I'll take the leader!

EXT. SPACE

Wedge shoots down the TIE fighter.

INT. WEDGE'S X-FIGHTER — COCKPIT

WEDGE: They're heading for the medical frigate.

EXT. SPACE

Lando steers the Falcon through a complete flip, as his crew fires at the TIEs from the belly guns.

INT. MILLENNIUM FALCON — COCKPIT

NAVIGATOR: Pressure steady.

EXT. SPACE

The copilot Nien Nunb chatters an observation.

INT. MILLENNIUM FALCON — COCKPIT

The giant Imperial Star Destroyer waits silently some distance from the battle. The Emperor's huge Super Star Destroyer rests in the middle of the fleet.

LANDO: Only the fighters are attacking . . . I wonder what those Star Destroyers are waiting for.

INT. SUPER STAR DESTROYER

Admiral Piett and two fleet commanders watch the battle at the huge window of the Super Star Destroyer bridge.

COMMANDER: We're in attack position now, sir.

PIETT: Hold here.

FLEET COMMANDER: We're not going to attack?

PIETT: I have my orders from the Emperor himself. He has something special planned. We only need to keep them from escaping.

INT. EMPEROR'S TOWER — THRONE ROOM

A worried Luke watches the aerial battle fireworks out of the window as Rebel ships explode against the protective shield.

EMPEROR: As you can see, my young apprentice, your friends have failed. Now witness the firepower of this fully armed and operational battle station. *(into comlink)* Fire at will, Commander.

Luke, in shock, looks out to the Rebel fleet beyond.

INT. DEATH STAR — CONTROL ROOM

A button is pressed, which switches on a panel of lights. Controllers pull back on several switches. A hooded Imperial soldier reaches overhead and pulls a lever. Commander Jerjerrod stands over them.

JERJERROD: Fire!

INT. DEATH STAR — BLAST CHAMBER

A huge beam of light emanates from a long shaft. Two stormtroopers stand to one side at a control panel.

EXT. DEATH STAR

(CONT'D)

CONTINUED

The giant laser dish on the completed half of the Death Star begins to glow. Then a powerful beam shoots out toward the aerial battle.

EXT. SPACE — AIR BATTLE

The air is thick with giant ships. Now an enormous Rebel cruiser is hit by the Death Star beam and blown to dust.

INT. MILLENNIUM FALCON — COCKPIT

The ship is buffeted by the tremendous explosion of the Rebel cruiser. Lano and his copilot are stunned by the sight of the Death Star firepower.

LANDO: That blast came from the Death Star! That thing's operational! *(into comlink)* Home One, this is Gold Leader.

INT. REBEL STAR CRUISER — BRIDGE

Ackbar stands amid the confusion on the wide bridge and speaks into the comlink.

ACKBAR: We saw it. All craft prepare to retreat.

INT. MILLENNIUM FALCON — COCKPIT

LANDO: You won't get another chance at this, Admiral.

INT. REBEL STAR CRUISER — BRIDGE

ACKBAR: We have no choice, General Calrissian. Our cruisers can't repel firepower of that magnitude.

INT. MILLENNIUM FALCON — COCKPIT

LANDO: Han will have that shield down. We've got to give him more time.

EXT. FOREST — GENERATOR BUNKER

Meanwhile, the forest battle is raging, too.

THREEPIO: We're coming!

Artoo and Threepio make it to the door, as Han and Leia provide cover fire.

HAN: Come on! Come on!

The little droid moves to the terminal and plugs in his computer arm.

THREEPIO: Oh, Artoo, hurry!

A large explosion hits near Artoo, knocking him backwards. The stubby astrodroid's head is smoldering. Suddenly there is a loud sprooing and Han and Leia turn around to see Artoo with his his compartment doors open, and all of his appendages sticking out; water and smoke spurt out of the nozzles in his body.

THREEPIO: My goodness! Artoo, why did you have to be so brave?

HAN: Well, I suppose I could hotwire this thing.

Han turns to the terminal.

LEIA: I'll cover you.

A walker lumbers forward, shooting laser blasts at frantic Ewoks running in all directions. Two Ewoks are struck down by laser blasts. One tries to awaken his friend, then realizes he is dead.

EXT. SPACE — DEATH STAR

The Rebel fleet continues to be picked off by the Death Star's deadly beam.

INT. MILLENIUM FALCON — COCKPIT

Lando steers the Falcon wildly through an obstacle course of floating giants. He's been yelling into the comlink.

(CONT'D)

CONTINUED

LANDO: (*desperately*) Yes! I said closer! Move as close as you can and engage those Star Destroyers at point-blank range.

INT. REBEL STAR CRUISER — BRIDGE

ACKBAR: At that close range we won't last long against those Star Destroyers.

INT. MILLENIUM FALCON — COCKPIT

LANDO: We'll last longer than we will against that Death Star ... and we might just take a few of them with us.

EXT. SPACE — IMPERIAL STAR DESTROYER

The Rebel cruisers move very close to the Imperial Star Destroyers and begin to blast away at point-blank range. Tiny fighters race across the giant surfaces, against a backdrop of laser fire.

INT. REBEL COCKPIT

REBEL PILOT: She's gonna blow!

EXT. SPACE

The control tower of a Star Destroyer blows up.

INT. REBEL Y-WING — COCKPIT

Y-WING PILOT: I'm hit!

EXT. SPACE — IMPERIAL STAR DESTROYER

The damaged Y-wing plummets toward a Star Destroyer, and crashes into it, exploding.

INT. EMPEROR'S TOWER — THRONE ROOM

Out of the window and on the viewscreens, the Rebel fleet is being decimated in blinding explosions of light and debris. But in here is no sound of battle. The Emperor speaks to Luke, and Vader watches him.

EMPEROR: Your fleet is lost. And your friends on the Endor moon will not survive. There is no escape, my young apprentice. The Alliance will die ... as will your friends.

Luke's eyes are full of rage.

EMPEROR: Good. I can feel your anger. I am defenseless. Take your weapon! Strike me down with all of your hatred and your journey towards the dark side will be complete.

Luke can resist no longer. The lightsaber flies into his hand. He ignites it in an instant and swings at the Emperor. Vader's lightsaber flashes into view, blocking Luke's blow before it can reach the Emperor. The two blades spark at contact.

EXT. FOREST

The battle rages on.
    Chewie swings on a vine to the roof of one of the walkers. Two Ewoks cling to him. They land with a thud on the top of the lurching machine.
    One of the Ewoks peeks through the window.

WALKER PILOT #1: Look!

WALKER PILOT #2: Get him off of there!

The walker pilot opens the hatch to see what's going on. He is yanked out and tossed overboard before he can scream. The two Ewoks jump into the cockpit and knock the second pilot unconscious. As the mighty machine careens out of control, outside Chewie is almost knocked overboard; he sticks his head into the hatch with a series of angry barks. The Ewoks are too busy and frightened to listen to the Wookiee's complaint. Chewie slips inside the walker.
    Chewbacca's walker moves through the forest, destroying another Imperial walker, and firing laser blasts at unsuspecting stormtroopers. The Ewoks shout and cheer as the giant machine helps turn the tide of the battle in their favor.

(CONT'D)

CONTINUED

A speeder bike chases Ewoks through the underbrush. As the scout rounds a tree, he is knocked off his bike by a vine tied between two trees.

As a walker moves in, Ewoks cut vines restraining two huge logs that swing down and smash the walker's head flat.

A walker marches through the undergrowth blasting Ewoks as it goes. An Ewok warrior gives the signal, and a pile of logs is cut loose. The logs tumble under the walker's feet, causing it to slip and slide until it finally topples over with a great crash.

A scout bike races past and is lassoed with a heavy vine. The other end of the vine is tied to a tree, and the bike swings around in ever-tightening circles until it runs out of rope and crashes into the tree with a huge explosion.

EXT. FOREST – GENERATOR BUNKER

Han works furiously at the control panel as he attempts to hotwire the door. Leia is covering him.

HAN: I think I got it. I got it!

As the connection is made, with loud squeaks, a second door slides across in front of the first.

Han frowns and turns back to the wires again. Leia suddenly cries out in pain, her shoulder hit by a laser blast.

THREEPIO: Oh, Princess Leia, are you all right?

HAN: Let's see.

LEIA: It's not bad.

STORMTROOPER: *(offscreen)* Freeze!

They freeze.

THREEPIO: Oh, dear.

STORMTROOPER: Don't move!

Leia holds her laser gun ready, behind Han, out of view of the two stormtroopers moving toward them. Han and Leia's eyes lock; the moment seems suspended in time.

HAN: I love you.

Another shared look between them, as she smiles up at Han.

LEIA: I know.

STORMTROOPER: Hands up! Stand up!

Han turns slowly, revealing the gun in Leia's hand. She disposes of the stormtroopers in a flash. As Han turns back to Leia, he looks up to see a giant walker approach and stand before him, its deadly weapons aimed right at him.

HAN: *(to Leia)* Stay back.

The hatch on top of the walker opens and Chewie sticks his head out and barks triumphantly.

HAN: Chewie! Get down here! She's wounded! No, wait … I got an idea.

INT. EMPEROR'S TOWER – THRONE ROOM

Luke and Vader are engaged in a man-to-man duel of lightsabers even more vicious than the battle on Bespin. But the young Jedi has grown stronger in the interim, and now the advantage shifts to him. Vader is forced back, losing his balance, and is knocked down the stairs. Luke stands at the top of the stairs, ready to attack.

EMPEROR: *(laughing)* Good. Use your aggressive feelings, boy! Let the hate flow through you.

Luke looks momentarily back at the Emperor, then back to Vader, and realizes he is using the dark side. He turns off his lightsaber, and relaxes, driving the hate from his being.

VADER: Obi-Wan has taught you well.

(CONT'D)

CONTINUED

LUKE: I will not fight you, Father.

Vader walks back up the stairs to Luke.

VADER: You are unwise to lower your defenses.

Vader attacks, forcing Luke on the defensive. The young Jedi leaps in an amazing reverse flip up to the safety of the catwalk overhead. Vader stands below him.

LUKE: Your thoughts betray you, Father. I feel the good in you ... the conflict.

VADER: There is no conflict.

LUKE: You couldn't bring yourself to kill me before and I don't believe you'll destroy me now.

VADER: You underestimate the power of the dark side. If you will not fight, then you will meet your destiny.

Vader throws the laser sword and it cuts through the supports holding the catwalk, then returns to Vader's hand. Luke tumbles to the ground in a shower of sparks and rolls out of sight under the Emperor's platform. Vader moves to find him.

EMPEROR: *(laughs)* Good. Good.

EXT. SPACE — AIR BATTLE

The two armadas, like their sea-bound ancestors, blast away at each other in individual point-blank confrontations. The Falcon and several fighters attack one of the larger Imperial ships.

INT. MILLENNIUM FALCON — COCKPIT

LANDO: Watch out. Squad at point oh-six.

INT. REBEL COCKPIT

REBEL PILOT: I'm on it, Gold Leader.

INT. WEDGE'S X-FIGHTER — COCKPIT

WEDGE: Good shot, Red Two.

EXT. SPACE

The dogfight rages.

INT. MILLENNIUM FALCON — COCKPIT

LANDO: Now ... come on, Han, old buddy. Don't let me down.

EXT. FOREST — GENERATOR BUNKER

Chewie's walker stands in front of the door to the bunker.

INT. BUNKER CONTROL ROOM

Controllers watch the main viewscreen on which a vague figure of an Imperial walker pilot can be seen. There is a great deal of static and interference.

HAN/PILOT: *(voice-over)* It's over, Commander. The Rebels have been routed. They're fleeing into the woods. We need reinforcements to continue the pursuit.

The controllers are delighted.

CONTROL ROOM COMMANDER: Send three squads to help. Open the back door.

SECOND COMMANDER: Sir.

EXT. FOREST — GENERATOR BUNKER

As the door to the bunker opens and the Imperial troops rush out, they're surprised to find themselves surrounded by Rebels, their weapons pointed at them. Ewoks holding bows and arrows appear on the roof of the bunker.

(CONT'D)

CONTINUED

INT. BUNKER

Han, Chewie and several troops have rushed into the control room and plant explosive charges on the control panels.

HAN: Throw me another charge.

INT. EMPEROR'S TOWER – THRONE ROOM

Vader stalks the low-ceilinged area on the level below the throne, searching for Luke in the semi-darkness, his lightsaber held ready.

VADER: You cannot hide for ever, Luke.

LUKE: I will not fight you.

VADER: Give yourself to the dark side. It is the only way you can save your friends.

Luke shuts his eyes tightly, in anguish.

VADER: Yes, your thoughts betray you. Your feelings for them are strong. Especially for . . .

Vader stops and senses something.

VADER: Sister! So . . . you have a twin sister. Your feelings have now betrayed her too. Obi-Wan was wise to hide her from me. Now his failure is complete. If you will not turn to the dark side, then perhaps she will.

Luke ignites his lightsaber and screams in anger.

LUKE: No!

He rushes at his father with a frenzy we have not seen before. Sparks fly as Luke and Vader fight in the cramped area.
    Luke's hatred forces Vader to retreat out of the low area and across a bridge overlooking a vast elevator shaft. Each stroke of Luke's sword drives his father further toward defeat.
    The Dark Lord is knocked to his knees, and as he raises his sword to block of another onslaught, Luke slashes Vader's right hand off at the wrist, causing metal and electronic parts to fly from the mechanical stump. Vader's sword clatters uselessly away, over the edge of the platform and into the bottomless shaft below. Luke moves over Vader and holds the blade of his sword to the Dark Lord's throat. The Emperor watches with uncontrollable, pleased agitation.

EMPEROR: Good! Your hate has made you powerful. Now, fulfill your destiny and take your father's place at my side!

Luke looks at his father's mechanical hand, then to his own mechanical, black-gloved hand, and realizes how much he is becoming like his father. He makes the decision for which he has spent a lifetime in preparation. Luke switches off his lightsaber.

LUKE: Never!

Luke casts his lightsaber away.

LUKE: I'll never turn to the dark side. You've failed, Your Highness. I am a Jedi, like my father before me.

The Emperor's glee turns to rage.

EMPEROR: So be it . . . Jedi.

EXT. FOREST – GENERATOR BUNKER

Han and Rebel fighters run out of the bunker and race across the clearing.

HAN: Move! Move! Move!

The bunker explodes, followed by a spectacular display as the huge shield-generator radar dish explodes along with the bunker.

INT. REBEL STAR CRUISER – BRIDGE

(CONT'D)

CONTINUED

Ackbar, sitting in his control chair, speaks into the radio.

ACKBAR: The shield is down! Commence attack on the Death Star's main reactor.

INT. MILLENNIUM FALCON – COCKPIT

LANDO: We're on our way. Red Group, Gold Group, all fighters follow me.
(laughs) Told you they'd do it!

EXT. SPACE – DEATH STAR SURFACE

The Falcon, followed by several smaller Rebel fighters, heads toward the unfinished superstructure of the Death Star.

INT. EMPEROR'S TOWER – THRONE ROOM

Luke stands still, as the Emperor faces him at the bottom of the stairs.

EMPEROR: If you will not be turned, you will be destroyed.

The Emperor raises his arms toward Luke. Blinding bolts of energy, evil lightning, shoot from the Emperor's hands at Luke with such speed and power the young Jedi shrinks before them, his knees buckling.
   The wounded Vader struggles to his feet, and moves to stand at his master's side.

EMPEROR: Young fool ... only now, at the end, do you understand.

Luke is almost unconscious beneath the continuing assault of the Emperor's lightning. He clutches a canister to keep from falling into the bottomless shaft as the bolts tear through him.

EMPEROR: Your feeble skills are no match for the power of the dark side. You have paid for the price of your lack of vision.

Luke writhes on the floor in unbearable pain, reaching weakly up toward where Vader stands watching.

LUKE: *(groans)* Father, please. Help me.

Again Vader stands, watching Luke. He looks at his master, the Emperor, then back to Luke on the floor.

EMPEROR: Now, young Skywalker ... you will die.

Although it would not have seemed possible, the outpouring of bolts from the Emperor's fingers actually increases in intensity, the sound screaming through the room. Luke's body writhes in pain.
   Vader grabs the Emperor from behind, fighting for control of the robed figure, despite the Dark Lord's weakened body and gravely weakened arm. The Emperor struggles in his embrace, his bolt-shooting hands now lifted high, away from Luke. Now the white lightning arcs back to strike at Vader. He stumbles with his load as the sparks rain off his helmet and flow down over his black cape. He holds his evil master high over his head and walks to the edge of the abyss at the central core of the throne room. With one final burst of his once awesome strength, Darth Vader hurls the Emperor's body into the bottomless shaft.
   The Emperor's body spins helplessly into the void, arcing as it falls into the abyss.
   Finally, when the body is far down the shaft, it explodes creating a rush of air through the room. Vader has collapsed beside the bottomless hole. Luke crawls to his father's side and pulls him away from the edge of the abyss to safety. Both the young Jedi and the giant warrior are too weak to move.

EXT./INT. SPACE BATTLE – FIGHTERS AND DEATH STAR

Rebel fighters accompany the Falcon across the surface of the Death Star to the unfinished portion, where they dive into the superstructure of the giant battle station, followed by TIE fighters.

WEDGE: I'm going in.

LANDO: Here goes nothing.

The X-wing leads the chase through the ever-narrowing shaft, followed by the Falcon and four other fighters, plus TIE fighters who continually fire at the Rebels.
   Lights reflect off the pilots' faces as they race through the dark shaft.

LANDO: Now lock on to the strongest power source. It should be the power generator.

(CONT'D)

CONTINUED

WEDGE: Form up. And stay alert. We could run out of space real fast.

The fighters and the Falcon race through the tunnel, still pursued by the TIE fighters. One of the X-wings is hit from behind and explodes.

LANDO: Split up and head back to the surface. And see if you can get a few of those TIE fighters to follow you.

PILOT: Copy, Gold Leader.

The Rebel ships peel off pursued by four of the TIEs, while Lando and Wedge continue through the main tunnel. It narrows, and the Falcon scrapes the side dangerously. Two other TIE fighters continue to chase them.

LANDO: That was too close.

Nien Nunb agrees.

INT. REBEL STAR CRUISER – BRIDGE

The battle between the Rebel and Imperial fleets rages on.

ACKBAR: We've got to give those fighters more time. Concentrate all fire on that Super Star Destroyer.

EXT. SPACE

Rebel craft fire at the giant Super Star Destroyer.

INT. VADER'S STAR DESTROYER – BRIDGE

CONTROLLER: Sir, we've lost our bridge deflector shields.

Admiral Piett and a commander stand at the window. They look concerned.

PIETT: Intensify the forward batteries. I don't want anything to get through.

EXT. SPACE

Outside the window a damaged Rebel fighter is out of control and heading directly toward the bridge.

INT. VADER'S STAR DESTROYER – BRIDGE

PIETT: Intensify forward firepower!

INT. REBEL FIGHTER COCKPIT

The Rebel pilot screams.

INT. VADER'S STAR DESTROYER – BRIDGE

COMMANDER: Too late!

The Rebel ships hits the Star Destroyer, causing a huge explosion.

EXT. SPACE

The giant battleship loses control.

INT. REBEL STAR CRUISER

There is excitement on the bridge as the battle rages on all sides. They cheer as the giant Star Destroyer is destroyed.

EXT. SPACE – SURFACE OF DEATH STAR

The giant Star Destroyer crashes into the Death Star, and explodes.

INT. DEATH STAR – MAIN DOCKING BAY

Chaos. For the first time, the Death Star is rocked by explosions as the Rebel fleet, no longer backed against a wall, zooms over, unloading a heavy barrage. Imperial troops run in all directions, confused and desperate to escape.

In the midst of this uproar, Luke is trying to carry the enormous deadweight of his father's weakening body

(CONT'D)

CONTINUED

toward an Imperial shuttle. Finally, Luke collapses from the strain. The explosions grow louder as Vader draws him closer.

VADER: Luke, help me take this mask off.

LUKE: But you'll die.

VADER: Nothing can stop that now. Just for once let me look on you with my own eyes.

Slowly, hesitantly, Luke removes the mask from his father's face. There beneath the scars is an elderly man. His eyes do not focus. But the dying man smiles at the sight before him.

ANAKIN: *(very weak)* Now ... go, my son. Leave me.

LUKE: No. You're coming with me. I'll not leave you here. I've got to save you.

ANAKIN: You already have, Luke. You were right. You were right about me. Tell your sister ... you were right.

LUKE: Father ... I won't leave you.

Darth Vader, Anakin Skywalker ... Luke's father dies.

EXT. DEATH STAR

A lone X-wing is just in front of the Millennium Falcon on its swerving bomb run through the immense superstructure of the half-built Death Star. They are pursued by TIE fighters.

INT. WEDGE'S X-FIGHTER – COCKPIT

WEDGE: There it is!

EXT. DEATH STAR

The Rebels home in on the main reactor shaft. It is awesome.

INT. FALCON COCKPIT

LANDO: All right, Wedge. Go for the power regulator on the north tower.

INT. WEDGE'S X-FIGHTER – COCKPIT

WEDGE: Copy, Gold Leader. I'm already on my way out.

EXT. DEATH STAR

The X-wing heads for the top of the huge reactor and fires several proton torpedoes at the power regulator, causing a series of small explosions.
The Falcon heads for the main reactor, and Lando fires the missiles, which shoot out of the Falcon with a powerful roar, and hit directly at the center of the main reactor.

INT. FALCON COCKPIT

Lando winces at the dangerously close explosion.

EXT. DEATH STAR

He maneuvers the Falcon out of the winding superstructure just ahead of the continuing chain of explosions.

INT. REBEL STAR CRUISER

Ackbar leans on the railing of the bridge, watching the large screen showing the Death Star in the main briefing room.

ACKBAR: Move the fleet away from the Death Star.

EXT/INT. DEATH STAR – IMPERIAL SHUTTLE

An Imperial shuttle, with Luke at the controls, rockets out of the main docking bay as that entire section of the Death Star is blown away.

INT. WEDGE'S X-FIGHTER – COCKPIT

(CONT'D)

CONTINUED

Wedge is relieved to escape the Death Star.

EXT/INT. DEATH STAR – FALCON COCKPIT

Finally, just as it looks like the Falcon will not make it, Lando expertly pilots the craft out of the exploding superstructure and whizzes toward the Santuary Moon, only a moment before the Death Star super-novas into oblivion.

INT. MILLENNIUM FALCON – COCKPIT

Lando and Nien Nunb laugh and cheer in relief.

EXT. SPACE

The Death Star super-novas into oblivion behind the Falcon.

EXT. ENDOR FOREST

Han and Leia, Chewie, the droids, the Rebel troops and the Ewoks all look to the sky as the Death Star reveals itself in a final flash of self-destruction. They all cheer.

THREEPIO: They did it!

Han looks down from the sky to Leia, a look of concern on his face. Leia continues to look at the sky as though listening for a silent voice.

HAN: I'm sure Luke wasn't on that thing when it blew.

LEIA: He wasn't. I can feel it.

HAN: You love him, don't you?

Leia smiles, puzzled.

LEIA: Yes.

HAN: All right. I understand. Fine. When he comes back, I won't get in the way.

She realizes his misunderstanding.

LEIA: Oh. No, it's not like that at all. He's my brother.

Han is stunned by this news. She smiles, and they embrace.

EXT. ENDOR FOREST – NIGHT

Luke sets a torch to the logs stacked under the funeral pyre where his father's body lies, again dressed in the black mask and helmet. He stands, watching sadly, as the flames leap higher to consume Darth Vader – Anakin Skywalker.
    In the sky above, fireworks explode and Rebel fighters zoom above the forest.

EXT. EWOK VILLAGE SQUARE – NIGHT

A huge bonfire is the centerpiece of a wild celebration. Rebels and Ewoks rejoice in the warm glow of firelight, drums beating, singing, dancing, and laughing in the communal language of victory and liberation.
    Lando runs in and is enthusiastically hugged by Han and Chewie. Then, finally, Luke arrives and the friends rush to greet and embrace him.
    They stand close, this hardy group, taking comfort in each other's touch, together to the end.
    Rebels and Ewoks join together in dancing and celebration. The original group of adventurers watches from the sidelines. Only Luke seems distracted, alone in their midst, his thoughts elsewhere.
    He looks off to the side and sees three shimmering, smiling figures at the edge of the shadows: Ben Kenobi, Yoda, and Anakin Skywalker.

FADE OUT

END CREDITS OVER STAR FIELD

THE END

(CONT'D)

THE OFFICIAL
Formula 1™
SEASON REVIEW 2007
FOREWORD BY BERNIE ECCLESTONE

Published in November 2007

A catalogue record for this book is available from the British Library

ISBN 978 1 84425 453 8

Library of Congress control no. 2007931176

Editor Bruce Jones
Managing Editor Steve Rendle

Design Lee Parsons, Richard Parsons

Contributors Adam Cooper (overview and grand prix reports), Tony Dodgins (round table, technical review and grand prix sidebars)

Photographs All by LAT (Steven Tee, Lorenzo Bellanca, Charles Coates, Glenn Dunbar and Andrew Ferraro)
Group Operations Manager LAT Tim Wright

Technical illustrations Paul Laguette
www.studiopdesign.com
Illustrations Alan Eldridge

Publishing Manager Nairn Miller
Publishing Directors Peter Higham, Mark Hughes

Published by Haynes Publishing
in association with Haymarket Consumer Media

Haynes Publishing, Sparkford, Yeovil,
Somerset BA22 7JJ, UK
Tel: +44 (0) 1963 442030
Fax: +44 (0) 1963 440001
E-mail: sales@haynes.co.uk
Website: www.haynes.co.uk

Haymarket Consumer Media, Teddington Studios,
Broom Road, Teddington, Middlesex TW11 9BE, UK
Tel: +44 (0) 208 267 5000
Fax: +44 (0) 208 267 5022
E-mail: F1Review@haymarket.com
Website: www.haymarket.com

Printed and bound by J. H. Haynes & Co. Ltd,
Sparkford, Yeovil, Somerset BA22 7JJ, UK

CONTENTS

FOREWORD

So much went on during the year. This World Championship was a bit different to normal, with all the scandals and so on. The spy story kept people talking. I wish it hadn't happened, but it did, and we lived with it. And that's what it's all about really, the public like to read about things like that.

The nice thing is that the best race we've had for a long time was the last race, because that's what people remember. A finish like that is always my dream. It was about as close as you can get – I've always said we wanted the result on the last corner of the last lap, and that's more or less what we got.

Kimi has done a good job this year, and he's won six races. I hope he starts making himself more available and talking to people. He was very good in the TV interview after Brazil – he hasn't spoken as much in the whole year! I've always thought that he's been under his shadow and he'll come out when necessary, and I hope that's what happens. He's a super guy.

I was disappointed for Felipe, because he certainly had the ability and everything, but he was a bit unfortunate.

In some ways, it's good for Lewis that he didn't win the title, and obviously in some ways it's not good. He's got a lot of attention this year, which he deserves. In the end, it's not so terrible that he didn't win, because what can he do after that? Whereas, at the moment, he's going to be wanting to win the World Championship next year, and everybody will be following it.

Fernando put himself under a lot of pressure, and was put under a lot of pressure. So he was never really that relaxed, as he was in the past. When he was at Renault, he was very relaxed and laid back. I used to pop into their motorhome an hour before the race and he was playing cards with Briatore. I told him: "When you get to McLaren, it won't be like that!"

BMW have done a good job and are clearly going to be a nuisance to the top teams next year. Some of the others have got to pull their socks up. It's usually a people problem.

As for the new drivers, Kovalainen looks good, and I think Vettel has got an awful lot of talent, and that will eventually show through. But there are quite a few young guys out there that we don't even think about yet who will get the job done.

Fuji turned out alright, and Valencia and Singapore are both going to be good – Singapore is going to be interesting because it's a night race. Overall, I think next year is going to be very good, and I am already looking forward to it. Meanwhile, enjoy the story of 2007!

BERNIE ECCLESTONE

THE SEASON

When competition heats up, things can get nasty. And it's safe to say that this is how it was between Ferrari and McLaren in 2007, with great racing and a spying scandal too

The 2007 FIA Formula One World Championship will be remembered as one of the most competitive for some time, and also one of the most controversial. The season was dominated by the spying scandal, the first signs of which were seen in the season-opening Australian GP, when McLaren challenged the legality of Ferrari's floor.

It was only much later that we learned that the team had been receiving information from Nigel Stepney, and that the Ferrari Race and Test Technical Manager's relationship with McLaren Chief Designer Mike Coughlan had subsequently become far more involved, leading to a complete breakdown in the frosty relationship between the two teams.

The bottom line was that just before the Belgian GP in September McLaren was thrown out of the constructors' championship, and given an unprecedented $100 million fine. Thankfully, the drivers' contest was not affected.

And what a fight it was. It was apparent from the very start of the season that the top two teams had drivers capable of winning races, and thus we would have a four-way fight for the title and no team orders. It became a three-way fight with just a couple of

The battle between Ferrari and McLaren at the front was echoed all the way down the grid

Everyone breathed a sigh of relief when Robert Kubica survived this dreadful accident in Canada

Bernie Ecclestone continues to be the heartbeat of the paddock

Lewis Hamilton wasn't the only rookie who flew. Watch out for Toro Rosso's Sebastian Vettel in 2008

grands prix to go as Felipe Massa lost ground, and the final outcome could hardly be closer as Kimi Räikkönen edged McLaren's Lewis Hamilton and Fernando Alonso by a point apiece.

There is no question that Räikkönen is a deserving World Champion. He won the opening race in Melbourne's Albert Park, but then had a rough time in the first third of the season before things began to go his way. He qualified on pole position on only three occasions, but six wins put him two ahead of any of his rivals. He also steered blissfully clear of any controversy by cocooning himself away from any outside pressures and focusing on the things that mattered to him: driving racing cars and enjoying himself when away from the paddock.

In truth, it should have been the year of his team-mate Massa. The Brazilian qualified more often on pole and scored three great victories before handing what would have been his fourth to Räikkönen at Interlagos. But a string of unfortunate problems cost him dearly, including a retirement in Italy and qualifying dramas in Australia and Hungary. Massa also got himself disqualified with a silly mistake in Canada. Had things fallen his way, he could have been Ferrari's main contender in the closing races, but the chance slipped away. Massa's turn could come next year, but it's hard to escape the fact that Räikkönen's title could make him the team's main focus.

It was an incredible season for McLaren, too, and yet the team ended it empty-handed. What looked on paper like a dream team of a double World Champion and an eager rookie proved to be anything but when Hamilton made it clear from the start of the season that he was not intending to play a supporting role. And why should he? Hamilton was seriously fast from the off, and that rattled Alonso.

Hamilton did very little wrong for the bulk of the season, performing brilliantly both in and out of the car. Two wins on the North American leg of the world tour suggested that he really could hang on to the points lead he established early on. Things began to go awry a little in Hungary, where he won, but only after contributing to a major controversy in qualifying when he ignored team instructions.

Hamilton's title challenge was finally derailed by his awful mistake in the Chinese GP, when he slid into a gravel trap in the pit entry on impossibly worn tyres, and then he fluffed the first lap in Brazil before a gearbox glitch then cost him the championship. It was the only gremlin he suffered in a race all year.

It would be cruel to accuse Hamilton of cracking at the critical time, because he had thrived on enormous pressure all season and done a far better job than anyone could possibly have expected. We can only guess at how strong he will be next year, having learned so much in 2007.

As time went by, Alonso became increasingly convinced that the team was being built around Hamilton, and he made little effort to integrate himself in the camp. He regularly dropped dark hints to the media about his treatment, and then in Hungary he tried to put McLaren boss Ron Dennis in a difficult position by revealing that he had some evidence

relating to the spying scandal – a move that led directly to the FIA's sanctions. After that, it seemed that his relationship with the team was no longer tenable but, with a world title at stake, everyone ploughed on.

On track, there were some fantastic drives and Alonso took four wins, the most spectacular coming at the Nürburgring, but there were also some pedestrian performances where the Spaniard made little impact. Apart from qualifying for the French GP, when a ceramic bearing failed, he had no real technical gremlins and his only real mistake was a crash in Japan at a very critical time.

The rise of BMW Sauber was one of the more positive stories of 2007. In only the second year with manufacturer support, the team produced a car that shone in testing and was on the pace from the opening race in Australia to the last in Brazil. Nick Heidfeld and Robert Kubica knew that they could go to every race expecting to finish fifth and sixth, and then take advantage of any slip-ups ahead.

That happened on many occasions, and a string of fourth places showed that the team was usually close enough to deal with any McLaren/Ferrari stragglers. Heidfeld was particularly fast in Canada, where he

RULE CHANGES FOR 2007

As ever, a raft of rule changes gave the 11 Formula One teams much to think about over the winter of 2006–07, and some of these changes proved to have more significant consequences than others.

The FIA had put a block on engine development in order to keep costs in check, and thus each manufacturer had to hand over a 'reference' engine to the sport's governing body at the end of the 2006 season. They were allowed to make some modifications to adjust to a new 19,000rpm rev limit, and those changes were submitted in December. In fact, once the season was underway, engines were barely mentioned.

More significantly, Michelin's withdrawal left Bridgestone as sole tyre supplier a full year before the rules mandated that only one brand was to be allowed. Working in conjunction with the Japanese tyre manufacturer, the FIA came up with regulations that made sense for all concerned.

Bridgestone produced just four types of dry tyre – supersoft, soft, medium and hard – and decreed which two types of tyres were to be used as prime and option tyres at each venue. Crucially, each driver had to use both types of tyre at some stage during the grand prix (although, if wet tyres were used at any time, the rule no longer applied).

Early in the season, a white stripe around the circumference of the tyre was introduced to make identification easier for all concerned and to help television viewers to understand precisely what was going on and thus get more out of their spectating.

Each driver had 14 sets of dry tyres per grand prix meeting. Two sets of each tyre specification had to be returned to Bridgestone after Friday practice, which was a ploy that encouraged teams to take to the track rather than while away practice time in their garages (as did the fact that the two-race engines did not have to be used until Saturday).

New safety car rules were perhaps the biggest headache for the teams. For 2007, after the safety car message had been displayed, no car could enter the pitlane for the purpose of refuelling until the pitlane was declared open. Any driver whose car was already in the pit entry when the signal was displayed was allowed to refuel, and drivers could come in for repairs or to change tyres if they had been involved in an incident or had run over debris. Once the cars were stacked up behind the safety car, everyone was allowed to refuel.

Anyone who was forced to come into the pits to refuel before the pitlane was open again, or did so for strategic reasons, received a 10 second stop-and-go penalty. The first victims of this new punishment were Fernando Alonso and Nico Rosberg in the Canadian GP.

Another regulation change for 2007 saw lapped cars being waved around to rejoin at the back of the queue behind the safety car, a bonus handed to none other than Lewis Hamilton at the Nürburgring.

earned second place on merit. The downside was poor reliability that cost both drivers good results.

The first post-Alonso year was always going to be tough for Renault, but matters were not helped by the switch from Michelin to Bridgestone tyres, as the team had been so close to the French supplier. In addition, there were wind tunnel issues that contributed to flaws that made the car inconsistent and difficult to drive.

It did get better, but the dip in form was a massive disappointment to Giancarlo Fisichella, who saw his chances of succeeding Alonso as a title contender disappear at the start of the season. He had a terrible year and was left struggling for a seat at the end of it, but rookie Heikki Kovalainen did a superb job after an uncertain start, regularly picking up points and taking a brilliant second place in the rain in Japan.

Williams joined forces with Toyota and took a step towards recovering respectability after a disappointing 2006. Reliability was better but still not perfect, and the car was always hovering around the lower reaches of the top 10, at least in Nico Rosberg's hands. Despite getting few spectacular results, the German did his reputation much good with his consistent performances. However, he finished the career of

ABOVE The similarity between the Honda and the Super Aguri was at the heart of the customer-car debate

OPPOSITE McLaren rookie Lewis Hamilton brought legions of new fans to Formula One, boosting the gate at the British GP in particular

Alexander Wurz, who could not consistently match his pace. The Austrian veteran, however, did know how to bring the car home, earning a priceless third place in Canada and a fourth in Germany.

Red Bull Racing had a terrible time with reliability, and the situation didn't improve over the course of the year. That proved very expensive as it cost the team the chance to beat Williams. Mark Webber was a regular top 10 qualifier and took an excellent third in the rain at the Nürburgring, while David Coulthard, like Wurz, showed his considerable experience by bringing home points when they were on offer, notably in Spain, Germany and Japan. The new partnership with Renault worked well, and RBR sometimes even outran the factory team.

Toyota endured a disastrous season that saw the team score just 13 points and never finish higher than sixth. As ever, Jarno Trulli could put in a quick lap and was usually in the top 10, but race performances were often mediocre, and a poor launch system didn't help. Ralf Schumacher was a marginal presence for much of the season, but occasionally woke up and put in a respectable drive, notably in Hungary.

Scuderia Toro Rosso made a big step forward by having access to technology from its sister team – Red Bull Racing – but again reliability suffered and it took time for the developments to filter through. Scott Speed fell out with the team and was dropped after Germany, but Vitantonio Liuzzi bolstered his reputation with some solid drives. However, he was outshone at season's end by Sebastian Vettel, who went from hero to zero in Japan when he crashed out of third, then back to hero with fourth in China, where Liuzzi backed him up in sixth. Eight points in a day were worth their weight in gold. Like Super Aguri, the team had been under the dark cloud of the customer car row all year.

If Toyota had a poor season, Honda's was positively catastrophic. The 'earth car' concept was laudable, but alas the team had made fundamental errors at the design stage and the car was saddled with an aero problem that was partially addressed but never really went away. In essence, the aero balance moved when the car pitched, making it incredibly inconsistent on braking and turn-in. Jenson Button and Rubens Barrichello struggled manfully throughout the year, and often couldn't even get out of Q1. Button scraped home eighth in France and Italy and then took sixth place in China, but Barrichello failed to score at all.

Very often the Honda team was humbled by Super Aguri Racing, who moved from an ancient Arrows chassis to an update of Honda's RA106 that proved to be far more effective than the works RA107. Takuma Sato made it into Q3 in Australia and followed up with an eighth-place finish in Spain and sixth in Canada, where he actually passed Fernando Alonso on the road. Anthony Davidson was frequently quicker in qualifying but didn't get the breaks in the races. Then budget problems hit development, and the team was less competitive in the latter part of the season.

The opposite was true for Spyker, who had a new engine partner in Ferrari and a new technical boss in Mike Gascoyne. Much effort went into a B-spec car that first appeared at the Italian GP and allowed impressive rookie Adrian Sutil to run in midfield at Spa and take a point in Fuji. The German was often involved in incidents as he pushed harder than the car would allow, but it was Christijan Albers who lost his job mid-season after struggling to match his team-mate, and he was replaced by Sakon Yamamoto, who did better than many expected.

Next year sees the arrival of a common ECU, and thus the absence of traction control. It's going to be fascinating to see who gains and who loses from that dramatic change…

THE PANEL

ROUND TABLE

Formula 1 always elicits debate, and here are the insiders' thoughts on prize money, chassis-sharing, how best to encourage overtaking, Lewis Hamilton and spying

To talk over the many highs and lows, as well as the leading trends and topics of 2007, we assembled an eight-man panel in the Spyker hospitality area at the Belgian GP. Look at their job titles and it's clear that they cover the whole gamut of individual involvement.

There's a driver (Red Bull's Mark Webber/MW), top management (McLaren's Martin Whitmarsh/MWH, Toyota's John Howett/JH and Super Aguri's Daniele Audetto/DA), car shapers (Spyker's Mike Gascoyne/MG and Renault's Pat Symonds/PS), a driver-turned-television commentator (Martin Brundle/MB) and a journalist (Mark Hughes/MH). Fellow journalist Tony Dodgins/TD made them take time out from their regular jobs at the Belgian GP and asked the questions.

TD: *Mark, have the cars felt different this year, with spec Bridgestone tyres and the 19,000rpm limit?*

MW: From the cockpit, it's just lower grip levels in slow and medium speed corners. Aerodynamically, the cars are still very strong.

TD: *Does anyone feel that taking away two competitive variables – tyres and engine competition – made it even harder to overtake in 2007?*

MW: I think that one of the biggest things to help overtaking was when you had different strengths at different parts of the lap. The last sector at Magny-Cours, for example, was traditionally a bad one for Bridgestone, but they were quick in the middle sector, which made it interesting car to car. On spec' tyres you lose that and we can't turn up the engines anymore. You need to have a performance advantage, for whatever reason, to overtake.

MB: Yeah, with the 19,000rpm limit you can see people running out of revs when they get in the slipstream, and I do feel that taking away tyre competition has taken a level of interest and uncertainty from the weekend.

MG: If you are a team like us at the back, one of the things we were able to do with the old tyre situation was to run softer ones because we were easier on them. Taking that away has undoubtedly made our lives more difficult.

BELOW **Red Bull racer Mark Webber checks to see that his point has been understood by all**

TD: *John, these things tend to be done for cost reasons. Do you think it has been a good move, or do you feel the racing has suffered as a result?*

JH: Testing-wise it has had a fairly big impact on cost. Before, we used to wear grooves in the tracks testing tyres and not always doing a lot of development on the car. But I don't think limiting the engines to 19,000rpm makes much difference to cost at all.

TD: *So you'd have preferred to keep freedom of development?*

JH: Yes, a degree of freedom of development. We are great believers that technology doesn't always cost money and sometimes it's cheaper.

TD: *Does anyone have any strong feeling about the Overtaking Working Group (OWG)?*

MB: I think they've established that a lot of the changes over the past decade were going the wrong way. Once all the addenda to bodywork, to give downforce or reduce drag, gets in turbulence, you can see the drivers struggling.

MW: Yeah, the wake is massive.

MH: Is it noticeably worse this year than last?

MW: We were blaming our car, but then you hear other guys saying they can't get close enough. I think some of the teams don't understand the stability issue in traffic.

MWH: I think the OWG is positive, because it's the first time that there has been some properly funded technical work aimed at solving the problems. It's good that Renault, McLaren and Ferrari are working well together and taking a sensible approach. There is a proper process: analysis and wind-tunnel testing and then understanding that in the simulator. You will never get it to the level of where the driver can come up behind a car and not feel any effect from the hole that the car ahead is punching though the air, but we can make it better, and I do think that the OWG will achieve that. It's a good initiative and the sort of thing we should be reproducing for all sorts of other affairs, both technical and commercial, in F1.

TD: *With aerodynamics blamed for overtaking problems and the sport open to environmental backlash, should we spend so much time in wind tunnels?*

MG: Well, you're always going to spend all your time on the thing that gives you performance and even if you halve the amount of downforce it is still going to be the most significant thing you've got to make the car quicker. I think the work done by Jean Claude Migeot at Fondmetal has been good. They have made progress and, as Martin said, shown that we have made things significantly worse over the last 10 years. The drivers reported that when we moved the front wing up. But, rather than make huge changes to the cars, we ought to implement those which are fairly simple and cost-effective, as soon as possible, and see what results we get before doing anything a lot more radical.

MH: Is [FIA President] Max Mosley's stated aim of trying to get it so that you have a car behind intrinsically faster than the one in front, realistic?

MG: What you can do is reduce the downforce loss and especially reduce the balance change, so if you are in a car that's quicker you may be losing downforce but you may still have the same as the car in front and don't get a massive balance change. The work that was done on the CDG wing showed that the thing would have been on an absolute knife-edge. There was a sweet spot where it supposedly worked, but you had to be under half-a-car-length behind. Drop a metre further back and the balance of the car changed by 20% and you lost 30% of your downforce. So, unless you were incredibly brave and barrelled in right behind someone, it was never going to work. The work done is definitely going to be an improvement, but whether it will be enough is a different matter.

MW: You have to get the balance right as well. The slipstreaming with the wide tyres they had in the past worked a lot better, but the cars are a lot more efficient now and so the tow is not as good. But you don't want it like the IRL [Indy Racing League], when they tried that very draggy wing where you've got guys passing each other a thousand times a lap. I've raced Formula Ford at Bathurst and you cannot pull away from people, even if you are a second a lap faster. If you are a better driver in a better car, you should be able to pull away. You don't want guys sitting in behind you, getting a tow and saving fuel and all that s**t that they've got in America.

TD: *Moving on to another key issue: do we know what the definition of a constructor is for 2008?*

DA: Not yet.

MG: Do we know what it is for 2007..?

DA: We knew very well what it was for 2007 and we wait to know what it is for 2008.

TD: *The rules say that we need to know by October 31, so what is the current status?*

DA: It is not for us to make the rules, it is for the FIA. When it publishes them, we will follow them.

MWH: I don't think there's any doubt what the definition of a constructor is. It's about how the money is shared. Do you accept the philosophy that a non-constructor should be entitled to revenue, and at equal levels or a proportion of the revenue level of a constructor? That's the debate.

TD: *Yes, and it's a fundamental change to the fabric of F1. What do you think the impact of being able to purchase customer cars is going to be?*

MWH: I think we have to be very careful, because an interesting ingredient of F1, good or bad, has been that to be a competitor you had to be a constructor. F1 has to be cautious before it discards that element of its make-up. It's something which has been a differentiator of F1. Philosophically, McLaren has consistently voiced its concerns that we might change that definition. On the other hand, if you can do it, then we will try to do it and have a go at working with other teams. Whether that's hypocrisy on our part... It's rather like single ECUs as far as I'm concerned. McLaren was the team most strongly against it and the only team to finally vote against it, but if that's what F1 wants, then we will try and play our part. We voiced our concerns with Max six months ago and said to him, are you really going to do it? And he said yes, and on that basis we made it clear we were prepared to work with another team. If it doesn't happen, it doesn't happen. We are not wedded to the idea. If those with the power say we shouldn't have customer teams, fine.

DA: When we signed the Concorde Agreement in 2005, when we entered the World Championship, it was guaranteed to Aguri Suzuki and to me that we can share identical cars without losing benefits. On this basis, we signed. We tried, with the support of Bernie [Ecclestone] and Max, to bring that forward one year for 2007, but because one vote was against, it wasn't possible. But it was clear to us that the way forward was to have 12 competitive teams. If you have 12 competitive teams, and they are close together, it is better than having a constructor like Minardi a few years ago that was 4–5s behind. So we prefer to have 24 competitive cars regardless of whether they are customers or constructors. The teams have to be protected financially. If you are a manufacturer you have a large budget, but if you are an independent team you have a small budget and we don't want to lose the commercial benefit just because we are independent.

TD: *Do you therefore see effectively two championships developing: a manufacturers and a customer-car championship?*

DA: No, it is a team championship like it always has been. You never had 12 constructors in the 50 years of F1. All the time you had Ferrari, but now you have Mercedes, Renault, BMW, Honda, Toyota, etc. At the end of the day, the manufacturers come and go, but the teams are always there, so I think it is very good what Max is trying to do to protect the small teams.

MG: Yeah, but we have a different view in that if we finish outside the top 10 and don't receive revenues, that has a large impact on our budget. We are a reasonably competitive racing car manufacturer, even though we are at the back. We obviously think that if

people are buying cars or being given cars, it can put a big problem on us. So, if you want 12 competitive teams and independent teams, you've got to ensure that we share the revenue.

DA: We twice proposed to share the revenue among 12 teams and not 10. That will stop all animosity and discussion, but unfortunately I have not been supported. Because the big teams still only want to share among the top 10.

TD: *What do you think, John?*

JH: Well, it was a constructors' championship and, although one discusses revenue, the point is that the customer cost is much cheaper, because they are basically receiving a car or buying a car cheaper and the development cost is significantly less. Fundamentally, there should be some sort of equality because I think the independent constructor teams are the lifeblood of F1 to some extent. And I go back to Bernie saying that F1 is a great brand. He needs to understand what the key part of that brand is and I believe it is individual constructor's cars. If he doesn't support and keep a strong element of that, there is a possibility that F1 will change. We believe that independent constructors should be supported and should get more revenue.

PS: I absolutely agree with that. One of the things I find strange is that all these things tend to be self-regulating. F1 has been around a long while now, it's survived well, it's sorted itself out and we

Spyker Chief Technical Officer Mike Gascoyne bats an answer back at MC Tony Dodgins

seem to be hell-bent on steering it in directions it probably doesn't need steering. We absolutely need independent teams. Manufacturers are relatively new. Look back over history and you had support for independent teams from automotive suppliers – the Dunlops, Shells, etc. Then we went through this false era of cigarette advertising. They'd all got a lot of money and everything changed. As we moved out of that, we all wondered what was going to take its place and quite a few of us thought it might turn out to be high-tech firms, but it turned out to be manufacturers. They won't be around forever, particularly with the way we are spending money. We will need the independent teams when the manufacturers are gone, so let's look after them.

DA: Excuse me, I want to say something. For us, being allowed to have TV revenues, the difference is $20–$25 million. For a big manufacturer, such an amount means little. But for a small team like us, it means survival or death. That's why I don't understand why they are so strong against allowing the independent teams to share the TV revenue.

JH: The only thing I'd like to say is that Red Bull is also a very wealthy company and we tend to refer to manufacturers. There are other companies who have significant revenue and significant budget, so it's not only car companies.

MWH: But there's no doubt we need to keep the small independent teams. I think F1 made a big mistake in losing Cosworth. That was a crime really.

And I think we have to make sure we don't lose any of the independent teams, whether they are developing their own chassis or not. But it does seem fair to me that if a constructor is bearing the cost of designing and developing a car, it ought to be recognised in the way the prize money is split.

PS: I agree with you Martin, it does. The point I was making is that we can't kill the independents, but neither should we look after them too much. Take the thing with the engine subsidy. Why should we, as manufacturers, take some of our money and give it to our competitors?

MWH: I do believe it was in our interests to have kept Cosworth because, as we've just agreed around this table, the core business of manufacturers is making and selling cars. At the moment, F1 is an attractive environment to get brand exposure and differentiation, but that might well change. It's in the aftermath, if we don't have the small independents used to running on relatively small budgets, that F1 could collapse. If two of the automotive manufacturers pulled out tomorrow, F1 would be in a tailspin crisis.

MB: But it makes no sense that the bottom two teams, which are always going to be the poorest two teams, are cut out of the finances. From a manufacturers' point-of-view, though, a Renault or a Mercedes-Benz can't be on the back of the grid.

MWH: If you asked the top three teams if the money should go to all teams, I don't think you'd have a problem. Where you've got a problem is with the teams that think they are going to be eighth, ninth and 10th. They want to maintain the differentiation from the 11th and 12th teams, and they are fighting

for that, so you can see the dynamics that create the dilemma. But I do think there should be some formula that provides an incentive for a team to design and develop its own car.

TD: *It seems to me that if you are an independent without manufacturer support, it's unfeasible to remain a constructor in the future?*

MG: No, I don't agree. If you look at the Concorde Agreement the way it is for next year, if we are receiving 10th-place money, we have a business plan that allows us to be, I think, a competitive manufacturer. You have to set your sights differently, but I think we can deliver a competitive racing car.

MWH: I think Mike put his finger on something there. The reality is that we talk about the issues among the teams, but what the teams need to do is ensure that F1 is maximising its revenues and that those revenues are equally shared out. I think for years we have not been doing that well enough. So I think the new Concorde Agreement actually gives all the teams quite a lot more money and a greater proportionate increase in their budgets. I think you can run a good independent team if you want to.

TD: *Hasn't there's always been this sense that F1 shouldn't be self-funding and that if you are always at the back you shouldn't be guaranteed a living?*

MWH: Yes, it shouldn't be self-funding, but I think at the same time the teams at the back aren't enjoying being at the back, so those tensions and dynamics exist and we don't need to push people to the edge and say if you don't succeed you drop out of the top 10 and into Armageddon because you're not getting that money anymore.

TD: *Daniele, have there been any repercussions from your team actually embarrassing the works Honda team this year with a year-old car?*

DA: Well, we have to clarify. I disagree with Mike that our car is not a new car because the rules have changed from last year and we had to pass five crash tests and we had to manufacture our car. We have a composite department and an autoclave and everything, but for the future we think it is better to share the same car with a top team. We think that is the way forward.

MG: Where are you going to get one of those from?

PS: Yes, I was wondering who that is?

DA: Well, it will be Honda.

PS: Oh sorry, I thought you said top team...

MWH: The good thing about F1 is you can get everyone sat down and they can forget their petty grievances and look at the big picture!

TD: *Had Prodrive turned up this year and fielded a McLaren-Mercedes, where would they have ranked?*

DA: With a winning car. Very competitive.

MWH: Last, as if they'd used this year's car, they would have been thrown out!

DA: It would have been good for F1 to have four competitive McLarens.

PS: There's a bit more to it than that though, because we've seen Sauber-Ferraris in 2004-2005 and it didn't move forward that much, they didn't do that well with it. And there's a lot to running a car and racing it.

DA: Exactly. You remember the Benetton and Ligier a few years ago. The Ligier was not a competitive car.

MB: I know. I was driving it...

TD: *What of Lewis Hamilton's performance? Is he an exceptional talent or was it merely indicative of what a good driver can do in a strong car with a lot of testing?*

MW: He's a very good talent, no question. It's very difficult to know how much Fernando was struggling on the tyres because he's a phenomenal driver, as he's shown since he came into F1. How would Lewis have gone in a Renault last year against Fernando? Maybe it would have been different, maybe it would have been the same. The cars are quite a bit easier to drive on these tyres, not in terms of getting a lap time out of them, but in terms of being punished for your mistakes. They are very forgiving tyres and if you make a small mistake under braking you can still get to the apex, that sort of thing. Lewis has still done an amazing job in qualifying and the races, but the hardest cars I've driven in terms of being quick were sportscars. You had a lot of power, no toys, and being one of the quickest guys was an achievement. But you see someone like Sebastian Buemi come and test our car and he's within half a second in a day.

PS: Mark, how do you think Lewis compares with Jacques Villeneuve? It's a similar thing as he did loads of testing, went to all the tracks and had a successful first year?

MW: I guess in that situation, in the best car, it's just reassuring to know that if you drive a few average laps you're going to be OK. Lewis's race at Silverstone was one of his poorest races, and yet he still ended up on the podium. But if you drive a car half-a-minute behind its pace in the midfield group, bloody hell mate, you finish 15th or 16th. It was the same for Jacques. He could go out, do a pretty average lap and still be on the front row with that Williams. Not a bad problem to have. That car had an even bigger advantage than this year's McLaren.

PS: It's like race strategy. Everyone asks how you do it, but there's only one strategy and that's to have the quickest car.

MW: Yeah, like Ross [Brawn] was amazing with Ferrari and Michael [Schumacher], wasn't he... You could do anything you wanted. Four stops at Magny-Cours or one, you could still do the business.

MH: Pat, you ran Ayrton Senna in his rookie year at Toleman in 1984. If you'd run him in a McLaren, would he have been vying with Alain Prost for the World Championship?

PS: Yeah, I think he would. By the end of that season, he was definitely giving them grief. He qualified third and finished third at Estoril. And, remember, he'd been hampered all that season by not having the same tyres. The only other race when he was on the same tyres as everyone else was Monaco, which he nearly won.

MG: Mark made a good point about being able to have a poor race, finish on the podium and still look great. If you compare Lewis with Adrian Sutil, who raced against him in F3 and was sometimes quicker, Adrian's tugging around at the back in a Spyker and if he does a great race or a bad one, who cares? The thing about Lewis though, is that he hasn't made mistakes, China apart. You'd always expect a rookie to have the odd fall-off.

MB: That's the important thing. Take away his McLaren, which has probably been the best car this year, and he's won races from the front under tremendous pressure with a World Champion on his tail. His overtakes have been absolutely extraordinary. He's delivered. But when I drove the Williams at Silverstone in May I was pretty staggered at how good it was. I can see how kids just get in these cars and get within half a second. They just do what you want them to.

PS: Were you within half a second then, Martin?

MB: No... but I wasn't much further away!

BELOW **As an ex-racer, Martin Brundle knows his subject, especially since his run in a Williams**

MW: Martin, was that on the National track with two corners?

MB: No, it was on the Grand Prix circuit.

TD: *Martin, what about you? Have you been surprised?*

MWH: We knew he was an extraordinary talent, but we couldn't have expected him to do what he has done. The lack of mistakes has been incredible.

MW: He's similar to Michael in one way. You see him making quite a lot of mistakes on Friday, but they don't happen on Saturday or Sunday. Michael would lock up and be a bit messy exploring the limits, but not when it mattered.

TD: *Looking to the future, Pat made the point in Monza that we shouldn't look at things like overtaking in isolation, but as part of a complete package of changes taking in the sporting and technical regulations. We do think about F1's tradition, but is it time we threw away the rule book and had a different sport and a better show?*

PS: It's hard to answer because there's an awful tendency to fix things that aren't broken, so let's not get too radical. We've actually got a damned good audience and people are enjoying it at the moment. Having said that, there are far too many races with people saying it's boring, and a lack of overtaking is part of that. The worst thing you can do is put the

Pat Symonds believes that the lack of overtaking must be addressed, perhaps in radical way

fastest cars at the front and say come back in an hour and a half and let's see what's happened. We all know what's going to happen and that's where it all goes wrong. No matter what you put on the cars, whether it's different aerodynamics, push-to-pass devices like kinetic-energy-recovery systems (KERS), boost buttons or whatever, they can all be negated by poor sporting rules. So, I don't think you should lay the blame completely at the feet of the tech guys.

TD: *What sporting regulations would anyone like to see?*

MG: I agree with Pat, at the moment I think it's not bad. You don't want sporting rules where it's all totally false and you just reverse the grid. You want to keep an element of purity and supply some element which is going to give some entertainment the next day. What we've got can be tweaked.

MB: It's clear that the great races are when the conditions are changeable.

PS: Yes, and people are out of position. That's one of the things I liked about the one-lap qualifying. It did get people out of position. Take that fantastic race at Suzuka in 2005. People had made mistakes, so there were quick cars at the back and a bit of chaos was actually good.

MB: Would that not be perceived as false?

MH: Well it was chaos, but it wasn't like you were sticking weight on the cars, which is false, it was just random circumstances.

TD: *Mark, you wrote in a column that you'd like to see qualifying separate from the race, not necessarily dictating it?*

MH: The thought process behind that was just to decouple it, because people like to see who is ultimately fastest, which they don't at the moment. And, at the same time, the great races have been when the grid is mixed up. So maybe we could have points for qualifying and then do something like run the grid as the reverse of fastest laps from the previous race, forcing people to overtake.

DA: You could also use a ballast system.

MW: Ballast is bullshit, I think. I mean, why should you get penalised? That is pure showbiz.

PS: I think it probably is a step too far. But ballast is interesting in one way as it's probably the one thing that evens out budgets. There really is no point in spending millions on something if it's going to get handicapped out at the next race.

MB: I hate qualifying with fuel. You suddenly realise on Sunday that the guy on pole was net fifth.

PS: The trouble is, if you take the fuel out then you are definitely going to put the fastest cars at the front. What about if at the end of qualifying everyone published their fuel loads instead of spending Saturday night working it out. Because we all know by the time the race starts, within a lap.

MB: It depends who we are trying to please here. Is it the fans on TV and at the circuit?

PS: Absolutely.

MB: Well, they cannot get their heads around three-and-a-half-tenths per 10 kilos of fuel. I can explain that as many times as I like on the TV and even my family still comes and asks me about it.

PS: But Martin, at all costs we must avoid just putting the fastest cars at the front.

MB: I think the GP2 system works quite well.

MW: Did refuelling cause these problems?

PS: Actually, it's very interesting. Refuelling absolutely changed F1. It made it very spectacular, but it's probably gone a bit too far. And it was another driver-skill thing to make tyres last through a race. Mark, you must know from sportscars.

MW: Yeah, we did have to look after our tyres and save fuel and everything. I suppose if you look at it, Prost was one extreme and Michael the other, when all those rules came in slicing the race down into three it was perfect for him, good for his pace, his fitness and everything.

PS: Mark, what would you rather do?

MW: Well, I don't particularly like driving around with 200 litres of fuel…

TD: *Martin, what would help broadcasters to put out a better show?*

MB: I ask experienced people who don't always come to the races: what's it like sitting at home watching ITV? What don't we tell you? What's the whole package like? Are we talking bollocks? Both Geoff Willis and Ross Brawn have said completely independently that they now realise how little information we get and how much surmising we have to do. But there's no point telling people that so-and-so is coming in on lap whatever. They want to see the story unfold. For us, it's really all about access. People want to know what the guy is really like, and what's going on at the pit wall?

MH: Why don't we have all the radios?

DA: American motor racing is much better at that.

PS: Yes, I can't understand that. In F1, we have all this silly secrecy.

MG: Maybe we should be publishing fuel weights and discussing strategies and having links to commentators on the pit wall.

MB: Yeah, it's inclusion. People want to feel right at the heart of it.

TD: *You go out live and that's difficult. Is there not a case for a follow-up highlights show with a group of guys in a studio explaining what happened?*

PS: Absolutely.

MB: Magazine programmes don't get the audience.

PS: That is what I would do rather than televise qualifying, which is not very exciting. But if we're televising qualifying and we've got a gap between sessions, why don't we have a studio at the end of the pitlane and if you get knocked out you've got to go in and explain where you messed up.

MG: Yeah, there should be far more during a race that we are forced to talk to the media about and give information out.

PS: The Indy stage show I thought was really good, I watched it on TV.

MW: You don't want to be too cheesy, but Bernie is at the other extreme, liking to be very exclusive and professional.

MB: I'd like a camera in the drivers' briefing, but it would change the dynamics of that. If we want to

move it on, that's the sort of access we have to get. But the drivers would say completely different things if there was a camera there.

MW: But over time that would loosen up a bit.

TD: *Finally, the spy saga. Was it really damaging?*

MH: I don't see why the FIA needed to get involved. Why couldn't it just have been a civil case and then if there was a guilty verdict maybe the FIA could then have looked at disrepute.

PS: I find it amazing that at the beginning of the year someone can be walking around with a drawing of another person's car with someone else's title on that drawing, give it to the FIA and nothing was said about it. And then all hell is let loose about McLaren.

MG: I think it's the consistency thing. If that's the rules, fine, but then let's make sure they are applied consistently. And I don't think there's anyone sitting around this table who thinks that they are.

JH: I agree. Firstly, intellectual property and who owns it is a very grey area anyway. But, in the end, it's belief in the consistency of the application of the regulations to all people equally. I tend to agree with Mike.

MG: I mean, we would argue that there are a couple of teams on the grid who have got a lot of drawings from someone else's car! And why is that OK?

MW: I'm massively disappointed with what happened. Look at the lead-time to build these cars. The best drivers have been in the silver cars this season and they have also been consistently the best

John Howett and Martin Whitmarsh prove that round table discussions can entertain

team. The other team was gifted the constructors' championship which is just a mess this year.

MB: I think it's very significant how nervous we all are to say something and how carefully we choose our words. Millions of people watch F1. Is it because of the overtaking? It certainly isn't. There is intrigue and skulduggery and politics, and that's an element of F1, but all this went way too far.

MG: I looked at the information that was passed from Ferrari to McLaren and it's fairly irrelevant. If you are going to exclude someone from the championship, you have to know that their car has gone quicker because of it, and I don't think they did.

DA: It's the price of popularity. In Italy, we have the most controversy in football and Formula 1. There is never any complaint about ping pong!

MW: I think we can learn from other sports. As soon as they come off the pitch, footballers are interviewed, and they can go for it. You still want some of that rawness. But I suppose they are not protecting a Mercedes, a Bridgestone or whomever.

MWH: The reason everyone is restrained is not Bridgestone or Mercedes, it is the environment in which F1 is being conducted. The minute you say something, you are bringing the sport into disrepute. Apparently you can go to ITV and say a team principal is a liar. But only one person can get away with that. Nobody else can say a damned thing…

THE DRIVERS

The thought of a rookie topping the rankings would have been fanciful at the start of the campaign, but that was counting without Lewis Hamilton

To rank the 26 drivers who entered a grand prix in 2007, and fully take into account all the factors they faced, we narrowed the panel of judges to former Formula One drivers who have become commentators, and thus have to watch every facet of a driver's year, observe how they cope with the equipment at their disposal.

Mark Blundell, Martin Brundle, Christian Danner, Bas Leinders and Marc Surer are all regulars, with five-time grand prix winner John Watson an occasional on the Formula One beat, but with a clear understanding of what is good. Leinders is the least well-known, but adds a balancing view as not only is he the one with the most contemporary racing knowledge but, having driven for Minardi, he is able to appreciate what it's like trying to weave magic with a car that falls short of the best. Likewise, Danner had to struggle with tail-end cars.

That Lewis Hamilton came top was down not only to his astounding speed and attacking excellence, but also to his relatively mistake-free debut season. If the others follow close to championship order, perhaps that's as it should be, but there are always roses among the thorns, and Nico Rosberg's performance for Williams is the most notable exception, as he is ranked above Felipe Massa and the rock-steady Nick Heidfeld.

1 LEWIS
HAMILTON
McLAREN

"It was difficult to know what to expect. I remember being at McLaren last November and having a photo taken next to Ron after he said I'd got the seat, and just sitting there thinking 'I hope I do a good job'. I have a lot of belief in myself as a driver, but never in a million years would I have thought that coming into my first year I'd be challenging for the championship. So it was a big surprise.

Perhaps someone, somewhere, didn't want me to win the title. I've had a few tyre problems, I made a mistake in the previous race and then something happened to me at the beginning in Brazil, but that's racing. To think I've come from GP2 to be ranked number two in the world is a positive thing and I know we'll be strong next year. We'll do a better job, for sure, and I can't wait.

I came into the season just hoping to do a good job and it's just been a mind-blowing season for me, and I think for my whole team and for everyone in the Formula One paddock with everything that's gone on.

It's been a bigger learning year for me than anyone. I've had to come in as a rookie and grow day by day with the sport and get to understand the way people work, understand the way the team works, and understand what it takes to be a professional F1 driver. I can't really point out the most difficult thing or the biggest surprise to me this year, but for sure one that I wasn't expecting is what goes on in the paddock and what is said: the politics. Whatever negative was thrown at me, I turned into a positive.

I don't think there's one thing that particularly stands out. I've made certain mistakes, though, and won't make them next season. I'll come back fitter and more experienced. I'm looking forward to next year.

It's been a crazy year and I can't honestly say I'm really gutted, because I'm not. After a year without problems, it's just unfortunate that we had a little one in Brazil. Everyone has had their fair share of bad luck, but most of mine has all come at the end of the year.

China definitely didn't make me more nervous. If anything, it took the pressure off my shoulders and I think I came out of it even stronger. I thought it would knock my confidence and put me onto my back foot, but I went away and I thought about the weekend, and I feel I'm even stronger than I was, for whatever reason. It was a good learning experience.

I have to say congratulations to Kimi, he's done a fantastic job. He's been a phenomenal force all year, and I've got so much respect for him. We did a great job ourselves this year. The gap is only one point, and it was very, very close at the end. Any of us deserved it. He did a great job in the final few races, and it's all about consistency, and he did an honest job.

I had a great opportunity to compete for the best team. I went to the first race and wanted to do a good job, and I finished third. From there, it was continuing to try to do a good job and to learn and hopefully get some more podiums. Then we won in Montréal and Indianapolis, so it started to become reality that maybe we could win the championship this year.

I think it was quite a strange experience. All these years I've dreamed of being an F1 driver. I was in GP2, which was a great category for me, I was there, I was watching F1, I was wondering 'I'm good enough to win in GP2, but will I be good enough to win in F1?' And that's the big question that every driver has. So eventually I got to F1, and it was everything I anticipated and more. As a youngster, you dream about it, and you only think about driving the car. But there's so much around F1, and really it's been quite a phenomenal experience for me this year. I'm always smiling because I'm always having good fun.

I've set some good records. There are still more to be beaten, and there's still a long, long way to go. I'm only 22. I'll be here for a while. I'm very proud to be in the McLaren team, and fingers crossed, they'll keep me for a while. Like with any relationship, it has been growing throughout the year and through rough times that I had in life it struck me how they stuck by me.

This year, we have worked extremely hard to improve the car and challenge for the World Championship, and we have gone through some hard times and we have stuck together. So, for sure the bond has grown and we get on as well as ever, so I am going to continue to try and do a good job for McLaren and stay in their good books."

British
7/1/85

Stevenage, England
17
4
6
2
109
GP2 Champion 2006, European F3 Champion 2005, British Formula Renault Champion 2003, World Kart Champion 2000

2 KIMI RÄIKKÖNEN

↑ +1   FERRARI

NATIONALITY Finnish
DATE OF BIRTH 17/10/79
PLACE OF BIRTH Espoo, Finland
GRANDS PRIX 122
WINS 15
POLES 14
FASTEST LAPS 25
POINTS 456
HONOURS F1 World Champion 2007, British Formula Renault Champion 2000, Finnish & Nordic Kart Champion 1998

"For sure, we were not in the strongest position at some points of the world championship season, but we always believed that we could recover, that we could do a better job than the other teams. And, even in the hard times, everybody at Ferrari was sticking together and we didn't give up.

It was good because as we saw in the end that even from a long way behind we could reduce the gap and go ahead and win the World Championship, not just the constructors' championship, but also the drivers', and I need to thank the team, as they did a really great job all year.

We had some hard times when we suffered some reliability problems and we lost quite a lot of points. At one point, people were saying that we weren't in the championship any more, but we showed them that they were wrong. We were able to come back and we came back strongly in the end, and it was great teamwork from all the people, from Felipe and the guys on the team, so it was a great season.

Like I said, we had some hard times with some problems, but we were always working hard to improve the situation and I think we had perfect teamwork, with Felipe helping all the time also. We had a hard fight with him all year, but then he unfortunately didn't score and couldn't be in the fight any more, so he's been a big help also. The sponsors have been a big bonus for us as well. The team is very close to them and they have been doing a great job for us, improving the fuel and everything to help us with the new regulations.

I came from pretty much nothing, but the family put in a lot of effort always, our friends, our cousins and all the sponsors in the beginning helped us to get here, but it was a long time ago. I've had great people behind me, great managers to help me here, and the teams that I've driven for have got close to the championship a few times, but I have never been able to really be there at the right moment.

This year it looked as though it was getting away again, but we have a great team at Ferrari, so we put everything together and just believed in ourselves and worked. Probably nobody else was thinking about us any more but we knew that we still had a chance, so I need to give a bit of thanks to the team.

I felt great after the final race in Brazil. It was a good feeling, but it has been a long season and it is hard to realise that we finally did it after many years and in my first year here at Ferrari, and also because it has not been in our minds to be a world champion because it seemed so far away, but we managed to come back and win it. So it is hard to believe that it happened.

I love the team, I have such a good time with the team, I enjoy Formula One much more now than last year. I have much better feelings from this year than any other year, so I must say to all the people who have been helping me: 'thanks' to them.

For sure, there have been hard times in the career, but that's normal for everybody and this is what I've always wanted and I've got it now, so anything that comes after this can only be a bonus. We're just going to try to do it again next year. It's going to be difficult, but we will see what we can do.

I enjoyed every moment with the team. I enjoy Formula One more this year than the last few years for many reasons, not because of the driving but for other reasons. And I am more than happy to win the championship with Ferrari, especially in my first year with the team. It has been a great year overcoming all the difficulties and Ferrari giving me such a nice big family and great people to work with. I would rather win with them than with anybody else.

For sure, I will have more appearances to make as World Champion, but it is not going to really change my life too much. People will probably look differently at me and make more stories about me and my stuff, but I am not going to change myself. I never have before. I am not going to worry about it and I am going to lead my life as I want and that's it."

3 FERNANDO ALONSO

↓ -1   **McLAREN**

NATIONALITY Spanish
DATE OF BIRTH 29/7/81
PLACE OF BIRTH Oviedo, Spain
GRANDS PRIX 105
WINS 19
POLES 16
FASTEST LAPS 11
POINTS 490
HONOURS F1 World Champion 2005, 2006, Formula Nissan Champion 1999, Italian & Spanish Kart Champion 1997, World Kart Champion 1996

"First of all, congratulations to Kimi. I said many times, the man who has more points at the last race deserves the championship, so in this case, I think Kimi did a great championship.

This season has been positive in a general view because I moved from Renault after winning the 2005 and 2006 Constructors' and Drivers' Championships, and I moved to McLaren with some doubts because 2006 had not been a great season for McLaren.

But the team did a fantastic job to have a competitive car in 2007, and so I was able to fight for the world championship until the final round, and I finished one point behind the champion. So, in that aspect, I think it has been a very positive season.

Outside the car, for sure we have had some difficulties this year, but I think this is normal in all jobs and you have ups and downs, better moments and worse moments. And as I said, I will have great memories of this year from my four victories I had in important places, where I had not won before, like Monza, and Monaco again for a second time. So, as I said, I will have great memories from this season.

I think it is difficult to know, or easy to know, when you lose a championship. We arrived in Brazil with only a three-points' advantage over Kimi, and it was not enough because we had a great opportunity to open this gap with the mechanical problems he had in some races. My chances were not very high because I was hoping for a problem or something wrong in Lewis's race and I had to avoid a 1–2 for Ferrari.

I think we lost a lot of points in Canada with a seventh place, I had a mistake in Japan and I didn't finish the race in the wet. So one or two points in some of those races and it would have changed the picture completely. From the team, I am very convinced they tried to give the same cars for both drivers, the correct approach, and you never know, a few points more to one driver and we would have won the championship now and not be second and third.

I had some difficulties with the team, it's not a secret. But in the end we tried to work together as hard as we could and we arrived at the last race fighting for the championship and we finished third in the Drivers' Championship, one point behind the World Champion. So I think at the end, I had a fantastic car, a very competitive car, great sponsors in the team and even if we have had a tough season, I've had great memories from this season: four victories and I feel comfortable.

As for Lewis, the media has been saying many, many things about us that weren't true. We never had problems with each other. We are obviously fighting on the track, but off the track we have had a very good relationship from day one and it's still the same.

We love competition and if we were not Formula One drivers then maybe we would be in a different sport or somewhere else competing against someone. It is our life. We enjoy it, this conflict. Away from the track, I think everyone has a different character and a different way to live, but in the paddock we do so much and sometimes we win and enjoy it more and sometimes we lose and have days of disappointments. But, after that, it is clear competition and we like that.

It's not too difficult to get away from all the comments in the media, all the attention that was around the team all year. But, for me, it was basically more difficult because I had some problems with the team as well, especially in the last part, but these things are normal in the sport.

I think you learn in every championship that you contest, in every season that you do. For sure, I learned things this year. It's not a secret that I didn't have the best relationship with the team. In a way, I am now stronger than last year.

For sure, I have some difficult moments and frustrating moments this season, but it's a competitive sport, and you always have good and not so good moments. This year, I suffered more difficult moments than I expected, but nothing bigger than what is normal in the sport."

"It's been an extremely positive year for me. It's really gone very well in general, even though a lot of the races didn't go perfectly. In some races I was in the wrong place at the wrong time, and in other races we had technical issues which we really need to sort out for 2008.

We really established ourselves as top of the midfield pack in the last few races, which is fantastic because everybody was saying that Williams was probably going to drop off in performance towards the end of the season, as the others pick up their development pace. And, in fact, we've been the ones developing quickest of all, pace-wise, so it's been very reassuring and very nice to see.

In your second year of Formula One, you use everything you've learned, and you just step up your game. I think that's normal. It just all comes together, really. The routine, the experience, the knowledge of the set-up, to know how to get the qualifying laps out. Everything just comes together.

I think I adapted very well to the tyres, I must say. Even though it was really not how I was used to driving, I managed to adapt really well. My driving style was the 100% opposite of a smooth driving style on corner entry. It takes time, especially because every time you get a new track you have to adapt, because you're not used to it on that track. It was a continuous thing through the year: it took time to get your head around it.

As a driver, you improve all the time, but as a team we also made a lot of small steps. It wasn't possible earlier in the season to qualify consistently within the top 10, and then in the last few races we were eighth and seventh or sixth, and it was very nice to see.

Overall, the package was a lot better than last year's, definitely. Reliability and performance were better. Towards the end of last year, we had little chance to qualify in the top 10. If we did it was ninth or 10th, but this year we were well within it, with a chance of scoring points every race, so our relative pace definitely improved.

We had a good engine [from Cosworth] last year and a good engine [from Toyota] this year, so there's not much in that. Reliability also helps you progress through the season, as if you're always stopping you don't get a rhythm. It stops you from developing, because you have to put the effort into it. This year, we could concentrate more on performance and on next year's car.

Having said that, we lost three races this year on my car because of technical issues, if you include Silverstone where I lost out in qualifying because of it. You really can't afford that, and if you really want to have a great season, you need to iron those things out. Next year for us that's very important. Otherwise, it's generally been very positive.

Everyone else was reliable too, but you shouldn't start depending on other people dropping out, you need to get up there! There were a few opportunities that got away from me this year. I learned a lot from the Nürburgring – it was a new situation that you can't prepare for, really. But that wasn't one of the most frustrating races.

I did not expect to beat Alex [Wurz] in qualifying so often. It's always positive for you as a driver if you are able to beat your team-mate. The team always did everything equal for both of us, but you do sense that the focus goes a little bit towards you if you're setting better lap times. Which is fair. If there are races where you are the one who has the only chance to score points, then that's normal.

Alex had a little bit of luck in some races, but he also did a great job. I have to also say that it's very, very important for me where we are in the constructors' [championship], so when Alex scored points and I was out of the race, like at the Nürburgring, I was happy. We needed the points, because it gives us more prize money and so an even better chance to create a great car next season."

4 NICO ROSBERG
⬆ +10 WILLIAMS

NATIONALITY German
DATE OF BIRTH 27/6/85
PLACE OF BIRTH Wiesbaden, Germany
GRANDS PRIX 35
WINS 0
POLES 0
FASTEST LAPS 1
POINTS 24
HONOURS GP2 Champion 2005, German Formula BMW Champion 2002

5 NICK HEIDFELD

⬆ +3 **BMW SAUBER**

NATIONALITY German
DATE OF BIRTH 10/5/77
PLACE OF BIRTH
Mönchengladbach, Germany
GRANDS PRIX 134
WINS 0
POLES 1
FASTEST LAPS 0
POINTS 140
HONOURS Formula 3000
Champion 1999, German F3
Champion 1997

"If someone had told me at the start of the World Championship that we would be third at the end of it, I would not have believed it. On the other hand, though, we were not far away either after testing. But back then I did expect Renault to be stronger than us, so our goal before the opening grand prix was to be fourth, and I thought that would be difficult.

In the very first roll-out, I had the feeling that the BMW Sauber F1.07 was a good car, but not as competitive for example as the 2001 Sauber. My first test run proved that it was a huge improvement over the F1.06. So, back then, I felt it was not going to be a bad season. Then we had out first test together with all the other cars, and that was when I knew for sure that it was looking quite good.

For sure the tyres were important, and the engineers did a very good job there, probably helped by the fact that we used Bridgestones not so long ago.

Also, our 2006 car was officially labelled a BMW Sauber car, but in fact was mainly developed by Sauber in a period when new people were still coming on board and BMW was coming on board. So, this was the first year that we had more or less the full power of BMW behind the car.

The first race is always the proof of where you stand against the other teams because, even with all the testing that you do with all the other teams, you never know what is going on. I didn't expect Ferrari to be that strong in Australia – Kimi just drove away and was nearly falling asleep. Luckily, after that, it got a bit more interesting at the front of the field.

It was great knowing that each grand prix weekend you can score some points, even more for myself than some of the other guys, because I haven't been in such a competitive team for years. I know what it's like to drive around in 10th or 15th place each weekend.

In most of the races, the four cars from McLaren and Ferrari were just too strong for us to compete, apart from Canada especially, and Indianapolis I think would have been a very good chance as well. In Canada, there was only one car quicker than me, Lewis Hamilton's McLaren, and I was quicker than Alonso and the two Ferraris, which was great.

Although the race was crazy with the safety car and Robert's crash and everything, I would have finished second no matter what. It was a great feeling knowing that it was obviously not far away from being a win, and it was also great knowing that it was not by luck, but we were really so strong.

At Indianapolis, I had a technical failure and the spin, and unfortunately not the best qualifying, but I think we had the pace there to beat at least one Ferrari if not both of them.

It was fantastic being on the podium in Hungary, especially the second time in a row after last season. But again it was more because the others made mistakes, like some of the races where I was able to beat a McLaren and Ferrari, it was because there was something not going right for the driver or the team, and I was there to jump in, which was nice.

The overtaking of Alonso in Bahrain stands out. That was great fun. But also on some other occasions we were together for quite a while, we had a good fight. In Japan, I overtook him again in the wet, obviously when his car was heavy. So I had some good fights with Alonso, and I remember those.

I had retirements in Spain, the US and Japan. It was a bit disappointing, but still if we look at laps completed compared to the other teams, we were quite good, but for me not good enough. That's something that we have to improve on if we want to fight for the title in a couple of years' time.

It was easy to improve on our form of the past few years, but it gets tougher the closer you get to the top. Also, half a second shows you the problem. If you are in the midfield now, you find a couple of tenths, you make a huge jump. But, from third to first, the step that we need to make is bigger. It will be difficult, but BMW is here to win, so there are no excuses."

6 FELIPE MASSA
↓ -2 FERRARI

"I'm very glad to help the team to win the championship. One day I hope it can be me, but I'm happy for Kimi. For sure I need to say thanks to the whole team who worked very hard, even during the difficult times when we were criticised because the reliability was not good enough. But, in the end, it was good to see the team as champions.

I had many good races. I had three victories, which was very good, I had many other good results, many podiums. And sometimes some bad luck as well.

I'm quite happy with the way the whole season was going, for sure. I'm not very happy with the problems we had this year, though, as I think they cost us a lot of points.

All of the victories were very good races, so it's difficult to say which one was the best! Bahrain was a very good race, starting from pole and winning, Barcelona as well, and also Turkey. I also had the opportunity to win at the Nürburgring, where I was leading throughout and then I suddenly had a problem at the end of the race.

It's been a very good season I think, in terms of fighting, in terms of competition. I'm quite happy, but for sure not very happy with the points I lost.

I was quite comfortable straight away with the new regulations on the tyres. I had to change the way of driving with these tyres. But for me it was not so difficult to change from one kind of construction and compound of tyres to another one we introduced this year. Also we could manage to improve the car a lot during the season. The way of driving now is not so different compared to the way of driving last year.

I feel very comfortable inside the team. I've been an official race driver for Ferrari for two years, and I was test driver before. Last year was my first year in Ferrari, and I think I was learning a lot. This year I had much more experience, much more maturity. I had a very good learning year last year, especially with Michael, and I could manage to put everything I learned and all my experience into this year and doing even better."

NATIONALITY Brazilian
DATE OF BIRTH 25/4/81
PLACE OF BIRTH São Paulo, Brazil
GRANDS PRIX 88
WINS 5
POLES 8
FASTEST LAPS 9
POINTS 201
HONOURS Euro F3000 Champion 2001, European Formula Renault Champion 2000

7 HEIKKI KOVALAINEN
RENAULT

"I think we can't be happy about the beginning of the season. Our car was not as competitive as it should have been, and it was very inconsistent. But also I made a few mistakes that I should not have made. Giancarlo was driving better at the beginning of the season, and he scored more points.

To be honest, when we went to Melbourne we didn't know that the gap was so big to the leaders. We went there thinking we won't be in front of Ferrari and McLaren, but we will be there or thereabouts.

Qualifying 13th for my first grand prix wasn't good at all! It was a bit of a shock, and the next few races not being on the pace at all was definitely a bit of a disappointment for us. We realised that we didn't have the pace and we had a bit of work to do.

The Spanish GP was the first one where the pace was actually alright and I qualified in the top 10. But then in Monaco I was really not on the pace all weekend. I was never really comfortable with the car, I didn't find good settings there, and I didn't really

make up places in the race. It was a really disappointing weekend, and after that I had some meetings with the engineers and they told me that I really needed to pull my finger out and I was not good enough.

In Canada, I had the accident and engine failure and it was still going wrong, but since the race there things turned around – I don't know why!

I started to understand the set-up and how to get more out of the car and make it better for the race, and also driving a little bit smoother and less aggressive, not attacking as much as before. It took just a little bit too long for me to put it all together.

In the second half of the season, we improved our car all the time, up to the Turkish GP. We made some good steps, and we got our place, which was seventh or eighth fastest all the time in normal conditions. Then we started to score points regularly, and I got a podium in Japan.

I think it's been a positive season anyway. I've learned a helluva lot this year"

NATIONALITY Finnish
DATE OF BIRTH 19/10/81
PLACE OF BIRTH Suomussalmi, Finland
GRANDS PRIX 17
WINS 0
POLES 0
FASTEST LAPS 0
POINTS 30
HONOURS World Series by Nissan Champion 2004

8 ROBERT KUBICA

↑ +7 BMW SAUBER

"The season was very good for all the team, and for sure as a team we were not expecting to be so competitive, and our car has made big steps compared to 2006. But it's also true especially with my car we have lost a lot of points due to technical problems.

In that way, I am happy for the team and what we have achieved as a group, and for the guys in Hinwil and Munich it's very positive and a very good achievement, but in some ways I'm also a bit disappointed.

For sure, the winter testing was a different approach, because this year I knew that I was working for myself, and that I had to prepare as much as possible for the new season, the new challenge. Last year I was working more or less as a team player for Nick and Jacques [Villeneuve]. This year we don't have any more tyre testing, we have a different work set-up and now I could set up the car more for what I like and what I don't like.

There were some days where we were able to fight with McLaren and Ferrari, depending on which track. And in fact we finished some races in front of them. But in the global picture we were safe in third position. There were two or three grands prix where Renault was close to us. Silverstone and Magny-Cours came at what was a crucial point of the season, because at that point Renault was catching us, but we made good races there.

Two races where I was pretty competitive were Hungary and Monaco. Unfortunately, I didn't manage to achieve 100% of the result that was possible on either occasion, Monaco because of strategy and in Hungary we had gearbox trouble in qualifying, and I was starting in P8. I finished P5, three seconds behind Nick. It was a very good race for myself, and I was not expecting to be so competitive there. Encouragingly, this year's car was very good also in tracks where we were not expecting it to be.

However, there were some occasions when you feel you can achieve something like a podium and something goes wrong, and that's always disappointing."

NATIONALITY Polish
DATE OF BIRTH 7/12/84
PLACE OF BIRTH Krakow, Poland
GRANDS PRIX 22
WINS 0
POLES 0
FASTEST LAPS 0
POINTS 45
HONOURS World Series by Renault Champion 2005, German & Italian Junior Kart Champion 2000, Polish Junior Kart Champion 1997

9 MARK WEBBER

↑ +2 RED BULL

"When I went to Red Bull, there were a lot of familiar faces from the Jaguar days. Management-wise, obviously it was different, with Christian Horner at the helm and Adrian Newey in charge technically, but I was going back to the same team effectively. I've driven for three F1 teams instead of four, if you like! It did make a difference for me to settle in, no question about it, but then I settled in very quickly at Williams. You do settle in to new environments pretty fast if you make the effort.

Clearly, we underperformed in terms of delivering a reliable racing car, that's the first thing you need to have to get you to the flag. So you can question our design or diagnostic skills or whatever you want, but we've got to do a better job over the winter this year, and going into next year we have to have a better product to work with. It's frustrating when you have a car that's fragile.

It's swings and roundabouts, sometimes it's been my side of the garage, sometimes it's been David's. In Bahrain, we both had it, which cost us points as well. Everyone's got their sob story for where they've lost points this year and where it's all gone wrong, but at the end of the day consistency is the key and the scoreboard never lies, because that's exactly what you've achieved as a team.

The Nürburgring was a highlight. There were eight pit stops done by the team, and David and I finished fifth and third. There were no dropped wheelnuts, no inters on one side and wets on the other. The team did a bloody good job. It started off with me qualifying sixth, and my first stint with intermediates put me in a good position. It was a challenging day for everyone and there was some attrition, but there was no attrition in terms of cars breaking down in front of me, apart from Kimi.

Budapest was a very, very strong race, as was Spa. Magny-Cours and Monaco were probably the two toughest races, but we've generally been on the fringe of the points, and other teams have moved around us a little bit. Which in some ways, if you walk a mile in Toyota or Honda's shoes, is not bad, but of course we want to do better."

NATIONALITY Australian
DATE OF BIRTH 27/8/76
PLACE OF BIRTH Queanbeyan, Australia
GRANDS PRIX 104
WINS 0
POLES 0
FASTEST LAPS 0
POINTS 79
HONOURS Formula Ford Festival winner 1996

10 JARNO TRULLI
← = →   TOYOTA

"I have to express the fact that this has been a poor season. If we look at our results and we look at our points, we cannot say anything else. We expected more, and we didn't even reach the lowest target, so it's a bit frustrating.

We had poor rear traction and braking stability, and we were always quite down on top speed. The main problem we always had is that we were very light on tyres, and we suffered a lot of problems warming them. That's why we were more competitive in extreme hot conditions like Bahrain and Malaysia, and then once the conditions were normal or cold, we struggled. When it was wet, it was even worse. On top of that, we have missed some good opportunities, especially Canada, the Nürburgring or Fuji.

I think I've had some races where I drove very well and was quick, like at Spa or Monza, but the points didn't come. At Spa, I was unlucky at the start because Heidfeld just went out and came around so I had to brake just after the corner, and I lost several positions. Then you don't recover, especially when you battle for one-tenth difference between one car and the other, it's nearly impossible then to recover three or four positions. It was the same in Hungary: I lost positions at the start with the launch, and the same at Monza.

We also had some races where clearly things didn't work right. In Spain, I had a problem with the fuel pump at the start. That was frustrating because we were quick. At the beginning of the season we looked, I would say, more competitive than the rest of the season. It looked as though the others caught us up and overtook us in terms of performance, and we struggled more and more to qualify in the top 10.

At the beginning, it was difficult but still possible. Later, to get it in I really had to put in a fantastic lap, at the very last second, hoping that I got it right, otherwise with one-tenth you're out. I don't want to go back and say I could have done this and that, anyone can say that. The problem is that the results of our team were not so great, and this is clearly shown by the points."

NATIONALITY Italian
DATE OF BIRTH 13/7/74
PLACE OF BIRTH Pescara, Italy
GRANDS PRIX 184
WINS 1
POLES 3
FASTEST LAPS 0
POINTS 183
HONOURS German F3 Champion 1996, World Kart Champion 1995, European Kart Champion 1994

11 JENSON BUTTON
↓ -6   HONDA

"This definitely hasn't been the year that we thought it would be. Last winter, we thought we had a good chance to challenge for the title, but when we drove the car in January we knew it wasn't a quick car, and we knew we couldn't just fix it with changing a few things.

Every time I drove the car, I thought it can't be as bad as I remember and I'd be positive, but after two laps you'd be so angry about how bad the car was. It was so frustrating, because the car was so inconsistent. It would do something different every time.

We made changes and it got a bit better, but the reason why it didn't make a big step forward was because of the direction we'd started with in 2006, mid-season, with the aero package and the ideas behind it.

If you look at the car around the sides and the bargeboard area, it's very different to everyone else's. We've built up the downforce over the years, but the problem is that it's downforce that you can't really use. You get it on the straights, you've got a lot of drag, and then you get to a corner and under braking the car lost all its rear downforce. The balance moved all the time, at different speed ranges. To try and have a consistent car was impossible.

Having a slow car is bad enough, but having a car that's different every time you hit the brakes, and you don't know what it's going to do, gives you no confidence at all.

We kept adding downforce, but it wasn't anything you could use. Sometimes it would even make it worse, because you'd get the grip and you'd hit a bump, or get a different camber, and everything would change. Suddenly, you'd lose that grip. It just made all the problems worse. You felt confident and then suddenly everything went, you lost all downforce in certain parts of the corner, on bumps, and also following cars.

The reason why it was quick in Monaco was that we could chuck the downforce on it and the drag didn't matter. Whereas in Hungary you need efficient downforce, which we didn't have, and that's why we were so slow. France was fantastic, we got the best out of the car, and we couldn't have gone any quicker."

NATIONALITY British
DATE OF BIRTH 19/1/80
PLACE OF BIRTH Frome, England
GRANDS PRIX 136
WINS 1
POLES 3
FASTEST LAPS 0
POINTS 229
HONOURS Formula Ford Festival winner 1998, European Super A Kart Champion 1997

12 ADRIAN SUTIL
SPYKER

"Last year, I think I just got a feeling for an F1 car, but it was just a few Fridays that I did, and I couldn't learn so much on the technical side – I was just testing tyres and doing the simple work.

This year, I learned more about all the programme, especially from Saturday to Sunday when you learn a lot more, such as all the procedures and all about the racing. So it was a big step this year, a big difference compared to being a test driver.

The early races were disappointing. The car was not strong enough to be better than the second last or last position, and I had a few accidents. But it told me how difficult it is to be at the back from which it's nearly impossible to gain some places!

I think I was trying too hard, but I became a little bit more calm after these early races. You can't push, you just have to see where there is a gap and then try to go in there, and really be careful.

I had a good race in Barcelona, but nobody noticed it because we were racing on our own! But we did nearly our maximum, and had a little fight with the Honda. Indianapolis was even better, it was the first time we could really race some other cars. I was in the midfield, racing and fighting, and it was a good step. It then went better and better in the final few races.

To get out a B-spec car during the year was a good step, and I think we could be happy about that. It was clear that the car was a bit better. The first race in Monza was a little bit of learning, because we didn't have so much testing before, and when you have a new car you need some testing to understand everything. Spa, though, was clear evidence of a better car.

At Fuji, we had a little bit of luck, as we gambled on a good rain set-up for the race. I think on my side I made no mistakes, and in these difficult conditions just to stay on the track was quite difficult, and it was the most important thing on the day. It was a very good feeling, it was like a little win for myself, and we got our point."

NATIONALITY German
DATE OF BIRTH 11/1/83
PLACE OF BIRTH Graefeling, Germany
GRANDS PRIX 17
WINS 0
POLES 0
FASTEST LAPS 0
POINTS 1
HONOURS Swiss Formula Ford Champion 2002

13 GIANCARLO FISICHELLA
↓ -7 RENAULT

"It's been a tough season for us! We were quite optimistic before the start of the season that we could fight for the title, but straight away we understood that our competitiveness compared to the cars of Ferrari, McLaren and BMW was not good enough.

From the outset, the car was inconsistent on braking, with a lot of understeer in high-speed corners, and the grip level was quite poor. It was an aerodynamic problem.

Before Australia, we knew that it was tough, it was difficult and we were not quick enough, but we didn't expect to be that far away. Especially just afterwards, in Malaysia for example, we were probably 1.5 seconds slower than the leaders. It was a real disaster.

After a few races we were quite close, and in Monte Carlo I was fourth, which was a good result. It was a completely fantastic weekend, fourth on the grid, fourth in the race.

At real circuits, where you need downforce, and where there are a lot of high-speed corners, the pace was far away. The main problem I think was coming from the wind tunnel. The figures were good but, on the track, they were completely different. A few months ago, we understood the problem, but it was too late. Considering all the problems, and the time we lost at the start of the season, the team did a very good job. They made a very big effort and they were working night and day but, unfortunately, it was not enough.

We made a big step forward from the beginning of the season, but in August we stopped development of the 2007 car because there was nothing to do for this year, and it was better to concentrate on next year's car.

Montréal was probably the biggest disappointment. I would have been on the podium, but the problem with the red light at the pit exit stopped me! It was disappointing, because I didn't score many points in the second half of the season. I had problems with qualifying: once I was penalised, once I had an accident, so it wasn't good.

It's been a difficult season, but considering the pace was not good, to finish third in the [constructors'] championship was good."

NATIONALITY Italian
DATE OF BIRTH 14/1/73
PLACE OF BIRTH Rome, Italy
GRANDS PRIX 196
WINS 3
POLES 3
FASTEST LAPS 2
POINTS 267
HONOURS Italian F3 Champion & Monaco F3 GP winner 1994

14 DAVID COULTHARD

↓ –5 RED BULL

"We've achieved our target of finishing fifth in the constructors' championship. It's been a season of ups and downs for us more than others because of the reliability issues we've had. I've stopped several times during qualifying – Bahrain, Magny-Cours and the Nürburgring – with gearbox-related issues. That's very frustrating, because you've then got to try and make it all up in the races.

On average I've been a tenth quicker than Mark in the races, and he's been on average a tenth quicker in qualifying.

The car was a definite improvement this year. Obviously, we've moved to a single tyre manufacturer and had to adapt to Bridgestone. Those who've run on Bridgestones before clearly had an advantage, so I'm quite happy with the way I've picked up and improved in understanding the Bridgestone's performance.

And there has been a learning process of Adrian Newey understanding the tools at his disposal. There have been a few changes in the aero department and some strengthening of the design side, so everything would appear to be in place running into 2008.

Our relationship with Renault has worked extremely well. They are very professional, and everything I remember. They are a very good engine partner, and there have been a few times when we have been in front of the works team. Of course our lack of reliability was frustrating, and what I've always maintained is that it's as frustrating for me as it is for various people within the factory whose department that falls within. I don't believe for one minute that it's due to a lack of effort, but clearly there's been a lack of response and understanding. As team members, we have to support those people and either give them better tools to fix it or, if they are not capable, replace them. That's what you do, that's what Christian Horner is charged with.

I care about the team moving forward and believe that slowly we are. I think that this year has very much been crossing the 't's and dotting the 'i's in making sure that everything is in place for 2008. There's inevitably a high expectation of what we will be able to do."

NATIONALITY British
DATE OF BIRTH 27/3/71
PLACE OF BIRTH Twynholm, Scotland
GRANDS PRIX 229
WINS 13
POLES 12
FASTEST LAPS 18
POINTS 527
HONOURS Macau F3 winner 1991, British Junior Formula Ford Champion 1989, Scottish Kart Champion 1988

15 ALEXANDER WURZ

WILLIAMS

"I had two extremely good races this year in Montréal and at the Nürburgring, and a few other good races. My racing was usually always on a very good level and speed, but in some of the later races I seemed to be a bit stuck, but that can happen.

I have to say I was a bit caught on the back foot at the Australian GP with the qualifying format, when I had been very fast the whole weekend and then suddenly everything happened so quickly, it was a bit too much.

It took a while to get used to things again, but it was not so much the qualifying, it was more the tyres. In fact, you had to be super gentle in your driving style to get the best out of them, and I tended to be a bit more of an aggressive driver.

For me, one of the best weekends this year was Monaco. I really like that race. I made no mistakes through the entire race, and kept pushing like hell. Most of the time I was in relatively clean air, and in the end I just had to defend from Kimi. It wasn't difficult, and the only thing I had to make sure was not to make a mistake, because I had enough tyre life so my traction was good.

I also enjoyed very much Malaysia, and Silverstone was great. The racing is a little bit of a mirror of the position where you are in the midfield, so you have good and bad ones.

At Spa, we all got a bit over-excited on the second lap, and I think four guys tried to go two-wide at the chicane. I hadn't spun since Monza 2006 in free practice, so I was a bit annoyed with that! It was the dot on the 'i' of a very bad weekend.

I was very happy for the team that the package improved. When I joined last year, I saw that there were some weak areas, but Frank, Patrick and Sam spotted this and, from a downward spiral, they turned it around. Now the team is making a real upwards move, and it's really nice to see because it's a good bunch of people.

We pretty much knew the weaknesses of the 2007 car, and improved it, and that's very important in terms of knowing what to do for next year's car."

NATIONALITY Austrian
DATE OF BIRTH 15/2/74
PLACE OF BIRTH Waidhofen, Austria
GRANDS PRIX 69
WINS 0
POLES 0
FASTEST LAPS 1
POINTS 45
HONOURS Le Mans 24 Hours winner 1996, Austrian F3 Champion 1993, Austrian & German Formula Ford Champion 1992, World BMX Champion 1986

16 SEBASTIAN VETTEL
BMW SAUBER & TORO ROSSO

"I wasn't happy at the start of the season. At first you get told that you are going to do all the Fridays, and then all of a sudden it stops! I mean, I can understand the decision that BMW made at that stage, because they were doing very well, and you want to do everything possible to improve the performance over the weekend, and obviously that was another step to achieve that, me not driving any more on Fridays.

Racing at Indianapolis was a bonus. The first corner was a little bit of a mess, and without that with the race pace and so on we were able to fight for fifth and sixth place. Even my eighth place was a good result, and it was good that everybody could see that it was quite OK.

There was some bad press going around, which for me was not much of a problem, because I don't care. But you have a lot of people believing everything that's written in the press, and it was going around that I was too slow, not experienced enough, and blah, blah, blah. So it was good to have the race in Indianapolis to show everybody.

I wanted to drive, I wanted to race, and as there was an opportunity with Toro Rosso, I wasn't thinking about it too much, I just grabbed it. It took some time in the beginning I think to get confident with the car and the team, and basically to understand them better.

Obviously, I was quite sad in Fuji because we were up for a podium finish, and the more positive thing is that we would have finished on the podium not because of everybody retiring, but just because we had the pace. The fourth place in China was a kind of revenge!

In the end, I'm quite happy with the choice I made, getting more and more experience, and driving the races. Of course it's a smaller team, and if you just look at the results they are not as successful as BMW. But obviously you have to give a bit of time to the team. We are a small team and we are growing, and on the other hand I'm a young driver and I need to learn a lot as well."

NATIONALITY German
DATE OF BIRTH 3/7/87
PLACE OF BIRTH Heppenheim, Germany
GRANDS PRIX 8
WINS 0
POLES 0
FASTEST LAPS 0
POINTS 6
HONOURS German Formula BMW Champion 2004, European Junior Kart Champion 2001

17 TAKUMA SATO
↑ +3 SUPER AGURI

"We should be happy with our second year, as the performance has been much higher than expected. To be honest, we have to talk a little about how we started. Last year we weren't really a grand prix team at the beginning. From the project start-up, we built a car in 100 days, and I think at that time we really bonded, all the factory guys. And, even now, more than 90% of the people are the same.

That's why the learning curve continued towards the end of last season, and then we were in much better shape going to the pre-season tests. The environment was a lot more comfortable coming into 2007, as everything had been prepared. The car we prepared also had good reliability and performance so we could perform well straight away in Melbourne. This was a great surprise and we already achieved our target, which was that we wanted to start where we finished in Brazil at the end of 2006. A top-10 start was a dream come true. I had such a fantastic feeling.

Of course, the race was a bit different and it was not that easy in the next few races. But then we had a major update at Barcelona. That again raised our performance so that we scored our first championship point, which was very emotional. I had been involved in this team from Day One, working together, so everything was very memorable. Eighth place, one point, might be a very small thing in global terms in F1, but for us it was mega! I had to push the whole way through the race, it wasn't an easy eighth place. That was a real race that I built up from the start, tenth by tenth.

The sixth place in Canada was still fantastic, but it was a very different feeling for me. It was nothing like as emotional, it was just pure fun and excitement. The Canada race was a bit crazy, and so many things did happen but, to the end of the race, and in the last stint especially, I was pushing like hell. I think we genuinely had the pace, because I qualified 11th, just missing the top 10 by a tenth or something. Overtaking some of the works teams, including one of the McLarens, was – from a pure driving point-of-view – so exciting! I really had fun…"

NATIONALITY Japanese
DATE OF BIRTH 28/1/77
PLACE OF BIRTH Tokyo, Japan
GRANDS PRIX 87
WINS 0
POLES 0
FASTEST LAPS 0
POINTS 44
HONOURS British F3 Champion 2001

18 ANTHONY DAVIDSON
SUPER AGURI

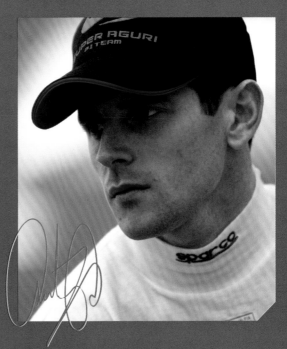

"I think in general it's been a really good year for me. I think I've done exactly what I wanted to do. In terms of speed, that's always been there. Sometimes the luck hasn't been with me, especially earlier in the year. But once I got settled into the weekends, how they run, and I stopped having bad luck, suddenly the results started coming – especially in qualifying.

Yes, I sit here with no points, but I feel I should have scored some. Especially after Canada, where I was one of the only drivers who managed to stay on the track in tough conditions, and was running in a strong position when I had bad luck by hitting the animal on the track. I think in reality I should have points, and I think everyone else knows that as well. The two people I was fighting were Alex Wurz and Ralf Schumacher, and I was in the middle of them. Alex was on the podium and Ralf was eighth, so I would have been in a points-scoring position for sure. It's a shame that the points are only in my head!

I'm happy with how the rest of the year has gone. I think one of my strongest races was actually very early on in Bahrain. It was a very positive weekend as I qualified 13th and was running in 13th position chasing the Renaults hard until five laps from the end, when the engine failed. I think because that was so long ago everyone forgets that, but in my mind I still remember that as a great weekend, and an early showing of what was to come.

The last few races were very good. I got a real handle on qualifying, I feel, and a good understanding of the tyres and just the way the whole weekend pans out now. I go at it in a much more relaxed frame of mind from where I was at the beginning of the year, when it was all a new experience.

Above all I've just been loving racing again. The racing environment has just been fantastic. At the beginning of the year, all I could really focus on was qualifying, and then see what happens in the race. But now I can definitely do both as well as each other."

NATIONALITY British
DATE OF BIRTH 18/4/79
PLACE OF BIRTH Hemel Hempstead, England
GRANDS PRIX 20
WINS 0
POLES 0
FASTEST LAPS 0
POINTS 0
HONOURS European F3 Champion 2001, Formula Ford Festival winner 2000, British Formula Ford Champion 1999

19 RUBENS BARRICHELLO
↓ –12   HONDA

"The overall feeling about this year is that it has been a disappointing and bad season. I've had no results at all! On the other hand, I've always been positive, and I've been working hard.

At the beginning of the year, some people said this is a bad car and no effort could make up for it, and they threw away the towel. But I've been working quite a lot. Although it was a bit of a fantasy to come to a weekend thinking that you can finish somewhere in the points, that's what I've been doing for the whole time.

To be honest, the problems really came home to me whenever we changed the car big time, and nothing improved. Before that, we always said we're going to have an upgrade, so you had the feeling that it will be OK. It was Canada, I think, where they brought everything, and there was no real change. The main problem was a shift in balance when you touched the brakes that was far too big, and that caused all the problems. It was not that it was draggy and you're keeping the downforce, it was going away whenever you were touching the brake pedal.

I think the car was suitable for some circuits. The test that I had at Paul Ricard, and then the race that I had at Monaco, were good. I quite enjoyed that. But then whenever we moved on from there in the aerodynamic package, we just made it worse again.

Jenson had two competitive races, Magny-Cours and Monza, where he finished eighth, with some people dropping out, and then fifth in China. In the ones where I was more competitive, everybody finished. In Silverstone everybody finished! I should have scored a few points. Hungary was the worst for me. People say you finished last, how does it feel? It's not that, it was the fact that I was driving a bad car, not that I was last or 14th.

What I want and what I asked the team is to put the right people in the right places, that's all. If you have a committee with everyone talking, you never get to the problem. I'm thinking that next year is going to be a lot better. But they know that they don't have to find one second, they have to find three! And that's a big task."

NATIONALITY Brazilian
DATE OF BIRTH 23/5/72
PLACE OF BIRTH São Paulo, Brazil
GRANDS PRIX 252
WINS 9
POLES 13
FASTEST LAPS 15
POINTS 519
HONOURS British F3 Champion 1991, European Formula Opel Champion 1990

20 RALF SCHUMACHER
↓ -4 TOYOTA

"It's been a very disappointing year for everybody, because everybody worked hard, it's just the outcome wasn't good enough. We did not develop at the right speed. Our car was sometimes competitive, but most of the time it wasn't. And in a situation like that everybody is giving 100%, you try to push, and sometimes mistakes happen as well.

When we started with the new car, it looked quite promising, and balance-wise we made a step. It's just the other teams made a bigger step! The problems for us were driveability, stability under braking and turn-in, and traction. That's what we struggled with this year. To point the finger at one area of the car is not appropriate – I think it was a combination of things.

The new tyres were so different to last year's that switching early didn't really help us. I think a lot of teams underestimated the new tyre situation, and so did we. It took us a while until we understood them. And I think 2006 would have been stronger on the Michelins rather the Bridgestone tyres!

It was different, it was not like driving an F1 car like it used to be. With those tyres, you needed a completely different style. I did adjust, but it took me a while, because first of all tried to get the tyre right and the situation right, but it didn't work out. At a certain time, though, it was myself adapting a bit, and the tyre becoming a bit better.

This year the fight for the last few points was really hard between Red Bull, Williams, Renault and ourselves. It was very close this year as well. On the very few occasions when we had a really strong package, we sometimes struggled to be near the pack. We had some bad starts as well, which didn't really help us to stay in the points. So we had a lot of problems this year which made the season worse than it could have been.

Hungary was an outstanding race, because the car was suited to the track, and I myself like it as well. We were quick. We were a little unlucky in the pit stop strategy, because we could have done better, but still it was a decent race."

NATIONALITY German
DATE OF BIRTH 30/6/75
PLACE OF BIRTH Kerpen, Germany
GRANDS PRIX 181
WINS 6
POLES 6
FASTEST LAPS 8
POINTS 329
HONOURS Formula Nippon Champion 1996, Macau F3 GP winner 1995

21 VITANTONIO LIUZZI
↓ -2 TORO ROSSO

"I'm disappointed about the first half of the season. We suffered a lot from the fact that we received the car so late, and had to pay for the fact that we had no development.

We struggled to close the gap to our competitors because we had no testing in the winter, so it was like a blind start to the season. For sure, that was really upsetting, because we expected to have a much faster car at the beginning, and we wanted to fight for points in every race. So that was not the best position to be in.

It was a shame because we always got development really late. Red Bull Technology gave us a lot of opportunities to go forward, but we always struggled to make everything in time. We were always one month late compared to where we should have been. We had to fight really, really hard to achieve something that never came because of the lack of the speed of the car. But, by the end of the season we were putting more pieces on the car and we were getting closer and closer to top 10.

Also, we had a difficult atmosphere in the team before Scott left, but at the end of the day I cannot complain about my season, because I always showed that compared to my team-mate I'm doing a good job. So, at the end of the day, I have to be positive.

From my point-of-view I think I did a really good season. We had some great races, and for sure it became easier and easier to be in Q2. I think in all the races we showed that when we have a fight I'm always there and I never give up.

For sure, Monaco qualifying was really great, we would have had a great race if David had not hit me at the first corner! We deserved the points in China. In the last 20 laps Heidfeld was faster than me, but I was trying to use a better exit out of the corners, putting myself in the best position in the track, trying not to make a mistake. Even if we were not so fast on the dry tyres, because I had a lot of graining on the fronts, I did everything perfectly strategy-wise to keep him behind."

NATIONALITY Italian
DATE OF BIRTH 6/8/81
PLACE OF BIRTH Locorotondo, Italy
GRANDS PRIX 39
WINS 0
POLES 0
FASTEST LAPS 0
POINTS 5
HONOURS Formula 3000 Champion 2004, World Kart Champion 2001, Italian Kart Champion 1996

22 MARKUS WINKELHOCK
SPYKER

NATIONALITY German DATE OF BIRTH 13/4/80 PLACE OF BIRTH Stuttgart, Germany GRANDS PRIX 1 WINS 0 POLES 0 FASTEST LAPS 0 POINTS 0 HONOURS None

"It was a special day, my first F1 race, and in Germany. I was quite lucky that the team made a good decision to bring me in, and we immediately changed to wet tyres. It worked, and I overtook many cars. As soon as I left the pits I could see that I was much quicker with the rain tyres. There was so much water, it was not easy to hold the car on the track. I didn't want to take any risks, because for me it was the first time in an F1 car in rain conditions. I saw the pit board with P1 on, and asked the team 'am I really in P1?' They said 'yes you are, keep on pushing!' Unfortunately the safety car came out, but they would have caught me anyway. It was disappointing to have an electronic problem after the restart, but I must thank the whole team for a really nice weekend."

23 SCOTT SPEED
TORO ROSSO
⬇ -2

NATIONALITY American DATE OF BIRTH 24/1/83 PLACE OF BIRTH Manteca, USA GRANDS PRIX 28 WINS 0 POLES 0 FASTEST LAPS 0 POINTS 0 HONOURS European & German Formula Renault Champion, US Formula Russell Champion 2001

"It has been a great ride, but I am going home! Over the past five years, I have had the privilege of driving at some of the world's most exciting circuits. It didn't all go the way that I wanted, but F1 has been a great experience. Unfortunately, Toro Rosso's decision to remove me from my racing seat has left me to consider many other options. Red Bull has been most supportive of my talents and Dietrich Mateschitz became very excited about the possibility of my racing back in the USA. I'm really excited to race ARCA as it's a chance to learn a new animal – stock car racing – without being put under a spotlight. In ARCA, you have a field full of young guys like me trying to make a name. It's hard to judge the competition, but I'm jazzed about the thought of racing back home."

24 KAZUKI NAKAJIMA
WILLIAMS

NATIONALITY Japanese DATE OF BIRTH 11/1/85 PLACE OF BIRTH Aichi, Japan GRANDS PRIX 1 WINS 0 POLES 0 FASTEST LAPS 0 POINTS 0 HONOURS Japanese Formula Toyota Champion 2003

"It's been a good year for me, and GP2 and the F1 testing all went quite well. The Brazilian GP was a really good chance for me, so I have to say many thanks to the team, especially Frank, Patrick and Sam Michael.

The weekend in Brazil passed really quickly. It was a shame to have a really bad qualifying, and I made a lot of mistakes. It's something that I have to learn for next time, but I'm quite happy with the weekend as a whole.

Friday was really good and the race was good, apart from the pit stop! I'm so sorry for the mechanics I hit.

I had a good start, but lost some places at the first corner. The pace was really good and I could overtake some people like Takuma, and also Coulthard, so that was good for me and good for the team as well."

25 SAKON YAMAMOTO
SPYKER
⬆ +1

NATIONALITY Japanese DATE OF BIRTH 9/7/82 PLACE OF BIRTH Toyohashi City, Japan GRANDS PRIX 14 WINS 0 POLES 0 FASTEST LAPS 0 POINTS 0 HONOURS Japanese Kart Champion 1999

"This year was quite variable for me! At the beginning of the season I was a test driver for Aguri, and I raced in GP2 as a way to come back to F1. And I got a chance. The team was different, but it was a good opportunity to join Spyker, and I really appreciated that they give me a really good chance to drive in F1.

At the first race in Hungary everything was new, but at least I had experience from seven races last year, and I knew how I should work with an F1 team.

Spyker's B-spec car was a big improvement. For me, driving was much easier than before, and I could really push and get good results. I know I can do better if I have more time. I don't know what's going to happen, but I hope I can drive from the start of the season."

26 CHRISTIJAN ALBERS
SPYKER
⬇ -4

NATIONALITY Dutch DATE OF BIRTH 16/4/79 PLACE OF BIRTH Eindhoven, Netherlands GRANDS PRIX 46 WINS 0 POLES 0 FASTEST LAPS 0 POINTS 4 HONOURS German F3 Champion 1999, Benelux & Dutch Formula Ford Champion 1997

"It was a nice situation for me, as you just want to race and to focus on that, you don't want to get involved in other things. And a lot of things happened. It was quite hard to improve because we'd spent all the money on the B-spec car. So it was really difficult for me to improve myself and to get the car to my driving style. That took a long time, and in Magny-Cours and Silverstone it turned around a bit as we went to another electronic system. I was waiting for the B-spec car – I thought I could do much more with the rear of the car, as for me it was quite difficult to drive with the tyres. Straight after the British GP, a press release came and said that I was not racing any more. You do feel a little bit of pain, but on the other side also relief, because there was a lot going on."

THE TEAMS

Spec tyres were one of the major challenges facing the 11 teams. We find out from the technical chiefs how they coped with the change plus their other highs and lows

McLAREN

FERRARI

BMW SAUBER

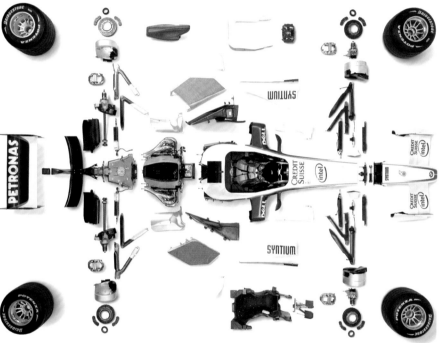

RED BULL

WILLIAMS

TORO ROSSO

SUPER AGURI

SPYKER

McLaren

THE TEAM

PERSONNEL

TEAM PRINCIPAL, CHAIRMAN & GROUP CEO
Ron Dennis
VICE-PRESIDENT MERCEDES-BENZ MOTORSPORT
Norbert Haug
CHIEF OPERATING OFFICER, McLAREN GROUP
Martin Whitmarsh (above)
MANAGING DIRECTOR, McLAREN RACING
Jonathan Neale
ENGINEERING DIRECTOR Paddy Lowe
DESIGN & DEVELOPMENT DIRECTOR Neil Oatley
HEAD OF AERODYNAMICS Simon Lacey
HEAD OF VEHICLE ENGINEERING Mark Williams
HEAD OF RACE OPERATIONS Steve Hallam
HEAD OF SIMULATION tba
CHIEF ENGINEER MP4-22 Pat Fry
CHIEF ENGINEER MP4-23 Tim Goss
TEAM MANAGER Dave Ryan
DRIVERS Fernando Alonso, Lewis Hamilton
RACE ENGINEER (Alonso) Mark Slade
RACE ENGINEER (Hamilton) Phil Prew
TEST TEAM MANAGER Indy Lall
TEST DRIVERS Pedro de la Rosa, Gary Paffett
CHIEF MECHANIC Pete Vale
TOTAL NUMBER OF EMPLOYEES 550 (McLaren Racing)
TEAM BASE Woking, England
TELEPHONE +44 (0)1483 261000
WEBSITE www.mclaren.com

TEAM STATS

IN F1 SINCE 1966 **FIRST GRAND PRIX** Monaco 1966
STARTS 630 **WINS** 156 **POLE POSITIONS** 133
FASTEST LAPS 134 **PODIUMS** 419 **POINTS** 3150.5
CONSTRUCTORS' TITLES 8 **DRIVERS' TITLES** 11

SPONSORS

Vodafone, Mobil 1, Johnnie Walker, Santander, Aigo, Henkel, Schuco, Hilton

1 **FERNANDO ALONSO**   2 **LEWIS HAMILTON**

EXCEEDING PRE-SEASON EXPECTATIONS

**By Martin Whitmarsh
(Chief Operating Officer)**

"The MP4-22 was good during winter testing, but a significant aspect was that the development team was able to improve it race-on-race. We targeted a 0.15s gain for every race and exceeded that. Increasingly, every team is improving at a faster rate than we were five or 10 years ago.

It stemmed from a good group of engineers who work together really well. We had some traumatic events and it's testimony that there was enough discipline not to be distracted. It was a great effort and we've come out a stronger group of people. Various assertions were made as to our competitiveness which caused offence to many of our engineers, but they realised they had to keep focus, and I'm incredibly proud of them.

The race team performed in an exemplary manner and we didn't have one mechanical failure. We did well tactically and strategically, China apart. We had some challenging races, Japan being one, and I think we did everything right, converting from a two- to a one-stopper at the right time and place.

GOOD AT RIDING THE KERBS

You look at any area where you are not the best, and I think that in long, high-speed corners – perhaps due to steering, turning or yaw sensitivity – we were not as good as Ferrari. But we narrowed the gap. In sharp turn-in, heavy-braking stability, traction and kerb riding, we had an advantage.

We adapted to Bridgestone fairly quickly. We had already won championships with them. I think Bridgestone had a lot of respect for our tyre analysis and simulation capabilities. We developed our own wind-tunnel-model tyres, probably uniquely, when we were last with Bridgestone.

We decided that we had tyre-development engineers and would disclose everything we had. Some of our experts were uncomfortable, thinking we were giving away the crown jewels, but it accelerated trust and information transfer between ourselves and Bridgestone.

Others suggest that putting Bridgestones on had little effect on us, but we lost 11 points of rear downforce. It was a big, big difference, but we were committed to pneumatic tyres in our wind tunnel. To aid fast transfer, we'd had a third party manufacture pneumatic wind-tunnel tyres. We now run with Bridgestone pneumatic model tyres, but we had made early provision by taking the Bridgestone profile, looking at its squash shape and having a third party produce them.

The tyres are a vital part of the package, so you have to take a tyre change very seriously. We had done a tremendous amount of work at the rear of the car looking at ride-height sensitivity, and it was optimised around the Michelin. When we switched tyres, a lot of that was negated.

MERCEDES INVESTMENT PAYS OFF

We didn't have one engine failure either, and that's a fantastic effort. Daimler has agreed to a significant investment programme at Mercedes High Performance Engines in Brixworth, taking it out of the old Ilmor buildings into a kind of mini MTC [McLaren Technology Centre]. It is designed to be the best race-engine design and manufacturing facility in the world.

We had the youngest driver pairing in F1, quite remarkable for an established team with high expectations. We had a proven product in Fernando and an unproven one in Lewis. What Lewis quickly established with those first nine consecutive podiums was unbelievable. We've been nonchalant about it, but it was stunning.

When we decided to give Lewis the seat, we were damned if we did and damned if we didn't! We got him an apartment in Woking, he came to work, sat with our engineers, our strategy people, went on the shop floor, in the simulator and in the gym, and physically he's much stronger. Mentally and technically, he was more informed too, and that all happened before the start of 2007.

PREPARING DRIVERS FOR THEIR ROLE

It was logical, but I don't know that a rookie has arrived so well prepared. Maybe that says something about how poor F1 is at developing talent. We knew he was quick, but to deal with the huge pressures was extraordinary. If he'd scored a point in his first race, and then had a sixth, it would have built up slowly, but you just couldn't prepare him for the phenomenal profile that his results created. He went from superstar kid to leading the championship to being favourite to win the title, almost overnight, and he took it all in his stride.

Fernando had this tremendous challenge of being a two-time champion in a new team and having a rookie outperforming him sometimes. Remember that Fernando is also still a young man and could not have expected it. He had never had a team-mate quicker, never mind being champion and having a rookie exert that much pressure.

POLICY OF EQUALITY MAKES LIFE HARDER

It's been daunting and challenging and that created some 'interesting' discussions. McLaren, rightly or wrongly, has a policy of equality, and I think people accept that we do a pretty good job of it. That has made our challenges for World Championships more difficult. A *de facto* number one is easier and sometimes more efficient, but we believe whoever wins the title should know they won it because they did the best job. It's undeniably the case that if you aren't willing to skew the effort, you make it harder to win. But when you do win, that title is worth more.

We believed Lewis could be a champion, but I don't know that anyone believed that it was reasonable to think it might happen in his first year. Some of his GP2 performances were extraordinary, but followed mistakes in qualifying or at the start. We said to him that if he was that much quicker it should be boring: you should get pole and drive away. So it might have been reasonable to expect some mistakes in F1, but he stood on the podium nine times in a row instead...

There hasn't been much wrong with Fernando's year either. He got a competitive car, the full support of the team, and had we not given that to Lewis as well, we'd all be hailing Fernando as the hat-trick hero."

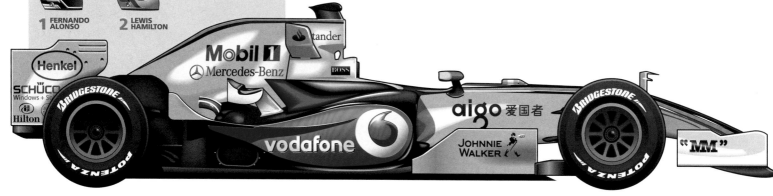

TECHNICAL SPECIFICATIONS

ENGINE
MAKE/MODEL Mercedes-Ilmor FO 108T
CONFIGURATION 2400cc V8 (90 degree)
SPARK PLUGS NGK
ECU McLaren Electronic Systems
FUEL Mobil 1
OIL Mobil 1
BATTERY GS Yuasa

TRANSMISSION
GEARBOX McLaren
FORWARD GEARS Seven
CLUTCH McLaren

CHASSIS
CHASSIS MODEL
McLaren MP4-22
FRONT SUSPENSION LAYOUT
Inboard torsion bar/damper system, operated by pushrod and bellcrank with a double-wishbone arrangement

REAR SUSPENSION LAYOUT
Inboard torsion bar/damper system, operated by pushrod and bellcrank, with a double-wishbone arrangement
DAMPERS Koni
TYRES Bridgestone
WHEELS Enkei
BRAKE DISCS Hitco
BRAKE PADS AP Racing
BRAKE CALIPERS Akebono
FUEL TANK ATL
INSTRUMENTS
McLaren Electronic Systems

DIMENSIONS
LENGTH Undisclosed
WIDTH 1800mm
HEIGHT 950mm
WHEELBASE Undisclosed
TRACK front Undisclosed
rear Undisclosed
WEIGHT Undisclosed

Team McLaren Mercedes

1 McLaren was the first team to try a 'bridge' front wing, doing so as its nose was much lower than that of many of its rivals. It was first seen at the Spanish GP
2 A reprofiled rear wing was seen on the MP4-22 for the first time in Canada, with an unusually straight profile to the upper edge of its top section

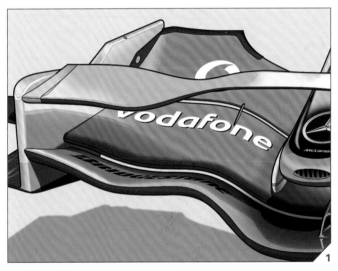

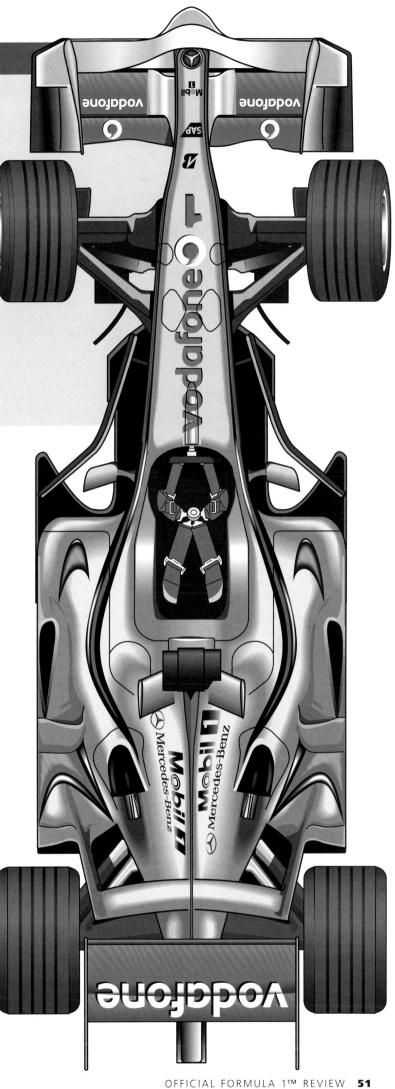

RENAULT

THE TEAM

PERSONNEL
PRESIDENT Bernard Rey
MANAGING DIRECTOR Flavio Briatore
DEPUTY MANAGING DIRECTOR (ENGINE) Rob White
DEPUTY MANAGING DIRECTOR (SUPPORT) Andre Laine
TECHNICAL DIRECTOR Bob Bell
EXECUTIVE DIRECTOR OF ENGINEERING Pat Symonds (above)
DEPUTY TECHNICAL DIRECTOR James Allison
HEAD OF VEHICLE TECHNOLOGY Tad Czapski
OPERATIONS DIRECTOR John Mardle
HEAD OF AERODYNAMICS Dino Toso
CHIEF DESIGNER Tim Densham
RS27 PROJECT MANAGER Axel Plasse
HEAD OF TRACKSIDE ENGINE OPERATIONS Denis Chevrier
SPORTING MANAGER Steve Nielsen
CHIEF RACE ENGINEER Alan Permane
DRIVERS Giancarlo Fisichella, Heikki Kovalainen
RACE ENGINEER (Fisichella) David Greenwood
RACE ENGINEER (Kovalainen) Adam Carter
TEST TEAM MANAGER Carlos Nunes
TEST/THIRD DRIVERS Nelson Piquet Jr, Ricardo Zonta
CHIEF MECHANIC Gavin Hudson
TOTAL NUMBER OF EMPLOYEES 790
NUMBER IN RACE TEAM 70
TEAM BASE Enstone, England
TELEPHONE +44 (0)1608 678000
WEBSITE www.ing-renaultf1.com

TEAM STATS
IN F1 SINCE 1977–1985 then from 2002 **FIRST GRAND PRIX** Britain 1977, then Australia 2002 **STARTS** 228 **WINS** 33 **POLE POSITIONS** 49 **FASTEST LAPS** 27 **PODIUMS** 88 **POINTS** 1046 **CONSTRUCTORS' TITLES** 0 **DRIVERS' TITLES** 0 **FASTEST LAPS** 0 **PODIUMS** 18 **POINTS** 306 **CONSTRUCTORS' TITLES** 0 **DRIVERS' TITLES** 0

SPONSORS
ING, Renault, Elf, Hanjin Shipping, PVAXX, Bridgestone

3 GIANCARLO FISICHELLA

4 HEIKKI KOVALAINEN

A YEAR SPENT PLAYING CATCH-UP

**By Pat Symonds
(Executive Director of Engineering)**

"We haven't had a good year. When you've won two championships in a row, it gets exponentially harder to maintain the level, but in spite of the realism that to continually win is near-impossible, it was still very disappointing to drop to a point where at the start of the season our performance was a good 2% off the pace of the front runners. That was hard to take.

While we're absolutely not proud that we got into that situation, we should be proud of the pragmatic approach we took to getting out of it. We still didn't have a front-running car at the end of the season, but it was consistent. What it lacked was the nine months of development time it took us to discover the problem and be rigorous in ensuring we had understood it. So we ended up with an R27 that was easier to drive, but an out-of-date car in real time.

TWO PARTICULAR PROBLEMS
The two main issues were not being able to use the Bridgestone tyres as well as we had the Michelins, and problems with lack of correlation between our wind tunnel and on-track data. They were separate issues and either one of them would have been troublesome. The combination of the two was particularly bad. And, when I say that either one of them would have been troublesome, we trawled back an awful long way and saw that part of the problem of correlation actually started when we were still on Michelins. So we mustn't just point in one direction.

Part of the trouble was that over the years the expectations from the wind tunnel just got better and better. Years ago we checked everything, but it got to the point where the correlation was actually so damn good that we didn't check it anymore, and it slipped away without us realising. The fix took longer than I expected. When we really crashed into it, by mid to end of February, we said, 'look, this is massive!'

We use pneumatic tyres in the wind tunnel, so the model tyres are real representations. Not too long ago we used to use carbon-fibre wheels and tyres and they were all solid. Now, they are made of rubber, inflated and the construction is done such that when scale loads are applied, they deflect to the same shape as a real tyre. So they are immensely sophisticated little things. With the Bridgestone model tyre that we changed to towards the end of last year, the shape, when loaded, was not a precise replication of the real thing. It deflected differently, and that is an incredibly critical area in terms of aerodynamics.

You can have a car that hasn't got downforce but is easy to drive, like a saloon car, but it's slow. You can also get very critical aerodynamics that switch between states. If you imagine a bit of airflow that attaches and detaches repeatedly – it's unstable. You have a car that is quicker one minute than it is the next, which is terribly difficult to drive. That was our problem at the beginning of the season. And it's why it reflected so much on Heikki Kovalainen. You must give a rookie a

car that's easy to drive, that he can trust, because rookies make mistakes. We gave Heikki a car that was pretty well different at every corner he turned into. Giancarlo's experience allowed him not to overdrive the car and get a better result than Heikki out of it. He knew the thing was going to bite him, so he kept it at a level where it didn't.

REACHING A TURNING POINT
People ask about highs and lows. Well, our low lasted from March through to about June! The high was not specifically one race, it was the realisation, as we came back from the North America trip, that we really had solved our problem and could start racing. Giving him a stable car to race in Canada was the turning point for Heikki. Up to then, as Flavio said, it was his 'brother', and on Saturday night in Canada Heikki came back to the fold and just didn't put a foot wrong thereafter. It was like flicking a switch. Friday and Saturday he'd done nothing but throw cars at the wall, Sunday he drove a brilliant race and never looked back.

Actually that was a bit of a high point too – getting Heikki's car out in qualifying on Saturday in Canada after he'd hit the wall in Turn 4. It was something else – I was really proud of the team. In the latter part of the season, Fisi had some unfortunate results and a few things transpired against him – and I don't think I really want to say much more than that.

By year-end, the car had established itself as fourth-fastest on the grid. Reliability has been very good. We had one engine change, at Spa, which was due to a massive oil leak. I think the homologated engines have worked very well. I can't remember in all the years that I've been in F1 where everyone seems to accept that the engines are all pretty much of a muchness. But while they're pretty equal on power, I think we've got a nice driveable engine.

I'm very optimstic about next year. This year's problems apart, what I do know is that if you do a good job and you've got a good group, which we have, you know that you're going to produce a car that's there or thereabouts.

MOVING THE TROOPS AROUND
Organisationally, we made a few changes this year. I've enjoyed moving aside a little and seeing the new guys move in and take over a bit. Alan Permane is doing a fantastic job as Chief Race Engineer.

He's a bit of a chip off the old block – strong and doing very well. It's given me a lot more time to work on other projects and future regulations, which I find very interesting.

James Allison was also instrumental in that he's been the project leader in the investigation of our problem. He worked so hard and did a thorough, logical, stunning job. And Dino Toso really attacked the aero problem and is now looking at our next stages and our new CFD centre.

It might sound perverse but, due to the problems we had in 2007, we learned such a lot – and I'm still very much a sponge for learning!"

TECHNICAL SPECIFICATIONS

ENGINE
MAKE/MODEL Renault RS27
CONFIGURATION 2400cc V8
(90 degree)
SPARK PLUGS Champion
ECU Magneti Marelli
FUEL Elf
OIL Elf
BATTERY Renault F1 Team

TRANSMISSION
GEARBOX Renault F1 Team
FORWARD GEARS Seven
CLUTCH Undisclosed

CHASSIS
CHASSIS MODEL Renault R27
FRONT SUSPENSION LAYOUT
Carbon-fibre top and bottom wishbones
operating an inboard rocker via a pushrod
system connected to a torsion bar and
damper units

REAR SUSPENSION LAYOUT
Carbon-fibre wishbones operating
vertically-mounted torsion bars and
horizontally-mounted damper units
DAMPERS Undisclosed
TYRES Bridgestone
WHEELS OZ Racing
BRAKE DISCS Brembo
BRAKE PADS Brembo
BRAKE CALIPERS
AP Racing
FUEL TANK ATL
INSTRUMENTS Renault

DIMENSIONS
LENGTH 4800mm
WIDTH 1800mm
HEIGHT 950mm
WHEELBASE 3100mm
TRACK front 1450mm
rear 1400mm
WEIGHT 605kg (including
driver and camera)

RENAULT F1 Team

1 Renault was one of many teams changing its front wing through the year in
the quest for more grip from the Bridgestones. This is the wing used in Australia
2 The winglet atop the R27's sidepods cleverly included the rear-view mirrors.
Note, too, the flow conditioners to tidy up the airflow off the front of the car

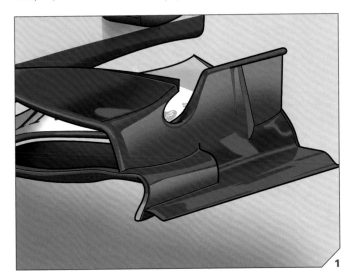

FERRARI

GOING FOR GOLD IN LIFE AFTER MICHAEL

**By Aldo Costa
(Head of Chassis)**

"The F2007 was a good development of the previous year's car. One of the more evident modifications was the wheelbase, which was longer. It allowed us better aerodynamic development and had some positive aspects and no big negative.

I don't think we were handicapped by it on the tighter circuits. In Hungary, for example, we had a problem in qualifying but our race pace was good.

We have to develop our cars a little for bumpier tracks or kerb-riding because I think McLaren was stronger there. It is about coping with the higher load variations that you can have in these circumstances. On the other hand, we had an advantage on overall aerodynamic efficiency.

WORKING WITH THE COMPOUNDS

Some of the performance this year was tyre-dependent and it's true that in Monaco we had problems managing the super-soft tyre, and also in Canada. We worked to understand that and in Hungary and Brazil we demonstrated that we had no more problems with that. So it was definitely a learning curve there.

The spec' Bridgestones were from the same family as the 2004/5 tyres, but in winter testing we saw that they were completely different animals and we had to adapt the car around them. The compounds were different compared to last year's tyres and so, again, we had to re-write the book and learn how to manage them.

The game was completely different from 2006. Last year it was about trying to develop the tyres and you could look at the previous five or 10 years to help make the car faster. We were focusing with Bridgestone on developing a lot of new tyres – both compounds and constructions. It was probably why this year we found our competitor stronger on bumpy circuits and the kerbing because over the last few years we didn't concentrate very much on that. It was much better to invest time on new tyres, new tyres and more new tyres. We did the development for Bridgestone pretty much single-handed for three or four years. We were the only ones really pushing because nobody else was with us apart from the smaller teams.

ALL CHANGE FOR 2007

This year was completely different. You had four tyres, four compounds, and you had to optimise your car around them. That's your fixed constraint and then you have to think about the various possibilities to gain performance from the pressure management, from camber settings, toe settings, tyre warmers and everything surrounding the tyres. Probably McLaren, in Monte Carlo, understood better than us how to manage the super-soft tyre – and maybe not only McLaren.

We started the season very competitively in Australia. There was then talk about the floor stay clarification costing us quite a lot. But, by then, it was a pretty well-used system in F1. There was a clarification which we accepted and we

changed it but, in the end, if I plotted ride height on a diagram, I wouldn't see anything greatly significant. I think it was a diversion, an excuse.

WIND TUNNEL BREAKAGE

We still use a single wind tunnel and are happy that it is the most efficient way to organise ourselves at the moment. We did have a wind tunnel breakage in April, which hurt us a little bit. It was a stoppage of a couple of weeks but we run it 24 hours, so while it wasn't fundamental, it was definitely a loss.

We had several aerodynamic developments during the year. Some were more evident, others less so, but the aero development was present throughout the year. In Spain, we had a big aero package but in terms of lap time gain there were also significant developments elsewhere. We had a pretty big new package at Magny-Cours and at Silverstone and, although the races were quite close together, for Spa and Fuji also. Overall, we have to be pleased with the level of car development throughout the season.

RELIABILITY PROBLEMS

We had some reliability issues this year and it's difficult to judge precisely why. We are trying to fix it with new procedures and new methods of analysis, but we cannot deny that they happened. We had three DNFs – an issue with Felipe in Melbourne in qualifying and another problem with Felipe in Silverstone. The fuel issue with Felipe in Hungarian qualifying was not a technical problem, it was a team problem. Kimi had an electronic problem in Spain and a hydraulic issue in Germany. That was cause for a little bit of frustration initially, but it was great to see that it did not cost him the championship in the end.

It was a mixture between procedural problems, quality control and tight design. If you run things which have got nice co-efficients of safety, you run safely, no problem, but then your car is very slow. And, when you are looking to push every detail to the limit, of course you need to improve your level of checking. You need to have stronger procedures.

LIFE AFTER MICHAEL

For many years, we had Michael Schumacher driving the development programme and benefited from all of his ability and experience. Of course, there were a lot of worries because Michael was stopping, but I have to say that both Kimi and Felipe have done a very good job. Felipe, as everyone saw from his 2006 season alongside Michael, made a very good step. He did so again and was much stronger again this year.

Kimi took a while to match him and to build those new team relationships and in general to understand how to work best with the team. But he really grew and now we are very happy about the feedback we get from both drivers. They work in the same direction. They are competitors, of course, but they were not fighting each other in a negative way. They were collaborators and they were open. This, for us, was a big plus."

THE TEAM

PERSONNEL

PRESIDENT Luca di Montezemolo
CEO & TEAM PRINCIPAL Jean Todt
TECHNICAL DIRECTOR Mario Almondo
SPORTING DIRECTOR Stefano Domenicali
ENGINE DIRECTOR Gilles Simon
TRACK OPERATIONS Luca Baldisserri
HEAD OF CHASSIS Aldo Costa (above)
CAR DESIGN & DEVELOPMENT CONSULTANT Rory Byrne
CHIEF DESIGNER Nikolas Tombazis
CHIEF AERODYNAMICIST John Iley
HEAD OF CAR PERFORMANCE Marco Fainello
HEAD OF STRUCTURES DEPARTMENT Davide Terletti
RACE & TEST TECHNICAL MANAGER David Lloyd
RACE ENGINE MANAGER Mattia Binotto
DRIVERS Felipe Massa, Kimi Räikkönen
RACE ENGINEER (Massa) Rob Smedley
RACE ENGINEER (Räikkönen) Chris Dyer
TEST DRIVERS Luca Badoer, Marc Gené
TEST TEAM MANAGER Luigi Mazzola
CHIEF MECHANICS (Massa) Salvatore Vargetto (Räikkönen) Giuseppe Rizzo
TOTAL NUMBER OF EMPLOYEES 900+
NUMBER IN RACE TEAM 90
TEAM BASE Maranello, Italy
TELEPHONE +39 0536 949450
WEBSITE www.ferrariworld.com

TEAM STATS

IN F1 SINCE 1950 **FIRST GRAND PRIX** Britain 1950
STARTS 758 **WINS** 201 **POLE POSITIONS** 195
FASTEST LAPS 204 **PODIUMS** 602 **POINTS** 3849.5
CONSTRUCTORS' TITLES 15 **DRIVERS' TITLES** 15

SPONSORS

FIAT, Marlboro, Shell, AMD, Bridgestone, Martini, Acer, Alice

5 FELIPE MASSA

6 KIMI RÄIKKÖNEN

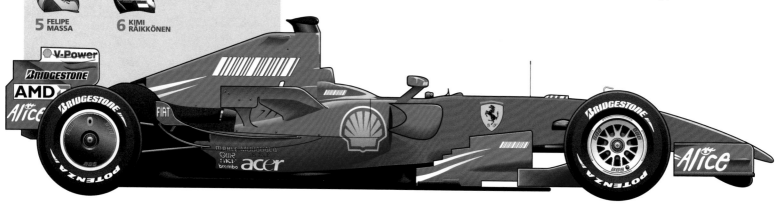

TECHNICAL SPECIFICATIONS

ENGINE
MAKE/MODEL Ferrari 056
CONFIGURATION 2398cc V8
(90 degree)
SPARK PLUGS NGK
ECU Magneti Marelli
FUEL Shell
OIL Shell
BATTERY Magneti Marelli

TRANSMISSION
GEARBOX Ferrari
FORWARD GEARS Seven
CLUTCH ZF Sachs

CHASSIS
CHASSIS MODEL Ferrari F2007
FRONT SUSPENSION LAYOUT
Double wishbones with pushrod-
activated torsion springs
REAR SUSPENSION LAYOUT
Double wishbones
with pushrod-activated
torsion springs
DAMPERS ZF Sachs
TYRES Bridgestone
WHEELS BBS
BRAKE DISCS Brembo
BRAKE PADS Brembo
BRAKE CALIPERS Brembo
FUEL TANK ATL
INSTRUMENTS
Ferrari/Magneti Marelli

DIMENSIONS
LENGTH 4545mm
WIDTH 1796mm
HEIGHT 959mm
WHEELBASE 3135mm
TRACK front 1470mm
rear 1405mm
WEIGHT 600kg (including
driver and camera)

1 Ferrari espoused the fitting of wheel shrouds in order to reduce drag by
drawing the air through from the ducts fitted on the chassis side of the wheel
2 These swept-back flow conditioners appeared at the French GP, sprouting from
the nose to channel air off the front wing to prevent lift and increase downforce

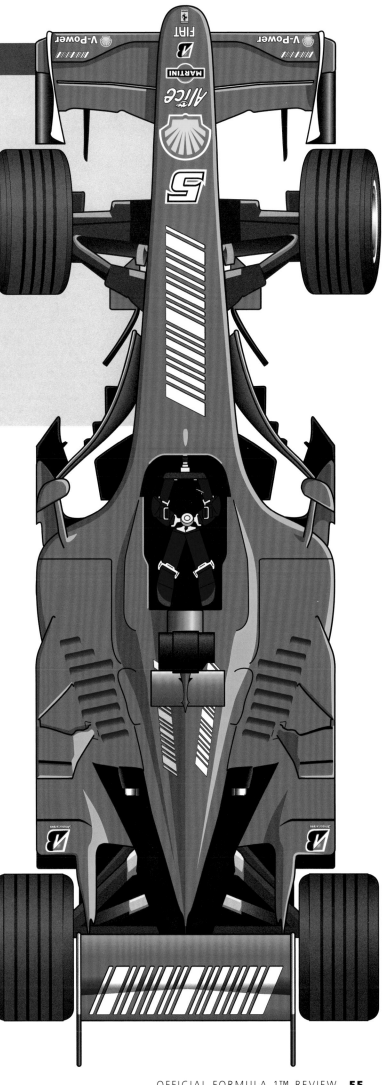

HONDA

THE TEAM

PERSONNEL

CHAIRMAN Yasuhiro Wada
CHIEF EXECUTIVE OFFICER Nick Fry
SENIOR TECHNICAL DIRECTOR Shuhei Nakamoto
ENGINEERING DIRECTOR Jacky Eeckelaert (above)
DIRECTOR OF STRATEGY & BUSINESS PLANNING
Otmar Szafnauer
OPERATIONS DIRECTOR Gary Savage
CHIEF DESIGNER Kevin Taylor
HEAD OF AERODYNAMICS Loïc Bigois
CHIEF ENGINEER, VEHICLE ENGINEERING
Craig Wilson
CHIEF TEST ENGINEER Simon Cole
SPORTING DIRECTOR Ron Meadows
DRIVERS Rubens Barrichello, Jenson Button
RACE ENGINEER (Barrichello) Jock Clear
RACE ENGINEER (Button) Andrew Shovlin
TEST TEAM MANAGER Andrew Alsworth
TEST/THIRD DRIVERS Mike Conway, Christian Klien
CHIEF MECHANIC Alastair Gibson
TOTAL NUMBER OF EMPLOYEES 640
NUMBER IN RACE TEAM 80
TEAM BASE Brackley, England
TELEPHONE +44 (0)1280 844000
WEBSITE www.hondaracingf1.com

TEAM STATS

IN F1 SINCE 1999, as BAR **FIRST GRAND PRIX** Australia
1999 **STARTS** 153 **WINS** 1 **POLE POSITIONS** 3
FASTEST LAPS 0 **PODIUMS** 18 **POINTS** 312
CONSTRUCTORS' TITLES 0 **DRIVERS' TITLES** 0

SPONSORS

Honda, Celerant, Eneos, NTN, Ray Ban, Seiko

7 JENSON BUTTON   **8 RUBENS BARRICHELLO**

TYRES WERE THE PRINCIPAL PROBLEM

By Jacky Eeckelaert
(Engineering Director)
"I don't think it needs saying that we had a tough 2007. We had one of the quickest cars on Michelins in 2006, and in the last three or four races we were quicker than Kimi's McLaren and sometimes were even on the rear wing of Alonso's Renault. Then, in November, when we swapped from Michelin to Bridgestone, five weeks after Brazil, suddenly our competitive car was not competitive any more.

In Brazil 2006, we were two-tenths faster than McLaren. A month later we were six-tenths slower. Looking at the data, it was the aerodynamic effect of the tyres on the car. Apparently, this effect was not there on the McLaren. The problems were compounded by the fact that the design of the RA107 started in June/July and the Bridgestone tyre data was only available at the end of October. We developed our aerodynamic concept in totally the wrong direction for the Bridgestone. So the new car was actually worse than the RA106.

TYRE SHAPE AFFECTS AIRFLOW

A critical factor was airflow around the front tyres. The tyre deformation was very different between the Michelin and the Bridgestone. The shape is different statically, but under loads – hard braking and downforce – there was an even bigger difference. The wake profile is different and we suffered a lot from that.

We had a lot of braking instability problems. It wasn't all due to the problem of the tyres. The car was reasonable at the start of 2006, developed in our old wind tunnel, and mid-season we had a loss of performance. We put in a lot of effort to get out of that situation and, from Hockenheim on, it was competitive. But, by putting so much effort in on that car, the new wind tunnel – which was ready mid-season and in which we started work on the RA107 – was not properly calibrated, causing a lot of problems. *Mea culpa* problems.

Also, perhaps we were too focused on the mechanical, rather than the aerodynamic, side. The car that used the Michelin best was the Honda – because mechanically it was the best car in 2006. But aerodynamics are important too, and I think we compromised that side too much.

Sometimes you have to give away stiffness and not go for the best suspension kinematics, as the wishbones won't be in the best position aerodynamically. We pushed too much towards the mechanical aspects at the expense of our aero.

FAST IN SLOW CORNERS, BUT...

The car was one of the lightest, with a very low centre of gravity, a very high level of ballast and it was very stiff. Aerodynamically, it was not so good. Speed traps at the apex of low-speed corners always showed us and the Super Aguris fastest, but the high-speed traps were a different story.

To have a high top speed, we had to run low downforce and that meant sliding through the corners. The balance also had a big shift under braking, which meant locking the rear wheels. Trying to sort that, you tended to reduce the front aero balance, but that gave power understeer.

We first saw the problems in November when we took the old car and put it on Bridgestones. We saw that it was much more sensitive to balance shift. But everything was already designed. We hoped the new car would be less sensitive to that problem, but it was worse. It's the same concept pushed further. And, Wind Tunnel 2, in which the car had been developed, was not properly calibrated, so we made the mistake of working too quickly in that tunnel. We stopped, went through a recalibration period and now the tunnel is good.

SUSPENSION MODIFICATIONS PAY OFF

We had new front suspension for the French GP. It improved the balance under braking and acceleration, and the layout was more aerodynamically driven, so we had better control of the wake from the front wheels. It wasn't the geometry that was the improvement, it was getting the wishbone up out of the wake. From the Italian GP, we did a similar thing with the rear suspension and that was also a positive.

When we tried the cascade front wing, it didn't give us any more efficiency, it was just more front wing. So you can either add the cascade wing or just turn the flap up a bit more. There didn't seem any benefit in adding the cascade wing, but the whole front-wing assembly area was one of our weaknesses. We suspect none of it worked as it should, and what we were doing with the upper wing was probably very different from McLaren.

Computational fluid dynamics gives you much better-optimised aero sections. We've probably developed our aero sections in the tunnel, whereas others do CFD to get the sections and use the tunnel to get the assembly. When I arrived in 2006, it was true that the team was quite poor in terms of CFD capacity compared to Sauber, where I'd come from. And CFD has become more important.

In the tunnel, you only measure results: you don't see the mechanism driving those results. But CFD can show you what is interesting, and it allows you to throw away 95 out of 100 ideas and just make five to try out. This is the way that Ferrari, McLaren, BMW and Williams have been doing it for the last four or five years, but not yet at Honda – for reasons of history.

DRIVERS HELD BACK BY THE CAR

It was a frustrating season for the drivers, but they worked hard. Jenson is not influenced by the stop watch, which is quite rare. If he's seventh and the car is awful, that's what he tells you. But if he's 18th and the balance is reasonable, he'll tell you it's OK. That's valuable, as so many drivers' comments are tainted by what the timing screens say.

Jenson has really matured, and his performances at Monza, where we were less handicapped in lower-downforce spec, and China, where he was fifth, were superb. There were also aspects of this year's package that were better suited to Rubens, who had some problems in 2006, and many times Jenson and Rubens were evenly matched. But we have to say that because of the problems with RA107 neither of them was in a position to perform to the level of their ability."

TECHNICAL SPECIFICATIONS

ENGINE
MAKE/MODEL Honda RA807E
CONFIGURATION 2400cc V8 (90 degree)
SPARK PLUGS NGK
ECU Honda PGM
FUEL Elf
OIL Nisseki
BATTERY NGK

TRANSMISSION
GEARBOX Honda F1
FORWARD GEARS Seven
CLUTCH Undisclosed

CHASSIS
CHASSIS MODEL Honda RA107
FRONT SUSPENSION LAYOUT
Wishbones and pushrod-activated
torsion springs and rockers, with a
mechanical anti-roll bar
REAR SUSPENSION LAYOUT
Wishbones and pushrod-activated
torsion springs and rockers, with a
mechanical anti-roll bar

DAMPERS Showa
TYRES Bridgestone
WHEELS BBS
BRAKE DISCS
Undisclosed
BRAKE PADS
Undisclosed
BRAKE CALIPERS
Alcon
FUEL TANK ATL
INSTRUMENTS
Honda F1

DIMENSIONS
LENGTH 4700mm
WIDTH 1800mm
HEIGHT 950mm
WHEELBASE
Undisclosed
TRACK
front Undisclosed
rear Undisclosed
WEIGHT Undisclosed

1 The front wing was apparently the RA107's Achilles' heel, and Honda
introduced this development at the European GP in a bid for aero efficiency
2 Getting clean air flow to the rear of the car was the aim when introducing this
arrangement of bargeboard, sidepod and chimney at the Monaco GP

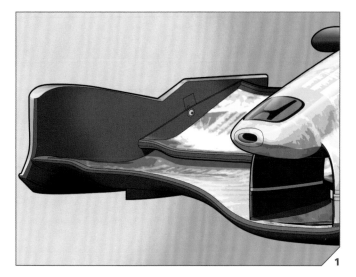

BMW SAUBER

AN EVOLUTION WITH DETAIL CHANGES

By Willy Rampf
(Technical Director)

"After a 2006 season in which we had increased the head count significantly, this process was largely finished, and for the 2007 World Championship everything stabilised from the people and processes points of view. That meant that we could largely concentrate on development of the car rather than the infrastructure of the team and its facilities.

BOOSTING THE COMPUTER POWER
We have increased the wind-tunnel head count from 35 to 85 people to be able to run three shifts, six days a week, basically 24 hours a day. This year, the wind tunnel was basically on-stream throughout the whole year.

We also introduced Albert 2, a more powerful version of the team's supercomputer, which uses 1,024 Intel processor cores, has a total memory of 2,048GB and a maximum power of 12,288 GigaFlops. On average, Albert 2 is around three times faster than its predecessor, Albert 1, and can perform calculations with greater accuracy than before. Yet, even now, we are thinking about increasing our computer capacity again, because all the simulation work we have to do is getting more and more detailed.

DEVELOPMENT RATHER THAN REVOLUTION
The regulations for 2007 were more or less the same, apart from some safety features. The car was an evolution but with a lot of detail changes. The basic dimensions were not so different, but we had much more time to develop the car compared to the year before. We also drastically revised the cooling system, which was a good step forward, and the front suspension was a huge change. We made sure too that we had more flexibility with weight distribution and aero balance on this year's car, because of the single supplier (Bridgestone) of standard tyres. That was important because when we actually did the concept work on the F1.07, nobody had any information about the tyres.

The gearbox was problematic at first, but that was no real surprise. A quick-shift 'box is a delicate system, and you can do some development on a bench, but the fine-tuning you do on a test track. If you get your shift-timing wrong by a few milliseconds, you have to open the gearbox because there is a major mechanical clash, but we managed it in a reasonably short time.

Overall, we were very reliable. We had a problem with the pit stop in Spain, with a wheelnut issue, but then we had 100 per cent finishes up until Robert's hydraulic problems in China.

FAIR COMPETITION BETWEEN THE DRIVERS
We were happy with both drivers. They are both good, but we don't have this Alonso/Hamilton situation. There is fair competition, which is absolutely right. Their lap times were very close together. In some races, Robert was really unlucky and could not get the maximum out of the car, because performance-wise they are very similar, but Nick got many more points than Robert.

We did not expect this level of performance. Finishing fifth last year, the target was to be fourth, and it was a nice surprise that we were third at the beginning of the season. We were very careful not to be too optimistic, but then it turned out that we stabilised in that position and in all the races we were the third-best team.

In Monaco, we were not so happy with the result. We gambled that there might be a safety-car period, which was the case for the five years before. We tried to win in Monaco, that's why we did it, and we split the cars' strategies.

DIFFERING DRIVING STYLES
At the start of the year, I think Robert was affected as much as anybody by the change to the different tyres. He improved, but the tyres do not favour his style. For Nick, it was easier and he was much quicker to adapt to the tyres. With Robert's driving style it was more difficult with these tyres because of the lateral and longitudinal characteristics. He turns in more aggressively than Nick, and the car has to respond very quickly and stay stable during this phase. He tuned the set-up in this direction and I don't think there's now a difference between the two guys, whereas at the beginning of the season there was.

We stopped using Sebastian Vettel as a third driver on Fridays, largely because the drivers requested as much track time as possible. The drivers wanted to select the tyres and everything themselves. I think that overall the most efficient way to engineer the car was for the race drivers to do the set-up work and the tyre selection.

AERO PROGRESS REQUIRED
We are pleased with the season, but we want to close the gap to the top teams, and the main area is still aerodynamics. We were also strong on the electronic side and always got good starts. We will lose out a bit there next year under the new rules, because we won't have the electronic flexibility. We may lose a little bit more than other teams there – it's possible.

I am very pleased and proud of the season overall, but the glory goes to the people in Hinwil and Munich, because we had the same people. They have done a good job in the past, but with limited resources. It really makes a huge difference whether you run the wind tunnel 10 hours a day or 24 hours a day, and if you have a computer that can do ten times the calculations. You can work in many more areas in more detail. We do much more simulation than in the past.

LOOKING TO MAKE THE FINAL JUMP
Of course, making the final jump to the McLaren/Ferrari level is the toughest thing, but it's where we are aiming.

It will be quite interesting to see where we are at the beginning of next season. The target is to move forward, but it will be difficult and we have to remember that Renault, last year's World Champions, had problems in 2007. They dropped back this year, but nobody should expect that they will stay there next season."

THE TEAM

PERSONNEL
MOTORSPORT DIRECTOR Mario Theissen
TECHNICAL DIRECTOR Willy Rampf (above)
HEAD OF POWERTRAIN Markus Duesmann
PROJECT MANAGER Walter Riedl
HEAD OF AERODYNAMICS Willem Toet
TEAM MANAGER Beat Zehnder
CHIEF RACE ENGINEER Mike Krack
DRIVERS Nick Heidfeld, Robert Kubica, Sebastian Vettel
RACE ENGINEER (Heidfeld) Giampaolo Dall'Ara
RACE ENGINEER (Kubica, Vettel) Mehdi Ahmadi
CHIEF ENGINE ENGINEER Tomas Andor
TEST/THIRD DRIVERS Sebastian Vettel, Timo Glock
CHIEF MECHANIC Urs Kuratle
CHIEF ENGINEER TEST TEAM Ossi Oikarinen
TOTAL NUMBER OF EMPLOYEES 700
NUMBER IN RACE TEAM 80
TEAM BASE Hinwil, Switzerland
TELEPHONE +41 44 937 9000
WEBSITE www.bmw-sauber-f1.com

TEAM STATS
IN F1 SINCE 1993, as Sauber **FIRST GRAND PRIX** South Africa 1993 **STARTS** 252 **WINS** 0 **POLE POSITIONS** 0 **FASTEST LAPS** 0 **PODIUMS** 10 **POINTS** 333 **CONSTRUCTORS' TITLES** 0 **DRIVERS' TITLES** 0

SPONSORS
Petronas, Intel, Credit Suisse, Dell, Syntium

9 NICK HEIDFELD **10 ROBERT KUBICA** **10 SEBASTIAN VETTEL**

TECHNICAL SPECIFICATIONS

ENGINE
MAKE/MODEL BMW P86/7
CONFIGURATION 2400cc V8
(90 degree)
SPARK PLUGS NGK
ECU BMWi
FUEL Petronas
OIL Petronas
BATTERY Undisclosed

TRANSMISSION
GEARBOX BMW Sauber
FORWARD GEARS Seven
CLUTCH AP Racing

CHASSIS
CHASSIS MODEL
BMW Sauber F1.07
FRONT SUSPENSION LAYOUT
Upper and lower wishbones,
inboard springs and dampers activated
by pushrods

REAR SUSPENSION LAYOUT
Upper and lower wishbones,
inboard springs and dampers
activated by pushrods
DAMPERS Undisclosed
TYRES Bridgestone
WHEELS OZ Racing
BRAKE DISCS Brembo or
Carbone Industrie
BRAKE PADS Brembo or
Carbone Industrie
BRAKE CALIPERS Brembo
FUEL TANK ATL
INSTRUMENTS BMW Sauber
Electronics

DIMENSIONS
LENGTH 4580mm
WIDTH 1800mm
HEIGHT 1000mm
WHEELBASE 3110mm
TRACK front 1470mm
rear 1410mm
WEIGHT 605kg (including
driver and camera)

BMW Sauber F1 Team

1 As early as the second race, in Malaysia, BMW Sauber introduced a new rear wing with revised profiling to help harness the air flow off the engine cover
2 The first race of the European season, the Spanish GP, was where the F1.07 first raced with this new front wing, sporting a deeply recessed middle section

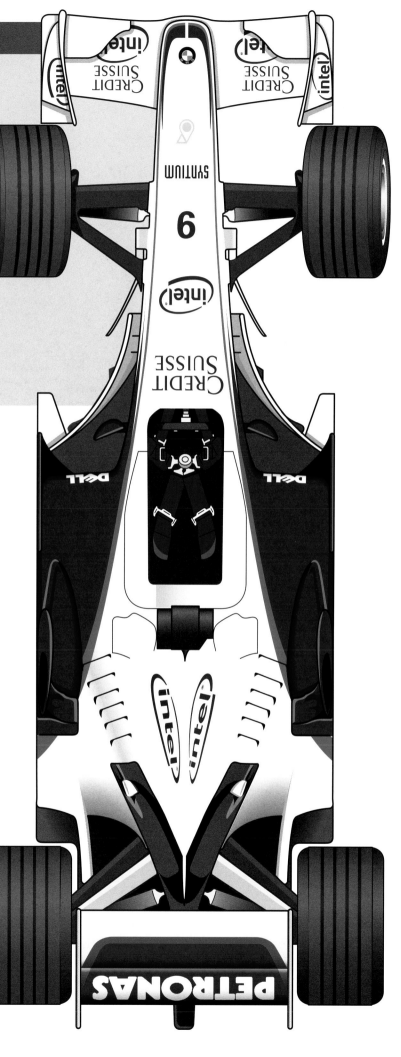

TOYOTA

Panasonic
DENSO

THE TEAM

PERSONNEL

CHAIRMAN AND TEAM PRINCIPAL
Tadashi Yamashina
PRESIDENT John Howett
ADVISOR Ove Andersson
EXECUTIVE VICE-PRESIDENT Yoshiaki Kinoshita
SENIOR GENERAL MANAGER, ENGINE
Luca Marmorini
SENIOR GENERAL MANAGER, CHASSIS
Pascal Vasselon (above)
DIRECTOR, TECHNICAL CO-ORDINATION
Noritoshi Arai
HEAD OF AERODYNAMICS Mark Gillan
TEAM MANAGER Richard Cregan
DRIVERS Ralf Schumacher, Jarno Trulli
CHIEF RACE & TEST ENGINEER Dieter Gass
RACE ENGINEER (Schumacher) Francesco Nenci
RACE ENGINEER (Trulli) Gianluca Pisanello
TEST DRIVERS Franck Montagny, Kohei Hirate & Kamui
Kobayashi
CHIEF MECHANIC Gerard Lecoq
TOTAL NUMBER OF EMPLOYEES 600
NUMBER IN RACE TEAM 80
TEAM BASE Cologne, Germany
TELEPHONE +49 (0)223 4182 3444
WEBSITE www.toyota-f1.com

TEAM STATS

IN F1 SINCE 2002 **FIRST GRAND PRIX** Australia 2002
STARTS 105 **WINS** 0 **POLE POSITIONS** 2
FASTEST LAPS 1 **PODIUMS** 6 **POINTS** 163
CONSTRUCTORS' TITLES 0 **DRIVERS' TITLES** 0

SPONSORS

Panasonic, Denso, Kingfisher Airlines, KDDI, Ebbon-Dacs,
Magneti Marelli, Dassault Systemes, EMC²

11 RALF SCHUMACHER **12 JARNO TRULLI**

A YEAR OF UNDER-ACHIEVEMENT

By Pascal Vasselon
(Senior General Manager, Chassis)
"The season was massively disappointing. We had two major problems. First, our car was not quick enough to achieve our targets – which included fighting for the podium. Ferrari, McLaren and BMW were faster and we were stuck in the midfield together with Renault, Williams and Red Bull. Sometimes we were ahead of them, and sometimes not. So, clearly, we were simply not fast enough in 2007.

The second problem was that we simply didn't score the points that our car performance was capable of. Renault, for instance, was a good benchmark and we can conclude that we had roughly the same car performance. And yet they scored a lot more points than we did.

RELIABILITY WAS STILL A PROBLEM

There were several reasons. First, we had a few reliability issues, a lot less than in 2006, but still a factor. Jarno had his fuel-system problem in Barcelona when he was P6 on the grid, for example, and Ralf had the wheel-fixing issue at Silverstone when he was also P6.

We had some disastrous pit stops – such as at the Nürburgring when Ralf's pace was quick in both the wet and the dry. We had a brake-caliper temperature issue in Monaco, where Jarno is always fast, but because of this could not race to his full potential.

LOSING GROUND AT THE STARTS

Probably a bigger issue than any of that, in terms of why we could not score the points our pace warranted, though, was our starts. We were struggling in this area and we can continue the parallel with Renault, as they usually gained one, two or even three places at the start and we lost one, two or three. They qualified in the midfield pack and were often ahead of it by Turn 1, whereas we were doing the opposite.

It was not only an issue surrounding the start itself, but also up to the first corner. And then, actually, more than once we had a decent start and were involved in an incident at the first corner.

The start itself is complex, as it's the integration of several specialities. There are four main factors: the tyre grip, the clutch control, the engine response and the driver, who is absolutely not a passenger. We have been struggling for the last 18 months with the start, and it seems our overall package is not robust enough. We have identified all the causes and worked on all of them, but obviously not quickly enough.

For sure, next year, with the ban on driver aids and a manual start, it will change, but some parameters will still be there – clutch controllability and tyre grip for instance, and the driver will step up in the order of importance.

The homologated V8 engines helped with reliability because manufacturers cannot push for power, and the maximum rpm was obviously limited to 19,000. We also saw an improvement in reliability from the chassis side. We were very reliable in testing and that was satisfying after dedicating more resources and a different structure to manage reliability.

We did not have problems with the adaptation to Bridgestone control tyres from an aerodynamic point of view. A tyre is highly deformable and the front is steered, so if the car is sensitive to a tyre change it means that the flow structure around the car is not robust enough.

WORKING FROM TYRE INSENSITIVITY

The only sensible way to develop an F1 car is to be tyre insensitive but, as long as a tyre deforms, that is very difficult. Tyre shape is not controllable so, in terms of aero-development direction, you try to be tyre insensitive and have a flow structure not too related to the tyre. That's an ideal picture, of course, but in terms of overall aero performance we did not suffer too much. But, saying that, we did not switch from Michelin to Bridgestone.

What did change massively was the character of the tyres. And it was a total change. It is still about extracting the best from the tyres, and optimisation is never easy, but it was not as difficult as 2006 for two reasons.

Firstly, the compounds this year were less critical, whereas before they were at the peak of grip and flirting with major performance destructors like blistering or graining. This season, usually, we were on the safe side.

Secondly, we were using the same tyres all year, and so we had a data base. Last year we had very peaky tyres that were always changing, and so we were always trying to understand the character of the latest compound and what the problems were. Now the tyres are easier to handle.

For some of the drivers, though, it was a big change. The major problem was that from the 2006 construction to '07, the tyres went towards oversteer. If you bolted a 2007 set of Bridgestones on to an '06 car, you got oversteer, to the point where it forced the teams to develop understeering cars to compensate. That was simply because with the tyre characteristics, if you kept oversteer you got instability and could not maintain a consistent balance.

DESIGNING UNDERSTEER INTO THE CAR

So we all put understeer into the car. For some drivers, that was just perfect. For others drivers, such as Kimi, Fernando, Ralf – those who like a neutral to oversteering car – it was not possible to have stability and consistency. So they had to adapt their styles to avoid over-driving the tyres. For them, it was a major change and some coped better than others.

For sure, we managed to improve the potential without generating instability, and Ralf also changed a bit from his side. Jarno, however, likes understeer and so the change to the 2007 tyres was into a window he felt comfortable with, so that he did not really struggle.

There is no denying that we want and need to improve and we are already well advanced on the 2008 car design based on our understanding from this season. We are strongly focused on the aerodynamic development."

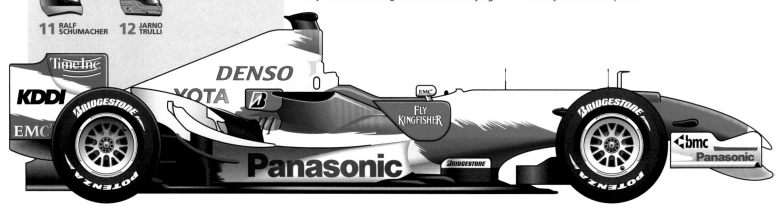

TECHNICAL SPECIFICATIONS

ENGINE
MAKE/MODEL Toyota RVX-07
CONFIGURATION 2398cc V8 (90 degree)
SPARK PLUGS DENSO
ECU Toyota/Magneti Marelli
FUEL Esso
OIL Esso
BATTERY Panasonic

TRANSMISSION
GEARBOX Toyota
FORWARD GEARS Seven
CLUTCH Undisclosed

CHASSIS
CHASSIS MODEL Toyota TF107
FRONT SUSPENSION LAYOUT
Carbon-fibre double wishbones with
carbon-fibre trackrod and pushrod
REAR SUSPENSION LAYOUT
Carbon-fibre double wishbones with
carbon-fibre toelink and pushrod

DAMPERS Penske
TYRES Bridgestone
WHEELS BBS
BRAKE DISCS Hitco
BRAKE PADS Hitco
BRAKE CALIPERS Brembo
FUEL TANK ATL
INSTRUMENTS
Toyota/Magneti Marelli

DIMENSIONS
LENGTH 4530mm
WIDTH 1800mm
HEIGHT 950mm
WHEELBASE 3090mm
TRACK front Undisclosed
rear Undisclosed
WEIGHT 600kg (including
driver and camera)

Panasonic TOYOTA *Racing*

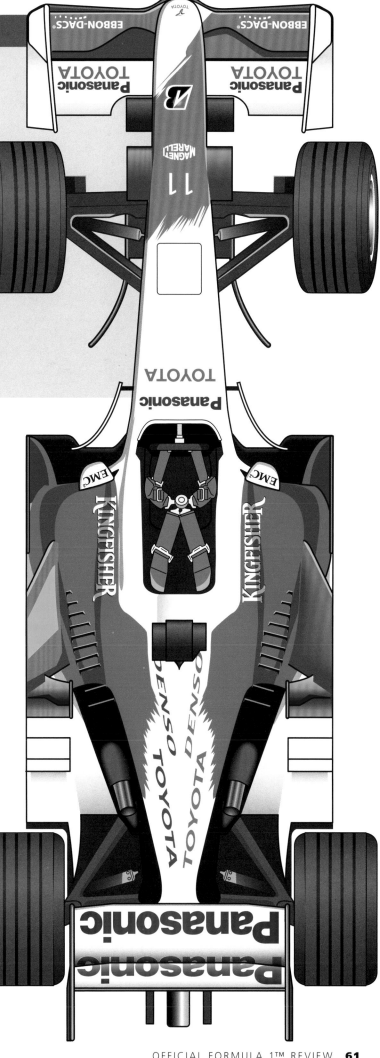

1 This late-season nose wing was designed to make an impact on Toyota's visit to its home race at Fuji, but other elements of the package were discarded
2 This is the regular set-up, with a pair of miniature wings atop the airbox, but a second pair was added for Monaco to help channel airflow on to the rear wing

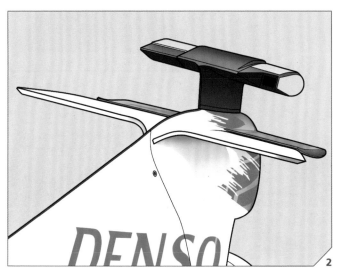

RED BULL

THE TEAM

PERSONNEL

CHAIRMAN Dietrich Mateschitz
TEAM PRINCIPAL Christian Horner
CHIEF TECHNICAL OFFICER Adrian Newey (above)
TECHNICAL DIRECTOR Geoff Willis
HEAD OF RACE & TEST ENGINEERING Paul Monaghan
CHIEF DESIGNER Rob Marshall
HEAD OF DEVELOPMENT Anton Stipovich
HEAD OF AERODYNAMICS Peter Prodromou
HEAD OF R&D Andrew Green
CHIEF OPERATING OFFICER Keith Saunt
TEAM MANAGER Jonathan Wheatley
CHIEF ENGINEER ENGINES Fabrice Lom
DRIVERS David Coulthard, Mark Webber
RACE ENGINEER (Coulthard) Guillaume Rocquelin
RACE ENGINEER (Webber) Ciaron Pilbeam
TEST TEAM MANAGER Tony Burrows
TEST DRIVERS Michael Ammermuller, Sébastien Buemi
CHIEF MECHANIC Kenny Handkammer
CHIEF TEST ENGINEER Ian Morgan
TOTAL NUMBER OF EMPLOYEES 540
NUMBER IN RACE TEAM 85
TEAM BASE Milton Keynes, England
TELEPHONE +44 (0)1908 279700
WEBSITE www.redbullracing.com

TEAM STATS

IN F1 SINCE 1997 as Stewart Grand Prix then Jaguar Racing
FIRST GRAND PRIX Australia 1997 **STARTS** 188
WINS 1 **POLE POSITIONS** 1 **FASTEST LAPS** 0
PODIUMS 7 **POINTS** 162 **CONSTRUCTORS' TITLES** 0
DRIVERS' TITLES 0

SPONSORS

Red Bull, Rauch, Metro International, Renault, Quehenberger

14 DAVID COULTHARD   **15 MARK WEBBER**

A SEASON OF RECURRING PROBLEMS

By Adrian Newey
(Chief Technical Officer)

"It's been a learning year in as much as we are still a team in its third season with work to do to get the infrastructure together in the managerial and personnel sense. In terms of the big bits of equipment – wind tunnels, CFD, etc – I am reasonably happy. The year has gone about as well as expected, but our reliability has been poor.

Top-10 level of performance is where we hoped to be, but we had a lot of recurring problems. Problems do happen, but the golden rule is making sure they don't happen again and we didn't achieve that.

Was it manufacturing, quality control or packaging? Tick all the boxes really. It was partly design not being as good as it could have been, and partly manufacture, assembly and operational problems. But In the last few races the reliability was better. The problems reduced our winter test mileage and we threw away a lot of points early in the year as we were recording DNFs when we should have scored a seventh or whatever.

The change to Renault engines gave us a lot of work in a short space of time, as the deal was done quite late, but we did a good job of accommodating that. The regulations are sufficiently restrictive that there is not a huge difference when it comes to installation. We had cooling issues with the Ferrari in 2006, but that was not so much the engine itself as a bit of optimism in how much cooling was needed.

I was very pleased with the service we had from Renault. They have been completely professional and we have had complete equality of service and product between Enstone and ourselves.

DRIVERS MAKE THEIR EXPERIENCE COUNT

Both drivers did a very good job. Mark was particularly strong in qualifying, putting the car in the top 10 at nearly 70% of the races. If you ask did the car deserve to be there or was it Mark who put it there, I don't know how you answer that one.

In Japan, Mark was definitely on for second, and he could have won. David raced pretty well too. Mark generally outqualified him, but there was little to choose between them in the race. The great thing about David, both drivers in fact, is that they are experienced and that brings a lot of feedback. Both were very good at coming to the factory and sitting down with the engineers, going through the strengths and weaknesses.

Our performance in the wet seemed to be higher than in the dry, but at some races – the ones that stand out are Spain, Montréal and Germany – we were the leader of the midfield group.

Looking at the highs and lows of 2007, when the car first came out it had some unexpected problems which we tried to solve with a fair degree of success. We qualified seventh in Melbourne, for instance, so I was pleased with the way we reacted and got a sensible level of performance for the first race. But, after that, we lacked consistency of pace. At times we have been the quickest team behind 'The Big Three' and at other times we have been towards the back end of the midfield. We need to establish a higher level of consistency, and it's about understanding our strengths and how they relate to particular circuits.

I think overall we've got a good engine package. Reliability hampered our development through lack of track time, and I think aerodynamically and mechanically the car has been a good solid base and we now need to take it on from there. We had upgrade packages through the year, the first at Melbourne, the next significant one for Barcelona, and then through the mid-season we did struggle to put performance on the car. Some parts didn't work as well as we wanted and others we couldn't introduce as quickly as we wanted because of reliability. We had an upgrade for Germany and then another one for the last three races.

INFRASTRUCTURE IS STILL BEING SORTED

In terms of the infrastructure, we are not all the way there with facilities and personnel, and still not totally there with our wind-tunnel correlation. We have one or two areas that need developing, but we made a lot of progress over the last 12 months and will continue pushing.

It's difficult to put a timescale on it. Wins in 2008 is a tall order if you look at the competition. I think a few people rather cheekily put around that we are the Chelsea of F1, but the fact is that our budget is seventh on the grid, just ahead of Williams and behind a lot of others. So we have actually managed to punch above our weight.

The thing that helps now is having key people in position. Peter Prodromou as head of aerodynamics has had his feet under the table for a year. Rob Marshall has been through a cycle with RB3 as chief designer. Geoff Willis's arrival was a huge boost to me in particular, in terms of leaving me free to be involved in things I want to do. Geoff's a very good organiser and is doing a great job of taking on the team's technical operation.

Mark Smith was a valued and well-liked member of Red Bull Racing, but we needed to change the job description of Technical Director from the way Mark was operating it. Like all things, it is only a title not a job description. And so we gave a new position of Technical Director to Geoff and offered Mark a different position, which unfortunately he declined.

CONCENTRATING ON PERFORMANCE

Everyone labels me an aerodynamicist, and I certainly enjoy it and spend a significant part of my time on it, but I try to operate as somebody who concentrates on performance. I dabble in lots of areas. But the importance of aero is reflected in people's budgets. You have a finite budget and you are free to decide how to spend it. Most teams spend more on aero than any other area.

We are not where we aspire to be but, given the age of the team and where it is, we performed satisfactorily, but dropped the ball in terms of reliability. We're now at 540 staff. Even if you have the budget you have to be careful about growing too quickly because that can actually cause more problems than it solves."

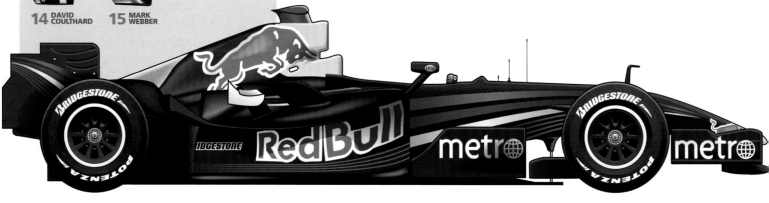

TECHNICAL SPECIFICATIONS

ENGINE
MAKE/MODEL Renault RS27
CONFIGURATION 2398cc V8 (90 degree)
SPARK PLUGS Champion
ECU Magneti Marelli
FUEL Elf
OIL Elf
BATTERY Panasonic

TRANSMISSION
GEARBOX Red Bull Racing
FORWARD GEARS Seven
CLUTCH AP Racing

CHASSIS
CHASSIS MODEL Red Bull RB3
FRONT SUSPENSION LAYOUT
Aluminium alloy uprights with upper and lower wishbones and pushrods. Torsion bar springs and anti-roll bars

REAR SUSPENSION LAYOUT
Aluminium alloy uprights with upper and lower wishbones and pushrods. Torsion bar springs and anti-roll bars
DAMPERS Multimatic
TYRES Bridgestone
WHEELS AVUS Racing
BRAKE DISCS Hitco
BRAKE PADS Hitco
BRAKE CALIPERS Brembo
FUEL TANK Undisclosed
INSTRUMENTS Red Bull Racing

DIMENSIONS
LENGTH Undisclosed
WIDTH 1800mm
HEIGHT 950mm
WHEELBASE Undisclosed
TRACK front Undisclosed
rear Undisclosed
WEIGHT Undisclosed

1 Red Bull kept experimenting with its front wing, moving on from this to follow McLaren's lead in fitting a single wing above its nose, doing so for Turkey
2 Red Bull kept its rear wing simple and added to it by fitting a small wing ahead of it that sloped up to the dorsal fin on the engine cover to which it was attached

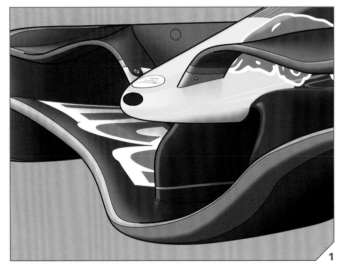

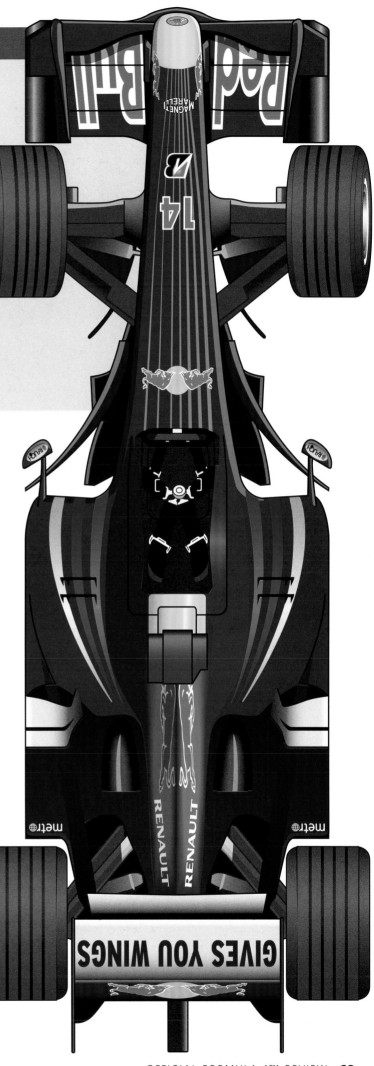

WILLIAMS

THE TEAM

PERSONNEL

TEAM PRINCIPAL Sir Frank Williams
DIRECTOR OF ENGINEERING Patrick Head
CHIEF EXECUTIVE OFFICER Adam Parr
TECHNICAL DIRECTOR Sam Michael (above)
CHIEF OPERATIING OFFICER Alex Burns
CHIEF DESIGNER Ed Wood
HEAD OF AERODYNAMICS Jon Tomlinson
SENIOR SYSTEMS ENGINEER John Russell
CHIEF OPERATIONS ENGINEER Rod Nelson
TEAM MANAGER Tim Newton
DRIVERS Kazuki Nakajima, Nico Rosberg, Alexander Wurz
RACE ENGINEER (Rosberg) Tony Ross
RACE ENGINEER (Wurz, Nakajima) Xevi Pujolar
TEST TEAM MANAGER Dickie Stanford
TEST DRIVERS Narain Karthikeyan, Kazuki Nakajima
CHIEF MECHANIC Carl Gaden
SENIOR TEST ENGINEER Peter Harrison
TOTAL NUMBER OF EMPLOYEES 520
NUMBER IN RACE TEAM 70
TEAM BASE Grove, England
TELEPHONE +44 (0)1235 777700
WEBSITE www.attwilliamsf1.com

TEAM STATS

IN F1 SINCE 1973 **FIRST GRAND PRIX** Argentina
1973 **STARTS** 550 **WINS** 113 **POLE POSITIONS** 125
FASTEST LAPS 129 **PODIUMS** 294 **POINTS** 2545.5
CONSTRUCTORS' TITLES 9 **DRIVERS' TITLES** 7

SPONSORS

AT&T, RBS, Lenovo, Philips, Petrobras, Allianz, Reuters, ORIS, alrasia.com, Tata, Hamleys, Mobilecast, MAN, Randstand

16 NICO ROSBERG **17 ALEXANDER WURZ** **17 KAZUKI NAKAJIMA**

A STEP FORWARD IN TERMS OF RELIABILITY

By Sam Michael
(Technical Director)

"Our main target in 2007 was to improve reliability, as last year we had 11 mechanical DNFs. This year, with three races to go, we'd had just three. We changed that by early planning of the engine installation with Toyota. And we had a simpler seamless-shift concept to the one we had. We also put in John Russell to concentrate 100% on reliability and changed a lot of systems in-house.

Toyota was reliable anyway in 2006, but the main thing we worried about was packaging. Four of our DNFs in 2006 were because we hadn't had enough time to package the Cosworth properly. There were two or three things that were difficult to solve, such as water-pipe failures, because of the way it was packaged. But we started much earlier with Toyota, to get around those issues.

A GREAT RELATIONSHIP WITH TOYOTA

Our relationship with the Toyota guys is really good. A lot of that has come through their side – right from the beginning they have bent over backwards to try to help us. They made sure we had enough time to package the engine, and understand the implications on airbox, exhaust and cooling systems. We used their dynos very heavily to do the gearbox work. That's been essential in achieving gearbox reliability.

Reliability-wise, it took a lot of attention to keep the old gearbox running. This year's is easier, better in every way. We designed it so all of the internals and dimensions comply with the 2008 regulations. And it will do '08 mileages – it's a four-race gearbox. We don't run it like that because we don't have to, but the 'box has already been tested to 2008 spec. We did that because we felt that if we tried to meet 2008 gearbox requirements in one winter and we had a problem with it, we could have big problems. It's a lot lighter too.

The first time we did a race distance in 2006 was when we finished the opening Grand Prix, in Bahrain. This year, by the time we went to the first race we'd done about 10 race distances, six on the track and four on the (Toyota) dynos at Cologne.

The next target, in our first year with a new engine supplier, was to get back up on performance from our eighth in the constructors' championship in 2006. We had new technical people – people like Jon Tomlinson and Rod Nelson. Many came in too late to affect the design, so they've been involved quite heavily in R&D. I hope to see more of their influence in FW30.

A big change over the winter of 2005/06 was the single tyre supply. Bridgestone changed the casings and compounds, so everyone had to get used to that from a mechanical point of view. Everything from mechanical set-up to driving style and aerodynamics was affected, and that is still ongoing. The only real advantage we had from changing to Bridgestone a year earlier was knowing the engineers. The actual tyres were completely different to what we raced in 2006.

Our drivers didn't take too long to adjust but it was an ongoing process. I don't know, it's pretty subjective to judge when they moved forward. Nico was pretty strong all year except for a couple of races, but he did change his driving style through the year. We've discussed it in great detail, but where it actually made a difference is very difficult to identify. Because as well as him changing his style, we're also changing the car, both aerodynamically and mechanically.

Nico did produce some strong qualifying performances, whereas Alex struggled more with that, as he admitted. The main thing was trying to get enough grip on new tyres/low fuel. A lot of that was changing set-up. I think it's fair to say that our car was one of the kindest to its tyres, but I'm not sure that's something to be proud of, as it could just be because you're running 1s per lap slower than McLaren and Ferrari.

WEIGHT DISTRIBUTION CRITICAL

The new tyres also impacted on weight distribution. A lot of that is obviously judgement, allied to testing over the winter. The key is really getting as much ballast as you can so that if you do find something in testing that says you want to go hard forward or hard back, you've got enough mass to be able to achieve it. There are two ways to achieve the weight distribution. One is having a lot of ballast, the other is geometrically positioning your wheels, changing them relative to the engine.

Overall, I think the FW29's performance window was quite good. That's shown by the fact we didn't have many bad races. We're weren't fast enough, sure, and that 1s gap to Ferrari/McLaren is what we have to find over the winter. Our best track was Monaco, where we were 0.6s off, and our worst was Silverstone, where we were 1.5s away. But the average was about 1s. If you look at Monza, Spa and Istanbul, in previous years we had not been very strong there, but at all those tracks this year we were not bad. Relative to the chasing pack, we were in front of it for those three races and scored points because of it. Also, it's because the car doesn't have any nasty windows where you get to a track and suddenly find yourself in a nightmare. That didn't really happen this year.

SIGNS OF ENCOURAGEMENT

Our development rate was about the same as last year. If you look back at where we were in the first couple of races, our race pace was quite strong relative to the pack behind Ferrari/McLaren/BMW. It was only our qualifying where we suffered. We picked our qualifying up after three or four races and qualified where we were racing. In the first three races, I think we were at the front of that pack by one or two tenths. Then from race four to seven or eight, we were in the pack because Red Bull got stronger and so did Renault. Then, in the last few races, it changed back again so we were where we were in the first few races.

Although our points total is better than in 2006, last year wasn't where we wanted to be. We were effectively fifth, chasing a lucky fourth. Our target for next year is to close that gap to the top guys, to at least put ourselves top three. There are signs of a turnaround at least, which gives you encouragement you're doing the right things."

TECHNICAL SPECIFICATIONS

ENGINE
MAKE/MODEL Toyota RVX-07
CONFIGURATION 2398cc V8 (90 degree)
SPARK PLUGS Denso
ECU WilliamsF1/Toyota
FUEL Petrobras
OIL Lubrax
BATTERY Undisclosed

TRANSMISSION
GEARBOX WilliamsF1
FORWARD GEARS Seven
CLUTCH AP Racing

CHASSIS
CHASSIS MODEL Williams FW29
FRONT SUSPENSION LAYOUT
Carbon-fibre double wishbones with composite toelink and pushrod-activated torsion springs

REAR SUSPENSION LAYOUT Double wishbones and pushrod-activated torsion springs and rockers
DAMPERS WilliamsF1
TYRES Bridgestone
WHEELS RAYS
BRAKE DISCS Carbone Industrie
BRAKE PADS Carbone Industrie
BRAKE CALIPERS AP Racing
FUEL TANK ATL
INSTRUMENTS WilliamsF1

DIMENSIONS
LENGTH 4500mm
WIDTH 1800mm
HEIGHT 950mm
WHEELBASE 3100mm
TRACK front 1470mm
rear 1420mm
WEIGHT 605kg (including driver and camera)

WILLIAMS F1

1 The way that the third plane of this FW29 front wing met the nose was new at the French GP in July, but it failed to give the team much of a performance boost
2 Anxious for improvement, Williams introduced entirely new upper bodywork at the Monaco GP in their quest for extra downforce, this sprouting winglets galore

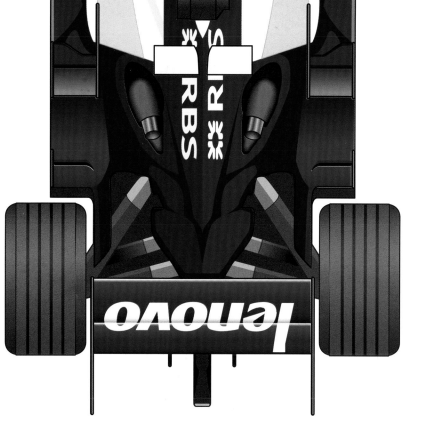

TORO ROSSO

THE TEAM

PERSONNEL

TEAM OWNERS Dietrich Mateschitz & Gerhard Berger
TEAM PRINCIPAL Franz Tost
GENERAL MANAGER Gianfranco Fantuzzi
TECHNICAL DIRECTOR Giorgio Ascanelli (above)
CHIEF ENGINEER Laurent Mekies
TEAM MANAGER Massimo Rivola
DRIVERS Vitantonio Liuzzi, Scott Speed, Sebastian Vettel
TECHNICAL CO-ORDINATOR Sandro Parrini
LOGISTICS MANAGER Domenico Sangiorgi
RACE ENGINEER (Liuzzi) Riccardo Adami
RACE ENGINEER (Speed/Vettel) John McGill
CHIEF MECHANIC Paolo Piancastelli
NO 1 MECHANIC (Liuzzi) Alberto Gavarini
NO 1 MECHANIC (Speed/Vettel) Marco Campoduni
NO 1 MECHANIC (T-car) Gabriele Marianelli
SENIOR TEST ENGINEER Gianvito Amico
SENIOR ENGINE ENGINEER Ernst Knoorst
RACE ENGINES MANAGER Mattia Binotto
TOTAL NUMBER OF EMPLOYEES 146
NUMBER IN RACE TEAM 60
TEAM BASE Faenza, Italy
TELEPHONE +39 (0)546 696111
WEBSITE www.tororosso.com

TEAM STATS

IN F1 SINCE 1985, as Minardi **FIRST GRAND PRIX** Brazil 1985 **STARTS** 376 **WINS** 0 **POLE POSITIONS** 0 **FASTEST LAPS** 0 **PODIUMS** 0 **POINTS** 47 **CONSTRUCTORS' TITLES** 0 **DRIVERS' TITLES** 0

SPONSORS

Red Bull, Hangar-7, Amik, Bridgestone

18 VITANTONIO LIUZZI **19** SCOTT SPEED **19** SEBASTIAN VETTEL

A YEAR SHORT OF TIME AND RESOURCES

By Giorgio Ascanelli
(Technical Director)

"I started in early April when the basic things were already done. It was an uphill year. The car arrived late and that conditioned our capacity for testing, learning and making good use of it. And then the car wasn't quite what we expected. We are a small team, but on the other hand it was clear that some small teams had done a better job than us.

Reliability was important, as well as performance, and we were neither reliable nor fast. The big struggle was recovering reliability, which by the end of the season was quite decent.

There was performance improvement touching many areas: brakes, fuel systems, differential, suspension, and we really started to get it together. I enjoy life at Toro Rosso, the commitment of the team and the goodwill, but we have to admit that this car has been quite a revolution for the team's mentality. There was potential in it and you had to deal with that by giving it more attention than the team was used to. But, remember, we are only 146 people from the cleaning lady to Mr Tost.

ENGINE DEVELOPMENT WAS CRUCIAL

A significant thing was engine development, not the engine itself of course, but its interaction with the car. We explored the cooling of the exhaust, and the airbox and fuel system in conjunction with Ferrari. It was fuel-system development rather than fuel development.

The second point, and probably the most important, was weight distribution: height and centre of mass. We also had some interesting results from brake work. There was continuous development in the wind tunnel too, but that is normal. The product of time multiplied by resources is a constant and we were short of both.

People need to be trained to think in a certain way. A classic example was Japan. Sebastian Vettel did a fantastic job for us in qualifying and we found ourselves in Q3, and at that point we made a mistake, which was calling him in at the wrong time, with the result that we lost the chance to set a lap time on new rubber. We missed the flag by 13s, so it was not a large mistake, but it probably cost us two places on the grid.

In the race, Alonso had a few troubles and we were actually overtaking him. This had never happened! You have to run your race in a completely different way. If you are behind, you've got to have limited ambition and take relatively low risk, but in front you have to have a totally different perspective.

THERE WERE DRIVER ISSUES...

We obviously had some driver issues throughout the year but Vitantonio and Scott and Vitantonio and Sebastian had quite decent relationships. They weren't trying to out-fox each other and they were pretty much team players, which was good.

Scott was extremely decisive on what he wanted to do, generally had a good feeling about the car and I got on with him well. But I don't think he was happy to be with us and I don't think our boss was happy with him. To make a wedding, you need two, and this relationship didn't work. I don't think badly of him as a driver. As much as I enjoyed his company as a human being, it was difficult for a young team to accept the challenge of such a character. He was cocky. My rule is that everyone makes mistakes and we try to stick together, and I always tell everyone that a mistake from a driver is the same as that of a mechanic or engineer – just more apparent. Scott's expectations were higher than the team could deliver.

Tonio, I think, was more committed although the situation is not that dissimilar because Tonio was not that happy with the situation he was in. I found Tonio put more effort in, and had a perfectly understandable moment of difficulty after the mishap in Canada. So for a race or two he wasn't quite on the ball, but otherwise produced everything he could in good spirit.

Sebastian, for a young guy, is interesting. He's on a steep learning curve, but if he keeps learning I think he has some justified ambitions. Bourdais I have not yet worked with, but he has won championships, so he knows how to do it.

I am always extremely sceptical about the move from the States to here though, essentially because the cars are so different. In the States, they are much heavier, and I remember when I engineered Michael Andretti at McLaren, I used to tell him that he couldn't hassle an F1 car. It's a young lady in high heels and silken stockings, rather than something you can force. Cars in the USA are a bit more robust and you can have a tangle without necessarily destroying the car. Here, collisions have to be avoided.

TESTING IS NOT YET OPTIMISED

We have a small test team at Toro Rosso and there's a large overlap of material that has to be shipped from races to a test. We have to accept that as we are pooling developments, and most of them are based on modelling and lap testing, you are going to have to find your good performance at the races. So the testing is not really at the leading edge of your technology, it is more like one step back.

We have been at every test, but we have not run enough miles due to reliability and physically too few resources. That is part of the problem.

On top of every other consideration, there is also the wallet. A team like Toro Rosso has to satisfy the brief of Mr Mateschitz, who said that Red Bull is there to try to win races and the second team has to promote the brand and train young drivers, but to a limited budget. We are thankful for being here, but we can't be in the same league.

Ron Dennis told me in 1991 that to win one race is relatively easy, to win one championship is not that difficult but to be consistently at the top of motor racing is incredibly tough. To be honest and reasonable, Toro Rosso had a set-up which allowed us to be between eighth and ninth, but poor reliability was letting us down until it all came good in Japan and we advanced to seventh. However, at whatever level you are, consistency is what's difficult to achieve."

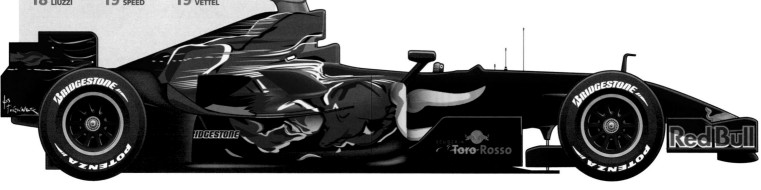

TECHNICAL SPECIFICATIONS

ENGINE
MAKE/MODEL Ferrari 056
CONFIGURATION 2398cc V8
(90 degree)
SPARK PLUGS Undisclosed
ECU Magneti Marelli
FUEL Shell
OIL Shell
BATTERY Undisclosed

TRANSMISSION
GEARBOX Undisclosed
FORWARD GEARS Seven
CLUTCH AP Racing

CHASSIS
CHASSIS MODEL Toro Rosso STR02
FRONT SUSPENSION LAYOUT
Upper and lower carbon wishbones
and pushrods, torsion-bar springs and
anti-roll bars

REAR SUSPENSION LAYOUT
Upper and lower carbon wishbones
and pushrods, torsion-bar springs
and anti-roll bars
DAMPERS Koni
TYRES Bridgestone
WHEELS AVUS Racing
BRAKE DISCS Hitco
BRAKE PADS Hitco
BRAKE CALIPERS Brembo
FUEL TANK ATL
INSTRUMENTS
Scuderia Toro Rosso

DIMENSIONS
LENGTH 4685mm
WIDTH 1800mm
HEIGHT 950mm
WHEELBASE
Over 3000mm
TRACK front 1480mm
rear 1418mm
WEIGHT 600kg (including
driver and camera)

SCUDERIA
Toro Rosso

1 Nose-mounted upper wings were in vogue in 2007, and Toro Rosso eventually went a stage further at the Belgian GP and fitted a beam wing over the nose
2 Scuderia Toro Rosso experimented with sidepod-mounted winglets and tall chimney vents in their quest for aerodynamic efficiency and chassis balance

SPYKER

THE TEAM

PERSONNEL

MANAGING DIRECTOR & TEAM PRINCIPAL
Colin Kolles
CHIEF TECHNICAL OFFICER Mike Gascoyne (above)
CHIEF OPERATIONS OFFICER Patrick Missling
TECHNICAL DIRECTOR James Key
CHIEF DESIGNER John McQuilliam
HEAD OF R&D Simon Gardner
HEAD OF AERODYNAMICS Simon Phillips
TEAM MANAGER Andy Stevenson
DRIVERS Christijan Albers, Adrian Sutil, Markus
Winkelhock, Sakon Yamamoto
CHIEF ENGINEER Dominic Harlow
RACE ENGINEER (Albers, Winkelhock, Yamamoto)
Jody Eggington
RACE ENGINEER (Sutil) Brad Joyce
TEST/THIRD DRIVERS Ernesto Viso, Markus Winkelhock
HEAD OF CAR BUILD Nick Burrows
CHIEF MECHANIC Andy Deeming
TEAM CO-ORDINATOR Hadley Donaldson
TOTAL NUMBER OF EMPLOYEES 230
NUMBER IN RACE TEAM 60
TEAM BASE Silverstone, England
TELEPHONE +44 (0)1327 850800
WEBSITE www.spykerf1.com

TEAM STATS

IN F1 SINCE 1991, as Jordan then Midland **FIRST GRAND
PRIX** USA 1991 **STARTS** 285 **WINS** 4 **POLE POSITIONS** 2
FASTEST LAPS 2 **PODIUMS** 20 **POINTS** 288
CONSTRUCTORS' TITLES 0 **DRIVERS' TITLES** 0

SPONSORS

Spyker, Etihad Airways, Aldar Abu Dhabi, Superfund,
McGregor Fashions, Medion, Exact Computers, MAN

20 ADRIAN SUTIL **21** CHRISTIJAN ALBERS **21** MARKUS WINKELHOCK **21** SAKON YAMAMOTO

MAKING THE MOST OF A SMALL BUDGET

By Mike Gascoyne
(Chief Technical Officer)

"At the end of 2006, the team had been through lean times and had new owners. We had a plan in place and to some extent it panned out, but the investment didn't turn out as expected. Budget-wise things were tight and we were able to do some things, such as the Aerolab deal to expand our wind-tunnel facilities, but far from everything.

Aerolab, run by Jean-Claude Migeot, came on board in January. I'd worked with them at Toyota. It's an operation that does a full aerodynamic service, including model design, and work with your own aerodynamic department. That meant we were able to do an update early in the year.

The car had been produced by James Key and his team, who did a good job before I arrived at the team, but the first three races were difficult. We didn't do the Bahrain or Malaysia tests. Getting back to Europe, we expected to be at the back of the grid. F1 was very competitive this year: we were regularly less than 3s from the pole, which, most years, would have seen you reasonably competitive in the midfield. This year, it meant we were half a second off the back.

PROGRESS WITH THE B-SPEC CAR

We planned an update for the Turkish GP, but that went back a race when we failed the rear-impact test. That B-spec car was a good step forward and we had our best race of the year at the Belgian GP. Even with that new package, though, we were compromised by the lack of finances and the lack of wind-tunnel testing. We'd hoped to get our tunnel running around the start of June, and that only really happened in the middle of September.

We haven't moved forward as much as we planned, but we finished the year racing Toro Rosso and Super Aguri. We were overtaking Toyotas and Hondas at Spa, too, and for a team with our limited resources, that's a good effort.

Basically, the car had far too much drag, which was significantly reduced with the B-spec car. We have the same engine as a couple of other teams, from Ferrari, but we were struggling with straight-line speed and our fuel consumption was noticeably higher. That fell back into line with the others with the B-car, so clearly we've made a step.

CARRYING CONTINUITY THROUGH INTO 2008

The B-spec car is the basis for our 2008 car and we've already introduced next year's gearbox and rear suspension, so mechanically the car is sound, we've got continuity of engine and we can concentrate on key areas such as aerodynamics.

I think the change to spec' tyres hurt us, because if you've got less downforce you can afford to run a slightly softer tyre and this year you weren't able to do that. There were races when we struggled to get the tyre working in the right window and put enough heat into the rubber. That undoubtedly improved with the B-spec car.

The fact that we didn't have the downforce was not the only reason that we, exclusively, were able to run soft, soft, hard rather than hard, hard, soft through the three race stints at Spa. I think

people missed a trick there. We wanted to target a very aggressive first stint and that's just an example of how the team has functioned well and made good strategy calls. Third in the list of laps led this year is Spyker – which is an interesting statistic! I don't think we made any risky calls. I just think we made the right ones.

NURTURING A DEVELOPING TALENT

The whole team has done a really professional job. The drivers have made quite a few mistakes, but undoubtedly Adrian Sutil has been learning and has got better throughout the year. We valued him as a real talent and he's shown that. Up to the middle part of the season, he made too many silly mistakes and went off the road too often, such as at Monaco, Canada and Silverstone for instance. People say, "Oh, it's because of the car," but any driver just has to drive the car as quickly as it can go without falling off.

Adrian learned, though. He's a very good, quick driver, and mentally he has the ability. He just has to learn to remain focused. He's made the mistakes you'd expect any rookie to make. The only thing is that everyone's comparing people to Lewis, who's set the bar a lot higher, but he had the benefit of a lot of McLaren testing. I expect Adrian to be a real asset to the team next year.

Christijan Albers struggled to match the pace of his team-mate. He can be quick, but we knew from working with him for a couple of years that he can be quite fragile emotionally. Often you'd see that he'd be quick on Friday and then, as the pressure came on, he couldn't quite deliver. I think there were a lot of pressures on him externally – Team Netherlands and the Dutch press, sponsors and all of that. He's the sort of driver who doesn't need that, especially when he had a quick team-mate. It just all snowballed for him.

I've been very impressed with Sakon Yamamoto. He's a pleasant young man, has a very good work ethic and has done a very professional job for a guy who's treated as a pay-driver, if you like. He's done a lot better than that, really impressed everyone and ended up pushing his team-mate quite hard on occasions.

THE ART OF LEADING RACES

Of course, Markus Winkelhock led his first grand prix at the Nürburgring, where his Dad did his last F1 race. To be leading by 30s on the second lap, having started from the back, was one hell of a story! It was a shame the race was red-flagged, as we were on top of everything that was happening.

I said to everyone at the start of that weekend that I wanted Markus to walk away saying he'd had a great weekend, even if it's his only ever F1 race. The greatest story of the year for me was actually after that race, sitting down with Markus when they played the highlights. As they showed that clip of him overtaking Räikkönen for the lead, he sort of looked at it strangely and said; "That's me... I'm leading!" He must have noticed at the time, but as he watched it afterwards it sort of sunk in and this big smile came all over his face. He's a lovely lad and good luck to him..."

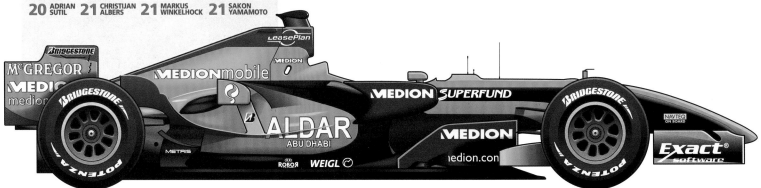

TECHNICAL SPECIFICATIONS

ENGINE
MAKE/MODEL Ferrari 056
CONFIGURATION 2398cc V8
(90 degree)
SPARK PLUGS NGK
ECU Magneti Marelli
FUEL Shell
OIL Shell
BATTERY Undisclosed

TRANSMISSION
GEARBOX Spyker F1
FORWARD GEARS Seven
CLUTCH AP Racing

CHASSIS
CHASSIS MODEL Spyker F8-VII
FRONT SUSPENSION LAYOUT
Composite pushrods activating
chassis-mounted in-line dampers
and torsion bars, unequal length
composite aerodynamic wishbones,
front anti-roll bar

REAR SUSPENSION LAYOUT
Composite pushrods activating gearbox-
mounted rotary dampers and
torsion bars, unequal length
composite aerodynamic wishbones
DAMPERS Penske
TYRES Bridgestone
WHEELS BBS Racing
BRAKE DISCS Hitco
BRAKE PADS Hitco
BRAKE CALIPERS
AP Racing
FUEL TANK ATL
INSTRUMENTS
Spyker F1

DIMENSIONS
LENGTH Over 5000mm
WIDTH 1800mm
HEIGHT 950mm
WHEELBASE Over 3000m
TRACK front 1480mm
rear 1418mm
WEIGHT 601kg (including
driver and camera)

Spyker

1 The rear end of the F8-VII came in for attention when the debut of Spyker's
B-spec car was delayed for failing a mandatory crash test before appearing at Spa
2 Many of the suspension and aerodynamic changes through the course of the
season were aimed at getting more heat into the tyres to make them work better

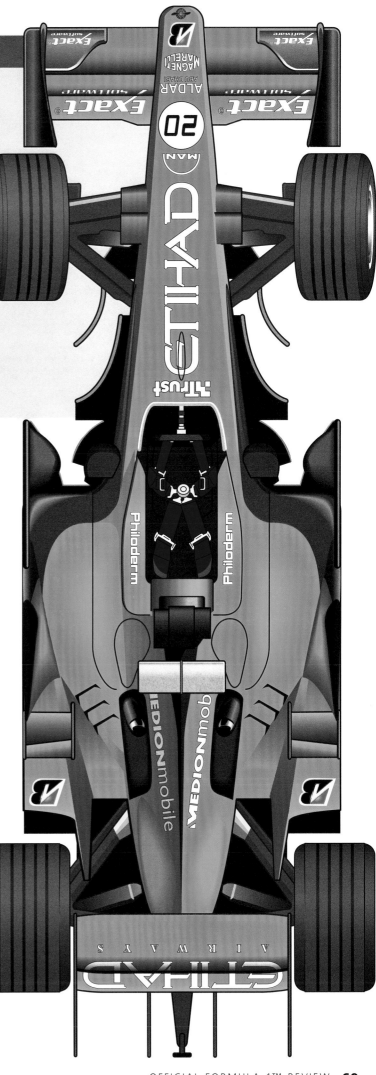

SUPER AGURI

THE TEAM

PERSONNEL

TEAM PRINCIPAL Aguri Suzuki
MANAGING DIRECTOR Daniele Audetto
TECHNICAL DIRECTOR Mark Preston (above)
SPORTING DIRECTOR Graham Taylor
CHIEF DESIGNER Peter McCool
CHIEF AERODYNAMICIST Ben Wood
HEAD OF R&D Graham Taylor
OPERATIONS DIRECTOR Kevin Lee
TEAM MANAGER Mick Ainsley-Cowlishaw
DRIVERS Anthony Davidson, Takuma Sato
RACE ENGINEER (Sato) Richard Connell
RACE ENGINEER (Davidson) Antonio Cuquerella
TEST/THIRD DRIVER James Rossiter
CHIEF MECHANIC Phill Spencer
TOTAL NUMBER OF EMPLOYEES 152
NUMBER IN RACE TEAM 43
TEAM BASE Witney, England
TELEPHONE +44 (0)1993 871600
WEBSITE www.saf1.com

TEAM STATS

IN F1 SINCE 2006 **FIRST GRAND PRIX** Bahrain 2006
STARTS 35 **WINS** 0 **POLE POSITIONS** 0
FASTEST LAPS 0 **PODIUMS** 0 **POINTS** 4
CONSTRUCTORS' TITLES 0 **DRIVERS' TITLES** 0

SPONSORS

Honda, Bridgestone, Samantha Kingz, Life Card, Taisei

22 TAKUMA SATO

23 ANTHONY DAVIDSON

ADAPTING THE STAFF TO START MOVING UP THE ORDER

By Mark Preston
(Technical Director)

"By the end of 2006 we were organised, had a good winter and came out of the box well. In Melbourne, we started 10th (Sato) and 11th (Davidson), which was a big shock. The goal was to get through Q1. We'd done a few calculations around what we'd do for fuel in Q3, but we weren't expecting to need them!

We didn't race so well, and over the next few races we changed things in terms of strategy and organisation. We were constantly making changes. At the Japanese GP, for example, we decided we weren't moving the tyres around correctly as we had a bit of a running into each other at Spa when the cars came in a lap apart. So we organised the garage better. Just logistics really.

CREATING A BATTLE ROOM

The Spanish GP was really the first example. We had all the engineers out on the pit wall and our radio systems aren't the best in the world. We decided we weren't communicating well and so all of the engineers came into the truck and we called it 'the battle room' and thought about things better. That's one of the reasons why we got a point.

But, in Canada, we were all in the back of the truck and there was no engineer on the pit wall, so we didn't see Anthony coming in after he'd hit the groundhog. After that, one person went back on the pit wall. Because we know we're not competing to win, we can try different things, and that's why Alonso got caught out on different tyres in Montréal with Taku. We'd thought about the fact that the option tyre just wasn't working in the race, and so when the safety car came out we had the chance to switch back to the other tyre.

TRYING DIFFERENT FRONT WINGS

Most of our progress has come from the aero side – trims and gurneys here and there, and changes to diffusers. The most visual thing we tried was a different front wing, one that goes up on to the nosebox, but we only ran that a few times in practice. We had a very powerful front wing and one that was more efficient, but that one was never quite the right thing. We seem to have had to run more front wing than we expected, and the other wing has never really come into its own.

We used the wind tunnel at the National Physics Laboratory in Teddington, which McLaren used until 2002. It's 50% and it's not all-singing, all-dancing, but it's reliable. Using the SA07 this year was such a huge change, and every race we brought aero bits. When we qualified so well in the first race, we thought, that's actually pretty good, let's keep going and not change everything for the sake of it, because we are not big enough.

I think we knew that we would slowly drop back. A few years ago, Sauber used to come out of the box well and slowly fall back through the season. In terms of people, we haven't expanded. The changes, as I say, have been procedural, things that you can't see, like the way you quarantine failed parts, organise the car on the grid, really subtle things. You go and look at McLaren on the grid and maybe copy some of the procedures or make little changes. That continues to get better.

In our first year, it was nice to prove that you could take an old monocoque and if you put enough downforce on it you could get it fairly close to the other teams on the grid. There were other parameters that weren't close enough, like centre of gravity and height, and they were the benefits of doing the SA07 with help from Honda Japan.

Budgetary limitations impacted, though. They limited us to going racing and doing the best we could on a weekend, but that's not enough to compete with even the Spykers, as they brought their new car and continued to put new bits on and you could see us trickle back. It was a question of 'what can we do for no money?' The answer was to organise ourselves and to perfect things.

ENJOYING THE RELATIONSHIP WITH HONDA

It was not until China that the works Honda team outscored us. I'm sure they hated it, but it's good for everyone to get beaten sometimes. We don't want to bite the hand that feeds us, though, because we get all of our engines, gearboxes and electronics from Honda Japan. They are quite behind Super Aguri, so we do have a fair amount of contact.

You can waste a lot of resource trying to get something like a gearbox working. We can take a lovely quick-shift 'box from Honda, that saves maybe 30 people, so it's a really big resource difference. At Arrows, we had a different engine every year, which meant you had to redesign the car and get to know the people. I can't stress enough how much of an effect that has. We have the same engineers, cooling and electronic settings from last year and that's so valuable, leaving you to get on with making the car go faster.

DAVIDSON MAKES STEPS FORWARD

On the driving side, Anthony Davidson is really coming on. The Turkish GP, for which he qualified 11th, was very impressive and he feels he's made an appreciable change in qualifying. Takuma has more experience in the races and seems to find his way through. He is also more mature since the start of last year, works well with the team, has gelled and is enjoying himself. People talk about Takuma's history of crashing, but he hasn't been doing that with us. He always makes great starts too.

Anthony races intelligently and is really good at making a one-stop race work, which Takuma doesn't like doing. In Canada, but for the groundhog, it looked as though even a podium might have been possible. Continuity with the drivers would be good, if we can keep both.

We did a reasonable amount of testing and one of the advantages we had is that we did go and do the early Bahrain and Malaysia tests. Williams didn't go testing in Bahrain and realised when they got to the Australian GP that perhaps they should have.

There is a crossover between the race and test teams, as we don't have the luxury of a completely separate test team. That's what it's like at this end of the grid with 140 people. You learn more, but you work harder. Maybe you can go and retire in a big team!"

TECHNICAL SPECIFICATIONS

ENGINE
MAKE/MODEL Honda RA807E
CONFIGURATION 2400cc V8
(90 degree)
SPARK PLUGS NGK
ECU Honda
FUEL ENEOS
OIL ENEOS
BATTERY Undisclosed

TRANSMISSION
GEARBOX Super Aguri
FORWARD GEARS Seven
CLUTCH Sachs

CHASSIS
CHASSIS MODEL Super Aguri SA07
FRONT SUSPENSION LAYOUT
Upper and lower wishbones, pushrod-activated torsion springs and rockers, with mechanical anti-roll bars

REAR SUSPENSION LAYOUT
Upper and lower carbon-wrapped steel wishbones, pushrod-activated torsion springs and rockers, with mechanical anti-roll bars
DAMPERS Showa
TYRES Bridgestone
WHEELS BBS
BRAKE DISCS Hitco
BRAKE PADS Hitco
BRAKE CALIPERS AP Racing
FUEL TANK ATL
INSTRUMENTS Super Aguri

DIMENSIONS
LENGTH 4680mm
WIDTH 1800mm
HEIGHT 950mm
WHEELBASE 3135mm
TRACK front 1460mm
rear 1420mm
WEIGHT 600kg (including driver and camera)

SUPER AGURI
F1 TEAM

1 The SA07 broke new ground when it turned up for the Malaysian GP with this truncated upper element, but it was changed for a more conventional upper wing
2 Displaying its Honda heritage, the SA07 followed the trend of running winglets at the front of its sidepod with a corresponding 'shadow' on the floor beneath

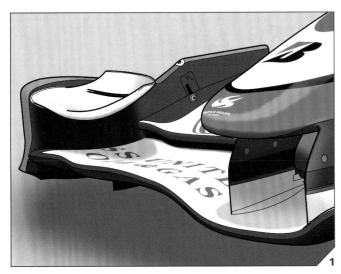

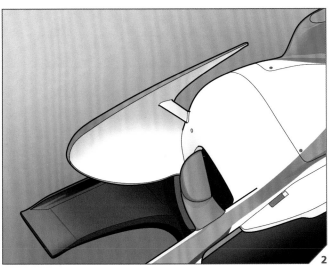

THE RACES

The 2007 season was the best for years as Ferrari and McLaren fought for honours, but there were cameo roles for the others, as outlined in the reports for all 17 races

2007 FORMULA 1™ ING AUSTRALIAN GRAND PRIX
MELBOURNE

RÄIKKÖNEN KICKS OFF

Kimi Räikkönen went to Ferrari to win races, and he started as he meant to go on. After the race, though, all talk was of Lewis Hamilton's stunning debut for McLaren

A safety car deployment would have helped to liven things up, especially as the new rules meant the pits would be closed for refuelling until the cars were lined up in race-position order, but for once we didn't get one at Albert Park.

Nevertheless, the Australian GP was an intriguing event with which to launch the post-Michael Schumacher era. With Kimi Räikkönen winning first time out at Ferrari, in many ways it seemed that little had changed. It had, of course, and the sensational arrival of Lewis Hamilton on the scene was an even bigger story than Räikkönen's win.

Räikkönen also took pole position on his maiden outing for Ferrari, but it was a frustrating Saturday for the Italian team as a gearbox problem afflicted Felipe Massa. So, after an engine change, the Brazilian would start at the back of the grid.

Hamilton was on the case from the outset, and especially in qualifying – under the most extreme pressure – he really showed what he was made of. He was fractionally faster than Fernando Alonso in Q1, and was again just in front after their first runs in Q2. Hamilton lost out to his Spanish team-mate when it mattered in Q3, but that was down to a two-lap

INSIDE LINE
LEWIS HAMILTON

McLAREN DRIVER

"This has been an absolutely unbelievable weekend for me. It is what I have been preparing for since I've been about 13 years old and, for me, it was literally living my dream. To lead on my first grand prix outing was a fantastic feeling, but it was an extremely tough race.

I had [my team-mate] Fernando Alonso behind me for a long time and it's pretty tough when you have a two-time World Champion behind you in your first race!

I made a pretty decent start, but the BMWs seemed to be extremely quick off the line and Robert Kubica got past me. There was no way that I could stay on the inside, so I dived back to the outside and managed to outbrake near enough everyone and gain a couple of places. I think Fernando got trapped behind Nick

Heidfeld, which helped me out.

It was good, but it was only the first corner of the race and you can't get too excited about it. That put me in second place and afterwards it was pretty much like any race when you are running up front: intense. You have to try to make sure you don't make any mistakes and, for sure, I did make one or two. It was another new experience for me and I am ecstatic about making it onto the podium in my first grand prix.

I had some problems on my second set of tyres, with some graining on the left front, and so I didn't have the pace to keep up with Fernando after he got ahead of me at the second round of pit stops. The key was to bring the car home, as I knew I had done enough for my first race! I was pushing as hard as I could, but I wasn't able to

close the gap to Fernando or keep up, so that was that.

Overall, though, I'm absolutely delighted. My team-mate is a World Champion, a great driver, this is my debut and I finished just behind him. Of course I'm happy! When I arrived in Melbourne and saw a McLaren with my name on it, I almost had to pinch myself. And I think the race was probably beyond my dreams. Just to be in Formula One was the dream and now, to come to the first race and have such a smooth start, is fantastic. This was everything I have been working for and hoping for. I'm loving it…"

difference in their fuel loads. The McLarens were split, though, by Nick Heidfeld in third, and the race was to prove that the BMW Sauber man had been running significantly lighter in Q3 than his rivals.

Räikkönen got away cleanly at the start, but things didn't quite go according to plan for Alonso. Even allowing for his lighter fuel load and soft tyres, Heidfeld got off the line extremely well, and exited the first corner in second place. Behind him, Hamilton pulled off an amazing manoeuvre to extricate himself from a blind alley on the pit wall side behind Robert Kubica in the second BMW Sauber by switching to the outside, in so doing not only passing the Pole but squeezing Alonso down to fourth place.

"Fernando is very intelligent, very confident in his own ability," said McLaren Chief Operating Officer Martin Whitmarsh. "He's a racing driver, and being overtaken by your team-mate at the first corner, who's come from two places back, isn't what you want to happen. Nick was light and had the option tyre, but he also had good traction off the line. That created a situation, and Lewis was very quick thinking, and decided, 'How do I respond to this?'

"He responded by going to his left and going out around the outside, by the time the situation evolved – and I don't think he got anything wrong – Fernando was boxed in going into that corner, and that allowed Lewis to come by. He would, at the time, not have been delighted by that..."

It was game over as far as taking the battle to Räikkönen was concerned, and that was a great shame. BMW Sauber might have improved, but even with his lighter fuel load Heidfeld was holding up the McLarens. It didn't look that way, because they weren't exactly breathing down his neck, but such is the way of modern Formula One, and passing so hard in Melbourne, that Hamilton and Alonso were obliged to hang back, bide their time and wait for the BMW

Sauber to make its pit stop. Back in the McLaren pit, there was some serious frustration.

"I think from an outcome-of-the-race perspective," said McLaren boss Ron Dennis, "our race was very much damaged by the Heidfeld strategy, which we just didn't understand. It was not the way to go. Once we were boxed in, we just lost touch with Kimi. All the time you're behind Heidfeld you're struggling in dirty air, and the cars are so sensitive to that. Unless you've got a good one-and-a-half seconds advantage, you are not going to be able to take them on, or you have to wait for the tyre situation to deteriorate, then attack."

By the time Heidfeld pitted on lap 14, Hamilton was 14.4s down on Räikkönen, and Alonso was a further 1.6s behind. Only a recurrence of Massa's qualifying gearbox failure could halt the Finn now, but the McLaren fight was becoming interesting, and their first pit stops were awaited eagerly.

Alonso had cut the gap to Hamilton to 1s when he came in at the end of lap 21, and Hamilton followed a lap later. Alonso's in and out laps were quicker, but that single extra lap with a light car was enough to ensure that Hamilton stayed ahead.

Intriguingly, Alonso was supposed to stop two laps before Hamilton, when traditionally the difference between team-mates has been one. However, the new safety-car rules, and the penalty inherent in being caught out when you are about to refuel, caused the team to spread the risk.

"We had already agreed that we would keep them apart," said Whitmarsh. "You don't ordinarily want the drivers in on the same lap and with the new safety-car regulations, having them make their pit stops on successive laps is not a good thing. So we wanted them apart by a couple of laps."

By having Massa start from the back of the grid, Ferrari kept its options open, and the same consideration played a part in BMW Sauber bringing

OPPOSITE TOP **Lewis Hamilton wowed the sport's insiders from the outset as he settled in at McLaren**

BELOW **Hamilton even had the affrontery to pass team-mate Fernando Alonso for second place at the first corner. Their positions were reversed after the second stops**

TALKING POINT
CUSTOMER CARS

This was always going to be thorny, and fundamental to the sport's very fabric. You can vindicate the decision to allow new teams to buy customer cars and engines. Manufacturer involvement has led to teams that build their own chassis and own engines and have approaching 1000 employees on their books to put two race cars on a track 17 times a year. The big spenders' bills are not far short of £500 million, which many consider ludicrous.

This means that there is a chasm between Formula One and every other branch of the sport. In short, no team from the lower echelons can realistically target graduation to Formula One because they simply do not have the infrastructure.

On the other hand, you have Williams – an entity that exists solely to go Formula One motor racing. It does not have the safety net of a manufacturer cash kitty, yet it has had to expand its wind tunnel capability and its infrastructure simply to remain even halfway competitive.

Suddenly, if new teams can go and buy a Ferrari or a McLaren, Sir Frank Williams' business model looks questionable at best, suicidal at worst.

At the Australian GP, Super Aguri Racing ran what was basically the 2006 Honda (the RA106) and Scuderia Toro Rosso fielded a Ferrari-engined version of this year's Red Bull RB3. Those that stood to be hit hardest by these entries included Williams and Spyker, who would reasonably have been expected to run ahead of the Super Aguri and Toro Rosso teams under 'normal' circumstances. Hence they would earn less money with these teams' improved form. And money is what it is always about.

When was a Super Aguri not a Honda? And a Toro Rosso not a Red Bull? When the intellectual property rights for the cars were owned by an independent company, of course. If this was said often enough, people might even start to believe it...

This is why it was amusing to find the works Hondas comfortably outqualified by both Super Aguris in Melbourne. Jenson Button had had high hopes for the 2007 season but, very rapidly, appreciated the need to lower his sights.

The question, predictable: "Jenson, just how surprised are you to be half a second slower per lap than the Super Aguris?"

His answer, unguarded: "Not at all. In fact, the surprise is that it wasn't closer to a full second..." After all, he had put that car on pole in 2006.

Oops, Jenson! No you didn't. Because it's not a Honda, is it?

A Spyker protest, kicked out on a technicality, was just the first salvo in an issue that was likely to be settled in the arbitration courts.

Heidfeld in well ahead of Kubica. A short early stint also allowed Heidfeld to have his compulsory run on the unfavoured soft tyres early.

As far as McLaren was concerned, the race fuel decision was made on the assumption that Alonso would be in front of Hamilton from the start. Now that he was behind, the Spaniard knew that he would have very little chance to reverse the situation at the first stops. He did his best by cutting the fuel deficit from two laps to one by dint of some economical driving and fuel mode knob twiddling – adding that one lap to his original 20 equated to a 5% gain.

"Lewis was going to come in a couple of laps later," said Whitmarsh, "but we were able to make a bit of fuel on Fernando's car. It was a combination of the driver and the engineers working together."

Stopping only one lap ahead of his team-mate wasn't enough to move him ahead of Hamilton, but it was worth a try. However, the race order was decided by what went into the cars at those stops. Alonso took on enough fuel to get himself to lap 45 (with some more economy driving), while Hamilton could go only to lap 43. As usual, the last man to pit had the advantage, and Alonso easily jumped ahead at the

second and final round of pit stops.

In effect, McLaren had decided which of the two drivers was going to finish second, assuming neither made a mistake, and Alonso got the nod. Dennis insisted that the stops panned out for Alonso as they had always been planned that way: "Our strategy was pre-set, we didn't vary from it. You've just got to have a realistic approach. You're not going to close that gap [to Kimi], and therefore you're then into engine and tyre conservation. Fernando sat patiently behind Lewis, dropping back occasionally to ensure that the engine stayed cool. And really the outcome was as good as we could have expected given the circumstances."

Hamilton dropped away from Alonso in the latter part of the race, but he had a huge margin on Heidfeld and nothing to gain by staying up close, especially as everyone had to take their engines on to hot and humid Malaysia for the following grand prix.

The McLarens may have been in cautious mode, but not too many people believed that Räikkönen was flat-out at the front, especially as he had gearbox conservation very much in mind. Given that he didn't have a working radio – the equivalent of racing with one hand tied behind your back – it was a faultless

OPPOSITE MIDDLE LEFT
Giancarlo Fisichella gives Jarno Trulli the chop after emerging from the pitlane right in front of him

OPPOSITE MIDDLE RIGHT
A gearbox problem resulted in Felipe Massa starting from the back, but he worked his way through to sixth

OPPOSITE BOTTOM **Fifteenth place was enough to convince Jenson Button that the 2007 season was set to be a tough one**

ABOVE **The calm before the storm for Scott Speed, but this wasn't to be the Toro Rosso driver's day**

performance. He did have one embarrassing grass-cutting moment when he allowed his mind to wander – something that his illustrious predecessor Schumacher was not averse to when on cruise control.

"The race was not as easy as it might have looked," Räikkönen insisted. "Just before the start my radio broke, so I didn't have a radio the whole race, but at least we had planned what we wanted to do, so I knew pretty much what I was meant to do, although in some places it wasn't an ideal situation. Anyhow, it was a good race for us. I didn't have to push too hard, just had to pace myself a bit and look what the others were doing."

From the outside, it appeared that he had cannily let Massa push the envelope in testing and waited until it mattered before stepping up a gear. Räikkönen had certainly staked his claim to be the team's title contender – which is of course what he and Jean Todt expected him to be when he signed up in the early stages of 2006, long before Massa emerged as a race winner and testing pacesetter.

Ferrari put the engine-penalised Massa on a one-stopper, starting on the soft tyres that so many were cautious about using. Ferrari Team Principal Jean

Todt took a lot of persuading that this was the way to go, but race engineering boss Luca Baldisserri sussed correctly that Massa would spend the early laps of the race in traffic, and thus the soft tyres wouldn't be particularly stressed. Massa eventually salvaged some points by climbing to sixth.

Heidfeld's solid fourth place was a sign of things to come for BMW Sauber, although team-mate Kubica dropped out with a gearbox problem. Giancarlo Fisichella took fifth as Renault came to terms with just how expensive the switch from Michelin to Bridgestone had been. Indeed, life was to get harder in the coming races. Rookie Heikki Kovalainen had a nightmare debut, losing track time in practice and finishing 10th. The final points on offer went to Nico Rosberg and Ralf Schumacher, as Toyota lost out to its customer team, Williams.

Toyota were at least in better shape than Honda, though, as Rubens Barrichello and Jenson Button finished back in 11th and 15th, with little hope of seeing any great improvement in the short term. Their performance was put into perspective by Takuma Sato, who managed to qualify his Super Aguri an impressive 10th. Strange times indeed...

SNAPSHOT FROM
AUSTRALIA

CLOCKWISE FROM RIGHT The Melbourne backdrop is one of the most distinctive on the Formula One tour; cricketer Shane Warne enjoyed life in the paddock as a guest of McLaren; Takuma Sato arrived in a British-liveried cab. Don't ask why; Mr and Mrs Ecclestone were in town; even in profile, you can detect that it's Murray Walker interviewing Rubens Barrichello; Kylie and Danni Minogue offer Jenson Button a good luck kiss. It didn't work; but at least they were prettier than these 'girls'

WEEKEND NEWS

■ McLaren made it clear over the course of the weekend that it was concerned about possible flexing of the floor of the Ferrari. The team wrote to the FIA seeking to clarify the situation, and by the time of the next race FIA Race Director Charlie Whiting had moved to ensure that its flexibility tests were strictly followed.

■ The customer car issue came to the surface in Australia when the Spyker team launched a protest against Super Aguri. The definitive Super Aguri had not been seen in public until the Thursday, and the protest was not accepted as it was made too late in the meeting. Nevertheless, the Anglo-Dutch team made its point.

■ Colourful Australian cricket star Shane Warne was present in Melbourne as a guest of McLaren. Also seen on race day were sisters Kylie and Danni Minogue. The former had previously been seen at the British GP, while Danni was a regular grand prix visitor when stepping out with Jacques Villeneuve in 1999.

■ Red Bull Racing launched its 2007 campaign with a Wednesday night party in Melbourne's upmarket docklands area, and took the opportunity to premiere a short 007-style film that saw its four race drivers flexing their acting muscles, with mixed results. Grammy winners and local heroes Wolfmother provided the musical entertainment.

■ A meeting of the World Motor Sport Council at the end of March signalled the end of traction control from 2008. Always a controversial subject, plans for its outlawing were made all the easier by the move to a common ECU, which would give the FIA more scope for policing electronics.

RACE RESULTS
MELBOURNE AUSTRALIA

Official Results © [2007]
Formula One Administration Limited,
6 Princes Gate, London, SW7 1QJ.
No reproduction without permission.
All copyright and database rights reserved.

RACE DATE March 18th
CIRCUIT LENGTH 3.295 miles
NO. OF LAPS 58
RACE DISTANCE 191.110 miles
WEATHER Sunny, 22°C
TRACK TEMP 40°C
RACE DAY ATTENDANCE 105,000
LAP RECORD Michael Schumacher,
1m24.125s, 141.016mph, 2004

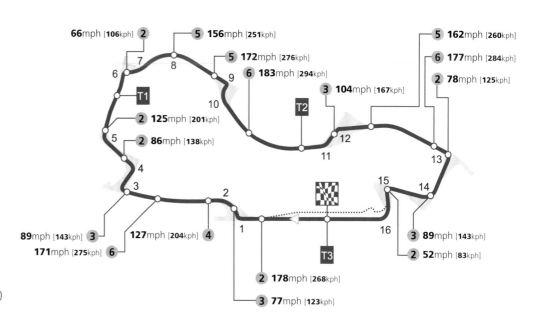

PRACTICE 1				PRACTICE 2				PRACTICE 3				QUALIFYING 1			QUALIFYING 2	
	Driver	Time	Laps		Driver	Time	Laps		Driver	Time	Laps		Driver	Time		Driver	Time
1	F Alonso	1m29.214s	23	1	F Massa	1m27.353s	32	1	K Räikkönen	1m26.064s	14	1	K Räikkönen	1m26.644s	1	F Alonso	1m25.326s
2	F Massa	1m30.707s	7	2	K Räikkönen	1m27.750s	33	2	G Fisichella	1m26.454s	18	2	L Hamilton	1m26.674s	2	N Heidfeld	1m25.358s
3	S Vettel	1m30.857s	22	3	L Hamilton	1m27.829s	29	3	L Hamilton	1m26.467s	12	3	R Kubica	1m26.696s	3	L Hamilton	1m25.577s
4	L Hamilton	1m30.878s	14	4	G Fisichella	1m27.941s	33	4	A Davidson	1m26.491s	17	4	F Alonso	1m26.697s	4	K Räikkönen	1m25.644s
5	J Button	1m31.162s	15	5	N Heidfeld	1m27.970s	27	5	F Massa	1m26.547s	14	5	F Massa	1m26.712s	5	R Kubica	1m25.882s
6	K Nakajima	1m31.401s	21	6	A Wurz	1m27.981s	31	6	N Heidfeld	1m26.753s	18	6	N Heidfeld	1m26.895s	6	G Fisichella	1m25.944s
7	D Coulthard	1m31.528s	9	7	F Alonso	1m28.040s	25	7	F Alonso	1m26.786s	10	7	M Webber	1m26.978s	7	M Webber	1m26.623s
8	H Kovalainen	1m31.571s	20	8	N Rosberg	1m28.055s	29	8	H Kovalainen	1m26.937s	13	8	A Davidson	1m26.986s	8	J Trulli	1m26.688s
9	M Webber	1m31.661s	16	9	R Kubica	1m28.281s	26	9	T Sato	1m27.266s	12	9	J Trulli	1m27.014s	9	R Schumacher	1m26.739s
10	R Barrichello	1m31.737s	12	10	D Coulthard	1m28.495s	23	10	A Wurz	1m27.322s	9	10	G Fisichella	1m27.270s	10	T Sato	1m26.758s
11	T Sato	1m31.782s	7	11	A Davidson	1m28.727s	28	11	M Webber	1m27.390s	13	11	R Schumacher	1m27.328s	11	A Davidson	1m26.909s
12	G Fisichella	1m32.011s	14	12	J Trulli	1m28.921s	33	12	R Kubica	1m27.753s	13	12	T Sato	1m27.365s	12	N Rosberg	1m26.914s
13	A Wurz	1m32.194s	18	13	T Sato	1m29.009s	23	13	R Schumacher	1m27.887s	13	13	A Wurz	1m27.479s	13	H Kovalainen	1m26.964s
14	A Sutil	1m34.043s	26	14	J Button	1m29.066s	30	14	J Trulli	1m27.897s	16	14	H Kovalainen	1m27.529s	14	J Button	1m27.264s
15	V Liuzzi	1m34.627s	8	15	R Barrichello	1m29.542s	12	15	R Barrichello	1m28.039s	16	15	J Button	1m27.540s	15	A Wurz	1m27.393s
16	C Albers	1m35.055s	10	16	R Schumacher	1m29.574s	26	16	N Rosberg	1m28.061s	5	16	N Rosberg	1m27.596s	16	F Massa	no time
17	N Heidfeld	1m37.249s	12	17	M Webber	1m29.801s	11	17	J Button	1m28.119s	21	17	R Barrichello	1m27.679s			
18	A Davidson	1m39.221s	6	18	H Kovalainen	1m30.097s	10	18	D Coulthard	1m28.208s	12	18	S Speed	1m28.305s			
19	K Räikkönen	1m39.242s	7	19	S Speed	1m30.383s	28	19	V Liuzzi	1m28.332s	15	19	D Coulthard	1m28.579s			
20	R Schumacher	1m39.550s	9	20	A Sutil	1m31.108s	35	20	S Speed	1m28.485s	9	20	V Liuzzi	1m29.267s			
21	S Speed	1m41.763s	9	21	C Albers	1m31.175s	32	21	A Sutil	1m28.678s	19	21	A Sutil	1m29.339s			
22	J Trulli	1m44.130s	11	22	V Liuzzi	1m31.693s	16	22	C Albers	1m30.547s	7	22	C Albers	1m31.932s			

Best sectors – Practice			Speed trap – Practice			Best sectors – Qualifying			Speed trap – Qualifying		
Sec 1	F Alonso	28.968s	1	K Räikkönen	191.1mph	Sec 1	F Alonso	28.371s	1	K Räikkönen	191.6mph
Sec 2	K Räikkönen	22.944s	2	A Wurz	190.3mph	Sec 2	N Heidfeld	22.704s	2	F Massa	190.7mph
Sec 3	K Räikkönen	34.128s	3	M Webber	190.2mph	Sec 3	K Räikkönen	34.002s	3	M Webber	190.5mph

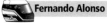 **Fernando Alonso**
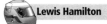 **Giancarlo Fisichella**
Felipe Massa
Jenson Button
Nick Heidfeld
Ralf Schumacher

"Kimi was just a bit quicker. I was so busy defending from Heidfeld that I could not stay ahead of him. I was then behind Lewis, but took second after the second stop."

"We knew that we were not on the leaders' pace. I got the best that I could from the package today, but I was struggling for grip, although we had good reliability."

"After engine failure in qualifying, and having to start from the back, it would have been hard to do better than sixth. I was able to run at a good pace even with a full load."

"I was heavy with fuel in the first stint. At my first stop I asked for front wing but because of a radio problem the team didn't respond. Then I had the drive-through."

"I had a very good start and got by Fernando. I hoped to stay in front, but the McLarens were quicker. Our pace is really good and fourth is a super start to the season."

"We had expected to be in the top 10, but to bring two cars home is great. Towards the end, I had a problem with pneumatic pressure but we made it to the finish."

 **Lewis Hamilton**
 **Heikki Kovalainen**
 **Kimi Räikkönen**
 Rubens Barrichello
 Robert Kubica
Jarno Trulli

"I'm ecstatic. Kubica got past at the start, but there was no room on the inside so I went left and outbraked he and Fernando into the first corner to take third."

"There is little to recall from my debut, and lots to forget. I made too many mistakes. I had hoped to move through the field, but I was struggling even to keep up."

"A fantastic win! The race was not as easy as it might have looked, as the radio failed. Luckily, I knew what I had to do. I was not flat-out all the time, adapting my pace."

"I had a competitive race, although I came 11th. The tyres were working well. I lost time behind Jenson in the first stint, but we have no team orders so I had to find a way by."

"My pace was good, but I got stuck in fifth gear. I was heavier than Nick and was able to match his speed. My strategy was to attack towards the end, but I didn't get that far."

"I lost two places into Turn 1, but gained one back on lap 1, then was held up by Ralf. I lost more time when Fisichella pulled out of the pits in front of me."

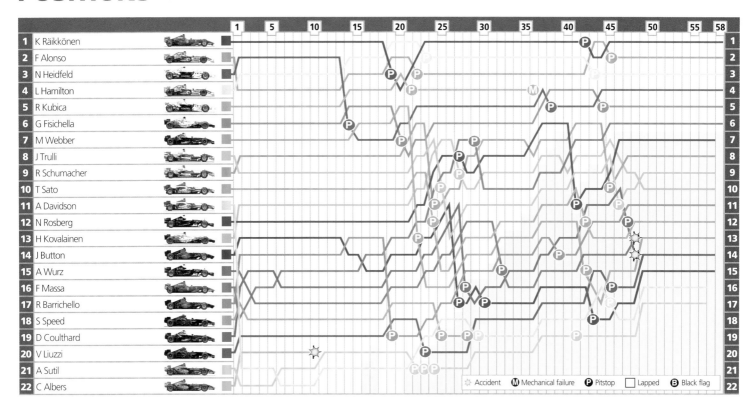

	Driver
1	K Räikkönen
2	F Alonso
3	N Heidfeld
4	L Hamilton
5	R Kubica
6	G Fisichella
7	M Webber
8	J Trulli
9	R Schumacher
10	T Sato
11	A Davidson
12	N Rosberg
13	H Kovalainen
14	J Button
15	A Wurz
16	F Massa
17	R Barrichello
18	S Speed
19	D Coulthard
20	V Liuzzi
21	A Sutil
22	C Albers

Legend: ✴ Accident   Ⓜ Mechanical failure   Ⓟ Pitstop   ☐ Lapped   Ⓑ Black flag

QUALIFYING 3

	Driver	Time
1	K Räikkönen	1m26.072s
2	F Alonso	1m26.493s
3	N Heidfeld	1m26.556s
4	L Hamilton	1m26.755s
5	R Kubica	1m27.347s
6	G Fisichella	1m27.634s
7	M Webber	1m27.934s
8	J Trulli	1m28.404s
9	R Schumacher	1m28.692s
10	T Sato	1m28.871s

GRID

	Driver	Time
1	K Räikkönen	1m26.072s
2	F Alonso	1m26.493s
3	N Heidfeld	1m26.556s
4	L Hamilton	1m26.755s
5	R Kubica	1m27.347s
6	G Fisichella	1m27.634s
7	M Webber	1m27.934s
8	J Trulli	1m28.404s
9	R Schumacher	1m28.692s
10	T Sato	1m28.871s
11	A Davidson	1m26.909s
12	N Rosberg	1m26.914s
13	H Kovalainen	1m26.964s
14	J Button	1m27.264s
15	A Wurz	1m27.393s
16	R Barrichello	1m27.679s
17	S Speed	1m28.305s
18	D Coulthard	1m28.579s
19	V Liuzzi	1m29.267s
20	A Sutil	1m29.339s
21	C Albers	1m31.932s
22*	F Massa	no time

*STARTED FROM BACK AFTER ENGINE CHANGE

RACE

	Driver	Car	Laps	Time	Avg. mph	Fastest	Stops
1	K Räikkönen	Ferrari F2007	58	1h25m28.770s	134.156	1m25.235s	2
2	F Alonso	McLaren-Mercedes MP4-22	58	1h25m36.012s	133.967	1m26.314s	2
3	L Hamilton	McLaren-Mercedes MP4-22	58	1h25m47.365s	133.671	1m26.351s	2
4	N Heidfeld	BMW Sauber F1.07	58	1h26m07.533s	133.150	1m26.722s	2
5	G Fisichella	Renault R27	58	1h26m35.239s	132.440	1m26.892s	2
6	F Massa	Ferrari F2007	58	1h26m35.575s	132.431	1m27.044s	1
7	N Rosberg	Williams-Toyota FW29	57	1h25m32.237s	131.754	1m26.721s	2
8	R Schumacher	Toyota TF107	57	1h25m55.972s	131.147	1m27.796s	2
9	J Trulli	Toyota TF107	57	1h26m03.643s	130.953	1m28.034s	2
10	H Kovalainen	Renault R27	57	1h26m04.110s	130.941	1m27.592s	2
11	R Barrichello	Honda RA107	57	1h26m05.009s	130.918	1m28.098s	2
12	T Sato	Super Aguri-Honda SA07	57	1h26m09.506s	130.804	1m28.487s	2
13	M Webber	Red Bull-Renault RB3	57	1h26m39.409s	130.052	1m27.501s	2
14	V Liuzzi	Toro Rosso-Ferrari STR02	57	1h26m46.364s	129.878	1m28.282s	2
15	J Button	Honda RA107	57	1h26m47.799s	129.842	1m28.387s	3
16	A Davidson	Super Aguri-Honda SA07	56	1h25m31.618s	129.458	1m28.489s	2
17	A Sutil	Spyker-Ferrari F8-VII	56	1h26m43.931s	127.659	1m28.687s	4
R	A Wurz	Williams-Toyota FW29	48	Crash damage	-	1m28.303s	1
R	D Coulthard	Red Bull-Renault RB3	48	Accident	-	1m27.706s	2
R	R Kubica	BMW Sauber F1.07	36	Gearbox	-	1m26.642s	1
R	S Speed	Toro Rosso-Ferrari STR02	28	Tyre	-	1m28.953s	1
R	C Albers	Spyker-Ferrari F8-VII	10	Accident	-	1m30.899s	0

CHAMPIONSHIP

	Driver	Pts
1	K Räikkönen	10
2	F Alonso	8
3	L Hamilton	6
4	N Heidfeld	5
5	G Fisichella	4
6	F Massa	3
7	N Rosberg	2
8	R Schumacher	1

	Constructor	Pts
1	McLaren-Mercedes	14
2	Ferrari	13
3	BMW Sauber	5
4	Renault	4
5	Williams-Toyota	2
6	Toyota	1

Fastest Lap
K Räikkönen 1m25.235s
(139.173mph) on lap 41

Fastest speed trap
A Wurz 192.3mph
Slowest speed trap
C Albers 184.3mph

Fastest pit stop
1	D Coulthard	20.963s
2	F Alonso	21.509s
3	G Fisichella	21.704s

David Coulthard
"I tried to have a go inside Wurz's car at Turn 3, but was too far back and messed it up. It was optimistic on my part. The crash was my fault, not Alex's, so apologies to him."

Nico Rosberg
"I started last year's first race from 12th and finished 7th, so I thought I could do it again. I was really happy when I took a chance to pass Ralf, but you've got to try it."

Vitantonio Liuzzi
"This has been a tough race for us. It was important for us to get to the chequered flag to get more kilometres under our belt, as we did very little testing this winter."

Christijan Albers
"I started in the spare car as I was not happy with my race car's balance. I put in some fast times in the first 10 laps, but unfortunately I made a mistake and went off."

Takuma Sato
"I had an exciting first lap, but with differing conditions, I was struggling for balance. At my second stop we lost time and that affected our finishing position."

Mark Webber
"The first stop didn't go well and when I rejoined I was having trouble maintaining speed into corners. I wasn't able to get the pace back that I'd had in the first stint."

Alexander Wurz
"After his second stop, I was aware that Coulthard was behind me. Then I felt an impact and straight after that I was his landing pad as the impact had sent him airborne."

Scott Speed
"I was on the pace of those ahead of me, but was struggling to stay on the track. This became worse and I had a bit of understeer, as we had a slow leak in both fronts."

Adrian Sutil
"I made up places at the start, but I had the clash with Davidson and fell back. When I got some free space I was running good times, but then had two drive-throughs."

Anthony Davidson
"The car went into anti-stall, so I was last into Turn 1. I went around one of the Spykers and they hit me. The car got pitched up, landed very heavily and I hurt my back."

2007 FORMULA 1™ PETRONAS MALAYSIAN GRAND PRIX
KUALA LUMPUR

McLAREN IN CONTROL

Massa started on pole for Ferrari, but was back in third after two corners as McLaren powered ahead, with Fernando Alonso racing on to his first victory for the team

McLaren supremo Ron Dennis looked every inch the proud father figure on the podium at Sepang as Fernando Alonso and Lewis Hamilton took the plaudits at the Malaysian GP. Dennis neatly ducked away before the champagne started flowing, and came down the stairs just in time to see Hamilton's half-empty bottle slip through the fingers of a mechanic after Lewis had passed it down from the podium. The unfortunate fellow caught it on the first bounce, and yet the Mumm bottle didn't break. The McLaren chief joked about it with his guys, perhaps aware that here was further confirmation that this was a day when nothing could go wrong.

"I'm proud for the team, above all else," he said as he walked away from the podium. "I'm obviously delighted with the result, as both drivers did an excellent job and we had a good strategy. Lewis was very controlled at the end, very cool, and did what was necessary to come second, which was his objective.

"I'm still basically letting it sink in. It was a great result, as it was a good strategic race, and I think that we showed we had the pace to beat the Ferraris, and I'm very pleased with the outcome, obviously. Inevitably, you go through peaks and troughs of

Felipe Massa tried his hardest to usurp Lewis Hamilton in the early laps, but he was the one who came unstuck

team and everyone in it works very hard. We knew we were there or thereabouts on qualifying pace, and I think we demonstrated that in Australia. We also knew in Australia that we were off the race pace, and we worked pretty hard on the car and set-up, so the engineers and the guys in Woking worked hard to see what we could do about that. I think we've demonstrated that we've made reasonable progress."

Specifically, the team was able to come to terms with the tyres. Everyone might have been testing on the same tyres since November, but Ferrari still had a huge amount of Bridgestone knowledge upon which it could call, and the others were still catching up. The test in Malaysia helped McLaren to close that gap.

There were other reasons why Ferrari was handicapped at Sepang, however. It was clear that for the hot flyaway races cooling had become an issue, and that created some aerodynamic compromises. More specifically, Räikkönen had to protect his engine. The saga of his Melbourne-winning engine – potentially damaged by the loss of water from a pipe – kept the media intrigued. It had been flown back to Maranello, a highly unusual occurrence when freight would normally go straight from Australia to Malaysia. Subject to the usual restrictions of it being sealed by the FIA, the finest brains in Gilles Simon's engine department did everything they could to ascertain if it was OK – some 10 detailed tests and inspections, including the use of a static dyno, were undertaken.

Meanwhile, another engine was tested on track at the Malaysia test with a similar loss of water simulated to provide useful data. The conclusion was that it was worth running the Melbourne engine come race weekend at Sepang, but to do so as gently as possible. The general feeling was that it would be better to take a punt and at least score some sensible points than take a guaranteed 10-place penalty.

While Felipe Massa made up for his Melbourne

competitiveness, and hopefully this will be a trend that we can continue."

It seemed that much had changed in the break since the opening race in Australia, when Kimi Räikkönen had romped home in front. While it's fair to say that Ferrari had a clear edge in Melbourne, there have been many races there when the advantage of the dominant team has for some reason been exaggerated. The interval of two weekends, and the chance to test in Malaysia, appeared to have allowed McLaren to haul in Ferrari.

"I think hard work pays off," said McLaren Chief Operating Officer Martin Whitmarsh, "and I think the

TALKING POINT
MASSA PANNED AT SEPANG

The new season could not have got off to a worse start for Felipe Massa.

Massa, according to those who know him best, benefited hugely from both his year's testing with Ferrari and then his 2006 season as race understudy to Michael Schumacher.

Honda's Engineering Director

Jacky Eeckelaert was the man who oversaw the first F1 tests of both Kimi Räikkönen and Massa, a year apart at Sauber. "The success we had with Kimi made Peter Sauber think that young drivers could make the step up to F1," said the Belgian, "and when he sold Kimi to McLaren we actively looked for another.

"Felipe was very quick, especially over one lap, but we threw him in at the deep end and I don't think he learned as quickly as Peter hoped. But he was too good to be lost from F1 and the Ferrari test year gave him much more confidence.

"At Sauber, if he was a second or two off the pace, he tried to find it in himself and he over-drove. But when he drove the same car as the World Champion, on the same tyres on the same day, and saw that he was only

a couple of tenths away, that gave him huge confidence. He started to learn to develop the car and was a different driver when he came back to Sauber in 2004. Then, in the race team at Ferrari, he learned from Michael without expectations being too high. He did very well. That was also invaluable to his confidence."

Over winter testing, with more experience of Bridgestone rubber than incoming team-mate Räikkönen, the little Brazilian started to look like stiff competition for Kimi. But, as always with intra-team rivalry, both men wanted a good start. Kimi got one, winning comfortably on his Ferrari debut in Melbourne. Felipe matched him for pace throughout practice but when it mattered, in qualifying, a gearbox problem relegated him to 16th on the grid.

Determined to hit back in Malaysia, Massa took pole at Sepang but then botched his start, not only letting Alonso through into Turn 1, but Hamilton's sister McLaren around the outside of Turn 2. With Alonso going away, Felipe knew he had to react quickly but, suckered by Hamilton, outbraked himself, ran onto the dirt at Turn 4 and dropped behind Räikkönen and Nick Heidfeld's BMW. Race over, effectively.

You wondered what Michael Schumacher, sitting on his sofa at home, would make of Felipe reversing his Ferrari into fifth place from pole. The pressure was on.

disappointment with pole position for Ferrari, Räikkönen had to settle for third with Alonso in between. Once again running with a heavier fuel load than his team-mate, Hamilton qualified fourth.

The start was a nightmare for Massa, who was beaten by both McLaren drivers in the run through the first two turns. He panicked as he tried to regain position. On lap 6, in his desperation to get back past, he ran wide at Turn 4, Langkawi, after Hamilton had brilliantly outfoxed him. His off-track excursion dropped the Brazilian behind Räikkönen and, more importantly, the BMW of Nick Heidfeld, and his race was ruined.

"I'm disappointed, definitely," Massa said later. "I expected something better from the weekend, as I was starting in pole position. I think I was not very lucky, as I lost a position at the start. You are behind, and it's very, very difficult to overtake here. So when I got a couple of chances, I tried to get by. Unfortunately I couldn't make it, but I'm not really angry that I tried. I think sometimes you need to try, and for sure in this kind of sport, where it's very difficult to pass, we need to try, and it's what I did."

Thereafter, it was a relatively straightforward

afternoon for McLaren, and Alonso and Hamilton ran free of pressure from behind, with Hamilton again getting the plaudits for a solid performance. Räikkönen was in conservative cruise mode throughout, doing just enough to ensure that he salvaged a handy helping of six points for finishing third.

Alonso was delighted to get his first McLaren win out of the way so early in the year: "When I was leading after the first corner and saw Lewis running in second place, well that helped a little bit the dream to win the race. We knew our chance was to overtake the Ferraris at the start and we were lucky to do it and, for sure, [it was] even better to have your team-mate in second place.

"But I was not confident until the final stint, to be honest, even on lap 40 or something like that, the team kept telling me to push because we thought Kimi was going very long for the second stint. So I was not confident until Kimi pitted for the second time when we realised the victory was in our hands, and after the race the team was extremely happy and very excited."

"At the moment, there's a reasonably small margin between ourselves and Ferrari," said Whitmarsh, "and I think it will continue to be a good battle between us.

Heikki Kovalainen was under pressure to atone for a weak Australian GP and started by outqualifying his team-mate, then came away with his first point

The strategy was good, the starts were fantastic, the job that Lewis did was great. Fernando, frankly, was driving within himself from a third of the way through the race. He is a lean, mean, killing machine. He just gets on and does the job."

Räikkönen clearly couldn't run his engine to its full potential, and that doesn't just mean the actual revs, but the way he had to drive to nurse it. There was no way he could ever be close enough at the end of either of Sepang's long straights to make a pass on a car of similar performance. Ultimately, though, the strategy of running his Australian GP engine paid off, as third place was undoubtedly better than he would have achieved with a 10-place penalty, as he would probably have started 14th or worse had he gone into qualifying with anything like a suitable fuel load for running a long first stint.

Räikkönen made it very clear that his hands had been tied: "The whole weekend was quite difficult, but I think we needed to compromise too many things and we lost too much speed because of those things. I think we knew that the engine was not 100% and we had to be a bit on the safe side, but there were some other things which were not perfect, so we could not

take risks to do anything stupid with what we had. Hopefully we can have all the right things in the car next race and be 100% again."

Massa, meanwhile, was stuck behind a very motivated Heidfeld, and even with a potential lap time advantage when running on his own, simply didn't have a chance of getting past. The way the strategies unfolded finished him off. As part of his quest for pole, Massa ran relatively light in Q3 and thus pitted on lap 17. Heidfeld confounded observers by going to lap 22, in total contrast to BMW Sauber's Australian GP strategy. Already with a five-lap advantage, BMW Sauber put in enough fuel at the first pit stop to get Heidfeld out still in front, and yet still with a two-lap fuel advantage over Massa at the second stop, which kept him ahead to the finish.

"We approached the race being a little bit aggressive in qualifying," said Ferrari engineering boss Luca Baldisserri. "The start compromised this kind of race, so we were behind people with more fuel. That forced us to run, let's say, a little bit heavier car in the second stint.

"A heavier car here is a penalty, and that is a penalty that I think at the end of the day we paid for

OPPOSITE Alexander Wurz pulls off a bold passing move on Ralf Schumacher on his climb from 19th on the grid to ninth place

BELOW Fernando Alonso made a great start and raced on from there to his first victory for McLaren

INSIDE LINE
FERNANDO ALONSO
McLAREN DRIVER

"Qualifying went pretty well and it was great to be on the second row for the second successive grand prix. It was good news when you consider that I started from zero, being new to the team, new to the car and new to the Bridgestone tyres. We are still on a learning curve, but it looked promising.

The race confirmed it. Ferrari was favourite coming to the Malaysian GP and I thought that our only chance to win was to lead into the first corner. Thanks to a good start and a good car, I was able to get down the inside of Felipe [Massa] into Turn 1. We were side-by-side, but I had the inside line. Then, when I looked in my mirrors as I accelerated out of Turn 2 and saw that my team-mate [Lewis] rather than Massa was second, that was even better!

During the practice sessions, we hadn't done more than about eight or nine laps on a set of tyres and so you are always a bit concerned about how the rubber was going to behave over 15 or 16 laps. That's never easy, but once I was able to open out a gap of 7–8s I felt rather more relaxed.

When you could see Ron [Dennis] on the pit wall signalling at the first pit stop, it was because from about lap 10 of the race I had no radio, just like Kimi [Räikkönen] suffered in the Australian GP. I was pleased that I saw the pit board! I saw the arrow, came in and just hoped that the guys would be there...

Ron was telling me that the radio was off, which obviously I knew, but they adjusted something and then it worked fine for the rest of the grand prix.

It's fantastic to have won so early in my McLaren career, and it's a wonderful surprise what we have achieved in such a short time. The team has put in a lot of effort, but we never expected to be that competitive.

It was a really tough race. It was extremely hot in the cockpit. You keep drinking water every five or six laps, but after 10 laps it's like tea, water at 60 degrees – not so pleasant to drink anymore!

It become tough during the last 20–25 laps, but I was lucky that I wasn't having a big battle with anyone and could take it a bit easier.

A second place and a win in the first two races with a new team is a bit of a dream for me. I felt proud for the whole team."

ABOVE Mark Webber had an uneventful weekend and finished where he started: in 10th position

BELOW LEFT Both Hondas ran in the midfield throughout the race, battling with Toyota and Toro Rosso

BELOW RIGHT High fives for the McLaren duo after their 1–2

most today. The car was not performing as it had on Friday. In fact, the car was not performing as it had in the last test, so we are analysing the data to understand why the package of car and tyres could not reproduce those runs."

There was also a question of Massa simply making the best of a bad situation. Throwing away a priceless pole position on the first lap and then going off a few laps later is hardly calculated to boost your confidence, and the Brazilian must have been driving to ensure that he at least brought home some points rather than trying any move on Heidfeld.

The unfortunate Massa took a pasting in the media, but at least he only had to wait a week for a chance of redemption in the Bahrain GP...

Behind Massa's Ferrari, Giancarlo Fisichella brought home some points but little joy for the Renault team in sixth place, while Jarno Trulli and Heikki Kovalainen completed the scorers, the Finn enjoying a much better weekend than he had in Melbourne.

Once again, it was a struggle for Honda, with Rubens Barrichello and Jenson Button finishing 11th and 12th, even on a day when the level of attrition was markedly low with only four drivers retiring.

SNAPSHOT FROM
MALAYSIA

CLOCKWISE FROM RIGHT The dancers brought a real taste of Malaysia to the grid; Fernando Alonso got down and dirty to celebrate his first McLaren win; Kimi Räikkönen shows off a new tattoo; the sun sets over the paddock; Fisichella's refuelling crew look a little on the small side; Petronas-sponsored BMW Sauber emphasises its link to Kuala Lumpur's Petronas Twin Towers; colouring in a white line on each soft compound tyre was a hit, but not with those doing the colouring

WEEKEND NEWS

■ After the failure of the near-invisible sidewall white spot at the Australian GP, the FIA mandated that henceforth the softer tyre would be identified by a white band around one of the grooves. Bridgestone was not impressed by the amount of extra work involved, but the new system proved an instant success.

■ The customer car issue rumbled on in Malaysia as Spyker this time focused its protest on Toro Rosso. The stewards again refused to accept the protest, mainly on the grounds that an independent process of arbitration had already been set in motion. The FIA, however, did confiscate some STR parts for possible use as evidence.

■ The silly season kicked off earlier than ever when stories linked Nick Heidfeld to a possible move to Toyota in 2008 – at the expense of the out-of-contract, very expensive and generally lacklustre Ralf Schumacher. Toyota denied any discussions, while for BMW Sauber the move would have left Sebastian Vettel on pole for a race seat.

■ Former Ferrari and McLaren man Giorgio Ascanelli returned to the paddock in Sepang as Technical Director of Scuderia Toro Rosso, having been wooed by his old pal Gerhard Berger. Meanwhile, former Ferrari technical chief Ross Brawn was mentioned in connection with a possible future role at struggling Honda.

■ Plans for a street race in nearby Singapore were gathering momentum and Red Bull Racing's Mark Webber visited the potential site in the run-up to the Malaysian GP. The nervous Malaysian GP organisers were less than reassured when Bernie Ecclestone pointed out that their eight-year-old venue was "starting to get a little shabby".

RACE RESULTS

MALAYSIA
SEPANG

RACE DATE April 8th
CIRCUIT LENGTH 3.444 miles
NO. OF LAPS 56
RACE DISTANCE 192.887 miles
WEATHER Sunny and humid, 36°C
TRACK TEMP 55°C
ATTENDANCE 115,000
LAP RECORD Juan Pablo Montoya,
1m34.223s, 131.595mph, 2004

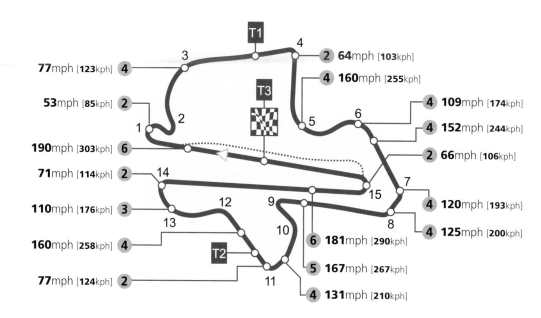

	PRACTICE 1		
	Driver	**Time**	**Laps**
1	F Massa	1m34.972s	17
2	F Alonso	1m35.220s	24
3	L Hamilton	1m35.712s	22
4	K Räikkönen	1m35.779s	20
5	N Rosberg	1m36.308s	21
6	M Webber	1m36.522s	20
7	J Trulli	1m36.597s	25
8	K Nakajima	1m36.885s	15
9	R Schumacher	1m37.052s	22
10	R Kubica	1m37.121s	12
11	D Coulthard	1m37.484s	7
12	S Vettel	1m37.837s	39
13	V Liuzzi	1m37.882s	20
14	H Kovalainen	1m38.143s	24
15	G Fisichella	1m38.300s	26
16	A Sutil	1m38.720s	29
17	T Sato	1m38.966s	10
18	S Speed	1m39.130s	9
19	R Barrichello	1m39.234s	21
20	J Button	1m39.331s	17
21	A Davidson	1m39.357s	9
22	C Albers	1m40.074s	25

	PRACTICE 2		
	Driver	**Time**	**Laps**
1	F Massa	1m35.780s	34
2	G Fisichella	1m35.910s	36
3	H Kovalainen	1m36.106s	37
4	K Räikkönen	1m36.160s	33
5	N Rosberg	1m36.523s	31
6	A Wurz	1m36.621s	21
7	R Kubica	1m36.717s	18
8	R Schumacher	1m36.760s	28
9	L Hamilton	1m36.797s	30
10	N Heidfeld	1m36.862s	25
11	M Webber	1m36.906s	18
12	F Alonso	1m37.041s	26
13	D Coulthard	1m37.203s	25
14	T Sato	1m37.282s	30
15	J Button	1m37.578s	29
16	J Trulli	1m37.712s	34
17	V Liuzzi	1m37.855s	26
18	A Davidson	1m38.334s	27
19	A Sutil	1m38.419s	28
20	S Speed	1m38.650s	20
21	R Barrichello	1m38.713s	20
22	C Albers	1m39.807s	23

	PRACTICE 3		
	Driver	**Time**	**Laps**
1	L Hamilton	1m34.811s	14
2	F Massa	1m34.953s	15
3	F Alonso	1m35.311s	11
4	R Kubica	1m35.385s	16
5	K Räikkönen	1m35.498s	7
6	N Rosberg	1m35.770s	16
7	N Heidfeld	1m36.160s	20
8	A Davidson	1m36.195s	19
9	R Schumacher	1m36.245s	20
10	M Webber	1m36.257s	17
11	D Coulthard	1m36.273s	13
12	V Liuzzi	1m36.297s	18
13	G Fisichella	1m36.434s	15
14	A Wurz	1m36.473s	16
15	S Speed	1m36.501s	14
16	T Sato	1m36.545s	18
17	J Button	1m36.658s	20
18	H Kovalainen	1m36.876s	6
19	R Barrichello	1m36.972s	19
20	J Trulli	1m37.473s	16
21	A Sutil	1m38.018s	20
22	C Albers	1m38.225s	20

	QUALIFYING 1	
	Driver	**Time**
1	F Alonso	1m34.942s
2	L Hamilton	1m35.028s
3	K Räikkönen	1m35.138s
4	R Kubica	1m35.294s
5	F Massa	1m35.340s
6	N Heidfeld	1m35.617s
7	J Trulli	1m35.666s
8	M Webber	1m35.727s
9	D Coulthard	1m35.730s
10	R Schumacher	1m35.736s
11	N Rosberg	1m35.755s
12	G Fisichella	1m35.879s
13	J Button	1m35.913s
14	H Kovalainen	1m36.092s
15	V Liuzzi	1m36.140s
16	T Sato	1m36.430s
17	S Speed	1m36.578s
18	A Davidson	1m36.816s
19	R Barrichello	1m36.827s
20	A Wurz	1m37.326s
21	C Albers	1m38.279s
22	A Sutil	1m38.415s

	QUALIFYING 2	
	Driver	**Time**
1	F Alonso	1m34.057s
2	F Massa	1m34.454s
3	L Hamilton	1m34.650s
4	K Räikkönen	1m34.687s
5	R Kubica	1m34.739s
6	N Heidfeld	1m35.203s
7	J Trulli	1m35.255s
8	N Rosberg	1m35.380s
9	M Webber	1m35.579s
10	R Schumacher	1m35.595s
11	H Kovalainen	1m35.630s
12	G Fisichella	1m35.706s
13	D Coulthard	1m35.766s
14	T Sato	1m35.945s
15	J Button	1m36.088s
16	V Liuzzi	1m36.145s

Best sectors – Practice			Speed trap – Practice			Best sectors – Qualifying			Speed trap – Qualifying		
Sec 1	L Hamilton	24.796s	1	K Nakajima	187.3mph	**Sec 1**	R Kubica	24.767s	1	K Räikkönen	186.3mph
Sec 2	L Hamilton	31.223s	2	K Räikkönen	187.0mph	**Sec 2**	F Alonso	30.873s	2	H Kovalainen	185.9mph
Sec 3	F Massa	38.632s	3	F Massa	186.7mph	**Sec 3**	F Alonso	38.383s	3	A Davidson	185.8mph

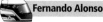

Fernando Alonso
"The key was to get in front to control the race. There was a problem with my radio after 10 laps, so I was not sure if the team was ready for me at the first stop."

Giancarlo Fisichella
"Sixth was the maximum, but it feels like a podium. I am proud of my race. The start was really good, I was able to be aggressive in Turns 1 and 2, and gain four places."

Felipe Massa
"It was a very tough race. It was almost impossible to overtake. I tried to attack Lewis, but made a mistake and ended up off track. I can't blame myself for trying."

Jenson Button
"Sutil drove over the side of my car and there was damage. How much difference it made I don't know, but during the first two stints I suffered a lack of rear grip."

Nick Heidfeld
"Robert hit me at Turn 1. Luckily, my car wasn't damaged. I passed Felipe when he went wide, and was surprised I could keep ahead and that he pitted earlier than me."

Ralf Schumacher
"The car didn't get away well and I had to avoid Jarno and lost places. Then I was stuck in traffic. After my first stop I had a slow puncture and needed to make an extra stop."

Lewis Hamilton
"That was my toughest race, as it was so hot inside the cockpit. I was able to pass Felipe and Kimi for second. Kimi was catching near the end as I struggled for balance."

Heikki Kovalainen
"My first F1 point is a nice feeling. The balance was similar to how it was in qualifying, unpredictable in high-speed corners which meant I had some moments in Turn 6."

Kimi Räikkönen
"I'm happy to have picked up six points, but sad the race didn't live up to expectations. We lacked a bit of speed. Turn 1? Fernando and Lewis were just better than us."

Rubens Barrichello
"For the last two grands prix, we've had a bad qualifying and the races have shown that we could have been closer to the points had we not suffered on Saturdays."

Robert Kubica
"Everything happened, from the gearbox to a puncture early on. In qualifying, the pace was good. Then in the race nothing worked. My big problem was braking instability."

Jarno Trulli
"The only pity was the start wasn't so great and I ended up behind Fisichella. I was quicker in the first stint but at this circuit whoever is in front tends to stay there."

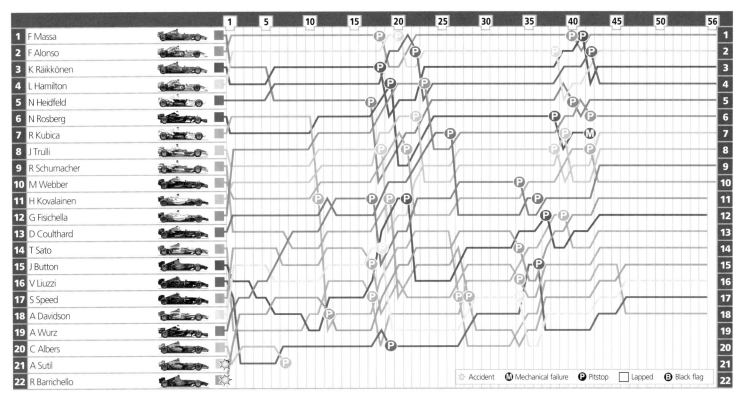

		1	5	10	15	20	25	30	35	40	45	50	56	
1	F Massa													1
2	F Alonso													2
3	K Räikkönen													3
4	L Hamilton													4
5	N Heidfeld													5
6	N Rosberg													6
7	R Kubica													7
8	J Trulli													8
9	R Schumacher													9
10	M Webber													10
11	H Kovalainen													11
12	G Fisichella													12
13	D Coulthard													13
14	T Sato													14
15	J Button													15
16	V Liuzzi													16
17	S Speed													17
18	A Davidson													18
19	A Wurz													19
20	C Albers													20
21	A Sutil													21
22	R Barrichello													22

☼ Accident   Ⓜ Mechanical failure   Ⓟ Pitstop   ☐ Lapped   Ⓑ Black flag

QUALIFYING 3

	Driver	Time
1	F Massa	1m35.043s
2	F Alonso	1m35.310s
3	K Räikkönen	1m35.479s
4	L Hamilton	1m36.045s
5	N Heidfeld	1m36.543s
6	N Rosberg	1m36.829s
7	R Kubica	1m36.896s
8	J Trulli	1m36.902s
9	R Schumacher	1m37.078s
10	M Webber	1m37.345s

GRID

	Driver	Time
1	F Massa	1m35.043s
2	F Alonso	1m35.310s
3	K Räikkönen	1m35.479s
4	L Hamilton	1m36.045s
5	N Heidfeld	1m36.543s
6	N Rosberg	1m36.829s
7	R Kubica	1m36.896s
8	J Trulli	1m36.902s
9	R Schumacher	1m37.078s
10	M Webber	1m37.345s
11	H Kovalainen	1m35.630s
12	G Fisichella	1m35.706s
13	D Coulthard	1m35.766s
14	T Sato	1m35.945s
15	J Button	1m36.088s
16	V Liuzzi	1m36.145s
17	S Speed	1m36.578s
18	A Davidson	1m36.816s
19	R Barrichello	1m36.827s
20	A Wurz	1m37.326s
21	C Albers	1m38.279s
22	A Sutil	1m38.415s

RACE

	Driver	Car	Laps	Time	Avg. mph	Fastest	Stops
1	F Alonso	McLaren-Mercedes MP4-22	56	1h32m14.930s	125.451	1m36.861s	2
2	L Hamilton	McLaren-Mercedes MP4-22	56	1h32m32.487s	125.054	1m36.701s	2
3	K Räikkönen	Ferrari F2007	56	1h32m33.269s	125.036	1m37.228s	2
4	N Heidfeld	BMW Sauber F1.07	56	1h32m48.707s	124.690	1m37.417s	2
5	F Massa	Ferrari F2007	56	1h32m51.635s	124.624	1m37.199s	2
6	G Fisichella	Renault R27	56	1h33m20.568s	123.981	1m37.879s	2
7	J Trulli	Toyota TF107	56	1h33m25.062s	123.881	1m38.016s	2
8	H Kovalainen	Renault R27	56	1h33m26.945s	123.840	1m37.810s	2
9	A Wurz	Williams-Toyota FW29	56	1h33m44.854s	123.445	1m37.864s	2
10	M Webber	Red Bull-Renault RB3	56	1h33m48.486s	123.366	1m38.540s	2
11	R Barrichello	Honda RA107	55	1h32m44.341s	122.560	1m38.566s	2
12	J Button	Honda RA107	55	1h32m45.062s	122.543	1m38.658s	2
13	T Sato	Super Aguri-Honda SA07	55	1h32m53.736s	122.353	1m38.496s	2
14	S Speed	Toro Rosso-Ferrari STR02	55	1h32m59.861s	122.219	1m39.098s	2
15	R Schumacher	Toyota TF107	55	1h33m10.875s	121.978	1m39.243s	2
16	A Davidson	Super Aguri-Honda SA07	55	1h33m17.142s	121.841	1m39.566s	2
17	V Liuzzi	Toro Rosso-Ferrari STR02	55	1h33m18.262s	121.816	1m38.447s	3
18	R Kubica	BMW Sauber F1.07	55	1h33m19.255s	121.795	1m38.874s	2
R	N Rosberg	Williams-Toyota FW29	42	Water leak	-	1m37.704s	2
R	D Coulthard	Red Bull-Renault RB3	36	Steering	-	1m38.098s	1
R	C Albers	Spyker-Ferrari F8-VII	7	Gearbox	-	1m41.495s	0
R	A Sutil	Spyker-Ferrari F8-VII	0	Accident	-	-	0

CHAMPIONSHIP

	Driver	Pts
1	F Alonso	18
2	K Räikkönen	16
3	L Hamilton	14
4	N Heidfeld	10
5	G Fisichella	7
	F Massa	7
7	J Trulli	2
8	N Rosberg	2
9	H Kovalainen	1
	R Schumacher	1

Fastest Lap
L Hamilton 1m36.701s
(128.224mph) on lap 22

Fastest speed trap
F Massa   187.9mph
Slowest speed trap
C Albers   177.7mph

Fastest pit stop
1	N Heidfeld	27.692s
2	G Fisichella	27.760s
3	K Räikkönen	28.169s

David Coulthard

"The brake pedal was rubbing on the steering column, so I lost some of the braking and also a little bit of the steering, so the only thing to do was to stop the car."

Nico Rosberg
"I lost sixth place to Kubica at the start. Later he made a mistake and I managed to claw the place back. From there, I gave it everything, but it all came to a halt."

Vitantonio Liuzzi
"It's a shame Sato pulled a crazy move at Turn 4. We collided and I also touched Scott's rear tyre and had to pit for a new nose. It was a shame, as my pace was good."

Christijan Albers
"It was such a shame to go out, as I really had confidence in the car. The guys in front were pulling away, but I could have got back up there. Then there was the gearbox failure."

Takuma Sato
"It was extremely tight into Turn 1 and Turn 2 and my car's nose was damaged. Into Turn 4, I was then side-by-side with the Toro Rossos and left with nowhere to go."

Mark Webber

"Tenth is about where we could have hoped to finish. The car ran reliably and the stops went well. Malaysia was a big test for the team and we got the car home."

Alexander Wurz
"I had a good pace on soft tyres in the first stint. Starting from 19th made it hard to fight Trulli and Kovalainen. It was disappointing to finish out of the points."

Scott Speed
"I've got blisters on my brake foot, but the car seemed more competitive than we'd expected. The guys worked very hard over the past few weeks so I'm glad for them."

Adrian Sutil
"I got past many cars at Turn 1 and was right behind Button. Under braking for Turn 4, something snapped at the back and I lost control, which was really sad."

Anthony Davidson
"It was a tough race after fighting off 'flu. I had a really good first lap, but then struggled for car balance. I still made a few rookie errors, but they can be ironed out."

	Constructor	Pts
1	McLaren-Mercedes	32
2	Ferrari	23
3	BMW Sauber	10
4	Renault	8
5	Toyota	3
6	Williams-Toyota	2

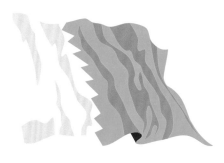

2007 FORMULA 1™ GULF AIR BAHRAIN GRAND PRIX

BAHRAIN

MASSA MAKES UP

Slated after Sepang, Felipe Massa took Ferrari back to the front at Sakhir. With Lewis Hamilton chasing him to the finish, it was time for the number twos to shine

Felipe Massa did a truly impressive job to bounce back from his Malaysian GP disappointment with pole position and a comfortable victory in Bahrain. It was just as well that he had only a few days to mull over what had happened when he tried to re-pass Lewis Hamilton at Sepang and fell off. When asked if he wanted to dedicate his win to anybody, he said: "To my girlfriend. This week was not so easy, but she had a lot of patience with me..."

Massa's recovery was due in no small part to his race engineer Rob Smedley, with whom he had been partnered since the middle of 2006. The no-nonsense Englishman had done a great job to get his man to make the most of his strengths and believe that he could really do it, talking the Brazilian through the post-Malaysia blues.

"To be honest with you, we took a lot of criticism," said Smedley after the race at Sakhir. "However, I think we understood the problems in Malaysia, we understood there was a problem at the start, we understood there was a problem with him trying to overtake where he did.

"It didn't really detract from the fact that he's been bloody quick from the end of last year until now. We

RENAULT'S MALAISE

Three grands prix into the new season, the Constructors' Championship points table read like this: McLaren-Mercedes, 49 points; Ferrari, 39 points; BMW Sauber, 18 points; Renault, 9 points. So there is no hiding from the fact that Renault – back-to-back champions in 2005–2006 – had had a dramatic fall from grace.

According to paddock flippancy, it was not hard to see why. Going out of the door in quick succession have been mass dampers, Fernando Alonso and Michelin tyres. Coming the other way has been Heikki Kovalainen, who had a truly awful start at the Australian GP, something which Flavio Briatore did not attempt to gloss over. "Terrible," said the Renault team chief. "That wasn't the real Heikki. Maybe it was his brother..."

There is a lot more to the decline than that, though. No team would like to lose a driver of Alonso's calibre, sure. In 2006, the reigning World Champion was, on average, around 0.15s quicker than Giancarlo Fisichella on fuel-adjusted qualifying pace. At this point in 2007, Renault was searching for around 10 times that margin to get back on terms with the pace-setting Ferraris and McLarens.

While McLaren had adapted well to the switch from Michelins to Bridgestone control rubber, Renault clearly did not.

"We've been a bit surprised at BMW Sauber's pace and at how some people were better able to use the soft tyre than us," said Renault engineering chief Pat Symonds at the season-opening grand prix in Australia.

The situation has not really improved and, with a race team as patently good as the Enstone outfit is, there have to be some deeper fundamentals.

"There are," says Symonds, "it's just that we can't put our finger on the problem. Rest assured, we will. There is a lot more to it than Fernando.

You don't punch above your weight for two years. You can do it for a race or two, but I'm not sure you can do it for much more than that. It was a sign of the team's class that we won back-to-back titles."

Fisichella scored points in each of the first three races (for fifth, sixth and eighth places) and Kovalainen took his first point with eighth place in Malaysia, but after the third race of the season, Renault was fighting to head an incredibly tight midfield group. Behind Ferrari, McLaren and BMW Sauber, it basically comprised everyone else bar Toro Rosso and Spyker. As the man at Super Aguri said: "If anyone had told us at the end of 2006 that we'd be fighting the defending champions on merit early in 2007, well... You just can't make it up!" Indeed.

saw two pole positions, two clean pole positions – even with the fuel he was extremely quick in Malaysia and here, and this time he was able to show what he could do in the race."

This turnaround for Massa meant that in both leading teams – McLaren and Ferrari – the incoming superstar was humbled in Bahrain by the supposed supporting act, as it was Lewis Hamilton and not Fernando Alonso who took the front row slot alongside Massa, while Alonso had to settle for fourth on the grid, having this time been given the heavier fuel load for the final qualifying segment.

"I think everything was OK on Friday," explained

World Champion Alonso, "but I lost a little bit of pace on Saturday morning, and overall grip, meaning that I was not happy with the car. I lost a little bit of the confidence, and that's all."

One key issue was the brakes. On switching from Renault to McLaren, Alonso had to find something that made him as comfortable as he had been at Renault. He did, but in Bahrain it became apparent on Friday that wear rates were too high with his preferred arrangement of pads and discs, so he had to switch to the disc and pad set-up that Hamilton had been using.

McLaren Chief Operating Officer Martin Whitmarsh explained: "Fernando was not as comfortable with the

BELOW Bahrain's rocky backdrop is distinctive, but Ralf Schumacher's run to 12th for Toyota was not, on a day when team-mate Trulli shone

brakes as Lewis over the weekend, and this is a circuit where there is some very big braking into high-speed corners. If you look at qualifying, his Q3 time fuel-corrected was almost spot-on the same as Lewis. Over one lap, if you get it right, you're OK. If you're not as comfortable in the race, though, it shows."

It says a lot for Hamilton's rapid ascent that there was almost a little disappointment that he didn't give Massa an even harder time than he did. This time there was no first-corner miracle, and he had to settle for second. The action was temporarily slowed by an immediate safety-car period after a first-lap tangle that eliminated Jenson Button and Scott Speed at Turn 3.

So impressive in Australia, Kimi Räikkönen seemed to be a little bit at sea in the lead Ferrari. Once again, he didn't make the most of his grid position, losing out to Alonso at the start. However, nothing characterised his problems more than his tardy performance at the safety-car restart, at which he crossed the start line a mammoth 1.3s down on Alonso when, in contrast, just 0.6s covered the top three. The team was at a loss to explain why their Finnish star had apparently fallen asleep. He later reeled in Alonso, but found himself well and truly stuck.

Meanwhile, Hamilton pushed leader Massa hard through the first stint, and the Briton was right there, just 1s behind, when he stopped on lap 19.

"Who knows what he could have done if he hadn't been behind Massa?" rued McLaren chief Ron Dennis. "Don't forget, he set several fastest laps behind Massa. If we had got to the first corner first, who knows what the outcome would have been..."

Massa went to lap 21 before pitting, and once he re-emerged, his advantage had grown to around 3.4s. There was to be no fight back from Hamilton, and instead that gap gradually stretched out to over 10s as the second stint progressed.

In fact, Hamilton had taken on five laps more fuel than Massa, and simple maths accounted for some of that increasing margin. Hamilton also probably found the car a little different to drive with 25 laps worth of fuel on board, as opposed to the 19 laps of fuel he had carried at the start of the race.

Having outpaced Alonso throughout the meeting, Hamilton was given priority for the first time on the lighter Q3 fuel load and thus came in earlier than Alonso for his first pit stop.

"We thought that we'd give Lewis the opportunity

ABOVE Rubens Barrichello is picked out in the blur of a pit stop, but he wasn't anywhere near the heat of the action on the track, racing to a lapped 13th place

ABOVE Nick Heidfeld was in superb form and passed Fernando Alonso in a bold manoeuvre to finish fourth for BMW Sauber

OPPOSITE The moment of atonement as Felipe Massa is shown the flag for his first win of 2007, making up for his Sepang *faux pas*

to give it a go in qualifying," said Whitmarsh. "At the first stop, we went fairly long with Lewis – based on the first-stint performance, we thought the best way to have a go at Massa was to run longer than him.

"The second stint in Malaysia was a very strong stint for Lewis. Here in Bahrain, we didn't have such a successful second stint and therefore couldn't use the fact that we were running a little bit longer... Also, Lewis ran into a little bit of traffic at the end of that second stint as well. He wasn't complaining of any particular issue, he just didn't quite have the pace and the grip that we wanted in that second stint."

Whitmarsh admitted that the team could have made changes at the first stop that might have improved the situation, but opted not to: "In fact, we tweaked a bit in the last stint, and Lewis was very quick then. I think both of our guys were quicker than the Ferraris in the final stint on the prime tyre, but that's either good fortune or good judgement."

Hamilton felt more comfortable in the third and final stint, kept pushing, and brought the gap down. As ever, Ferrari ensured that Massa went only as fast as he needed to, especially as his engine had to last for the Spanish GP as well, but the fact that it was

so close at the end – the final margin was just 2.36s – suggested that he probably didn't have a massive amount in hand.

Smedley acknowledged how worried Ferrari had been about Hamilton in the first part of the race: "Lewis was absolutely as quick as us in the first stint. We managed to keep him behind Felipe though. Then, at the end of the stint, when our car usually manages to look after the tyres a bit better, we managed to pull out a small gap. Lewis came in earlier, and from that point on we knew it was pretty much in the bag, as long as we kept putting the lap times in."

Räikkönen got by Alonso for third place at the first round of pit stops, but the Finn had a face like thunder on the podium.

"After that, it was too difficult to come back and challenge at the front," said Kimi. "I got past him, but we needed to go a little bit shorter in the middle stint to make sure we got in front of him. After that, it was too short to challenge Lewis. I came very close at the second stop, but it wasn't enough.

"There was also a bit of a mistake by me on the start button, but we got third place, and we know where we are losing time, so hopefully in the next test

INSIDE LINE
FELIPE MASSA
FERRARI DRIVER

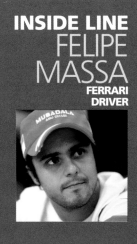

"I had a lot of negative press after the Malaysian GP and I want to dedicate this win to my girlfriend Rafaela, because I won't have been easy to be with these past few days! I'm actually relieved that it was only a short break before we were driving again in Bahrain, and not the usual couple of weeks. The best way to respond to all this media criticism was to take pole position and then win the race, which thankfully I did.

I was pleased to get pole again and be quick with both heavy and light fuel loads. I'm generally satisfied too that I've been getting everything out of the car and set-up. However, for one reason or another, I hadn't been able to show it. In Melbourne, I was quick but had the gearbox problem in qualifying. Then, in Malaysia, I didn't have a good first lap, got trapped behind other cars and wasn't able to demonstrate the race pace that we had, which was extremely frustrating.

I made a mistake in Malaysia, sure, but I wanted to win the race and, with Fernando getting away, I thought I had to pass Lewis. There was no point just sitting there. But my win in Bahrain has made up for the disappointment and so this is a good time to think about things. There is a long break before we next race in Spain and it will be nice to be looking back on this result. We put everything together and I'm happy for myself and the whole team. They did a great job here with the set-up, the strategy, everything, but we still need to push really hard because McLaren is very close.

In the first stint, the car was not perfectly balanced and I was suffering from a lot of oversteer. Lewis was quite close the whole time, but then the second stint was fantastic for me. The car was behaving very well on scrubbed tyres, I took away a bit of front wing and it was really much easier to drive, so I opened up a comfortable gap. Then, in the last stint, I just looked after my car and maintained my advantage through traffic to the flag.

This was an important win for me. My wins in Turkey and especially my home race in Brazil were great last year, but hopefully I'm now back looking at and fighting for the championship. It's very close and so it's fantastic to score some good points – really important points."

we can find something which is a bit better for me."

Nick Heidfeld had qualified fifth for BMW Sauber, and gamely hung on to the Alonso/Räikkönen battle in the opening stint. Later, he amazed even his own team by passing the troubled Spaniard around the outside at Turn 5, thereafter securing his third fourth-place finish in as many races.

It said a great deal about the competitiveness of the 2007 World Championship season that fifth-placed Alonso found himself in the unusual (for him) position of finishing in the points but not on the

podium. He still put on his best face.

"I was not competitive today, and I was not able to have the right pace," he shrugged. "For sure, the goal is always to be on the podium, and today I didn't achieve that. I found no confidence in the car, and overall grip was quite poor. I was having understeer and oversteer, and I was not able to sort it out at any stage in the race.

"You have good days and bad days, and good races and bad races, and this one was one of the bad. Hopefully, that's the only one we will have in the whole championship. Nothing to worry about…"

Once again, Robert Kubica was out of luck. Having started sixth, he dropped back from team-mate Nick Heidfeld and then lost time because an open fuel filler flap compromised his BMW Sauber's aerodynamics. Nevertheless, the Pole had an easy run to sixth place and his first points of the season.

Affected more than most by the headwind on the straight, Jarno Trulli struggled with a lack of top speed from his Toyota. Nevertheless, he got involved with a spectacular midfield fight, spending the early laps battling with both Williams drivers. He also passed both the Renaults on the way to an eventual seventh place, having held off Renault's Giancarlo Fisichella in the closing laps.

Fisichella was happier on the harder Bridgestone tyres in the final stint, and re-caught his fellow Italian before the flag, but was not able to get past. Team-mate Heikki Kovalainen endured another character-building weekend, starting 12th and just missing out on the points by finishing in ninth place.

The team personnel were now faced with an unusually long break of three free weekends before Alonso's home race in Spain. After the surprising start to the season, people wondered which of the top drivers would make best use of the time.

SNAPSHOT FROM
BAHRAIN

CLOCKWISE FROM RIGHT Those in the grandstand appreciated the shade as they watched Felipe Massa blast away from pole; she's pretty and can play the violin; there were some real dummies in the paddock; she's got all of the accessories: bottle of water, handbag, hookah pipe; flying in economy won't do for these aviators; Nick Heidfeld took time out to lap the Nürburgring Nordschleife in his BMW Sauber; Renault racers Heikki Kovalainen and Giancarlo Fisichella look on as boss Flavio Briatore blows out the candles on the birthday cake presented to him by the Renault team

WEEKEND NEWS

■ David Richards made his first appearance of the year, claiming to be in the region because of business interests in nearby Dubai. The Prodrive boss attended meetings of team bosses that related to 2008 and insisted that his plans were on track, despite a lack of news about his mooted McLaren deal.

■ A concerted public relations effort by the Bahrain GP organisers ensured that ticket sales were up on previous years. Increased interest in the region was good news too for the organisers of the Abu Dhabi GP, announced in February and due to join the World Championship calendar in 2009.

■ Jazz singer and pianist Jamie Cullum made his first appearance at a grand prix as a guest of the McLaren team, and played at a party at the royal palace. Also seen in the McLaren camp were British TV comedian Rory Bremner and Pink Floyd's Nick Mason, who had taken part in the 2006 Bahrain celebrity race.

■ Having kept a low profile for much of the winter, Michael Schumacher was busy at the end of April. He appeared at a Shell event in Poland and then a United Nations road safety event in London. In the same city, he presented the A1GP prize to the German team, which is owned by his long-time manager Willi Weber.

■ Nick Heidfeld was also kept busy in the gap before the Spanish GP with a PR visit to the Nürburgring on April 28, when he lapped the mighty Nordschleife in a BMW Sauber. The ride height was raised and he was running on ultra-hard 'demo' Bridgestones, but otherwise the car was as standard.

RACE RESULTS

BAHRAIN SAKHIR

Official Results © [2007]
Formula One Administration Limited,
6 Princes Gate, London, SW7 1QJ.
No reproduction without permission.
All copyright and database rights reserved.

RACE DATE April 15th
CIRCUIT LENGTH 3.363 miles
NO. OF LAPS 57
RACE DISTANCE 191.530 miles
WEATHER Sunny but windy, 31°C
TRACK TEMP 41°C
RACE DAY ATTENDANCE 42,000
LAP RECORD Michael Schumacher,
1m30.252s, 134.262mph, 2004

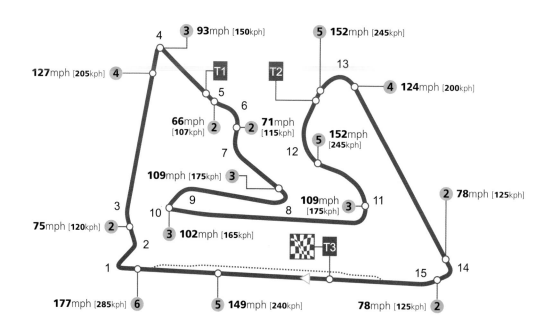

	PRACTICE 1				PRACTICE 2				PRACTICE 3				QUALIFYING 1			QUALIFYING 2	
	Driver	**Time**	**Laps**		**Driver**	**Time**	**Laps**		**Driver**	**Time**	**Laps**		**Driver**	**Time**		**Driver**	**Time**
1	K Räikkönen	1m33.162s	21	1	K Räikkönen	1m33.527s	33	1	L Hamilton	1m32.543s	12	1	F Massa	1m32.443s	1	F Massa	1m31.359s
2	F Massa	1m33.679s	17	2	L Hamilton	1m33.540s	33	2	K Räikkönen	1m32.549s	16	2	L Hamilton	1m32.580s	2	L Hamilton	1m31.732s
3	L Hamilton	1m34.110s	17	3	R Kubica	1m33.732s	37	3	N Heidfeld	1m32.652s	15	3	F Alonso	1m33.049s	3	K Räikkönen	1m31.812s
4	F Alonso	1m34.161s	15	4	F Massa	1m33.772s	28	4	R Kubica	1m32.755s	15	4	K Räikkönen	1m33.161s	4	N Heidfeld	1m32.154s
5	J Trulli	1m34.896s	26	5	F Alonso	1m33.784s	30	5	A Davidson	1m32.900s	20	5	N Heidfeld	1m33.164s	5	F Alonso	1m32.214s
6	N Heidfeld	1m35.076s	30	6	A Wurz	1m33.973s	26	6	F Massa	1m32.950s	12	6	J Trulli	1m33.218s	6	R Kubica	1m32.292s
7	R Kubica	1m35.248s	24	7	N Heidfeld	1m34.076s	34	7	F Alonso	1m33.235s	11	7	A Davidson	1m33.299s	7	J Trulli	1m32.429s
8	V Liuzzi	1m35.292s	23	8	N Rosberg	1m34.189s	34	8	M Webber	1m33.399s	14	8	R Kubica	1m33.348s	8	M Webber	1m32.808s
9	N Rosberg	1m35.375s	19	9	D Coulthard	1m34.359s	32	9	G Fisichella	1m33.602s	17	9	N Rosberg	1m33.349s	9	N Rosberg	1m32.815s
10	A Wurz	1m35.398s	20	10	J Trulli	1m34.366s	33	10	H Kovalainen	1m33.605s	14	10	H Kovalainen	1m33.467s	10	G Fisichella	1m32.889s
11	J Button	1m35.445s	24	11	R Barrichello	1m34.391s	28	11	N Rosberg	1m33.614s	14	11	M Webber	1m33.496s	11	A Wurz	1m32.915s
12	H Kovalainen	1m35.474s	21	12	H Kovalainen	1m34.585s	33	12	A Wurz	1m33.658s	17	12	G Fisichella	1m33.556s	12	H Kovalainen	1m32.935s
13	R Schumacher	1m35.573s	24	13	A Davidson	1m34.595s	29	13	V Liuzzi	1m33.700s	18	13	A Wurz	1m33.759s	13	A Davidson	1m33.082s
14	G Fisichella	1m35.697s	17	14	M Webber	1m34.677s	24	14	J Trulli	1m33.724s	22	14	R Barrichello	1m33.776s	14	R Schumacher	1m33.294s
15	S Speed	1m35.726s	22	15	G Fisichella	1m34.796s	34	15	D Coulthard	1m33.826s	14	15	R Schumacher	1m33.923s	15	R Barrichello	1m33.624s
16	T Sato	1m35.856s	15	16	T Sato	1m35.001s	35	16	J Button	1m34.023s	20	16	J Button	1m33.967s	16	J Button	1m33.731s
17	R Barrichello	1m35.911s	20	17	V Liuzzi	1m35.268s	38	17	T Sato	1m34.082s	21	17	T Sato	1m33.984s			
18	A Davidson	1m36.243s	6	18	R Schumacher	1m35.427s	29	18	R Barrichello	1m34.397s	17	18	V Liuzzi	1m34.024s			
19	M Webber	1m36.483s	18	19	V Liuzzi	1m35.582s	31	19	S Speed	1m34.791s	14	19	S Speed	1m34.333s			
20	D Coulthard	1m36.513s	7	20	S Speed	1m35.687s	34	20	R Schumacher	1m35.144s	11	20	A Sutil	1m35.280s			
21	A Sutil	1m37.084s	27	21	C Albers	1m35.835s	30	21	C Albers	1m35.395s	22	21	D Coulthard	1m35.341s			
22	C Albers	1m38.258s	29	22	J Button	1m36.079s	19	22	A Sutil	1m35.436s	18	22	C Albers	1m35.533s			

Best sectors – Practice
Sec 1	K Räikkönen	29.590s
Sec 2	F Massa	39.591s
Sec 3	L Hamilton	22.907s

Speed trap – Practice
1	K Räikkönen	194.2mph
2	A Wurz	194.2mph
3	N Rosberg	193.9mph

Best sectors – Qualifying
Sec 1	F Massa	29.315s
Sec 2	F Massa	39.154s
Sec 3	L Hamilton	22.832s

Speed trap – Qualifying
1	K Räikkönen	195.5mph
2	N Rosberg	194.9mph
3	N Heidfeld	193.7mph

Fernando Alonso
"I was struggling for grip. You always start believing you can win, but after six laps I knew it would be tough. I couldn't keep up with the Ferraris and Lewis."

Giancarlo Fisichella
"I was lighter than Kubica, but he held me up. The rears went off and I lost a few places, but it improved on the hard tyres, and I pushed Jarno hard."

Felipe Massa
"After the first two races didn't go well for me, we got it together. In my final stint, I had the harder tyres and focused on looking after the car."

Jenson Button
"I made up three places but at Turn 2 Taku squeezed me and I had to go on the dirt. DC went wide at Turn 3 then cut back and again I had nowhere to go."

Nick Heidfeld
"I didn't think I could pass Alonso, but in the second stint I was quicker. He had the better top speed, so I had to wait until he made a mistake."

Ralf Schumacher
"It was hard starting so far back. I struggled to adapt the car to suit me. I didn't get away well and that meant I was always going to be in traffic."

Lewis Hamilton
"We have closed the gap to Ferrari. I kept up with Felipe, then struggled for balance in the second stint and couldn't brake as late as I wanted."

Heikki Kovalainen
"I passed both Williams and Trulli's Toyota, but the rear tyres dropped off. Trulli passed, then I tried to defend against Rosberg, but he passed too."

Kimi Räikkönen
"I was in position to pass Lewis, but lost a place to Alonso. We passed him at the first pitstop, but then decided to shorten the second stint."

Rubens Barrichello
"I finished at least, but that's little consolation. The conditions were so blustery, the car so difficult. Now we have to put a poor few races behind us."

Robert Kubica
"This has been a very positive weekend and it is my first time in the points in 2007, so I know we will get there. Annoyingly, the fuel-filler flap wouldn't close."

Jarno Trulli
"It's my job to resist pressure and this result was due to experience and getting the best out of the car. The stops and the strategy were perfect."

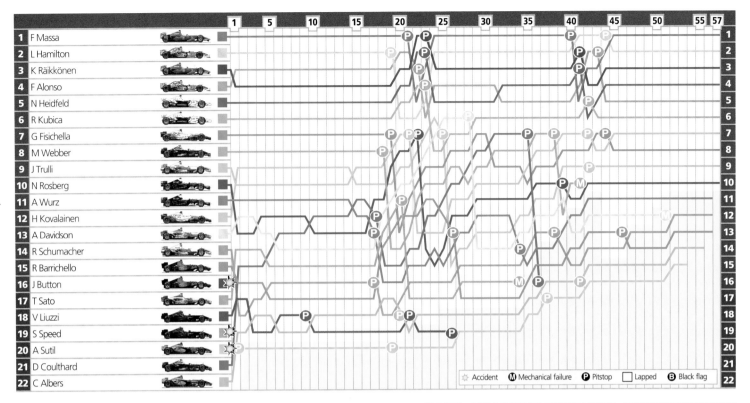

	Driver		1	5	10	15	20	25	30	35	40	45	50	55	57	
1	F Massa															1
2	L Hamilton															2
3	K Räikkönen															3
4	F Alonso															4
5	N Heidfeld															5
6	R Kubica															6
7	G Fisichella															7
8	M Webber															8
9	J Trulli															9
10	N Rosberg															10
11	A Wurz															11
12	H Kovalainen															12
13	A Davidson															13
14	R Schumacher															14
15	R Barrichello															15
16	J Button															16
17	T Sato															17
18	V Liuzzi															18
19	S Speed															19
20	A Sutil															20
21	D Coulthard															21
22	C Albers															22

☼ Accident Ⓜ Mechanical failure Ⓟ Pitstop ☐ Lapped Ⓑ Black flag

QUALIFYING 3

	Driver	Time
1	F Massa	1m30.000s
2	L Hamilton	1m32.935s
3	K Räikkönen	1m33.131s
4	F Alonso	1m33.192s
5	N Heidfeld	1m33.404s
6	R Kubica	1m33.710s
7	G Fisichella	1m34.056s
8	M Webber	1m34.106s
9	J Trulli	1m34.154s
10	N Rosberg	1m34.399s

GRID

	Driver	Time
1	F Massa	1m32.652s
2	L Hamilton	1m32.935s
3	K Räikkönen	1m33.131s
4	F Alonso	1m33.192s
5	N Heidfeld	1m33.404s
6	R Kubica	1m33.710s
7	G Fisichella	1m34.056s
8	M Webber	1m34.106s
9	J Trulli	1m34.154s
10	N Rosberg	1m34.399s
11	A Wurz	1m32.915s
12	H Kovalainen	1m32.935s
13	A Davidson	1m33.082s
14	R Schumacher	1m33.294s
15	R Barrichello	1m33.624s
16	J Button	1m33.731s
17	T Sato	1m33.984s
18	V Liuzzi	1m34.024s
19	S Speed	1m34.333s
20	A Sutil	1m35.280s
21	D Coulthard	1m35.341s
22	C Albers	1m35.533s

RACE

	Driver	Car	Laps	Time	Avg.mph	Fastest	Stops
1	F Massa	Ferrari F2007	57	1h33m27.515s	122.987	1m34.067s	2
2	L Hamilton	McLaren-Mercedes MP4-22	57	1h33m29.875s	122.935	1m34.270s	2
3	K Räikkönen	Ferrari F2007	57	1h33m38.354s	122.749	1m34.357s	2
4	N Heidfeld	BMW Sauber F1.07	57	1h33m41.346s	122.684	1m34.470s	2
5	F Alonso	McLaren-Mercedes MP4-22	57	1h33m41.941s	122.610	1m34.420s	2
6	R Kubica	BMW Sauber F1.07	57	1h34m13.044s	121.996	1m34.819s	2
7	J Trulli	Toyota TF107	57	1h34m48.886s	121.227	1m35.153s	2
8	G Fisichella	Renault R27	57	1h34m49.216s	121.220	1m35.200s	2
9	H Kovalainen	Renault R27	57	1h34m56.926s	121.056	1m35.475s	2
10	N Rosberg	Williams-Toyota FW29	57	1h34m57.431s	121.046	1m35.556s	2
11	A Wurz	Williams-Toyota FW29	56	1h33m38.906s	120.582	1m35.992s	2
12	R Schumacher	Toyota TF107	56	1h33m47.984s	120.388	1m35.845s	2
13	R Barrichello	Honda RA107	56	1h34m06.110s	120.002	1m35.842s	2
14	C Albers	Spyker-Ferrari F8-VII	55	1h33m42.820s	118.345	1m37.184s	2
15	A Sutil	Spyker-Ferrari F8-VII	53	1h33m43.110s	114.032	1m36.772s	3
16	A Davidson	Super Aguri-Honda SA07	51	Engine	-	1m36.111s	2
R	M Webber	Red Bull-Renault RB3	41	Gearbox	-	1m35.705s	2
R	D Coulthard	Red Bull-Renault RB3	36	Driveshaft	-	1m35.384s	2
R	T Sato	Super Aguri-Honda SA07	34	Engine	-	1m36.359s	1
R	V Liuzzi	Toro Rosso-Ferrari STR02	26	Hydraulics	-	1m35.723s	2
R	S Speed	Toro Rosso-Ferrari STR02	0	Collision	-	-	0
R	J Button	Honda RA107	0	Collision	-	-	0

CHAMPIONSHIP

	Driver	Pts
1	F Alonso	22
2	K Räikkönen	22
3	L Hamilton	22
4	F Massa	17
5	N Heidfeld	15
6	G Fisichella	8
7	J Trulli	4
8	R Kubica	3
9	N Rosberg	2
10	H Kovalainen	1
	R Schumacher	1

Fastest Lap
F Massa 1m34.067s
(128.720mph) on lap 42

Fastest speed trap
A Wurz 194.8mph
Slowest speed trap
S Speed 141.4mph

Fastest pit stop
1 R Kubica 28.055s
2 G Fisichella 28.100s
3 H Kovalainen 28.133s

	Constructor	Pts
1	McLaren-Mercedes	44
2	Ferrari	39
3	BMW Sauber	18
4	Renault	9
5	Toyota	5
6	Williams-Toyota	2

David Coulthard
"We were on an aggressive race strategy, which had been working well. The car and strategy were good, but we lost the right rear driveshaft."

Nico Rosberg
"On such a hard-braking track, it was difficult to pass as I didn't have a feel for the brakes. Also, every time I'd try, I'd get dirt on the tyres."

Vitantonio Liuzzi
"A hydraulics problem put me out, but we had a radio problem, so when I passed Ralf I was unaware it was a safety-car period, getting a drive-through."

Christijan Albers
"Even when running alone it was tough as I had oversteer and no radio. We made a change to the front wing, which made it better at the end."

Takuma Sato
"I made a very positive start and gained some places, but was struggling for grip then felt power loss from the engine mid-race before it failed."

Mark Webber
"The car had an open fuel flap in the second stint, like it did in Australia. After the stop, I got back in position, but then a gearbox part failed."

Alexander Wurz
"I couldn't attack the cars in front, even when they were slower. My car had the speed, but I couldn't pass as I was sliding out of the corners."

Scott Speed
"I got hit from behind at Turn 12 and the engine cut out so I couldn't do anything about it. Jenson thought he hit me, but I don't think we touched."

Adrian Sutil
"The cars in front stopped at Turn 4 and I lost the front wing. It took three laps for repairs and the car wasn't the easiest to drive after that."

Anthony Davidson
"This was my best F1 race to date: I was in the thick of the action; the stops were good; but near the end, I saw smoke and the team told me to stop."

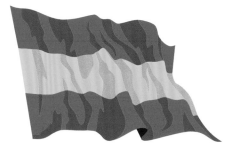

FORMULA 1™ GRAN PREMIO DE ESPAÑA TELEFÓNICA 2007
CATALUNYA

MASSA'S DOUBLE

Even a clash at the first corner couldn't stop Felipe Massa from controlling the race. Second was enough to put McLaren's rookie Lewis Hamilton into the points lead

Alas, the Circuit de Catalunya has very often produced afternoons of tedium, and this year it was particularly disappointing that the new chicane inserted at the final corner failed to achieve its aim of spicing up the show, especially as it robbed the fans packed into the grandstands of a sequence of corners that, while not offering quite Eau Rouge or 130R, still provided a pretty spectacular challenge.

While the race itself was not that enthralling at the front, there was plenty going on up and down the field, and a series of incidents ensured that there was much to discuss. Not least of these was a spectacular clash between Fernando Alonso and Felipe Massa at the first turn on the opening lap, from which the local hero emerged in fourth place, having lost two positions. That set the tone for a second successive frustrating race day for McLaren's leading man.

Lewis Hamilton's move into a two-point World Championship lead was the other major talking point, but that unfairly took the attention off another great performance from Massa. The Brazilian became the first of the title contenders to take a second 2007 win, while his pole position was his third of the season – remember he was thwarted by technical problems in the first race – and, counting the end of the 2006 season, it was his fifth in the past six races, which wasn't bad for a driver who not so long ago was perceived as a solid number two.

Once again, Massa had the edge over Kimi Räikkönen, and significantly that came after the Finn had been boosted by a good test at Barcelona. It had taken Räikkönen a while to get comfortable with the team, with the car and with the hard Bridgestone tyres, and it was felt that he had made a big step forward at the test. Come the race weekend, though, with the conditions inevitably different, he was not happy. Indeed, on Friday night, and with Michael Schumacher returning to the Ferrari camp to sit in on team meetings, he asked to switch chassis from his regular race car (261) to the T-car (262), which was the one he'd used in the test.

The team took some convincing because, as far as they were concerned, the two machines were identical, and they weren't too keen to get involved in all that messing about for what appeared to be psychological rather than practical reasons. Nevertheless, Räikkönen felt happier come Saturday. However, he was still beaten by Massa in both Q1 and

Q2, and once more when it really mattered.

The key to the race was the first corner, and Massa showed that he had learned from earlier disappointments by holding his ground on the inside line when Alonso came flying across. The Ferrari and McLaren made contact, and Alonso speared wide across the gravel. He did a brilliant job to maintain enough momentum to get back on the track, and incredibly only Hamilton and Räikkönen were able to take advantage, pushing him down to fourth place.

"He wouldn't have done that to Michael," said Massa's engineer Rob Smedley of the Spaniard's move, "and now he won't do it again to Felipe…"

Alonso made his displeasure clear after the race, but Massa insisted that since he was on the inside line, he had every right to claim the corner.

"Well, it was a little bit tight for both of us," said the eventual race winner, "but I was just inside and I went for it, so it was quite a risk for both of us. Looking at the competition and everything, the first corner is important. I just didn't want to lose out like I lost out in Malaysia. I was inside, so I just tried to stay there.

"We were both very close going into the corner. Fernando was trying to push me inside and we just

OPPOSITE Fernando Alonso attacked Felipe Massa at the first corner, but this run through the gravel cost him two places, to the disappointment of his home crowd

BELOW Alexander Wurz's race was a short one, his Williams suffering this damage on the opening lap after being caught out when Ralf Schumacher braked suddenly

touched each other. It was a very small contact, but I was also a bit afraid for my car afterwards, although fortunately nothing happened.

"It was just a normal race accident and as long as I am inside, close to the car going into the first corner, I will stay there. I will not move. So, if somebody was aggressive, it was Fernando, not me."

This was an important psychological gain by Massa, who later made it clear that he felt Alonso had underestimated him. After that, it was a pretty straightforward run for the Brazilian, aside from a scare at the first pit stop when a fuel spill led to a brief but spectacular fire. His clutch was dragging and thus he was marginally out of position, so that the hose came off at a slight angle. In such circumstances, the valve does not always close properly.

That glitch aside, everything ran like clockwork as Massa eased towards his second win of the season, with Hamilton following him home. Ferrari's Brazilian ace admitted that he was surprised to be able to pull away so easily in the opening stint: "A little bit, yes, especially in the beginning when in three or four laps I managed to pull away three seconds or something.

"Then I was getting half a second quicker per lap,

TALKING POINT
INTERNAL BATTLES

For the second grand prix in succession, the established 'star' drivers at Ferrari and McLaren – Kimi Räikkönen and reigning World Champion Fernando Alonso – were beaten by their respective team-mates, Felipe Massa and Lewis Hamilton.

In Spain, Massa again took pole position, this for the fifth time in six races with the only break being in Australia, where he had a gearbox problem. The Brazilian's second successive race win gave him 27 points, five more than Räikkönen.

At McLaren, Hamilton's third consecutive second place finish ensured he left Alonso's home turf as the youngest championship leader in history, at 22 years and 126 days. He took over the honour from his team's very own founder, Bruce McLaren, who was 22 years and 161 days when he won the season-opening Argentinian GP in 1960. Hamilton's 30 points put him two clear of Alonso.

This left F1 fans, as well as the sport's

insiders, salivating at the prospect of a genuine four-way battle for the title between team-mates. One of those lapping it up was three-time World Champion Niki Lauda.

"Alonso is quicker than Hamilton now – he has to be," said Lauda. "Because Hamilton is at the start of his experience line and Alonso is at the end, Alonso should be two- to four-tenths of a second quicker at every circuit we go to, but Hamilton is only going to get better and is the best guy around.

"Kimi is still struggling with the Bridgestones and doesn't yet know how to make the car go quick. If Massa loses his silly Brazilian inconsistency and continues to be fast, Kimi could have a similar problem."

Lauda was also optimistic that there would be no team orders.

"Those are decisions to be made at the end of the year. It's a principle, it's sport, and both teams are fortunate that the same situation exists with their main rival. It's perfect.

"I think McLaren will be OK. Ron Dennis likes Hamilton anyway because he's his driver. And with Todt at Ferrari it's pretty simple: if Todt's son is Massa's manager and the Todt relationship with his son is a good one, which I hope it is, the sympathies are at least not with Räikkönen, they are in the middle, so it means there will be no bias with strategy.

"But, if I was Kimi and Massa was breaking my balls, I'd certainly ask Mr di Montezemolo 'the number one guy at Ferrari racing, his son is the manager of my biggest competitor? How can this be? Please explain it to me...' I would certainly do that."

so that was a little bit of a surprise. I knew that Lewis was running a little bit heavier, looking at the times he did in qualifying, but it was still a little bit of a surprise. Anyway, I just took advantage of that to pull away and make the biggest gap I could to be a little bit more relaxed in the second part of the race."

Hamilton said he was not worried about the clear advantage enjoyed by Massa.

"They obviously had very good pace," he noted. "We were slightly heavier in the first stint and also in the second stint, but we just struggled at the beginning to warm the tyres up, leaving us with a bit of oversteer, and that enabled Massa to pull away. Then the car's balance came quite good and I was able to produce the same sort of times as him, but by then he had already got quite a big gap, although I kept pushing. It got to the second stint and, again, we just struggled a bit in traffic."

Alonso claimed third position, but only after an early retirement for Räikkönen. It had proved to be a real struggle in front of his home fans, but the points were useful. Alonso said later that the legacy of the first corner incident spoiled his race.

"I think the car was damaged all through the race

and unfortunately it was a little bit more difficult to drive," explained the reigning World Champion. "We also took the gamble when we fitted the prime tyre in the first stop, just to see if there was some advantage on these because we needed a miracle after being third, a little bit too far behind the first two on lap 15 or lap 16. So, we gave it a go, but it was not fantastic. So we went back to the option tyre for the final stint and the car became a little bit quicker. After the first corner, you need to risk too many things and it's hard for everything to go well after that."

Alonso's only comfort was that Räikkönen's weekend went from bad to worse. Yet again, the Australian GP winner lost out to Hamilton at the start of a race, but then managed to dive around the stranded Alonso to regain third. Through the early laps, Räikkönen kept pace with Hamilton, maintaining the gap at around 1.5s. It's not easy to follow anyone at Barcelona, and Ferrari seems to have a particular problem this year. He would probably have stopped before Hamilton, leaving McLaren with the chance to put Lewis on the optimal strategy for the second stint, so it seems unlikely that the Finn really could have secured second, as Ferrari folk later insisted.

BELOW Lewis Hamilton used all of the kerbs as he tried to keep the pressure on race leader Felipe Massa

OPPOSITE TOP David Coulthard ended a run of retirements to finish in a very strong fifth position

OPPOSITE BOTTOM Kimi Räikkönen ran third until his car retired with an electrical problem

INSIDE LINE
DAVID COULTHARD
RED BULL DRIVER

"After I failed to finish in the first three races and the team left the flyaway races without any points, it was good to have a competitive run to fifth place and put four points on the board for myself and the team.

We've made a massive step forward since the start of the season. The progress has all been down to aerodynamic parts – front wing, barge boards, sidepods and so on. The actual balance wasn't bad in the first three races. It's just that the car wasn't quick.

Towards the end of the race, the gearbox broke and I couldn't go below fourth. I had to avoid using the gears, which cost me time in the last sector, but I was still quick in the first two and had enough of a margin over Nico Rosberg not to lose fifth place. He was catching me at over a second a lap, but I managed to hold on. We are still marginal on reliability, but I would rather be seeing the performance and having a problem than trundling around at the back with a reliable car.

We had a number of cooling issues with the Ferrari engine in 2006, but Renault is giving us a good engine package all the time and the cooling is fantastic relative to last year. That's one of the reasons we wanted to go the Renault route, and the torque is also more progressive. It showed here when I could stay in fourth gear and not lose much lap time.

I was pleased to be on the BMW Sauber pace and I was only about 3s behind Kubica and catching him in the second stint, but I lost a bit of time coming into the pits when I nearly hit Liuzzi's Toro Rosso, which had a problem. That was a bit frustrating and, actually, Mark [Webber] had already mentioned the narrow pitlane to [Race Director] Charlie Whiting. It's the same at Spa, where they've done a load of paddock and circuit work but have given us a ridiculously narrow pitlane. It can completely screw your race for no good reason.

If Nick Heidfeld hadn't had his problem, I think it would have been marginal between him and me. The Renaults both had fuel-rig problems and had to make an extra stop, which helped us, but we had better pace.

It's definitely a very important step for the team. I'm happy. Monaco is next of course and, given my record there, I've got to be optimistic!"

Pole, while Heidfeld's race was spoiled when a wheelnut was not properly secured at the first of his two planned pit stops, and had to be retrieved by a nearby Toyota mechanic. The German later retired with a gearbox problem, ending his impressive start to 2007.

A major surprise was the fifth place scored by David Coulthard, who was really fired up and keen to prove a point after his team owner Dietrich Mateschitz had hinted that a more youthful line-up might be preferable at Red Bull for 2008. The Scottish veteran just held off Nico Rosberg, who had a good run for Williams

"I think David drove an excellent race," said Red Bull Racing technical chief Adrian Newey. "He withstood the pressure from Kovalainen, who was obviously on a very short fuel load in the middle of the race. Then he had to drive around at the end of the race after losing third gear while keeping Nico behind him."

Kovalainen followed Rosberg home in seventh, the Finn's race having been compromised by a problem with a fuel rig that didn't deliver its full load. The same problem afflicted his Renault team-mate Giancarlo Fisichella, who actually needed a late splash-and-dash. That gifted the final point to Takuma Sato, showing just how far Super Aguri Racing had come in a little over a year. Driver, crew and the Japanese media celebrated as if he had scored a grand prix victory.

The Spanish GP was another terrible race for the 'other' Honda team, and on this occasion the two cars even contrived to collide when Jenson Button came out of the pits and Rubens Barrichello didn't leave him much room. The British driver lost his front wing, and had to stop again, while Barrichello couldn't better 10th.

Toyota folk weren't much happier, after Jarno Trulli's excellent sixth place in qualifying was squandered by a fuel-pressure problem on the grid, while the hapless Ralf Schumacher managed to assault Alexander Wurz's Williams on the opening lap.

ABOVE A delighted Takuma Sato celebrates with the Super Aguri team after scoring its first point

BELOW Giancarlo Fisichella lost ground on the opening lap and became trapped behind Rubens Barrichello's Honda, ending the Renault driver's hope of points

All that was made academic however by an alternator failure that stopped Räikkönen after just nine laps. Keen to get home to watch the Ice Hockey World Cup on TV, he disappeared to the airport with some 27 laps to go, which was unusual behaviour for a Ferrari driver, especially as the visiting Schumacher attended the debrief, and he wasn't even driving...

With only three of the big four still running, a worthy fourth place went to Robert Kubica, keeping up the sequence established by his BMW Sauber team-mate Nick Heidfeld. It was a good drive by the

SNAPSHOT FROM
SPAIN

CLOCKWISE FROM RIGHT As expected, Vodafone made the most of their double World Champion, who happened to be Spanish...; Michael Schumacher added the experience of his seven world titles to the Ferrari effort; the Spanish grid girls continued to captivate; the start of the new European season meant new team headquarters, all bigger and better than before; there was no doubting who the home crowd wanted to win; and there's no doubting that all technical men always try to keep up with their rivals' technical developments

WEEKEND NEWS

■ Plans for a street race in Valencia from 2008 were announced in the Spanish city on the Thursday before the Spanish GP in a ceremony attended by Bernie Ecclestone. The new track includes part of the port area that was rebuilt for the 2007 America's Cup. McLaren had given a taster when it ran its cars on the streets in February.

■ Having been upstaged by the Valencia announcement, the Barcelona organisers acted quickly. Ecclestone appeared on Saturday for the announcement of an extension of the Spanish GP deal until 2016. He admitted that he hadn't always agreed with the Catalunyans, but said he was delighted with the new deal.

■ The Valencia news was quickly followed by confirmation from Singapore that they were also pushing ahead with plans for a street race for 2008, although the contract had not yet been signed. The tantalising question of whether the event would be held at night remained under discussion.

■ Bruno Senna created a stir by scoring his first GP2 victory in the main event on Saturday, heading home former Jordan driver Timo Glock. Among those cheering him from the foot of the podium were former Ayrton associates Jo Ramirez, Josef Leberer (ex-physio) and Betise Head (ex-PA/PR).

■ Sebastian Vettel was present in Spain, but BMW had decided for the time being that it was best to concentrate on giving its race drivers miles on Friday, a conclusion that seemed obvious to rival teams who had elected not to run third drivers on Fridays in 2007. Vettel had been placed in the World Series by Renault, rather than GP2, to avoid double booking on grand-prix weekends.

RACE RESULTS

SPAIN
CATALUNYA

Official Results © [2007]
Formula One Administration Limited,
6 Princes Gate, London, SW7 1QJ.
No reproduction without permission.
All copyright and database rights reserved.

RACE DATE May 13th
CIRCUIT LENGTH 2.818 miles
NO. OF LAPS 65
RACE DISTANCE 183.170 miles
WEATHER Dry and bright, 29°C
TRACK TEMP 50°C
RACE DAY ATTENDANCE 140,000
LAP RECORD Felipe Massa,
1m22.680s, 122.700mph, 2007

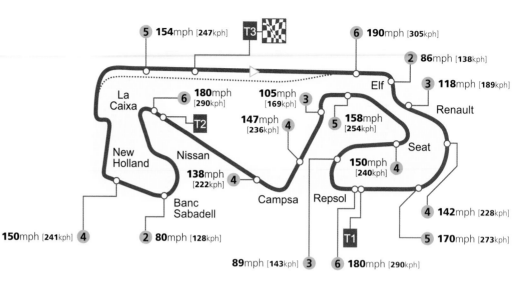

PRACTICE 1			
	Driver	Time	Laps
1	L Hamilton	1m21.880s	22
2	F Alonso	1m22.268s	21
3	K Räikkönen	1m22.291s	19
4	R Kubica	1m22.446s	21
5	F Massa	1m22.565s	15
6	A Davidson	1m22.665s	21
7	J Trulli	1m22.740s	28
8	R Schumacher	1m22.843s	23
9	N Rosberg	1m23.048s	28
10	J Button	1m23.114s	22
11	A Wurz	1m23.131s	23
12	N Heidfeld	1m23.170s	26
13	T Sato	1m23.316s	22
14	H Kovalainen	1m23.322s	24
15	G Fisichella	1m23.397s	21
16	D Coulthard	1m23.428s	21
17	M Webber	1m23.444s	21
18	R Barrichello	1m23.479s	23
19	A Sutil	1m23.954s	25
20	V Liuzzi	1m24.104s	24
21	S Speed	1m24.179s	19
22	C Albers	1m24.396s	25

PRACTICE 2			
	Driver	Time	Laps
1	F Alonso	1m21.397s	33
2	G Fisichella	1m21.684s	39
3	H Kovalainen	1m21.966s	38
4	F Massa	1m22.048s	31
5	L Hamilton	1m22.188s	37
6	K Räikkönen	1m22.251s	33
7	N Rosberg	1m22.415s	29
8	N Heidfeld	1m22.543s	40
9	M Webber	1m22.589s	39
10	S Speed	1m22.617s	35
11	R Kubica	1m22.710s	43
12	D Coulthard	1m22.719s	30
13	J Button	1m22.808s	39
14	R Barrichello	1m22.926s	40
15	A Wurz	1m22.950s	30
16	V Liuzzi	1m23.143s	29
17	R Schumacher	1m23.219s	28
18	J Trulli	1m23.307s	42
19	T Sato	1m23.493s	40
20	A Davidson	1m23.497s	49
21	A Sutil	1m23.609s	33
22	C Albers	1m23.736s	30

PRACTICE 3			
	Driver	Time	Laps
1	L Hamilton	1m21.233s	13
2	F Alonso	1m21.312s	13
3	R Kubica	1m21.364s	17
4	N Heidfeld	1m21.464s	17
5	D Coulthard	1m21.556s	12
6	F Massa	1m21.659s	14
7	K Räikkönen	1m21.829s	15
8	A Davidson	1m21.845s	15
9	N Rosberg	1m21.953s	16
10	H Kovalainen	1m22.067s	15
11	G Fisichella	1m22.140s	12
12	J Trulli	1m22.174s	25
13	R Barrichello	1m22.274s	15
14	T Sato	1m22.295s	21
15	S Speed	1m22.314s	16
16	R Schumacher	1m22.570s	21
17	J Button	1m22.744s	17
18	M Webber	1m22.759s	13
19	A Wurz	1m23.020s	16
20	V Liuzzi	1m23.367s	8
21	A Sutil	1m23.584s	22
22	C Albers	1m23.817s	22

QUALIFYING 1		
	Driver	Time
1	L Hamilton	1m21.120s
2	F Massa	1m21.375s
3	F Alonso	1m21.609s
4	N Heidfeld	1m21.625s
5	H Kovalainen	1m21.790s
6	K Räikkönen	1m21.802s
7	R Kubica	1m21.941s
8	N Rosberg	1m21.943s
9	G Fisichella	1m22.064s
10	T Sato	1m22.090s
11	A Davidson	1m22.295s
12	D Coulthard	1m22.491s
13	J Trulli	1m22.501s
14	R Barrichello	1m22.502s
15	J Button	1m22.503s
16	V Liuzzi	1m22.508s
17	R Schumacher	1m22.666s
18	A Wurz	1m22.769s
19	M Webber	1m23.398s
20	A Sutil	1m23.811s
21	C Albers	1m23.990s
22	S Speed	No time

QUALIFYING 2		
	Driver	Time
1	F Massa	1m20.597s
2	L Hamilton	1m20.713s
3	K Räikkönen	1m20.741s
4	F Alonso	1m20.797s
5	N Heidfeld	1m21.113s
6	R Kubica	1m21.381s
7	D Coulthard	1m21.488s
8	J Trulli	1m21.554s
9	H Kovalainen	1m21.623s
10	G Fisichella	1m21.677s
11	N Rosberg	1m21.968s
12	R Barrichello	1m22.097s
13	T Sato	1m22.115s
14	J Button	1m22.120s
15	A Davidson	No time
16	V Liuzzi	No time

Best sectors – Practice			Speed trap – Practice			Best sectors – Qualifying			Speed trap – Qualifying	
Sec 1	L Hamilton	22.816s	1	N Rosberg	193.7mph	Sec 1	K Räikkönen	22.550s	1	D Coulthard	193.0mph
Sec 2	N Heidfeld	30.386s	2	M Webber	193.0mph	Sec 2	L Hamilton	29.992s	2	T Sato	192.6mph
Sec 3	R Kubica	27.869s	3	J Button	192.7mph	Sec 3	F Massa	27.788s	3	K Räikkönen	192.3mph

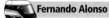

Fernando Alonso
"I was able to get a tow from Felipe and challenge into Turn 1. I was half-a-car-length in front, but we touched, and I had to go into the gravel to avoid a crash."

Giancarlo Fisichella
"I got squeezed on the run to Turn 1. Then I lost three places at Turn 9, which left me behind Barrichello, but I didn't have the speed to pass on the straight."

Felipe Massa
"The start was very tight, and we touched when Alonso came up the inside of me. Luckily, my car was undamaged, and I was able to pull away in the lead."

Jenson Button
"As I exited the pits after my first stop, I hit the kerb and was thrown offline. I lost my wing on Rubens' right rear and had to pit for a new nose."

Nick Heidfeld
"It was probably a gearbox problem, but my race was over after my front-right wheel came loose at my first stop. Until then, it looked superb."

Ralf Schumacher
"I made up two places at the start, but was hit from behind at Turn 10 and pitted to check for damage. Then the nose worked loose and I retired."

Lewis Hamilton
"Things just keep getting better. I was struggling to get heat into the tyres in the early stages. In the second stint, I was a bit unlucky with traffic."

Heikki Kovalainen
"This is my best finish so far, but I was quick enough to finish fifth. We had problems in our pit stops, and it meant we had to convert to three stops."

Kimi Räikkönen
"I lost a place to Hamilton, but made the most of the fight between Felipe and Fernando to get back to third before the car had an electrical problem."

Rubens Barrichello
"We just don't have the pace to improve our final position. I had left Jenson enough room at Turn 1. It was a shame, but it's just one of those racing incidents."

Robert Kubica
"I had problems with tyre degradation in the second stint when I was behind Alonso and Coulthard was closing in, but everything was under control."

Jarno Trulli
"The engine cut out at the end of the parade lap, so I took the restart from the pitlane. I did a few laps, but our fuel problem was too severe to continue."

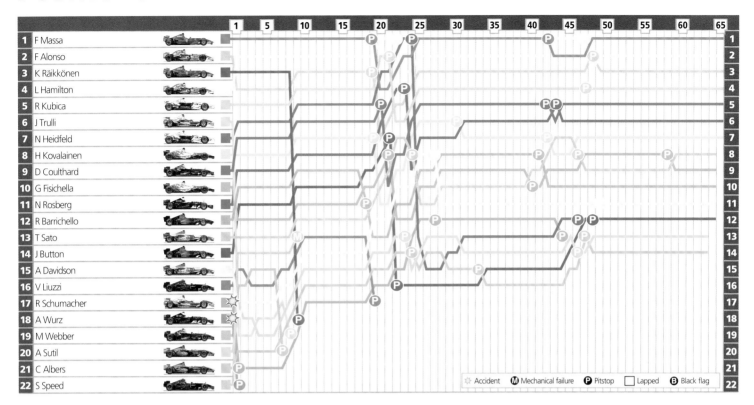

	1	5	10	15	20	25	30	35	40	45	50	55	60	65
1 F Massa														
2 F Alonso														
3 K Räikkönen														
4 L Hamilton														
5 R Kubica														
6 J Trulli														
7 N Heidfeld														
8 H Kovalainen														
9 D Coulthard														
10 G Fisichella														
11 N Rosberg														
12 R Barrichello														
13 T Sato														
14 J Button														
15 A Davidson														
16 V Liuzzi														
17 R Schumacher														
18 A Wurz														
19 M Webber														
20 A Sutil														
21 C Albers														
22 S Speed														

☆ Accident   Ⓜ Mechanical failure   Ⓟ Pitstop   ☐ Lapped   Ⓑ Black flag

QUALIFYING 3

	Driver	Time
1	F Massa	1m21.421s
2	F Alonso	1m21.451s
3	K Räikkönen	1m21.723s
4	L Hamilton	1m21.785s
5	R Kubica	1m22.253s
6	J Trulli	1m22.324s
7	N Heidfeld	1m22.389s
8	H Kovalainen	1m22.568s
9	D Coulthard	1m22.749s
10	G Fisichella	1m22.881s

GRID

	Driver	Time
1	F Massa	1m21.421s
2	F Alonso	1m21.451s
3	K Räikkönen	1m21.723s
4	L Hamilton	1m21.785s
5	R Kubica	1m22.253s
6*	J Trulli	1m22.324s
7	N Heidfeld	1m22.389s
8	H Kovalainen	1m22.568s
9	D Coulthard	1m22.749s
10	G Fisichella	1m22.881s
11	N Rosberg	1m21.968s
12	R Barrichello	1m22.097s
13	T Sato	1m22.115s
14	J Button	1m22.120s
15	A Davidson	No time
16	V Liuzzi	No time
17	R Schumacher	1m22.666s
18	A Wurz	1m22.769s
19	M Webber	1m23.398s
20	A Sutil	1m23.811s
21	C Albers	1m23.990s
22	S Speed	No time

* STARTED FROM THE PITLANE

RACE

	Driver	Car	Laps	Time	Avg. mph	Fastest	Stops
1	F Massa	Ferrari F2007	65	1h31m36.230s	123.044	1m22.680s	2
2	L Hamilton	McLaren-Mercedes MP4-22	65	1h31m43.020s	122.942	1m22.876s	2
3	F Alonso	McLaren-Mercedes MP4-22	65	1h31m53.686s	122.705	1m22.966s	2
4	R Kubica	BMW Sauber F1.07	65	1h32m07.845s	122.391	1m23.129s	2
5	D Coulthard	Red Bull-Renault RB3	65	1h32m34.561s	121.802	1m23.524s	2
6	N Rosberg	Williams-Toyota FW29	65	1h32m35.768s	121.775	1m23.693s	2
7	H Kovalainen	Renault R27	65	1h32m38.358s	121.719	1m22.980s	3
8	T Sato	Super Aguri-Honda SA07	64	1h31m50.941s	120.876	1m24.110s	2
9	G Fisichella	Renault R27	64	1h31m52.172s	120.850	1m23.560s	3
10	R Barrichello	Honda RA107	64	1h32m06.861s	120.528	1m24.287s	2
11	A Davidson	Super Aguri-Honda SA07	64	1h32m17.097s	120.305	1m24.291s	2
12	J Button	Honda RA107	64	1h32m44.602s	119.711	1m24.186s	3
13	A Sutil	Spyker-Ferrari F8-VII	63	1h31m49.413s	119.020	1m25.191s	2
14	C Albers	Spyker-Ferrari F8-VII	63	1h32m25.252s	118.250	1m25.260s	3
R	N Heidfeld	BMW Sauber F1.07	46	Gearbox	-	1m23.483s	2
R	R Schumacher	Toyota TF107	44	Loose nose	-	1m24.003s	2
R	V Liuzzi	Toro Rosso-Ferrari STR02	19	Hydraulics	-	1m25.207s	0
R	S Speed	Toro Rosso-Ferrari STR02	9	Tyre	-	1m26.238s	0
R	K Räikkönen	Ferrari F2007	9	Electrics	-	1m23.475s	0
R	J Trulli	Toyota TF107	8	Fuel pressure	-	1m26.094s	0
R	M Webber	Red Bull-Renault RB3	7	Hydraulics	-	1m26.323s	0
R	A Wurz	Williams-Toyota FW29	1	Crash damage	-	-	0

CHAMPIONSHIP

	Driver	Pts
1	L Hamilton	30
2	F Alonso	28
3	F Massa	27
4	K Räikkönen	22
5	N Heidfeld	15
6	R Kubica	8
7	G Fisichella	8
8	N Rosberg	5
9	D Coulthard	4
10	J Trulli	4
11	H Kovalainen	3
12	T Sato	1
	R Schumacher	1

Fastest Lap
F Massa 1m22.680s
(122.700mph) on lap 14

Fastest speed trap
A Davidson 193.3mph
Slowest speed trap
N Heidfeld 182.0mph

Fastest pit stop
1 G Fisichella 23.904s
2 G Fisichella 25.498s
3 L Hamilton 25.655s

David Coulthard

"I lost third gear, but I drove using only fourth gear and above, which lost me time in the last sector, but I was still able to be quick in the first."

Nico Rosberg

"This is the best result I've had in F1 so far. Trying to catch Coulthard late in the race was exciting, but I needed a couple more laps to get him."

Vitantonio Liuzzi

"I had a hydraulic problem at the start and lost three places. It's a shame as many other cars seemed to have problems and I was already up to 12th."

Christijan Albers

"The start was good, I could keep up with others, but it was disappointing to get the blue-flag penalty and then have the stall in the second pit stop."

Takuma Sato

"What a great performance from the team. Just one year plus four races and we're scoring a point in a head-to-head fight with Renault."

Mark Webber

"Poor reliability cost me a race finish. We'd planned to go for a long first stint, but it doesn't matter what strategy you have if you don't finish the race."

Alexander Wurz

"I had a good start and passed a few guys, but then I was lined up behind Ralf going into Turn 10 and he suddenly had to lift for someone in front."

Scott Speed

"The start and the first few laps were fun, going from last on the grid to 14th. I noticed the tyre was going down. Then it blew on the straight."

Adrian Sutil

"It was a good race. My first pit stop was OK, but in the second the engine stalled. I lost only 3–4s but it was enough to lose the place."

Anthony Davidson

"It is really good to score our first point; it's what we were all working for from the word go, but we got there. Next time, hopefully it will be me!"

	Constructor	Pts
1	McLaren-Mercedes	58
2	Ferrari	49
3	BMW Sauber	23
4	Renault	11
5	Williams-Toyota	5
6	Toyota	5
7	Red Bull-Renault	4
8	Super Aguri-Honda	1

FORMULA 1™ GRAND PRIX DE MONACO 2007
MONTE CARLO

ALONSO BY A HAIR

The race was close, very close, between the McLaren drivers, but some of the media thought that Hamilton deserved to be the winner rather than Alonso

Controversy took the shine off what should have been a great Monaco Grand Prix result for Ron Dennis and his McLaren team. Fernando Alonso may have scored a finely judged victory, but many observers thought that his runner-up and team-mate Lewis Hamilton should have won the race, but had been unfairly handicapped by the team. The following day, the FIA announced that it was to investigate the behaviour of McLaren during the race, specifically with regard to the possible illegal use of team orders to manipulate the result.

An investigation was quickly conducted, and just two days later the governing body announced that it was satisfied with the team's explanation that it had merely run a strategy to guarantee a 1–2 rather than favour a particular driver. It was a sensible and logical outcome, but one that didn't satisfy everybody.

In the weeks leading up to the Monaco Grand Prix, there had been a feeling that the principality would be the perfect place for Hamilton to score his first win. Indeed, he was blindingly quick throughout, and even a big impact with the Ste Devote tyre wall on Thursday failed to dampen his enthusiasm.

Strategy is always key at Monaco, and with the new safety-car rules creating potential problems if a

INSIDE LINE
RON DENNIS
McLAREN
TEAM PRINCIPAL

"I am obviously delighted that we have finished first and second in Monte Carlo, but my enthusiasm is tempered by the spin that some people appear to be applying, to suggest that we favoured one driver over another.

The primary objective of any grand prix team is for one of its drivers to win the race. If that can be achieved, we will try to ensure that our other car finishes second. That might sound an obvious statement to make, but the method of achieving it is not straightforward.

People need to bear in mind that we are operating under a different set of safety-car regulations in 2007 and that four of the previous five Monte Carlo races had safety-car interventions.

With no safety car during Alonso's first stint, there was a small but finite risk that it would come out during the five laps before Hamilton had to refuel. This would have put him behind the field and at a significant disadvantage to any car on a full (as opposed to optional) one-stop strategy. The latter cars would be expected to refuel at around lap 40 – that's to say after the safety car had pitted if it had come out during Hamilton's extra laps.

For similar reasons, Hamilton was called in early for his second pit stop, thus assuring his second place, with or without a safety car.

Had the car in front of Hamilton not been his team-mate, we might, and probably would, have decided to risk the safety car and let Hamilton run for as long as his fuel load allowed, in the hope that he would come out of the pits in the lead after one of his pit stops.

There is, however, no obligation on us to take that risk in order to overtake our own car. Indeed, it would be foolish to do so.

It is standard procedure for a team to tell its drivers to slow down when they have a substantial lead in a race. This is in order to minimise the risk of technical or other problems. It is also standard practice and entirely reasonable to ask the drivers not to put each other at risk. This would apply anywhere, but is especially relevant at a circuit as unforgiving as Monaco can be.

We were able to pursue an optimum team strategy because we had a substantial advantage over all other cars. We did nothing that could be described as interfering with the race result."

front-runner was due a fuel stop when a safety car was deployed, McLaren decided to play safe. The team split its drivers by around four or five laps of fuel in qualifying, so they would not be caught out at the same time in the race if a safety car came out.

Hamilton might not have been too excited when told he was going into qualifying with a fuel penalty of such significance relative to his team-mate, but he must have been confident that he could still put it on the front row. After all, Kimi Räikkönen was already out of the running after hitting the Swimming Pool barrier early in the second qualifying session.

It was close for Hamilton, though, as Ferrari's Felipe Massa was only 0.062s behind, the equivalent of a little over a lap of fuel. Had Ferrari been a little more aggressive, then Hamilton would have been down in third, and the story of the race would have been very different. As it was, Massa ran a lot further in the race than McLaren anticipated.

The upside for Hamilton was that he still had a chance of usurping Alonso. There was always the possibility that he could squeeze by on the run to the first corner, allowing for the fact that both men were fully aware of their responsibility not to hit each other. Had he got by, things would have been very interesting. Or had a safety car emerged in the window after Alonso's first pit stop, yet before his own, he would have gained a huge advantage.

The key advantage he had was that in having those five clear laps after Alonso pitted, he had a chance to bang in quick lap times and resolve the matter for himself by getting out of the pits in front.

To do that, he had to be as close as possible to Alonso when the Spaniard pitted, but this didn't work to plan. He was carrying that 0.3s penalty not just for qualifying, but for the first stint of the race as well. Indeed, after 10 laps, the gap was 3.1s. The other factor at play was the tyres. Both men started on new

soft tyres (the top runners had a few soft sets left, but had used all their supersofts in qualifying), and both suffered from front graining and understeer. Hamilton was a little worse off than Alonso, and as that kicked in, the gap grew from 3 to 7s between laps 10 and 14.

Then traffic became an issue as the pair fought their way past Ralf Schumacher, then Christijan Albers, Adrian Sutil, Anthony Davidson, Takuma Sato and Jarno Trulli. On lap 20 alone, Alonso was an astonishing 4s off the pace he had been running, and for a brief moment Hamilton seemed to be back in the game – but then he had a near identical delay on lap 21 as he fought his way past the same group, including an all-or-nothing move on Trulli that could have ended in tears.

Overall, Hamilton gained a little from this chaotic segment of the race, and his tyres also cleaned up. On lap 22 the gap was 5.5s, then it dipped to 4.2s by lap 25. Next time around, Alonso came in.

Hamilton, meanwhile, now had his chance. However, on the crucial laps 26 and 27 he was half a second off the times he had been running, before going half a second quicker on lap 28, with what turned out to be his fastest lap of the race. He then came in on lap 29, just three laps after Alonso.

Hamilton made it clear after the race that he hadn't fully understood why he had been called in earlier than expected. He'd taken that five-lap penalty in qualifying, and yet when it mattered he had only a three-lap advantage after Alonso's stop.

The conspiracy theorists suggested that the team didn't want Hamilton to enjoy any advantage he might have gained in those extra laps purely because they wanted to keep Alonso ahead. The more logical explanation, and the one accepted by the FIA, is that having got Alonso successfully in and out of the pits, and with no threat from behind, there was no point in leaving Hamilton out on track to run his fuel load

Kimi Räikkönen spent the entire race attempting to make up for qualifying only 16th, one-stopping with a heavy fuel load, but managing to climb only to eighth

This is how they ran, Fernando Alonso in front and Lewis Hamilton behind, with Felipe Massa holding a watching brief for Ferrari

TALKING POINT
POST-RACE INVESTIGATION

McLaren were in clover. With Kimi Räikkönen crashing strangely at the Swimming Pool section in Q2 and Felipe Massa a distant third behind their drivers, they had enjoyed a margin of superiority they couldn't have been expecting. And it was this superiority that allowed them to employ race tactics that covered the unexpected and did not leave them vulnerable to the new safety-car regulations, which state that the pitlane is closed until all cars are in order behind the official car. What that means, effectively, is that a faster two-stopping car loses its advantage and is vulnerable to a one-stopping car making its pit stop later in the race.

It was a majestic 1–2 by Ron Dennis's men but, immediately afterwards, it was clear that all was not well. Dennis looked serious-faced as he walked back from the podium, and in the post-race press conference Hamilton made it obvious he did not understand why he had not been permitted to run the extra laps his heavier fuel load allowed, which would have given him every chance of overhauling Alonso. Predictably, the British national media ran their "Lewis was screwed" stories. What should have been a joyous afternoon became a fire-fighting exercise for McLaren.

News came of an FIA investigation, with everyone reminded that on 28 October 2002 the F1 Commission decided by 23 votes to nil, with three abstentions, that it should be "prohibited to use team orders to interfere with the results of the race". This decision now appears as Article 39.1 of the 2007 F1 Sporting Regulations.

Sanity prevailed, however, and the FIA verdict backed up Dennis's explanation (see 'Inside Line').

The key facts, said the FIA, were these:
1. A two-stop strategy is the optimum at Monaco unless the safety car is deployed, in which case a one-stop strategy can sometimes be better.
2. The safety car has been deployed during four of the past five Monaco Grands Prix.
3. Under current rules, the choice between a one-stop and a two-stop strategy must be made before the start of the final qualifying period.
4. It is clear from FIA measurements taken after qualifying that McLaren fuelled Hamilton for five more laps than Alonso.
5. This allowed Hamilton the option of a one-stop strategy should the safety car have come out during his first stint.
6. The safety car was not deployed.
7. The McLaren was significantly faster at Monaco than any other car.

Conclusion: McLaren was entirely legitimate. No further action necessary.

down to zero. All it did was put him at risk of getting caught out if a safety car came out and left him with no choice but to refuel in a closed pit, and take the stop-and-go penalty. So, instead, McLaren took the zero-risk option.

The big question, therefore, was how aware Hamilton had been before the start of the the race that such a scenario might unfold? He accepted the heavy fuel load in qualifying, but then didn't reap the benefits come the race and, in the heat of battle, that caught him off guard. The FIA investigation was in large part a response to Race Control's monitoring of the team's radio traffic. Hamilton had a colourful response to what was being explained to him, and that triggered some suspicions within the FIA that perhaps all was not as it seemed.

In the end, those extra laps would have been academic. Firstly, he just wasn't quite close enough when Alonso pitted and, secondly, the reigning World Champion came out with a heavy fuel load (but new soft tyres) and banged in several super-fast laps that were more than enough to ensure that he would have stayed in the lead even if Hamilton had done those couple of extra laps before pitting.

ABOVE Felipe Massa had no time to admire the views as he raced to third. Unlike the rest, he wasn't lapped by the McLarens, but he was more than a minute in arrears

OPPOSITE Giancarlo Fisichella used a two-stop strategy to finish fourth, which is where he started

five laps after Alonso at the second stops. If he could catch him, then once again the chance was there to jump him. In the event, the team called a halt to any such thoughts for, a few laps after the first round of stops, the drivers were told to cool it.

"They were free to run as hard as they could until about five laps past the first stops," said Dennis. "And that's when we started to slow the cars."

The gap was as low as 3.6s on lap 33, and thereafter it drifted out to as much as 12s by the time Alonso pitted for a second time. This time Hamilton came in just two laps later, when he surely had the fuel to run at least five more. Again it was a question of getting the stop out of the way when it was pointless risking the arrival of a safety car. So, once again, Hamilton had been carrying more fuel than Alonso for a stint, for no benefit to himself.

Any pit-to-car discussions going on around this time may well have wound Hamilton up, because he emerged from that final stop in a fiery mood. For once on the same fuel load as his team-mate, and with scrubbed supersoft tyres now fitted, he brought the gap down to nothing and sat on Alonso's tail, as if to make a point to the world. He was then told by the team to drop back a little, presumably to avoid any possible distraction to the leader and to let a little more clean air into his radiators.

Dennis explained that there were sound technical reasons for not overstressing the cars, and not just the fact that the engines would have to be raced in the next race in Montréal: "We were extremely racy on brake material choice, and we knew we had to manage the brakes for the balance of the race."

Massa trailed home a distant third after a relatively lonely race that saw Ferrari well and truly beaten.

"McLaren definitely showed incredible pace today," the Brazilian admitted. "I think that even if I pushed 150% on the limit, it would have been the same in the end. They were pretty quick. There was nothing I could do with them. I could only expect some mistakes or something like that, or maybe a retirement. I was just thinking of finishing third, trying to score as many points as possible."

A light fuel load and early stop helped Giancarlo Fisichella to fourth on the grid, and the Italian did a great job to hold that position in the race, thoroughly trumping BMW Sauber. The Swiss-German cars had done the opposite and run heavy and, in effect, Robert Kubica and Nick Heidfeld each sacrificed a place to the Italian Renault driver. Alex Wurz had a good run to seventh and his first points for Williams.

Consigned to 16th on the grid after his crash in the second qualifying session, Räikkönen had a low-key race that saw him creep into the points in eighth place. He finished ahead of Scott Speed, who kept out of trouble and had a smooth race, plus the Hondas of Rubens Barrichello and Jenson Button. The latter pair would have done rather better but, concerned about the supersoft tyre, the team ran two stops when one would have done the job. Blocked by David Coulthard in qualifying and thus hampered by starting 15th, Renault's Heikki Kovalainen was a frustrated 13th.

Hamilton didn't win this time, but it was all too obvious that his time would come, and soon...

Nick Heidfeld struggled by starting on the supersoft tyres, yet gathered more points for BMW Sauber by finishing in sixth place

Lewis Hamilton may have been frustrated, but he was still able to smile and spray at the same time

"After the first stop," said Dennis, "at which time Fernando had saved some fuel, Lewis had an opportunity, a brief window of opportunity, to reverse the order. But he was struggling with a bit of understeer, and in the end Fernando had pulled out enough of a gap. But that is motor racing."

There was still a chance for the same procedure to unfold at the second round of pit stops. Not only did Hamilton clearly have some extra fuel in the car when he pitted, the stop timing suggested that he took on more fuel too, so that added up to him pitting at least

SNAPSHOT FROM
MONACO

CLOCKWISE FROM RIGHT It could only be Monaco, the undisputed jewel in Formula One's crown; David Coulthard putters the short commute from his appartment; 'Come along dear, but don't you think you've got enough jewellery already'; how to make your large motor yacht seem only average; it's still early in the day as the sun breaks around the corner of the appartment block at Mirabeau; not exactly haute couture, but it gets the message across; well, hello girls...

WEEKEND NEWS

■ A British spectator on Monaco's famous hillside overlooking the last part of the lap armed himself with a microphone and powerful loudspeaker system, and enjoyed himself by heckling VIPs as they walked from pitlane to paddock. In a nod to 2006, Michael Schumacher was told his car was illegally parked at Rascasse...

■ The Spyker team was given something to smile about on Saturday morning when torrential rain gave the drivers their first wet-weather experience on a 2007 race weekend. Adrian Sutil reminded everyone that he gave Lewis Hamilton a hard time in the European F3 series in 2005 by setting the quickest time of the session.

■ Following the *Ocean's 12*, *Star Wars* and *Superman Returns* arrangements, there were no major film tie-ups between teams and Hollywood at Monaco this year. There was, however, the inevitable paparazzi fuss when British movie star Jude Law made the trip over from Cannes and took a stroll down the pitlane.

■ Giancarlo Fisichella was penalised in 2006 for blocking David Coulthard in qualifying, but this year the Scottish driver was charged with impeding Fisichella's team-mate Heikki Kovalainen. Red Bull Racing boss Christian Horner admitted that the team had not informed their driver that the Finn was on a hot lap. Coulthard was excluded from top 10 qualifying session and docked two further places.

■ Rubens Barrichello has often amused himself by tinkering with his helmet design for special occasions, and for Monaco he had some fun by using a helmet decorated with heat-sensitive paint. It appeared black until it reached 27°C, at which point his traditional white, red and blue livery began to show through.

RACE RESULTS
MONTE CARLO MONACO

Official Results © [2007]
Formula One Administration Limited,
6 Princes Gate, London, SW7 1QJ.
No reproduction without permission.
All copyright and database rights reserved.

RACE DATE May 27th
CIRCUIT LENGTH 2.075 miles
NO. OF LAPS 78
RACE DISTANCE 161.850 miles
WEATHER Warm and dry, 24°C
TRACK TEMP 35°C
RACE DAY ATTENDANCE 120,000
LAP RECORD Michael Schumacher,
1m14.439s, 100.373mph, 2004

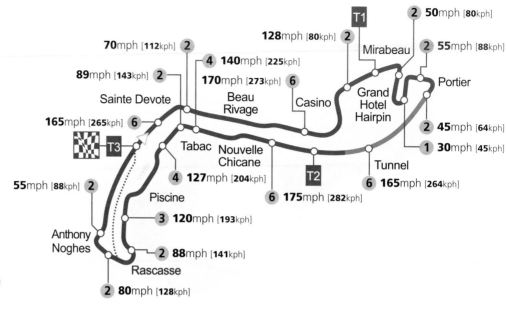

	PRACTICE 1				PRACTICE 2				PRACTICE 3				QUALIFYING 1			QUALIFYING 2	
	Driver	Time	Laps		Driver	Time	Laps		Driver	Time	Laps		Driver	Time		Driver	Time
1	F Alonso	1m16.973s	33	1	F Alonso	1m15.940s	40	1	A Sutil	1m36.612s	12	1	L Hamilton	1m15.685s	1	F Alonso	1m15.431s
2	L Hamilton	1m17.601s	14	2	K Räikkönen	1m16.215s	43	2	K Räikkönen	1m36.739s	13	2	F Alonso	1m16.059s	2	L Hamilton	1m15.479s
3	N Heidfeld	1m17.616s	31	3	L Hamilton	1m16.296s	19	3	L Hamilton	1m36.767s	15	3	K Räikkönen	1m16.251s	3	R Kubica	1m15.576s
4	G Fisichella	1m17.758s	27	4	J Trulli	1m16.354s	39	4	G Fisichella	1m36.784s	16	4	V Liuzzi	1m16.720s	4	N Heidfeld	1m15.733s
5	K Räikkönen	1m17.918s	28	5	G Fisichella	1m16.753s	41	5	S Speed	1m36.954s	15	5	F Massa	1m16.786s	5	F Massa	1m16.034s
6	M Webber	1m17.956s	19	6	F Massa	1m16.784s	37	6	F Alonso	1m37.020s	16	6	N Rosberg	1m16.870s	6	G Fisichella	1m16.054s
7	N Rosberg	1m18.074s	27	7	R Kubica	1m16.848s	48	7	H Kovalainen	1m37.214s	15	7	D Coulthard	1m17.204s	7	N Rosberg	1m16.100s
8	F Massa	1m18.189s	29	8	N Rosberg	1m16.852s	34	8	N Rosberg	1m37.388s	15	8	R Barrichello	1m17.244s	8	M Webber	1m16.420s
9	R Kubica	1m18.675s	28	9	M Webber	1m17.292s	16	9	J Button	1m37.442s	12	9	J Button	1m17.297s	9	R Barrichello	1m16.454s
10	R Barrichello	1m18.676s	22	10	D Coulthard	1m17.414s	16	10	R Barrichello	1m37.463s	14	10	N Heidfeld	1m17.385s	10	J Button	1m16.457s
11	A Wurz	1m18.869s	29	11	R Barrichello	1m17.449s	40	11	M Webber	1m37.732s	13	11	R Kubica	1m17.584s	11	D Coulthard	1m16.319s
12	S Speed	1m18.967s	27	12	J Button	1m17.457s	45	12	F Massa	1m37.997s	12	12	G Fisichella	1m17.596s	12	A Wurz	1m16.662s
13	D Coulthard	1m19.095s	16	13	T Sato	1m17.459s	47	13	T Sato	1m38.121s	14	13	J Trulli	1m17.686s	13	V Liuzzi	1m16.703s
14	T Sato	1m19.203s	27	14	N Heidfeld	1m17.486s	43	14	A Davidson	1m38.180s	17	14	M Webber	1m17.816s	14	J Trulli	1m16.988s
15	V Liuzzi	1m19.285s	24	15	A Wurz	1m17.516s	34	15	D Coulthard	1m38.302s	6	15	H Kovalainen	1m17.836s	15	H Kovalainen	1m17.125s
16	H Kovalainen	1m19.321s	27	16	V Liuzzi	1m17.898s	42	16	R Kubica	1m38.463s	13	16	A Wurz	1m17.874s	16	K Räikkönen	No time
17	J Button	1m19.332s	27	17	H Kovalainen	1m18.086s	41	17	A Wurz	1m38.876s	14	17	A Davidson	1m18.250s			
18	A Davidson	1m19.337s	22	18	S Speed	1m18.233s	40	18	N Heidfeld	1m38.899s	18	18	S Speed	1m18.390s			
19	J Trulli	1m19.496s	22	19	A Davidson	1m18.328s	25	19	C Albers	1m38.935s	14	19	A Sutil	1m18.418s			
20	R Schumacher	1m19.799s	25	20	R Schumacher	1m18.662s	38	20	R Schumacher	1m40.677s	17	20	R Schumacher	1m18.539s			
21	A Sutil	1m21.634s	19	21	C Albers	1m18.820s	35	21	V Liuzzi	1m41.108s	8	21	T Sato	1m18.554s			
22	C Albers	1m23.235s	5	22	A Sutil	1m19.358s	29	22	J Trulli	1m43.417s	22	22	C Albers	No time			

Best sectors – Practice
Sec 1	F Alonso	19.505s
Sec 2	M Schumacher	36.477s
Sec 3	G Fisichella	17.784s

Speed trap – Practice
1	F Massa	176.3mph
2	G Fisichella	176.0mph
3	F Alonso	175.5mph

Best sectors – Qualifying
Sec 1	M Schumacher	19.359s
Sec 2	K Räikkönen	36.293s
Sec 3	D Coulthard	17.522s

Speed trap – Qualifying
1	M Schumacher	179.0mph
2	G Fisichella	177.2mph
3	F Alonso	177.0mph

Fernando Alonso
"I didn't get off the line brilliantly, but I was able to keep the lead. However, as I was able to save fuel in my first stint I stayed out for two more laps than planned."

Giancarlo Fisichella
"The car had more grip thanks to a new wing, and the car's consistency was much better too. It was good to finish ahead of the BMWs for the first time."

Felipe Massa
"We tried to see if we could gain pace by using the extra-soft tyres in the second stint, but it did not make much difference. The main problem was traffic."

Jenson Button
"I was stuck in traffic in all three stints, so couldn't make the most of the strategy. It's disappointing, but we have to be encouraged by signs of improvement."

Nick Heidfeld
"On my second stint I lost quite a few seconds when I had to let the two McLarens by. It was enough to let Robert get just in front of me after his pit stop."

Ralf Schumacher
"I was stuck in traffic. We could clearly have been fighting for points for sure if we had qualified better. Qualifying was really where our race was decided."

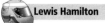

Lewis Hamilton
"My start was quite good, and I could run close to Fernando but it didn't make sense to try anything crazy as our job is to score maximum points for the team."

Heikki Kovalainen
"I got stuck behind Coulthard and though I got past him at the stops, it wasn't enough to catch the cars in front. At the end, the engine lost almost all its power."

Kimi Räikkönen
"I got a good start, quickly moving up to 12th, but it was only thanks to the strategy that I was able to make up some more places and get into the points."

Rubens Barrichello
"After my first stop I was held up by Wurz and that was that. I was a little bit faster than him and if I had got past there would have been a chance to get closer to points."

Robert Kubica
"I had a small problem with the brakes soon after the start and had to pump them all the time. Then I was stuck in traffic and at the end I had a sensor problem."

Jarno Trulli
"The car almost stalled, so I lost a lot of positions at the first corner. I was just keeping up with the cars in front of me and then the brakes started heating up."

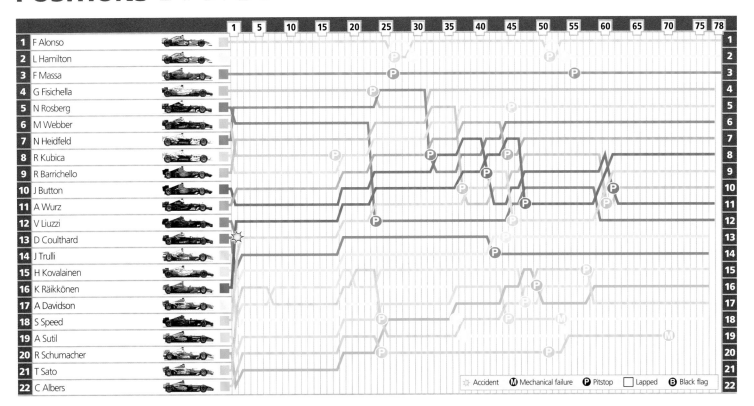

		1	5	10	15	20	25	30	35	40	45	50	55	60	65	70	75	78
1	F Alonso																	1
2	L Hamilton																	2
3	F Massa																	3
4	G Fisichella																	4
5	N Rosberg																	5
6	M Webber																	6
7	N Heidfeld																	7
8	R Kubica																	8
9	R Barrichello																	9
10	J Button																	10
11	A Wurz																	11
12	V Liuzzi																	12
13	D Coulthard																	13
14	J Trulli																	14
15	H Kovalainen																	15
16	K Räikkönen																	16
17	A Davidson																	17
18	S Speed																	18
19	A Sutil																	19
20	R Schumacher																	20
21	T Sato																	21
22	C Albers																	22

☼ Accident ⓜ Mechanical failure ⓟ Pitstop ☐ Lapped ⓑ Black flag

QUALIFYING 3

	Driver	Time
1	F Alonso	1m15.726s
2	L Hamilton	1m15.905s
3	F Massa	1m15.967s
4	G Fisichella	1m16.285s
5	N Rosberg	1m16.439s
6	M Webber	1m16.784s
7	N Heidfeld	1m16.832s
8	R Kubica	1m16.955s
9	R Barrichello	1m17.498s
10	J Button	1m17.939s

GRID

	Driver	Time
1	F Alonso	1m15.726s
2	L Hamilton	1m15.905s
3	F Massa	1m15.967s
4	G Fisichella	1m16.285s
5	N Rosberg	1m16.439s
6	M Webber	1m16.784s
7	N Heidfeld	1m16.832s
8	R Kubica	1m16.955s
9	R Barrichello	1m17.498s
10	J Button	1m17.939s
11	A Wurz	1m16.662s
12	V Liuzzi	1m16.703s
13*	D Coulthard	1m16.319s
14	J Trulli	1m16.988s
15	H Kovalainen	1m17.125s
16	K Räikkönen	No time
17	A Davidson	1m18.250s
18	S Speed	1m18.390s
19	A Sutil	1m18.418s
20	R Schumacher	1m18.539s
21	T Sato	1m18.554s
22	C Albers	No time

* BANNED FROM Q3 AND DEMOTED TWO PLACES FOR IMPEDING A RIVAL DURING Q2

RACE

	Driver	Car	Laps	Time	Avg. mph	Fastest	Stops
1	F Alonso	McLaren-Mercedes MP4-22	78	1h40m29.329s	96.655	1m15.284s	2
2	L Hamilton	McLaren-Mercedes MP4-22	78	1h40m33.424s	96.589	1m15.372s	2
3	F Massa	Ferrari F2007	78	1h41m38.443s	95.559	1m16.183s	2
4	G Fisichella	Renault R27	77	1h40m40.909s	95.233	1m16.254s	2
5	R Kubica	BMW Sauber F1.07	77	1h41m01.077s	94.916	1m16.006s	1
6	N Heidfeld	BMW Sauber F1.07	77	1h41m05.100s	94.853	1m17.041s	1
7	A Wurz	Williams-Toyota FW29	77	1h41m11.902s	94.746	1m16.658s	1
8	K Räikkönen	Ferrari F2007	77	1h41m16.120s	94.681	1m16.592s	1
9	S Speed	Toro Rosso-Ferrari STR02	77	1h41m25.886s	94.529	1m16.867s	1
10	R Barrichello	Honda RA107	77	1h41m27.029s	94.511	1m17.080s	2
11	J Button	Honda RA107	77	1h41m28.011s	94.496	1m16.802s	2
12	N Rosberg	Williams-Toyota FW29	77	1h41m32.877s	94.420	1m16.991s	2
13	H Kovalainen	Renault R27	76	1h40m26.634s	94.218	1m17.100s	1
14	D Coulthard	Red Bull-Renault RB3	76	1h40m41.607s	93.985	1m16.786s	1
15	J Trulli	Toyota TF107	76	1h41m07.463s	93.585	1m17.495s	1
16	R Schumacher	Toyota TF107	76	1h41m08.382s	93.570	1m17.231s	1
17	T Sato	Super Aguri-Honda SA07	76	1h41m08.970s	93.562	1m17.183s	2
18	A Davidson	Super Aguri-Honda SA07	76	1h41m09.518s	93.553	1m17.223s	2
19	C Albers	Spyker-Ferrari F8-VII	70	Driveshaft	-	1m17.689s	2
R	A Sutil	Spyker-Ferrari F8-VII	53	Spun off	-	1m17.678s	1
R	M Webber	Red Bull-Renault RB3	17	Gearbox	-	1m18.998s	0
R	V Liuzzi	Toro Rosso-Ferrari STR02	1	Spun off	-	-	0

CHAMPIONSHIP

	Driver	Pts
1	F Alonso	38
2	L Hamilton	38
3	F Massa	33
4	K Räikkönen	23
5	N Heidfeld	18
6	G Fisichella	13
7	R Kubica	12
8	N Rosberg	5
9	D Coulthard	4
10	J Trulli	4
11	H Kovalainen	3
12	A Wurz	2
13	T Sato	1
	R Schumacher	1

Fastest Lap
M Schumacher 1m15.143s
(99.430mph) on lap 74

Fastest speed trap
M Schumacher 179.8mph
Slowest speed trap
T Monteiro 170.8mph

Fastest pit stop
1	F Alonso	23.553s
2	K Räikkönen	23.555s
3	G Fisichella	24.510s

	Constructor	Pts
1	McLaren-Mercedes	76
2	Ferrari	56
3	BMW Sauber	30
4	Renault	16
5	Williams-Toyota	7
6	Toyota	5
7	Red Bull-Renault	4
8	Super Aguri-Honda	1

David Coulthard
"I clashed with Tonio and damaged my front wing and endplate, so had a lot of understeer. We debated if we should change it, but decided not to."

Nico Rosberg
"I had a good start but Fisichella closed in at the first corner and I had to back off. Maybe I should not have pitted and I might have had the chance to score points."

Vitantonio Liuzzi
"I was hit hard at the first corner and I think it must have damaged something. I tried to do one more lap, but as I came over the bump at Turn 3 I lost control."

Christijan Albers
"I struggled with the rear, but when I came in and changed to the normal soft tyres, it started to go really well, but then you are just lost in the traffic."

Takuma Sato
"Because of traffic before my second stop we missed a chance to improve my position. We tried our best and recovered well, but we needed more speed."

Mark Webber
"First, I had a small misfire, which wasn't really fantastic, especially through the Piscine section. Then I lost third gear and the car kept locking up."

Alexander Wurz
"It was critical for me to pull some laps out to get past the Hondas in the middle part of the race and then keep Räikkönen behind me at the end."

Scott Speed
"I got a good launch and made a move around the outside, and it paid off as I got around David. Maybe I should have pitted earlier, but Kimi was out of reach."

Adrian Sutil
"It was a good race until I crashed at Casino corner. I went a bit to the outside of the corner and there was so much rubber and dirt that I hit the barrier."

Anthony Davidson
"Massa was slowly catching me up, at 0.2s a lap, and I was waiting until he got closer to let him by. I was going to let him pass when we got a drive-through."

FORMULA 1™ GRAND PRIX DU CANADA 2007
MONTREAL

LEWIS IS A WINNER

Lewis Hamilton bounced back from the disappointment of Monaco in the best way possible by keeping his cool to win a much-interrupted race in Canada

Robert Kubica's accident in Montréal was the most violent seen in many years. Many of us thought the worst, but by the end of the race word had gone round the paddock that he had got away with only a broken leg, this the result of an erroneous report to Race Control from a local circuit doctor.

It was only later, after speaking directly to the hospital, that BMW Sauber team chief Mario Theissen was able to report the astonishing news that Robert wasn't injured at all. That left everyone free to enjoy Lewis Hamilton's wonderful maiden victory, and to try to make sense out of what was one of the most dramatic dry-weather races of recent times.

We could probably fill this book with the full story of the race, but let's focus on how the unfortunate Adrian Sutil helped to set everything in motion. The Spyker man's impact with the wall triggered a safety car on lap 23, and so commenced an extraordinary chain of events that turned the race on its head.

From the start of the season, the prospect of a safety-car introduction in the middle of a fuel window had kept everyone on their toes. Against the usual form, there was no intervention in either Melbourne or Monaco, and the one in Bahrain came on the opening

ABOVE Lewis Hamilton leads away from pole position, with Fernando Alonso already thinking about how to try to pass him at the first corner. Nick Heidfeld is third and Kimi Räikkönen fourth

lap, so the new rules – a closed pitlane to allow the cars to be bunched up – had no impact.

Some teams (including McLaren) had consistently ensured that their drivers were not pitting a single lap apart, in order to guarantee that a safety-car deployment wouldn't ruin both men's races. The downside of that was that one driver had to carry a more significant weight penalty in qualifying than he would have had in former days, which is what led to the controversy at the Monaco Grand Prix.

Hamilton had beaten Fernando Alonso to pole position in great style in Montréal, and the apparently rattled Spaniard had run wide across the grass at

Turn 1 as he attempted to redress the balance. He instead dropped behind Nick Heidfeld's BMW and, in effect, the race became Hamilton's to lose. The British driver was comfortably ahead when he made his first stop on lap 22. Alonso was due in next time around, but then Sutil went off at Turn 4 and brought out the safety car.

Alonso still had a little fuel in the tank – everyone does when they stop. With no way of knowing how long it would take to get the field together and so for the FIA to declare the pitlane open, staying out was not a gamble worth taking. So, along with the equally ill-starred Nico Rosberg, Alonso headed

INSIDE LINE
LEWIS HAMILTON
McLAREN DRIVER

"It's been a truly fantastic day. This is history. To come here, my first time in Canada, and win...

It has really been a fantastic season already, with a podium at every race, and I've been ready for the win for quite some time. It was just a matter of when and where. The team gave me

the best car. I had no problems during the race at all. There were a few safety cars, but no real problems.

I did hear about Robert Kubica's accident during the race. He's a good friend of mine and I was concerned, but I have to dedicate this win to my Dad because without him it would not have been possible.

When the lights changed, I made quite a poor getaway. I'm supposed to have a certain amount of revs and I went over it and then under it to try to compensate.

I saw Nick (Heidfeld) getting close, so I had to close the door, and then I saw Fernando fly past. Obviously I didn't want him coming past me, but he got onto the marbles and went straight on. I just took the corner as normal and then Fernando came flying back across my nose,

which was certainly quite exciting...

I had good pace and Nick wasn't very close to me, so I was able to maintain a good gap.

It was challenging when the safety cars were deployed: each time your tyres get cold, your brakes get cold and it's so easy to just put the car into the wall. That was the real challenge: warming up your tyres enough and not making any mistakes. It's a tricky circuit and if you make a single slip and get on the marbles, you're in the wall.

Actually, I don't think it's acceptable that we have that many marbles here. I doubt that it's just the rubber off the tyres. We had it in qualifying and Fernando probably lost pole position due to that. We've seen that in Turn 10 they did something to the circuit. We have had it numerous

times here apparently and, OK, we're the best in the world and should keep on-line, but we're talking about centimetres. You go off-line by just a fraction and you lose so much, or even crash.

In the end, I just calmed it all down, counted down the laps to the end of the race and enjoyed the moment. Five laps, four laps, keep off the kerbs, keep it controlled, and then an absolutely amazing feeling.

I just wanted to get out of the car and do cartwheels!"

straight into the pitlane knowing that he would later face a compulsory 10s stop-and-go penalty.

"Running one of our cars out of fuel behind the safety car didn't seem much of an option," said McLaren supremo Ron Dennis. "We had less than a lap's fuel when the safety car was deployed. What you then have to work out very quickly is how much fuel you are actually going to be able to conserve behind the safety car, and we worked it out as a little over two laps, which we thought was too marginal.

"So we knew we were going to be penalised, but that was better than running out of fuel. As it happens we probably would have had an egg-cup-full left, and made it, so with the benefit of hindsight we made the wrong call, which is why some of us don't feel great after the race, because it effectively made Fernando's race very difficult."

Alonso and Rosberg were not the only ones to suffer problems, however. When the pitlane was declared open, Felipe Massa led the charge in for fuel. When he reached the pit exit, he failed to notice the red light. It was on because the queue of cars was making its way past the pit exit, which in this case was down at the first-turn complex. Giancarlo Fisichella

followed him out of the pitlane, and eventually, both men were black-flagged and excluded.

"Felipe did not pay attention," said Ferrari chief Jean Todt of his driver. "He was concentrated on going out, and not having any car passing him. And we did not tell him anything."

The actual decisions didn't come for some time, because officials were soon preoccupied with something else. At the restart, Hamilton made his escape up front, leaving others fighting to make up for lost ground. Among them was Kubica.

The Pole had waited dutifully at the red light at the pit exit, despite the temptation to follow Massa and Fisichella out. However, when it turned green he was overtaken by Jarno Trulli, who was still moving and thus had momentum on his side.

Losing a position by obeying the rules would not have pleased Kubica, who was well aware that his car was much quicker than the Toyota, and he had to get back past it as quickly as possible. The best chance would be the first lap after the restart, and that was why he was urgently trying to find a way past on the approach to the hairpin.

Trulli said that he wasn't aware of the BMW's

Nick Heidfeld closed up to Hamilton after each safety-car period, but was never able to make a move for the lead

The backdrop is pretty, but the result wasn't for Spyker, with both cars retiring

The closest Alonso got to Hamilton was at the start when the British driver was slow away

ROBERT KUBICA'S HUGE ACCIDENT

The images playing out on the television monitors on lap 27 of the Canadian Grand Prix pitched the press room into silence. The sheer violence of Robert Kubica's accident was shocking. It was a horrifyingly bad one.

At more than 170mph on the run down to Circuit Gilles Villeneuve's hairpin, Kubica had moved to pass Jarno Trulli's Toyota. Trulli knew he was there, but first saw the Pole in his left-hand mirror and assumed that he would come down the inside of the left-hand kink following the previous chicane. However, Kubica went the other way, his left-front wheel making contact with Trulli's right-rear.

Kubica's car was launched by the grass verge and slammed into the concrete retaining wall at unabated speed, then launched itself into a series of barrel rolls, shedding debris as it flew back across the track, finally coming to rest on the opposite side of the circuit at the hairpin. Initially, there was no movement in the cockpit.

BMW Sauber team-mate Nick Heidfeld had been running in second place: "I saw the car upside down. I saw on the big screen that my team were putting their hands above their heads, so I knew there was something serious. There was no information for quite a long time. Then, later, in one of the safety-car phases, they told me that Robert seemed fine".

With such an impact, the part played by the HANS device cannot be underestimated. At first, there were reports of a broken ankle or leg but, unbelievably, Kubica escaped with just bruising. Trulli, one of the paddock's more sensitive souls, went to the Montréal hospital where Kubica was retained overnight for observation, but the Pole was permitted to leave the following day.

As far as Kubica was concerned, he would be driving at Indianapolis the following Friday morning, but the FIA medical staff thought not, as the fear of another impact so soon made discretion the better part of valour.

"It was a fantastic day in two respects," BMW's Mario Theissen said. "We got one driver onto the podium and the other driver back unhurt from a huge accident that I don't think would have been survivable 10 years ago".

It was glowing testimony to the effectiveness of the FIA's constant push towards better safety standards, specifically the HANS device and ever-tougher crash-testing demands. As Heidfeld said: "It can never be safe enough. I think we have been extremely lucky that we haven't seen a very bad accident over the last couple of years. You have to remember that if we do more than 200mph, open-wheel to open-wheel, anything can happen."

presence on his right. "I didn't move," said the Italian, "I just kept my line. The last time I saw Robert he was on the left-hand side, and apparently he turned to the right-hand side, so I have no idea what he was doing. I just know that I kept my line and I haven't done anything. Honestly, I spent my race thinking about this accident. I know that I am a driver, but I am also a human being, so obviously I was shocked..."

Kubica hit the Toyota's right rear tyre at full tilt, and that pushed the front of the BMW up. Losing part of the front wing at such a speed didn't do much for aero stability, and tyre marks showed that the front wheels bounced twice on the tarmac before he headed onto the grass, where an access road caused the front to rear up again, and air to get under the car.

At this point, there is a gap in the wall to allow retired cars to be retrieved, and he clipped the very end of the first part of the wall with the right-front wheel. Thankfully, this first impact caused the front to drop down before he struck the second part of the wall, and the car exploded into pieces.

We'll never know what would have happened had that first impact not lowered the front, but without it there was at least some chance that he would

have hit the second wall with the bottom of the car rather than the nose, and the result might have been very different.

The tumble that the car suffered after the initial impacts looked horrific, but all the while the car was dissipating energy. The key thing was that Kubica did not suffer a further heavy front-end impact, because his feet were extremely vulnerable by that stage. However, the HANS device, the foam headrest and the new-generation lightweight composite helmet, all things that have been pushed through by the FIA in recent years, did their jobs.

It took a while to clean up the mess, and after the restart Hamilton again opened up a lead on Heidfeld. Subsequent safety-car periods after incidents involving Christijan Albers and Tonio Liuzzi failed to derail him.

In an ironic twist, McLaren guaranteed Hamilton's win by pulling the same trick that so frustrated him – and created a media furore – in Monaco. He made his second stop with a significant amount of fuel in the car, as he had nothing to gain by staying out.

"We were covering Heidfeld," explained Dennis. "We had a lot more fuel. We could have gone another six laps I think, but if the safety car had come out in a

OPPOSITE Three shots from the mind-boggling sequence of Robert Kubica's spectacular accident. That he escaped uninjured is testament to the work the FIA has done on safety

ABOVE Takuma Sato would love to re-run the Canadian GP again and again. Especially the moment that he overtook Alonso *en route* to sixth

Alex Wurz used his racing brain, and the team's tactical nous, to survive 40 laps on the supersoft tyres and race from 19th to third

Lewis Hamilton had to keep his cool on the way to his maiden victory, before triggering considerable celebration, most particularly with his father Anthony

situation where we were penalised as we were with Fernando, he would have lost the race. The only thing that could lose us the race was the safety car in respect of Heidfeld, so we just covered Heidfeld, which was the logical thing to do.

"We could have gone much further, and then you think, the only way we can lose this race is a safety car. The problem was that stopping that early, you're then on the option tyre, so we then had the fuel to optimise the tyre use, but we couldn't use it because of the safety car. So then Lewis really had to look after his tyres, and he really did that well."

The big factor at play in strategy choice was the need to use both types of tyres at some point in the grand prix. Nobody wanted to get on the supersoft because of graining issues, but they had to find a time to use them.

Hamilton reeled off the laps to score a majestic first win, the safety-car periods ensuring that Heidfeld wasn't far behind at the flag. Williams took a huge gamble by putting Alex Wurz on supersofts for the last 40 laps of the race on a suitably heavy fuel load. The Austrian had a few problems, but the extra safety-car periods helped him nurse them and when it mattered at the end he had gone through the graining period and was in better shape than those on fresh supersofts, enabling him to secure a surprise third place.

Cleverly, Renault got Heikki Kovalainen onto the supersofts for a short stint in the middle of the race, so he was on the preferable harder prime tyre when it mattered at the end. He took fourth, ahead of a low-key Kimi Räikkönen (delayed by being stacked behind Massa in the first round of pit stops), while Takuma Sato earned an amazing sixth for Super Aguri Racing. Right at the end, the Japanese driver had the temerity to overtake Alonso, who had dropped back after his penalty and was struggling on the supersoft tyres.

"Fernando was super quick," said Dennis, "but what you needed to be was slower than that to hold the tyres in good condition. As soon as you pushed, you grained the tyres and got monster understeer. That was the problem. He fought well, and it was disappointing at the end that his tyres were completely finished, because he'd pushed so hard, which is why he was a sitting duck."

A final and very fortunate point went to Ralf Schumacher. Psyched out by the Kubica crash, his hapless team-mate Trulli had earlier crashed in slow motion while exiting the pits. It was that sort of day – one that provided a lucky escape not just for one driver, but for the whole sport.

SNAPSHOT FROM
CANADA

CLOCKWISE FROM RIGHT The Circuit Gilles Villeneuve is one of the few that can be reached by public transport; Alex Wurz gets intense with Sir Frank Williams; Gilles Villeneuve, gone but never forgotten; Jenson Button meets a future team-mate?; the Massa brothers weren't feeling this casual after Felipe's disqualification; Lewis Hamilton, read all about him...; Tsutomu Tomita bids his farewells to the Toyota team

WEEKEND NEWS

■ Emerson Fittipaldi watched the grand prix from a hospitality suite near the first corner, and afterwards raved about the performance of Lewis Hamilton. "The driver and car combination is outstanding to watch," said Emmo, who as winner of his fourth grand prix in 1970 remained ahead in the record books.

■ The Canadian Grand Prix was the final race appearance for Toyota Team Principal Tsutomu Tomita before he moved to a new role at Fuji Speedway, the new home of the Japanese Grand Prix. Tomita became Toyota's senior motorsport man in 1996, and he was instrumental in getting the Formula One project underway. He took over the main role in Cologne in December 2003.

■ Cycling fan Jarno Trulli had his helmet design modified to include an image of his friend Danielo di Luca, who had recently won the Giro d'Italia. Both men hail from Pescara, and have known each other for several years. The tribute didn't bring Trulli much luck, though, as he crashed when exiting the pits.

■ Appropriately enough, Alex Wurz's third place came on the 10th anniversary of his grand prix debut with Benetton at Montréal in 1997. The Austrian scored a third place at Silverstone that year, and added another for McLaren when subbing for Juan Pablo Montoya at Imola in 2005. However, as the latter came after Jenson Button's exclusion, he didn't make the podium on that occasion.

■ Giancarlo Fisichella announced that he had started a 'Motor Sport Academy' at Vallelunga, not far from his home in Rome. The plan was for the institute to train not just drivers but also mechanics and engineers. The GP2 team owner denied that he was making plans for his retirement...

RACE RESULTS

CANADA
MONTREAL

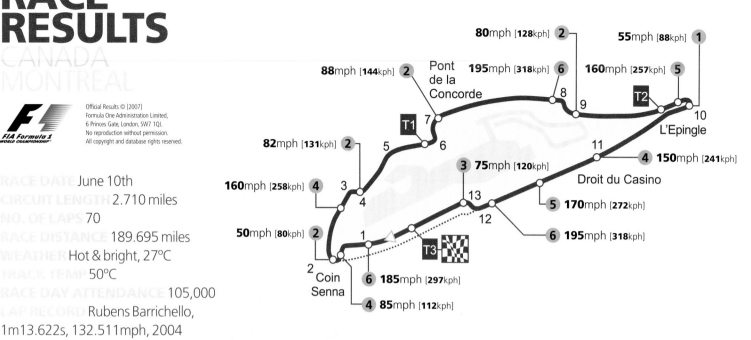

80mph [128kph] ②   55mph [88kph] ①

88mph [144kph] ②   Pont de la Concorde   195mph [318kph] ⑥   160mph [257kph] ⑤

T1 ⑦   8   9   T2   10   L'Epingle

82mph [131kph] ②   5   6   11

160mph [258kph] ④   3   ③ 75mph [120kph]   ④ 150mph [241kph]   Droit du Casino

4   13   ⑤ 170mph [272kph]

50mph [80kph] ②   12   ⑥ 195mph [318kph]

2   1   T3

Coin Senna   ⑥ 185mph [297kph]

④ 85mph [112kph]

Official Results © [2007]
Formula One Administration Limited,
6 Princes Gate, London, SW7 1QJ.
No reproduction without permission.
All copyright and database rights reserved.

RACE DATE June 10th
CIRCUIT LENGTH 2.710 miles
NO. OF LAPS 70
RACE DISTANCE 189.695 miles
WEATHER Hot & bright, 27°C
TRACK TEMP 50°C
RACE DAY ATTENDANCE 105,000
LAP RECORD Rubens Barrichello,
1m13.622s, 132.511mph, 2004

PRACTICE 1

	Driver	Time	Laps
1	F Alonso	1m17.759s	17
2	L Hamilton	1m17.967s	20
3	K Räikkönen	1m18.136s	21
4	F Massa	1m18.167s	21
5	M Webber	1m18.301s	21
6	G Fisichella	1m18.620s	24
7	N Heidfeld	1m18.634s	20
8	R Schumacher	1m18.652s	32
9	D Coulthard	1m18.717s	24
10	A Davidson	1m18.896s	16
11	T Sato	1m18.898s	20
12	J Trulli	1m18.925s	25
13	J Button	1m18.932s	24
14	H Kovalainen	1m18.997s	26
15	A Wurz	1m19.189s	22
16	S Speed	1m19.234s	29
17	K Nakajima	1m19.273s	30
18	R Barrichello	1m19.937s	18
19	V Liuzzi	1m20.331s	12
20	C Albers	1m21.251s	17
21	A Sutil	1m21.630s	25
22	R Kubica	No time	2

PRACTICE 2

	Driver	Time	Laps
1	F Alonso	1m16.550s	37
2	F Massa	1m17.090s	34
3	L Hamilton	1m17.307s	36
4	K Räikkönen	1m17.515s	37
5	N Heidfeld	1m17.827s	42
6	N Rosberg	1m17.992s	25
7	R Barrichello	1m18.108s	38
8	G Fisichella	1m18.130s	40
9	M Webber	1m18.181s	40
10	T Sato	1m18.309s	38
11	D Coulthard	1m18.316s	40
12	R Kubica	1m18.399s	29
13	J Button	1m18.474s	36
14	V Liuzzi	1m18.493s	33
15	A Davidson	1m18.545s	35
16	S Speed	1m18.602s	37
17	A Wurz	1m18.871s	25
18	J Trulli	1m18.895s	16
19	R Schumacher	1m19.331s	16
20	C Albers	1m19.453s	38
21	A Sutil	1m19.662s	25
22	H Kovalainen	1m20.519s	13

PRACTICE 3

	Driver	Time	Laps
1	L Hamilton	1m16.071s	12
2	K Räikkönen	1m16.459s	14
3	F Alonso	1m16.465s	9
4	F Massa	1m16.666s	13
5	T Sato	1m16.864s	12
6	N Rosberg	1m16.975s	14
7	M Webber	1m17.071s	11
8	R Barrichello	1m17.329s	16
9	D Coulthard	1m17.391s	11
10	A Davidson	1m17.391s	15
11	G Fisichella	1m17.454s	12
12	J Button	1m17.468s	15
13	R Kubica	1m17.601s	12
14	J Trulli	1m17.624s	17
15	S Speed	1m17.742s	12
16	R Schumacher	1m17.748s	13
17	V Liuzzi	1m17.799s	14
18	A Sutil	1m18.270s	13
19	N Heidfeld	1m18.428s	5
20	A Wurz	1m18.489s	11
21	H Kovalainen	1m18.758s	10
22	C Albers	1m18.933s	12

QUALIFYING 1

	Driver	Time
1	K Räikkönen	1m16.468s
2	F Alonso	1m16.562s
3	L Hamilton	1m16.576s
4	F Massa	1m16.756s
5	G Fisichella	1m16.805s
6	N Heidfeld	1m17.006s
7	R Barrichello	1m17.011s
8	N Rosberg	1m17.016s
9	R Kubica	1m17.267s
10	M Webber	1m17.315s
11	J Trulli	1m17.324s
12	S Speed	1m17.433s
13	D Coulthard	1m17.436s
14	T Sato	1m17.490s
15	J Button	1m17.522s
16	V Liuzzi	1m17.541s
17	A Davidson	1m17.542s
18	R Schumacher	1m17.634s
19	H Kovalainen	1m17.806s
20	A Wurz	1m18.089s
21	A Sutil	1m18.536s
22	C Albers	1m19.196s

QUALIFYING 2

	Driver	Time
1	L Hamilton	1m15.486s
2	F Alonso	1m15.522s
3	N Heidfeld	1m15.960s
4	F Massa	1m16.138s
5	N Rosberg	1m16.190s
6	M Webber	1m16.257s
7	G Fisichella	1m16.288s
8	R Kubica	1m16.368s
9	K Räikkönen	1m16.592s
10	J Trulli	1m16.600s
11	T Sato	1m16.743s
12	V Liuzzi	1m16.760s
13	R Barrichello	1m17.116s
14	D Coulthard	1m17.304s
15	J Button	1m17.541s
16	S Speed	1m17.571s

Best sectors – Practice

Sec 1	F Alonso	21.318s
Sec 2	L Hamilton	24.206s
Sec 3	L Hamilton	30.274s

Speed trap – Practice

1	A Wurz	200.8mph
2	G Fisichella	200.5mph
3	V Liuzzi	200.2mph

Best sectors – Qualifying

Sec 1	F Alonso	21.110s
Sec 2	L Hamilton	24.016s
Sec 3	F Alonso	30.255s

Speed trap – Qualifying

1	N Heidfeld	201.5mph
2	H Kovalainen	201.4mph
	R Kubica	201.4mph

Fernando Alonso

"The safety car being deployed so many times worked to Lewis's advantage. I pitted for the first time on lap 24 as I had no more fuel. There was nothing I could do."

Giancarlo Fisichella

"In terms of the incident coming out of the pits, I was concentrating on Kubica alongside me, and was so focused on beating him that I didn't see the red light."

Felipe Massa

"I was having a good race and could have scored. Unfortunately, when I left the pits I didn't look at the lights, partly as there were so many cars in pitlane behind me."

Jenson Button

"I went to select first, but there was nothing. I kept switching from neutral to first to try to clear it. The same thing happened when we tried to start from the pitlane."

Nick Heidfeld

"I am happy that Robert is OK. We hoped to get a podium, but didn't expect second. The best moment was the start when I got by Alonso and was right in Hamilton's wake."

Ralf Schumacher

"It's nice to score after starting 18th. We fuelled the cars heavily for the first stint. The car was short of straightline speed so it was hard to overtake into the chicane."

Lewis Hamilton

"I can't find words to describe how it feels to take my first win. It seemed each time I opened a gap, the safety car came out. It was only at the end that I noticed the fans."

Heikki Kovalainen

"I needed luck to score points after starting last, but you have to take advantage of your opportunities. I seemed to spend a lot of the afternoon overtaking other cars."

Kimi Räikkönen

"Being on the dirty side of the track, I didn't have much grip and hit Felipe's car with my front wing. Then, there were so many safety-car periods that it caused chaos."

Rubens Barrichello

"It was a crazy race and the last safety car ruined our strategy, which could have brought us home fifth. After Kubica's accident, my thoughts were with him."

Robert Kubica

On his release from the circuit's medical centre after his accident: "I feel fine. I was very lucky. It was a big accident, but fortunately nothing got hurt."

Jarno Trulli

"I hadn't moved from my line, but when Kubica hit me and rolled I was concerned. I pitted with a flat. But after I pitted for the last time, I pushed too hard and hit the wall."

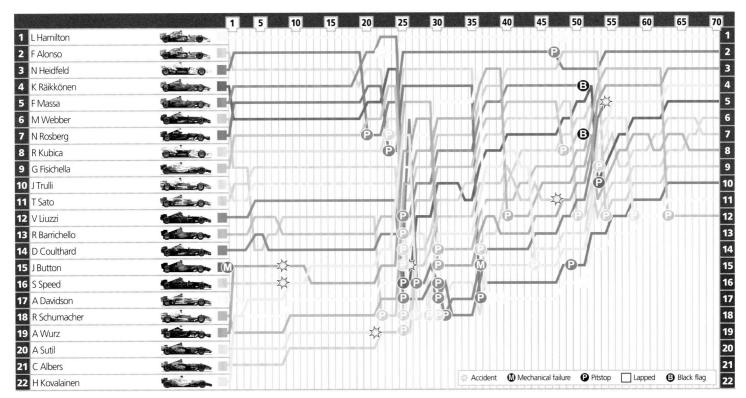

	Driver			Driver		
1	L Hamilton		1	L Hamilton		1
2	F Alonso		2	F Alonso		2
3	N Heidfeld		3	N Heidfeld		3
4	K Räikkönen		4	K Räikkönen		4
5	F Massa		5	F Massa		5
6	M Webber		6	M Webber		6
7	N Rosberg		7	N Rosberg		7
8	R Kubica		8	R Kubica		8
9	G Fisichella		9	G Fisichella		9
10	J Trulli		10	J Trulli		10
11	T Sato		11	T Sato		11
12	V Liuzzi		12	V Liuzzi		12
13	R Barrichello		13	R Barrichello		13
14	D Coulthard		14	D Coulthard		14
15	J Button		15	J Button		15
16	S Speed		16	S Speed		16
17	A Davidson		17	A Davidson		17
18	R Schumacher		18	R Schumacher		18
19	A Wurz		19	A Wurz		19
20	A Sutil		20	A Sutil		20
21	C Albers		21	C Albers		21
22	H Kovalainen		22	H Kovalainen		22

☼ Accident　Ⓜ Mechanical failure　Ⓟ Pitstop　☐ Lapped　Ⓑ Black flag

QUALIFYING 3

	Driver	Time
1	L Hamilton	1m15.707s
2	F Alonso	1m16.163s
3	N Heidfeld	1m16.266s
4	K Räikkönen	1m16.411s
5	F Massa	1m16.570s
6	M Webber	1m16.913s
7	N Rosberg	1m16.919s
8	R Kubica	1m16.993s
9	G Fisichella	1m17.229s
10	J Trulli	1m17.747s

GRID

	Driver	Time
1	L Hamilton	1m15.707s
2	F Alonso	1m16.163s
3	N Heidfeld	1m16.266s
4	K Räikkönen	1m16.411s
5	F Massa	1m16.570s
6	M Webber	1m16.913s
7	N Rosberg	1m16.919s
8	R Kubica	1m16.993s
9	G Fisichella	1m17.229s
10	J Trulli	1m17.747s
11	T Sato	1m16.743s
12	V Liuzzi	1m16.760s
13	R Barrichello	1m17.116s
14	D Coulthard	1m17.304s
15	J Button	1m17.541s
16	S Speed	1m17.571s
17	A Davidson	1m17.542s
18	R Schumacher	1m17.634s
19	A Wurz	1m18.089s
20	A Sutil	1m18.536s
21	C Albers	1m19.196s
22*	H Kovalainen	1m17.806s

* 10-PLACE GRID PENALTY

RACE

	Driver	Car	Laps	Time	Avg. mph	Fastest	Stops
1	L Hamilton	McLaren-Mercedes MP4-22	70	1h44m11.292s	109.259	1m16.494s	2
2	N Heidfeld	BMW Sauber F1.07	70	1h44m15.635s	109.183	1m16.696s	2
3	A Wurz	Williams-Toyota FW29	70	1h44m16.617s	109.166	1m17.947s	1
4	H Kovalainen	Renault R27	70	1h44m18.021s	109.142	1m18.368s	2
5	K Räikkönen	Ferrari F2007	70	1h44m24.299s	109.032	1m16.861s	2
6	T Sato	Super Aguri-Honda SA07	70	1h44m27.990s	108.968	1m18.035s	3
7	F Alonso	McLaren-Mercedes MP4-22	70	1h44m33.228s	108.877	1m16.367s	3
8	R Schumacher	Toyota TF107	70	1h44m34.180s	108.860	1m17.910s	2
9	M Webber	Red Bull-Renault RB3	70	1h44m34.252s	108.859	1m17.618s	2
10	N Rosberg	Williams-Toyota FW29	70	1h44m35.276s	108.841	1m17.156s	2
11	A Davidson	Super Aguri-Honda SA07	70	1h44m35.610s	108.835	1m18.780s	3
12	R Barrichello	Honda RA107	70	1h44m41.731s	108.730	1m18.543s	3
R	J Trulli	Toyota TF107	58	Spun off	-	1m19.092s	4
R	V Liuzzi	Toro Rosso-Ferrari STR02	54	Spun off	-	1m19.375s	3
D	F Massa	Ferrari F2007	51	Pit infringement	-	1m16.849s	1
D	G Fisichella	Renault R27	51	Pit infringement	-	1m17.411s	2
R	C Albers	Spyker-Ferrari F8-VII	47	Spun off	-	1m19.254s	1
R	D Coulthard	Red Bull-Renault RB3	36	Gearbox	-	1m18.981s	3
R	R Kubica	BMW Sauber F1.07	26	Spun off	-	1m17.529s	1
R	A Sutil	Spyker-Ferrari F8-VII	21	Spun off	-	1m19.452s	0
R	S Speed	Toro Rosso-Ferrari STR02	8	Collision	-	1m20.092s	0
R	J Button	Honda RA107	0	Transmission	-	-	0

CHAMPIONSHIP

	Driver	Pts
1	L Hamilton	48
2	F Alonso	40
3	F Massa	33
4	K Räikkönen	27
5	N Heidfeld	26
6	G Fisichella	13
7	R Kubica	12
8	A Wurz	8
9	H Kovalainen	8
10	N Rosberg	5
11	D Coulthard	4
12	T Sato	4
13	J Trulli	4
14	R Schumacher	2

Fastest Lap
F Alonso 1m16.367s
(127.768mph) on lap 46

Fastest speed trap
H Kovalainen 203.7mph
Slowest speed trap
J Trulli 196.1mph

Fastest pit stop
1	A Davidson	25.834s
2	D Coulthard	26.086s
3	R Schumacher	26.413s

David Coulthard
"I had a gearbox problem. It began to work again, but the gearbox temperatures had risen, so I had to park up. It's sad, as our strategy could have worked well."

Nico Rosberg
"I gained two places, but then I was unlucky. I had no fuel and had to pit when the safety car went out for the first time and, according to the new rules, I was penalised."

Vitantonio Liuzzi
"After Kubica's accident, I got debris caught under the car, but everything seemed fine. Unluckily, I went over the kerb at the final chicane, which put me in the wall."

Christijan Albers
"I touched the wall early on, but thought it was going to be OK. Then the car got ever more unbalanced until I arrived at Turn 8 and the car just went straight on."

Takuma Sato
"I pitted, as I saw a chance just as the safety car was deployed and the pitlane was still open. The team was on hand and this was the most beautiful day of my career."

Mark Webber
"I lost out to Rosberg and Kubica on the run to Turn 1 and had a battle with Kubica, but went off. I began to move through the field again, then the safety car came out."

Alexander Wurz
"The team did everything right in terms of strategy and keeping me informed. I had a close call when Speed and I touched and my rear wing got damaged."

Scott Speed
"Alex was quicker than me down the straight, but he made a mistake at the hairpin and another at the corner before I tried to pass. When I did try, there wasn't enough room for two."

Adrian Sutil
"I am disappointed not to have finished. I want to say sorry to the team as they worked so hard and it would have been easy to have a points finish if I hadn't mucked up."

Anthony Davidson
"It's a shame about the beaver! I was third then, behind the safety car, on a one-stop strategy, and it damaged the front wing, so I had to pit, taking the guys by surprise."

	Constructor	Pts
1	McLaren-Mercedes	88
2	Ferrari	60
3	BMW Sauber	38
4	Renault	21
5	Williams-Toyota	13
6	Toyota	6
7	Red Bull-Renault	4
8	Super Aguri-Honda	4

2007 FORMULA 1™
UNITED STATES GRAND PRIX
INDIANAPOLIS

TWO WINS
IN A ROW

Lewis Hamilton took his second straight
victory, this time beating his McLaren
team-mate Fernando Alonso in a
straight fight that was fast and furious

Lewis Hamilton followed up his maiden victory in Canada
with a second success in eight days as he scored a hugely
popular victory at the Indianapolis Motor Speedway. The
win confirmed that the 22-year-old Briton was becoming
a serious contender for the World Championship, and
that Fernando Alonso was painfully aware that he could
well lose his crown to his rookie team-mate.

Qualifying proved crucial to the outcome of the
United States Grand Prix, as Lewis just managed to
edge out Alonso, who had been quicker in every session
– except the one that really counted. In fact, the McLaren
drivers qualified with equal fuel loads, something they
did for the first time at the Canadian Grand Prix. The
team had the option to adjust the pit stops to suit,
either by bringing one driver in early to avoid safety-car
problems, or through a driver saving fuel and stopping
later, a feat that Alonso had already achieved several
times in 2007.

Hamilton held on to his advantage off the startline,
and remained in the lead after pitting one lap ahead of
the Spaniard, on lap 21. Immediately after the first round
of pit stops, Alonso began to catch Hamilton again, and
even had a go at overtaking him on the long drag down
the pit straight.

TALKING POINT
A CHAMPION'S DISCOMFORT

After the Canadian GP, Lewis Hamilton had made the front page of every British national newspaper. Perhaps it was as well for him that he'd not been home. Practice day at Indianapolis was just four and a half days later, but there had been time for Fernando Alonso to talk to Spanish radio. He wasn't totally comfortable at McLaren, he said. There were a couple of issues, but he wouldn't elaborate.

McLaren supremo Ron Dennis wouldn't either, but he did say that the team was open about the issues with Fernando and they had been discussed. He advised against amplifying them.

Seasoned Alonso watchers at Renault said that changing teams is like changing tyre supplier: you've got the data, but the human relationships take time. They didn't figure that Fernando would be demanding preferential treatment on testing, strategy or data access, they just thought that he'd been shocked by Hamilton's pace. As well as that, Lewis had been part of McLaren longer, so Fernando would feel like he was renting a room in Lewis's house rather than buying his own.

After the furore at the Monaco GP, McLaren had decided to fuel its drivers identically in Q3 to give them equal opportunity to gun for pole position, and Lewis took it with 1m19.997s, with Fernando second on 1m20.147s.

That was straightforward enough, surely? Lewis was quicker. Yet, it wasn't that simple, as Fernando ran the fuel burn-off Q3 much more conservatively than Lewis. You'd think that would make the tiniest difference to fuel consumption but, in fact, it makes enough difference to give the possibility of an extra lap in the first stint of the race. Fernando's first Q3 'in'-lap was fully 16s slower than Lewis's. The penalty, of course, is a slightly heavier car at the end of the session when you go for pole. Fernando suspected he might not beat Lewis to pole and he was right. As soon as he saw his S2 time on the last run, he knew it for sure and immediately swooped across the front straight to clean up the dirty part of the track from which the second qualifier would start the grand prix...

Fernando didn't care too much, as he'd been quicker than Lewis throughout practice and, so long as he could run with him, then the carefully planned extra lap should be key. However, when he ran in Lewis's choppy wake, the tyres grained more than expected, just as they had for Lewis at Monaco. Thus, the extra lap wouldn't be the answer, and neither could Fernando pass Lewis on the track, try as he did. When he failed, the jink towards the pit wall articulated the frustration. The quicker man would finish second. By such tiny margins are races being decided. Formula One 2007 – absorbing stuff.

OPPOSITE **The McLaren pit crew work in perfect harmony on Fernando Alonso's car at a pit stop**

BELOW **Lewis Hamilton resists Alonso's attack through Turns 1 and 2 as the midfield concertina behind**

Points leader Hamilton was not to be outpsyched, and held on. On the next lap, Alonso veered towards his pit and made a hand gesture that was caught by his on-board camera. He was apparently trying to make a point to the team, but afterwards both he and the management – with straight faces – said merely that he was trying to get out of the slipstream to cool everything down.

It wasn't the brakes or the engine that were getting overheated. In fact, Alonso had been asking to be waved through by his team-mate, feeling that he was quicker. Team boss Ron Dennis had to remind him that such orders were frowned upon by the FIA and, if he couldn't find a way past, he should stay put...

Mindful of the upcoming French Grand Prix, both men were told to turn their engines down at the same time in the interests of fairness, but they raced hard until the chequered flag.

"It was extremely close for the first couple of laps," reported Hamilton. "Then, obviously, I managed to pull out a slight gap and maintain that. Going into the middle stint, the first two laps were very good, and then my tyres just decided to grain. Maybe I pushed too hard on them immediately, so Fernando was right up my tail, and it was extremely difficult."

INSIDE LINE
SEBASTIAN VETTEL
BMW SAUBER DRIVER

"The decision for me to race in the United States Grand Prix came at the last moment – it was Thursday afternoon. All the previous week the team and Robert Kubica were confident that he was going to be able to race after his accident in the Canadian Grand Prix and I wasn't even thinking of making my debut at Indianapolis. Suddenly, after the FIA decision, I was called up. From then, it was important that I was always with the team so that I knew all the updates on the car performance-wise.

I had not done much mileage in the car, just the Friday sessions in Australia and Malaysia. Other than that, I had not done a single test. In that situation you cannot do a lot, so I just ran the same programme that Robert would have done, but obviously did a lot of laps on Friday to gain confidence in the car.

On Saturday I think I did quite a good job to qualify seventh. I was on heavier fuel than Nick and I think I could have maybe beaten Kovalainen and been sixth, but the target was to make it into Q3 and I made it.

The race start stays in the memory. Unfortunately, we changed the set-up for the start and I lost quite a lot of momentum. It wasn't a personal mistake, it was the software.

This meant that I lost contact with the cars at the front of the field and then the backmarkers were around me. I braked very late for the first corner. Maybe that was a mistake, but I was trying not to be passed. You see, I knew I was a carrying more fuel than most and so was heavier. But, as soon as the one-stop guys get past you, your race is effectively over. The guys in front of me were quite slow into Turn 1 and I approached pretty much on the limit. To avoid a crash with Heikki Kovalainen's Renault, I went across the grass. When I came back on, I was behind Nico Rosberg, who was on a one-stopper.

My whole race was compromised by that, but I was basically not in a position to overtake with that car. There was no chance to get Nico, not even into Turn 1.

Nevertheless, I finished eighth and scored a point on my debut. If I'd got a better start I'm convinced I could have mixed it with Kovalainen.

Overall, it was a good debut and I was fairly satisfied considering that I'd had no testing up to this point in the season."

"Obviously, he was in my slipstream the whole time so he would always catch me down the straight and whatever I gained [in the infield], I lost on the straight, so it was very, very tough. But he fought very well, very professionally, and at the end I managed to pull out a gap and was able to maintain that gap and control the remainder of the race."

Hamilton made a point of putting his arm around his team-mate as they appeared on the podium, but it was all too clear that Alonso was far from happy.

"There was no doubt at the start that they were being allowed to race one another," said McLaren CEO Martin Whitmarsh. "They were respectful. We've got two very intelligent drivers and they both want to win very badly. They pushed hard then, but with the appropriate respect for one another. Later in the race, it was no holds barred. They were racing each other from beginning to end.

"Frankly, in the middle of the race, Fernando was a bit quicker, but Lewis had track position – they were pushing hard, they were consuming engine life. It was the first weekend of new engines and we were pretty mindful of the fact that they were pushing their engines pretty hard in pursuit of each other.

"When we had to turn the engines down in the final section of the race, we did it simultaneously. It was done to the same extent on both cars so that they were able to continue racing. At various points in the race, it was clear that Fernando was a little bit quicker, but Lewis did a fantastic job in qualifying. He did a great start and robustly defended his position a couple of times at Turn 1."

Behind the McLarens, the Ferraris were left trailing, Felipe Massa heading home Kimi Räikkönen. Once again, the Finnish driver had a frustrating weekend. He was beaten by a lighter Massa in qualifying, although Ferrari, unlike in Canada, did not have to worry

about BMW Sauber, as Nick Heidfeld threw away a certain third place on the grid with a mistake at the penultimate corner of his final qualifying lap.

Räikkönen's biggest problem, though, was that in the second session of qualifying he had to take an unplanned extra run on new soft tyres, as he had slipped down the order and faced the very real risk that he would be bumped. The Finn made it through to the third qualifying session, but he went into the race with no fresh soft tyres available for the first stint, unlike his main rivals. Ferrari gambled on putting him on new medium tyres for the opening stint, hoping that would be a better compromise.

Once again, Räikkönen made a bad start, losing out to both Heidfeld and Heikki Kovalainen. They were on the preferable tyre and, as we'd seen elsewhere this year, the Ferrari appeared to be unable to do much when stuck behind another car.

Eventually, things fell Räikkönen's way. He caught Massa in the middle stint, setting the race's fastest lap along the way. Had he not lost so much ground behind Kovalainen in the early running – he was around 11s behind Massa when the Brazilian made his first pit stop – he might ultimately have been able to jump to third.

In the final stint, Räikkönen was on the quicker soft tyre, while those ahead were on the medium tyre, but it proved to be too little too late, and he was consigned to fourth place.

"To finish fourth is never good," Räikkönen reflected afterwards. "I think we paid a big penalty to have a not so good start. The car was pretty OK, once we got racing, but if you get stuck behind some people it's very difficult to get past.

"We ran on hard tyres from the beginning, as we didn't have any new softs and we didn't want to risk [scrubbed softs] at the start. Anyhow, we lost some places at the start. Once we put the soft tyres on, they

were good but, like I said, it didn't help, it was a bit late. If you are behind, that's the penalty that you pay."

Räikkönen was at least able to keep the pressure on Massa, although the team, like McLaren, tried to keep things fair and, as with McLaren, both drivers turned their engines down at the same time, in order to preserve them for the forthcoming French Grand Prix at Magny-Cours.

"We did the same on both cars, so it was an even affair," continued Räikkönen. "It was just too difficult to overtake. When you get close, even when you are faster, and you lose downforce, you cannot get close enough to overtake – that's the biggest problem.

"We were racing for third place, so it's normal that you try to get close and try to get by. Felipe made a mistake in one place and I got close to him. Unfortunately, it was in the wrong place, and you can't really get past there. I think we had a pretty good race car once we got clean air and on the soft tyre, but it was already just too late at that point. We need to look at the situation and improve our qualifying, but I think it looks worse than it is."

This was probably Räikkönen's best race relative to team-mate Massa for a while, an indication that the

OPPOSITE **Jenson Button was hit by his team-mate Rubens Barrichello in another race that Honda would prefer to forget**

BELOW **Nick Heidfeld locked his rear wheels at Turn 1 and rotated**

BOTTOM **Heikki Kovalainen enjoyed five laps in the lead before coming home fifth for Renault**

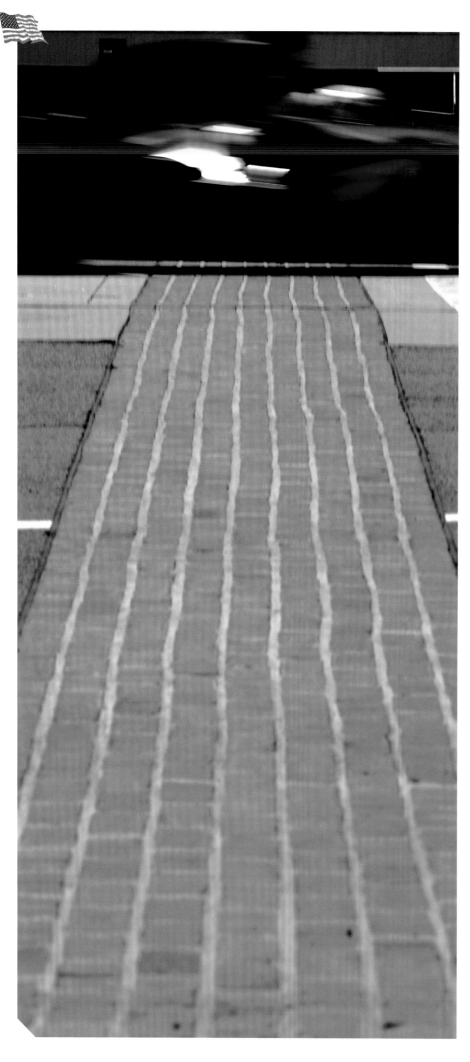

inevitable hurdles involved in settling into Ferrari and adapting to car and tyres were being overcome. The next two races were to provide even more evidence...

Kovalainen had a great run to secure fifth place and the tag of 'the best of the rest', making up for a frustrating early spin for his Renault team-mate Giancarlo Fisichella. A surprise sixth place was claimed by Jarno Trulli, who kept his head down and was in the right place at the right time as everyone's strategies unfolded. Seventh place went to Mark Webber, who finally had a clean run for Red Bull Racing.

The Williams was not as competitive as it had been in the Canadian Grand Prix, but a one-stop strategy put Nico Rosberg into contention for points until an oil leak created a fire and caused a late retirement.

The final point thus went to Sebastian Vettel, a late nomination for BMW Sauber after Robert Kubica was ruled out by the FIA following a medical check-up on Thursday. Despite not driving the car at all since Friday practice in Malaysia at the start of April, Vettel settled in well, and made the top 10 in qualifying. However, he nearly threw it away at the first corner.

"I braked quite late, I was on the edge," he admitted sheepishly. "Maybe it was too late, but I was trying to pull away from the field and trying to catch the guys at the front, or at least stay there. And then Kovalainen was fighting with a Ferrari, they were all tight, and they were quite slow turning into the first corner. I arrived quickly and therefore to avoid an incident with Kovalainen I decide to go straight and cut the grass. I thought 'damn' and fell behind Rosberg, which destroyed our strategy and our race.

"I'm happy to have come away with one point from my first grand prix, which is great for me personally. My target was to finish the race, and we did so. For sure, we could have been maybe two places higher if I hadn't messed it up at the first corner!"

Meanwhile, his team-mate Heidfeld's luck ran out at Indianapolis. He made the aforementioned mistake in qualifying, and then in the race a gearshift glitch caused him to have an early spin. The German was later to retire with a hydraulic problem.

The unhappiest team at Indianapolis was undoubtedly Honda. It was the turn of Rubens Barrichello to have a short day, as he got involved in a first-lap tangle that involved his own team-mate. He retired straight away with suspension damage, while Ralf Schumacher and David Coulthard were also eliminated. Jenson Button continued with a damaged car, but a refuelling delay at his pit stop meant he was not able to better 12th.

This was not a great grand prix, but it had plenty of interest. We didn't know it at the time, but it was also to mark the end of Formula One's Indianapolis adventure for the foreseeable future...

LEFT **Hamilton flashes over the brick strip at Indianapolis for his second straight victory for McLaren**

SNAPSHOT FROM
USA

CLOCKWISE FROM RIGHT The crowds were back in force in 2007; John Button is touched that Jenson didn't forget; preparation is everything to this trio; jetlag can hit at any moment; floodlighting was tested with a view to future night races; the portions tend to be on the large side in the USA...; Lewis Hamilton was the focus of media attention, both before and after the race

WEEKEND NEWS

■ Robert Kubica came to Indianapolis fully expecting to be allowed to take part, but a check-up by the FIA's Dr Gary Hartstein confirmed that he was still suffering the after-effects of his Montréal shunt – and Hartstein was not prepared to take the responsibility of allowing the Pole to race. Sebastian Vettel was only confirmed as his substitute at 4pm on Thursday.

■ On Thursday evening, the FIA conducted a test with a view to possible future night racing. Indianapolis was chosen not as a possible venue for such an event, but because US lighting company Murco wanted to demonstrate its products, which are used successfully to illuminate oval racing venues. The test, which was conducted with the medical and safety cars running around a stretch of track, was adjudged a success.

■ Hip-hop and rap music guru Pharrell Williams turned up at the Indianapolis Motor Speedway as a personal guest of Lewis and Anthony Hamilton. Part of the most successful producing team in the world, Williams has also forged a career as an artist in his own right. His car collection includes a Mercedes SLR, a Ferrari Enzo and a Rolls-Royce...

■ Nelson Piquet Sr made a rare appearance at a grand prix to catch up with his Renault test driver son, Nelsinho, and brought yet another junior Piquet with him. Also in the paddock was former Renault, Ligier and Arrows driver Eddie Cheever, while the current Indy Racing League ranks were represented by recent Indy 500 winner Dario Franchitti and Marco Andretti.

■ Several other likely visitors were busy at Le Mans. This year's race saw the event debut of Jacques Villeneuve, who was hoping to add victory in the 24 Hours to his earlier success in the Indianapolis 500, ChampCar series and World Championship. The Canadian finished fourth with Peugeot on his first race outing since the 2006 German GP.

RACE RESULTS
UNITED STATES
INDIANAPOLIS

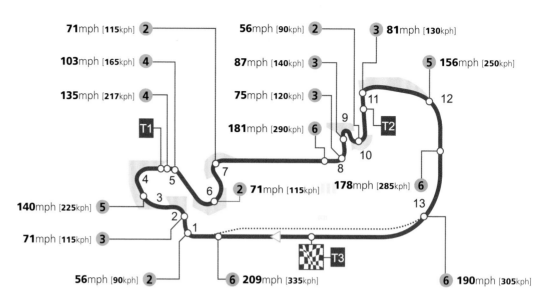

RACE DATE June 17th
CIRCUIT LENGTH 2.605 miles
NO. OF LAPS 73
RACE DISTANCE 190.139 miles
WEATHER Hot & humid, 35°C
TRACK TEMP 45°C
RACE DAY ATTENDANCE 120,000
LAP RECORD Rubens Barrichello,
1m10.399s, 133.229mph, 2004

PRACTICE 1

	Driver	Time	Laps
1	F Alonso	1m11.925s	16
2	N Heidfeld	1m12.391s	24
3	L Hamilton	1m12.628s	21
4	S Vettel	1m12.869s	33
5	K Räikkönen	1m12.966s	21
6	N Rosberg	1m13.020s	24
7	F Massa	1m13.040s	22
8	D Coulthard	1m13.159s	22
9	J Button	1m13.597s	23
10	M Webber	1m13.682s	26
11	J Trulli	1m13.777s	32
12	K Nakajima	1m13.786s	27
13	R Schumacher	1m13.819s	27
14	V Liuzzi	1m13.907s	28
15	S Speed	1m13.990s	24
16	G Fisichella	1m14.000s	19
17	T Sato	1m14.037s	20
18	R Barrichello	1m14.052s	23
19	H Kovalainen	1m14.189s	18
20	A Davidson	1m14.632s	10
21	C Albers	1m14.636s	28
22	A Sutil	1m14.810s	27

PRACTICE 2

	Driver	Time	Laps
1	F Alonso	1m12.156s	35
2	L Hamilton	1m12.309s	34
3	F Massa	1m12.435s	36
4	K Räikkönen	1m12.587s	38
5	N Heidfeld	1m13.026s	43
6	D Coulthard	1m13.042s	41
7	N Rosberg	1m13.057s	35
8	H Kovalainen	1m13.110s	48
9	R Barrichello	1m13.144s	40
10	J Button	1m13.202s	46
11	S Vettel	1m13.217s	50
12	M Webber	1m13.263s	21
13	V Liuzzi	1m13.332s	41
14	A Davidson	1m13.364s	46
15	G Fisichella	1m13.394s	44
16	A Wurz	1m13.539s	29
17	J Trulli	1m13.692s	42
18	S Speed	1m13.712s	34
19	T Sato	1m13.753s	46
20	R Schumacher	1m13.765s	39
21	C Albers	1m14.225s	30
22	A Sutil	1m14.513s	33

PRACTICE 3

	Driver	Time	Laps
1	F Alonso	1m12.150s	12
2	S Vettel	1m12.321s	27
3	L Hamilton	1m12.378s	14
4	H Kovalainen	1m12.574s	21
5	N Heidfeld	1m12.646s	24
6	K Räikkönen	1m12.692s	16
7	F Massa	1m12.709s	17
8	G Fisichella	1m12.710s	20
9	D Coulthard	1m12.940s	17
10	N Rosberg	1m13.031s	18
11	J Trulli	1m13.057s	23
12	R Schumacher	1m13.061s	23
13	A Davidson	1m13.203s	20
14	M Webber	1m13.289s	14
15	J Button	1m13.318s	20
16	V Liuzzi	1m13.415s	23
17	T Sato	1m13.476s	19
18	R Barrichello	1m13.573s	17
19	A Wurz	1m13.626s	18
20	S Speed	1m13.979s	18
21	A Sutil	1m14.142s	24
22	C Albers	1m14.402s	24

QUALIFYING 1

	Driver	Time
1	F Alonso	1m12.416s
2	N Heidfeld	1m12.543s
3	L Hamilton	1m12.563s
4	S Vettel	1m12.711s
5	F Massa	1m12.731s
6	K Räikkönen	1m12.732s
7	R Schumacher	1m12.851s
8	H Kovalainen	1m12.998s
9	N Rosberg	1m13.128s
10	A Davidson	1m13.164s
11	G Fisichella	1m13.168s
12	J Trulli	1m13.186s
13	R Barrichello	1m13.203s
14	J Button	1m13.306s
15	D Coulthard	1m13.424s
16	M Webber	1m13.425s
17	A Wurz	1m13.441s
18	T Sato	1m13.477s
19	V Liuzzi	1m13.484s
20	S Speed	1m13.712s
21	A Sutil	1m14.122s
22	C Albers	1m14.597s

QUALIFYING 2

	Driver	Time
1	F Alonso	1m11.926s
2	L Hamilton	1m12.065s
3	K Räikkönen	1m12.111s
4	F Massa	1m12.180s
5	N Heidfeld	1m12.188s
6	H Kovalainen	1m12.599s
7	G Fisichella	1m12.603s
8	S Vettel	1m12.644s
9	M Webber	1m12.788s
10	J Trulli	1m12.828s
11	D Coulthard	1m12.873s
12	R Schumacher	1m12.920s
13	J Button	1m12.998s
14	N Rosberg	1m13.060s
15	R Barrichello	1m13.201s
16	A Davidson	1m13.259s

Best sectors – Practice

Sec 1	L Hamilton	22.162s
Sec 2	F Alonso	29.348s
Sec 3	L Hamilton	20.345s

Speed trap – Practice

1	D Coulthard	209.0mph
2	M Webber	208.1mph
3	N Heidfeld	207.1mph

Best sectors – Qualifying

Sec 1	F Alonso	22.117s
Sec 2	F Alonso	29.311s
Sec 3	K Räikkönen	20.274s

Speed trap – Qualifying

1	M Webber	207.8mph
2	D Coulthard	206.2mph
3	H Kovalainen	205.9mph

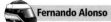

Fernando Alonso
"I finally managed to leave Indy with a trophy. The race was decided after Turn 1, and I didn't manage to get past. All I could do was stay as close to Lewis as possible."

Giancarlo Fisichella
"I lost the rear end going into Turn 4 on lap 2. We had planned to do a one-stop strategy and I was even able to pass a few cars off-line on the outside of Turn 6."

Felipe Massa
"We can't be satisfied with third. We need to make up the ground lost these past three races. In the last stint, Kimi got very close and I was struggling on hard tyres."

Jenson Button
"At the start, I was on the outside and was hit by Rubens, which damaged the front of my car. That forced me across the grass and left me almost at the back."

Nick Heidfeld
"I had a good start and passed Kimi. Later, when I was braking for Turn 1, the rear wheels locked and I spun. When I wanted to get going, I couldn't get a gear."

Ralf Schumacher
"It was very crowded going into Turn 1 and everyone is on cold tyres. I braked quite calmly, but my tyres locked. David came from the outside and we hit each other."

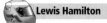

Lewis Hamilton
"I was under pressure all the way from Fernando. In the second stint, he managed to get really close when my tyres were graining, but I was able to keep him behind."

Heikki Kovalainen
"I passed Räikkönen at the start. When he pitted, with Heidfeld, I didn't even realise I was leading until I came into the pits. Sadly, the tyre performance wasn't there."

Kimi Räikkönen
"I paid a high price for places lost at the start. It's hard to overtake as you lose aero downforce. In the final stages, I closed on Felipe but there was never a chance to pass."

Rubens Barrichello
"It was just an unlucky first-corner racing incident. I tried to avoid a spinning Ralf and hit two cars, one of which was Jenson. The contact broke my front suspension."

Sebastian Vettel
"It was fun, but a longer race than I imagined. I am lucky to get away with a point, as the first corner was tight. To avoid an incident, I decided to cut Turn 2 and lost places."

Jarno Trulli
"I can't believe I finished in the points. For us, sixth place is like a victory. I was fighting with Webber and I didn't think I would come out ahead, but I managed it."

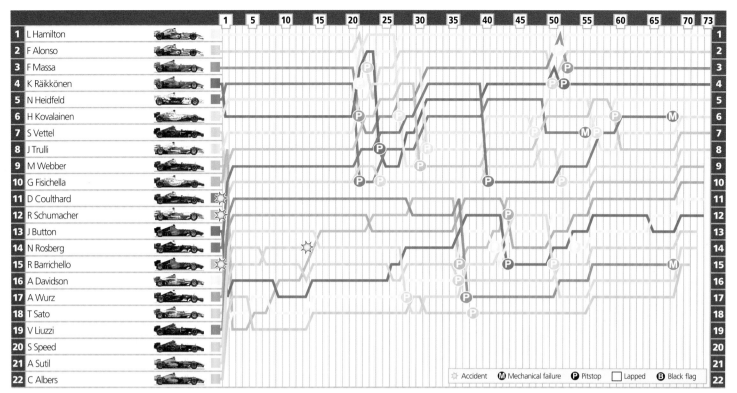

	Driver	
1	L Hamilton	
2	F Alonso	
3	F Massa	
4	K Räikkönen	
5	N Heidfeld	
6	H Kovalainen	
7	S Vettel	
8	J Trulli	
9	M Webber	
10	G Fisichella	
11	D Coulthard	
12	R Schumacher	
13	J Button	
14	N Rosberg	
15	R Barrichello	
16	A Davidson	
17	A Wurz	
18	T Sato	
19	V Liuzzi	
20	S Speed	
21	A Sutil	
22	C Albers	

☆ Accident Ⓜ Mechanical failure Ⓟ Pitstop ☐ Lapped Ⓑ Black flag

QUALIFYING 3

	Driver	Time
1	L Hamilton	1m12.331s
2	F Alonso	1m12.500s
3	F Massa	1m12.703s
4	K Räikkönen	1m12.839s
5	N Heidfeld	1m12.847s
6	H Kovalainen	1m13.308s
7	S Vettel	1m13.513s
8	J Trulli	1m13.789s
9	M Webber	1m13.871s
10	G Fisichella	1m13.953s

GRID

	Driver	Time
1	L Hamilton	1m12.331s
2	F Alonso	1m12.500s
3	F Massa	1m12.703s
4	K Räikkönen	1m12.839s
5	N Heidfeld	1m12.847s
6	H Kovalainen	1m13.308s
7	S Vettel	1m13.513s
8	J Trulli	1m13.789s
9	M Webber	1m13.871s
10	G Fisichella	1m13.953s
11	D Coulthard	1m12.873s
12	R Schumacher	1m12.920s
13	J Button	1m12.998s
14	N Rosberg	1m13.060s
15	R Barrichello	1m13.201s
16	A Davidson	1m13.259s
17	A Wurz	1m13.441s
18	T Sato	1m13.477s
19	V Liuzzi	1m13.484s
20	S Speed	1m13.712s
21	A Sutil	1m14.122s
22	C Albers	1m14.597s

RACE

	Driver	Car	Laps	Time	Avg. mph	Fastest	Stops
1	L Hamilton	McLaren-Mercedes MP4-22	73	1h31m09.965s	125.145	1m13.222s	2
2	F Alonso	McLaren-Mercedes MP4-22	73	1h31m11.483s	125.110	1m13.257s	2
3	F Massa	Ferrari F2007	73	1h31m22.807s	124.851	1m13.380s	2
4	K Räikkönen	Ferrari F2007	73	1h31m25.387s	124.793	1m13.117s	2
5	H Kovalainen	Renault R27	73	1h31m51.367s	124.204	1m13.998s	2
6	J Trulli	Toyota TF107	73	1h32m16.668s	123.673	1m14.016s	2
7	M Webber	Red Bull-Renault RB3	73	1h32m17.296s	123.623	1m14.004s	2
8	S Vettel	BMW Sauber F1.07	73	1h32m17.748s	123.613	1m13.862s	2
9	G Fisichella	Renault R27	72	1h31m44.282s	122.661	1m14.009s	1
10	A Wurz	Williams-Toyota FW29	72	1h32m11.721s	122.053	1m14.486s	1
11	A Davidson	Super Aguri-Honda SA07	72	1h32m13.434s	122.015	1m14.066s	2
12	J Button	Honda RA107	72	1h32m23.277s	121.798	1m14.703s	1
13	S Speed	Toro Rosso-Ferrari STR02	71	1h31m17.333s	121.552	1m15.092s	1
14	A Sutil	Spyker-Ferrari F8-VII	71	1h31m19.396s	121.506	1m14.858s	2
15	C Albers	Spyker-Ferrari F8-VII	70	1h31m16.671s	119.855	1m15.902s	1
16	N Rosberg	Williams-Toyota FW29	68	Oil leak	123.589	1m14.066s	1
17	V Liuzzi	Toro Rosso-Ferrari STR02	68	Water leak	121.426	1m15.426s	1
R	N Heidfeld	BMW Sauber F1.07	55	Hydraulics	-	1m13.414s	2
R	T Sato	Super Aguri-Honda SA07	13	Spin	-	1m16.680s	0
R	D Coulthard	Red Bull-Renault RB3	0	Accident damage	-	-	0
R	R Barrichello	Honda RA107	0	Accident damage	-	-	0
R	R Schumacher	Toyota TF107	0	Accident	-	-	0

CHAMPIONSHIP

	Driver	Pts
1	L Hamilton	58
2	F Alonso	48
3	F Massa	39
4	K Räikkönen	32
5	N Heidfeld	26
6	G Fisichella	13
7	R Kubica	12
8	H Kovalainen	12
9	A Wurz	8
10	J Trulli	7
11	N Rosberg	5
12	D Coulthard	4
13	T Sato	4
14	M Webber	2
15	R Schumacher	2
16	S Vettel	1

Fastest Lap
K Räikkönen 1m13.117s
(128.249mph) on lap 49

Fastest speed trap
S Speed 208.6mph
Slowest speed trap
D Coulthard 179.7mph

Fastest pit stop
1	M Webber	24.272s
2	J Trulli	24.351s
3	F Alonso	24.9s

Constructor
	Constructor	Pts
1	McLaren-Mercedes	106
2	Ferrari	71
3	BMW Sauber	39
4	Renault	25
5	Williams-Toyota	13
6	Toyota	9
7	Red Bull-Renault	6
8	Super Aguri-Honda	4

David Coulthard
"I kept a steady line off the start, making sure I left space on the inside. Ralf came together with another car behind me. That spun Ralf and he speared into my side."

Nico Rosberg
"I thought sixth was in the bag. We were on a good strategy and we've shown that we've made some progress and we would definitely have been in the points."

Vitantonio Liuzzi
"We were too slow in the first stint, after starting on hard tyres. I enjoyed a good fight with Fisichella, but I struggled with rear stability and a lack of rear grip."

Christijan Albers
"We were on a one-stop strategy, but when the leaders began to lap me, I lost time and got lapped again! In our position, you have to be aggressive with the strategy."

Takuma Sato
"I had a poor start and got passed by two cars. I avoided the incident at Turn 1 and lap by lap overtook people. But, then I got on the dirt and went off at Turn 3."

Mark Webber
"My race was a scrap with Jarno (Trulli) from start to finish. I would have liked slightly better balance in the middle stint, but it's good to get two points in the bag."

Alexander Wurz
"I made up places at the start. Our strategy was also good, but I ended up stuck behind Liuzzi, who was slower, and that cost me too much time to finish in the points."

Scott Speed
"The track was slippery and we needed more grip from the track for our car to work better. It was a tough race and just keeping the car on the track was in itself a challenge."

Adrian Sutil
"After a great start I was able to fight. There seems to have been a step forwards since Canada. I am happy to have made it to the end, especially as it was a hard race."

Anthony Davidson
"We opted to save the tyres by running more wing and it was hard work to get close enough to get a tow. There was a lot of passing, with a chaotic first corner."

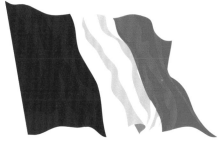

FORMULA 1™ GRAND PRIX DE FRANCE 2007
MAGNY-COURS

KIMI HITS BACK

Off the podium since Bahrain, Kimi Räikkönen bounced back to prove that there were two drivers at Ferrari who could win races, heading a Ferrari 1–2

A Ferrari comeback at Magny-Cours was nicely timed in terms of the World Championship but, even though he was beaten, McLaren's Lewis Hamilton didn't lose too much ground to his Italian rivals. Also, with Kimi Räikkönen's victory meaning that the big-four names now had two wins apiece, there was a pleasing symmetry about the results as we approached the halfway mark. Everything was still to play for.

Ferrari won in France fair and square, and the fact that Räikkönen was able to jump team-mate Felipe Massa at the second round of pit stops showed that it was not only at McLaren where an intense on-track rivalry was gathering momentum. However, the Maranello team was certainly helped by a below-par weekend for McLaren, whose management readily admitted that they didn't quite get things right.

The first signs of trouble for McLaren came on Friday, when Hamilton stopped early in the first session with an electronic problem. The car was returned to the pits and he eventually put in some laps later in the session, but his programme was disrupted. Quick times from Ferrari piled on the pressure.

On Saturday morning, it was Fernando Alonso's turn to hit trouble. Again it was a minor glitch, in

TALKING POINT
WHAT NOW FOR FRANCE?

As the trucks pulled out of Magny-Cours on Sunday night, after an uninterrupted 17 years, the future of the French GP was uncertain. The track was at the end of its FOM deal, remote and lacking infrastructure.

A venue as part of the Disneyland Paris theme park was talked about, but discussions with FOM are in their infancy. There was also the possibility of a street race in Versailles and a race on the Le Mans Bugatti circuit.

"A race in Paris would be a dream," said Jean Todt. "It would be like a grand prix in London, amazing, but I don't think it's practical."

A combined statement from Marcel Charmant (Président du Conseil Général de la Nièvre), François Patriat (Président du Conseil Régional de Bourgogne) and Gérard Dumas (Président de la Société du Circuit de Nevers Magny-Cours) on Sunday night expressed delight with the success of the day's race and confirmed a willingness to build 'Magny-Cours 2' with better facilities. It went on to ask the French motorsport authority (the FFSA) to apply for a date on the 2008 F1 calendar. People thought it too late for Magny-Cours, but they were to be proved wrong.

As Jean's son, GP2 team boss Nicolas Todt, said: "It's very hard to find backers for motorsport in France. At ART GP, we've had French drivers and very often the backing is via friends, parents and connections rather than commercially driven. I don't find any French sponsors."

A French driver would help, he said, and that's why he was involved with trying to bring triple ChampCar king Sébastien Bourdais into Formula One.

There was again talk that Todt Jr might become involved in a Ferrari junior team, possibly through buying into Toro Rosso. What did he have to say about that?

"First of all, I've never heard that Toro Rosso is for sale. Obviously people see me speaking to Gerhard Berger and Franz Tost, but we are talking about Sébastien, not the team."

But if something was possible, surely he would be interested? "I'm 29, quite young, and I want to achieve things. Obviously, one day, being part of a team or being a shareholder, yes, I would be interested. But you need to gather all the elements. Buying the team needs a lot of money. I would need to find the right partners and very often you hear that guys want to buy a team but don't have money to run it, so you need long-term vision."

With Prodrive talking to McLaren about running a satellite team, Ferrari admits it may look into running a 'B' squad. And with Todt Jr selling 30% of ART to Bahraini backers, is it really too fanciful to see a link?

Perhaps the future for French motorsport is not so glum after all.

this case a brake sensor, but it kept his McLaren in the pits until the very end of the session and meant he lost priceless track time in a session that's vital in terms of preparing for qualifying.

Then, at the start of Q3, Alonso soon realised after driving out of the pits that he had a problem and he came straight back in. It was a ceramic-bearing failure, something that had failed only once before in three years of use. He could take no further part in the session, and was thus doomed to start 10th with the fuel that was still in the car – a load that was only ever going to work if he was to start the race at the very front.

Meanwhile, Hamilton made a mistake, and when it all shook out Massa was on pole ahead of Hamilton and Räikkönen. There was quite a big margin to the Finn, but he knew he had qualified with a lot of extra fuel, and Alonso was down in 10th and clearly no threat.

All was not yet lost for Hamilton. He still had a chance of beating Massa into Turn 1, although that's never easy from the inside spot at Magny-Cours. The threat from Räikkönen was tempered by the knowledge that he had endured some pretty dire first laps.

Unfortunately for Hamilton, he had a poor time trying to get away from the dirty side of the grid, a problem

that also afflicted Robert Kubica, immediately behind. Normally by that stage of the weekend there would have been some rubber down on the pitwall side of the start/finish straight after two GP2 races, two Euro Formula Three races, and the Porsche Supercup, but rain in the morning had put paid to that. And a bad start from Lewis coincided with Räikkönen finally getting it right. In a flash, Hamilton was down in third with what the team had guessed was the lightest load of the three. This was the worst-case scenario.

Massa edged away in the opening laps, leaving his team-mate to hold off Hamilton. When Hamilton pitted very early on lap 16 and the two red cars stayed out, it became apparent that they were on different strategies, with Hamilton eventually pitting three times and the Ferrari drivers twice.

After that, there was no question of Hamilton challenging the Ferraris, but there was still some excitement at the front as Räikkönen stayed close to Massa before their second and final pit stops. Massa came in on lap 43 while Räikkönen stayed out until lap 46, and this was more than enough to allow the Finn to claim the lead from the frustrated Brazilian.

Massa said that traffic hadn't helped his defence

OPPOSITE MIDDLE LEFT
Lewis Hamilton returns to the grid, but his start from the 'dirty' pitwall side wasn't swift

OPPOSITE MIDDLE RIGHT
Heikki Kovalainen finds his Renault facing the wrong direction after clashing with Jarno Trulli at the hairpin on the opening lap

OPPOSITE BOTTOM Jenson Button raced hard and rose from 13th to eighth place to secure Honda's first point of the year

ABOVE Vitantonio Liuzzi's Toro Rosso is lifted clear after being hit by Anthony Davidson's Super Aguri on lap 1 and forced into retirement

INSIDE LINE
FERNANDO ALONSO

McLAREN DRIVER

"I thought that we were in good shape and I would be in the fight for pole position, but it all went wrong on the 'out'-lap in Q3. There was smoke coming from my car and the team radioed me to come in.

The adrenaline is flowing and you sit there hoping that you might be able to go out and do a lap, hoping for the miracle! But then they tap your helmet and tell you to get out of the car... It was a gearbox problem.

It meant starting in 10th place. Obviously, I'd been fuelled light to go for pole and a three-stop strategy, so I knew that starting P10 I was going to have a difficult race.

I couldn't afford to wait for the pit stops. I picked up a couple of places on the first lap when Trulli clipped Kovalainen at the hairpin and then I managed to pass Rosberg. I was quicker than Heidfeld and I tried a move on him at Lycée which worked, but I ran wide and he re-passed me. I knew I was light on fuel compared to the others and so I risked as much as I could.

I was still behind Nick at the first pit stop, and he ran longer than me, so he stayed in front, and so did Fisichella. It was hard to stay close enough through Turn 3 to make it down the inside of Adelaide hairpin, but I managed to pass Fisico. I knew I had to pass Nick on the track and open up a gap. I got a good exit before the fast chicane and just went for it. It was a bit tight... I thought that it was probably not enough and that I'd be behind them again after the second round of stops, and I was right.

We swapped to a two-stop strategy and that meant running a 33-lap stint on the last set of tyres. I damaged them a little when the fuel load was heavy and wasn't able to be aggressive in the last couple of laps fighting Fisichella again, so it was seventh place for me.

I really enjoyed the race and those moves, but when you cross the line and the team says seventh, it doesn't feel so good. Two seventh places in the past three races is not great for the championship. But in Canada there was a safety car on the lap I had to stop, and here there was the gearbox problem, neither of which I could do anything about. One day this will happen to the other guys."

of the lead. Having been 3.2s ahead on the lap before his final pit stop, he got caught behind a train of cars that included those of Ralf Schumacher, Mark Webber, David Coulthard and Alexander Wurz. When Räikkönen pitted after his three laps in the lead, he emerged clearly ahead of his team-mate, who was nearly 2s behind at the end of that lap. The Ferraris then ran in formation to the flag.

"Finally, the start worked for me and that helped a lot," said Räikkönen. "I think the car was good all the time, not exactly perfect, but I was very happy with the car. I just tried to push and keep up with Felipe. I knew that he was going to stop a bit later, so just before the first stop I had quite a bit of traffic, but then at the second stop I managed to get in front of him. It was a good day for me and the team.

"I think we had a bit of a hard time, but I kind of expected to have a bit of a difficult time. People always think that you've lost it when you don't have a good result, but we just work hard and try to get it right. Also, I think we can still improve and we're still not where we want to be, but we are definitely much happier with the car since the last test. In the last few races, we just couldn't get it together. It seems to have good speed now, so we must keep it up."

A clearly disappointed Massa said: "For sure I lost the race today because of the traffic, because in the first stint I was supposed to be more than 4s in front of Kimi, and it worked perfectly because the track was free, and I was 4.8s ahead or something. I came out in front of him again and then he had three laps more than me in the second stint, which is supposed to be the same, I was supposed to be more than 4s in front.

"But I was so disappointed with the traffic in the second stint. I lost too much time. Even when you are not very close to the car in front, you lose so much downforce that you can't follow the car and you lose speed and that was the biggest problem I had today.

Unfortunately, I lost the victory because of that, because the car was great throughout. Whenever I was alone I was doing very, very quick laps, so it was a shame."

Despite his personal disappointment, Massa said he was pleased with the overall outcome: "But anyway, it's very good for the team. I'm very happy and also looking at McLaren, who are still quite a bit in front, it is good to have a weekend like that."

When Hamilton came in for the first of his three stops, the option existed for him to run a longer second stint and run his race to a two-stop strategy. Yet, fearful of dropping him into traffic, the team decided to go short and keep him on a three-stop schedule. It was a strategy that raised a few eyebrows up and down the pitlane, but McLaren's theory was that beating the Ferraris was no longer an option, and the three-stopper was the best way to consolidate third.

"Sometimes you've got to be pragmatic, take the points, and move on to the next race," said McLaren boss Ron Dennis. "That's what it was, pragmatism. That's why we switched Lewis's strategy, it was a way to keep him out of trouble, keep him out of traffic. It wasn't designed to give him a shot at second, it was designed to make sure he came third."

There was also the issue of tyres. Nobody was very keen to go onto the softer option tyre, but they all knew they had to at some stage. A three-stopper would mean that Hamilton would only have to use the less favoured tyre in that short final stint.

Hamilton had one especially exciting moment when he came out of the pits just behind Kubica's BMW Sauber. Informed that he was racing the Pole for position, the McLaren driver immediately fought back and pulled off a great passing move of the type everyone had been waiting for him to demonstrate since his fireworks on the run to the first corner of the season's opening grand prix in Melbourne.

Funnily enough, Hamilton didn't have to do it, since

OPPOSITE Having started 10th, Fernando Alonso seemed to spend the entire race fighting to pass others. Here he grapples with Giancarlo Fisichella at the hairpin

BELOW Robert Kubica returned from injury to get straight back into the points with fourth place

Kimi Räikkönen had every reason to celebrate as he fought hard for his second consecutive win

Kubica was due to stop a few laps later, and thus he would have got his place back and stayed ahead after his own third stop by dint of some quick laps. Hamilton, though, is not the sort of driver to play a percentage game: he saw a rival and his instinct was to pass him come what may...

However, getting ahead at that stage did make his life easier and put third place beyond reasonable doubt. Crucially, it also allowed him to back off on the engine, which had also done the US Grand Prix, in the closing stages. By the end of the race, Hamilton was 29s down on the Ferraris.

There was a familiar pattern behind, as Kubica and Nick Heidfeld took fourth and fifth places for BMW Sauber, as usual taking advantage of a problem for one of the big two teams, on this occasion Alonso's qualifying misfortunes.

Giancarlo Fisichella gave Renault some comfort by taking sixth place in the company's home race.

Alonso was always going to have it tough from 10th, and in the end the only places he gained on the first lap were those vacated by Heikki Kovalainen and Jarno Trulli when they tangled. Over the course of the remaining 69 laps, the only driver he managed to successfully demote was Nico Rosberg, which was

a clear sign of just how difficult a job he had, having been stuck with the light fuel load at the start of the race when traffic was at its most dense.

It's worth noting that Jenson Button also managed to usurp Rosberg, and he did it with a Honda, from 13th on the grid!

And yet, Alonso pulled off some brilliant passes along the way, including one on Heidfeld that was as good as any seen all year. The problem was that he spent so much of the race in traffic. Clearly, there was speed in Alonso's car – he set a better fastest lap than Hamilton, one that was a huge 0.6s quicker than the best by fourth-placed Kubica, so the fact that the eventual outcome was a humble seventh for Alonso gave a graphic demonstration of the value of strategy and track position.

The final point went to Button. Incredibly, it was also the first point of the year for the troubled Honda team. Rosberg dropped to ninth, while Ralf Schumacher completed the top 10.

Most people left Magny-Cours with the impression that they would not be going back, ever, and few shed many tears. Against expectations a few weeks later, Bernie Ecclestone confirmed that the race had made it on to the 2008 calendar after all.

SNAPSHOT FROM
FRANCE

CLOCKWISE FROM RIGHT It was "welcome to Magny-Cours" but then very nearly "adieu" as well; Nicholas Hamilton had to make do with third place for his brother Lewis; Honda Racing added the support of a few friends to its world livery; the grid girls added their traditional sunny smiles to the show; doing PR events doesn't always get the drivers' votes, just ask Giancarlo Fisichella, Franck Montagny and Fernando Alonso...; Kimi Räikkönen dropped the winner's champagne to one of his mechanics, who just failed to hold the catch; Red Bull Racing would have settled for reflected glory, but neither driver could even make it into the top ten

WEEKEND NEWS

- Three people were killed in a helicopter accident to the north of Magny-Cours on the Saturday evening. Among those who died while en route to a local chateau were Quiksilver marketing man Emanuel Longobardi, and the pilot, former F3 driver Pierre Bennehard. Two others were injured, including a senior Bridgestone Europe employee.

- French soccer hero Zinedine Zidane was the highest-profile VIP guest at Magny-Cours. He was given a lap of the track by Michael Schumacher in the German's own jet-black Ferrari FXX. The outing was connected to their joint involvement in the ICM medical charity.

- Former Spyker tester Ernesto Viso had a hugely lucky escape from a dramatic accident in Saturday's GP2 race. The Venezuelan's car hit the back of another, rolled along a concrete wall, smashed through an advertising hoarding, and came to rest in an access road. The chassis was broken in half, but he escaped unhurt.

- Honda Racing announced that former Williams designer Loïc Bigois was to join the team as head of aerodynamics. The arrival of the erstwhile Prost employee couldn't come soon enough, as the latest incarnation of the RA107 represented only a modest step forward.

- Two days after the French GP, it was revealed that a McLaren employee had been suspended pending an investigation into possible espionage involving Ferrari and its Race & Test Technical Manager Nigel Stepney. It was soon revealed that the man in question was chief designer Mike Coughlan, and in the coming days the story exploded into a major scandal.

RACE RESULTS
FRANCE
MAGNY-COURS

Official Results © [2007]
Formula One Administration Limited,
6 Princes Gate, London, SW7 1QJ.
No reproduction without permission.
All copyright and database rights reserved.

RACE DATE July 1st
CIRCUIT LENGTH 2.741 miles
NO. OF LAPS 70
RACE DISTANCE 191.870 miles
WEATHER Bright, but humid, 25°C
TRACK TEMP 40°C
RACE DAY ATTENDANCE 72,000
LAP RECORD Michael Schumacher, 1m15.377s, 130.910mph, 2004

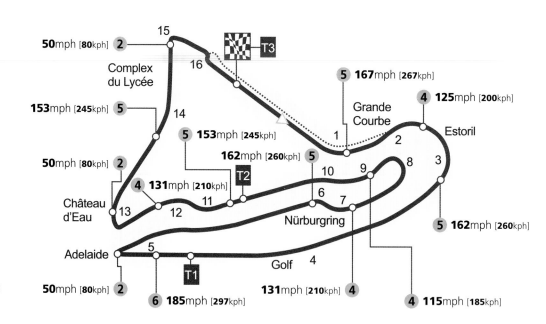

	PRACTICE 1		
	Driver	Time	Laps
1	K Räikkönen	1m15.382s	22
2	F Massa	1m15.447s	22
3	F Alonso	1m16.154s	19
4	N Rosberg	1m16.214s	24
5	D Coulthard	1m16.268s	24
6	L Hamilton	1m16.277s	20
7	N Heidfeld	1m16.338s	25
8	A Wurz	1m16.407s	23
9	R Kubica	1m16.441s	19
10	J Trulli	1m16.603s	26
11	V Liuzzi	1m16.895s	32
12	T Sato	1m16.967s	22
13	R Barrichello	1m16.990s	25
14	J Button	1m17.047s	24
15	S Speed	1m17.103s	33
16	A Davidson	1m17.166s	26
17	R Schumacher	1m17.168s	26
18	G Fisichella	1m17.226s	20
19	H Kovalainen	1m17.348s	21
20	M Webber	1m17.435s	26
21	C Albers	1m18.178s	28
22	A Sutil	1m18.419s	15

	PRACTICE 2		
	Driver	Time	Laps
1	F Massa	1m15.453s	38
2	K Räikkönen	1m15.488s	28
3	S Speed	1m15.773s	21
4	L Hamilton	1m15.780s	36
5	V Liuzzi	1m15.952s	40
6	D Coulthard	1m15.958s	36
7	N Rosberg	1m16.003s	39
8	F Alonso	1m16.049s	32
9	A Davidson	1m16.162s	25
10	R Schumacher	1m16.184s	41
11	G Fisichella	1m16.205s	43
12	R Kubica	1m16.236s	42
13	A Wurz	1m16.260s	38
14	J Trulli	1m16.285s	46
15	J Button	1m16.395s	43
16	M Webber	1m16.562s	17
17	H Kovalainen	1m16.735s	40
18	R Barrichello	1m16.950s	47
19	N Heidfeld	1m16.968s	18
20	T Sato	1m17.165s	49
21	A Sutil	1m18.213s	32
22	C Albers	1m18.708s	9

	PRACTICE 3		
	Driver	Time	Laps
1	L Hamilton	1m14.843s	8
2	F Massa	1m14.906s	16
3	K Räikkönen	1m15.276s	15
4	H Kovalainen	1m15.404s	19
5	G Fisichella	1m15.489s	20
6	R Kubica	1m15.535s	20
7	N Rosberg	1m15.735s	18
8	F Alonso	1m15.742s	4
9	J Trulli	1m15.801s	19
10	D Coulthard	1m15.802s	15
11	V Liuzzi	1m15.872s	22
12	J Button	1m15.902s	16
13	A Davidson	1m15.925s	20
14	R Schumacher	1m15.944s	24
15	N Heidfeld	1m16.060s	18
16	R Barrichello	1m16.102s	19
17	A Wurz	1m16.104s	16
18	S Speed	1m16.161s	18
19	T Sato	1m16.221s	18
20	M Webber	1m16.573s	14
21	A Sutil	1m17.517s	21
22	C Albers	1m17.705s	23

	QUALIFYING 1	
	Driver	Time
1	L Hamilton	1m14.805s
2	K Räikkönen	1m14.872s
3	F Massa	1m15.303s
4	F Alonso	1m15.322s
5	H Kovalainen	1m15.524s
6	M Webber	1m15.746s
7	R Schumacher	1m15.760s
8	R Kubica	1m15.778s
9	N Heidfeld	1m15.783s
10	D Coulthard	1m15.915s
11	S Speed	1m15.980s
12	G Fisichella	1m16.047s
13	N Rosberg	1m16.092s
14	J Button	1m16.113s
15	J Trulli	1m16.118s
16	R Barrichello	1m16.140s
17	V Liuzzi	1m16.142s
18	A Wurz	1m16.241s
19	T Sato	1m16.244s
20	A Davidson	1m16.366s
21	C Albers	1m17.826s
22	A Sutil	1m17.915s

	QUALIFYING 2	
	Driver	Time
1	L Hamilton	1m14.795s
2	F Massa	1m14.822s
3	K Räikkönen	1m14.828s
4	R Kubica	1m15.066s
5	F Alonso	1m15.084s
6	N Heidfeld	1m15.149s
7	G Fisichella	1m15.227s
8	H Kovalainen	1m15.272s
9	N Rosberg	1m15.331s
10	J Trulli	1m15.379s
11	R Schumacher	1m15.534s
12	J Button	1m15.584s
13	R Barrichello	1m15.761s
14	M Webber	1m15.806s
15	S Speed	1m16.049s
16	D Coulthard	No time

Best sectors – Practice		
Sec 1	K Räikkönen	21.955s
Sec 2	L Hamilton	28.510s
Sec 3	F Massa	24.136s

Speed trap – Practice		
1	N Rosberg	190.5mph
2	K Räikkönen	189.5mph
3	A Wurz	188.7mph

Best sectors – Qualifying		
Sec 1	F Massa	21.747s
Sec 2	L Hamilton	28.645s
Sec 3	K Räikkönen	24.164s

Speed trap – Qualifying		
1	N Rosberg	189.9mph
2	R Kubica	189.5mph
3	F Massa	189.0mph

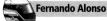

Fernando Alonso
"We knew it would be hard starting 10th with a fuel strategy for a top-three grid position. This meant that at the stops I was always ending up behind those I'd passed."

Giancarlo Fisichella
"I was able to keep Alonso behind me, so we are getting better. Ultimately, I lost one position. I had a small battle with Alonso early on, but he was much lighter."

Felipe Massa
"I was delayed by traffic in the decisive phase, when I had to build a lead over Kimi to stay ahead during the stops. When I had a clear track, I was quickest."

Jenson Button
"The car has improved a lot with the new package. It's nice to have a car which gives me confidence. Our race pace is improving, though we need to work on qualifying."

Nick Heidfeld
"Both Renaults went to the middle of the track, I tried to pass Fisichella on the right, but he moved over. The fight with Alonso was fun and useful for my result."

Ralf Schumacher
"On lap 1, when Jarno hit Kovalainen at the hairpin, I couldn't go anywhere and lost two places. I was a lot quicker than Barrichello but couldn't overtake."

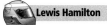

Lewis Hamilton
"I didn't have the best start, but my car was good in the opening stages, and I pushed to get past Kimi, but it didn't work out. We opted for a three-stop strategy."

Heikki Kovalainen
"I was in Turn 5 when Jarno spun me and punctured my right-rear tyre. I had to pit, lost nearly a lap and then it felt like I was slowing for blue flags almost every lap!"

Kimi Räikkönen
"It was vital I got past Hamilton and then I tried to stay with Felipe. I had a few laps in hand but, at my first pit stop, I hit traffic. At the second stop, I came out ahead."

Rubens Barrichello
"I was heavy for my opening stint and don't know if that hurt my tyres as I didn't have any pace. After that, the pace improved but it was too late to make any further progress."

Robert Kubica
"I made a good start, but we were on the dirty side with Hamilton. After that, I was close to him only when he exited the pits. The last 20 laps were about bringing it home."

Jarno Trulli
"The field was bunched on lap 1 and I misjudged it into the hairpin. I was not attacking, but I braked too late and hit Kovalainen. I am sorry for him as it spoiled his race."

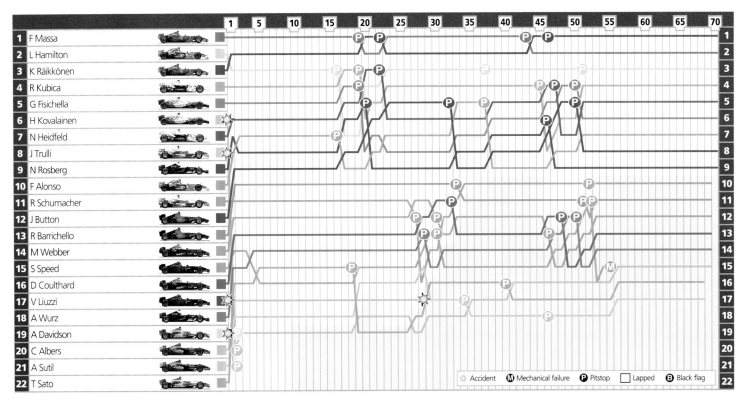

		1	5	10	15	20	25	30	35	40	45	50	55	60	65	70	
1	F Massa																1
2	L Hamilton																2
3	K Räikkönen																3
4	R Kubica																4
5	G Fisichella																5
6	H Kovalainen																6
7	N Heidfeld																7
8	J Trulli																8
9	N Rosberg																9
10	F Alonso																10
11	R Schumacher																11
12	J Button																12
13	R Barrichello																13
14	M Webber																14
15	S Speed																15
16	D Coulthard																16
17	V Liuzzi																17
18	A Wurz																18
19	A Davidson																19
20	C Albers																20
21	A Sutil																21
22	T Sato																22

☆ Accident ⓜ Mechanical failure ⓟ Pitstop ☐ Lapped ⓑ Black flag

QUALIFYING 3

	Driver	Time
1	F Massa	1m15.034s
2	L Hamilton	1m15.104s
3	K Räikkönen	1m15.257s
4	R Kubica	1m15.493s
5	G Fisichella	1m15.674s
6	H Kovalainen	1m15.826s
7	N Heidfeld	1m15.900s
8	J Trulli	1m15.935s
9	N Rosberg	1m16.328s
10	F Alonso	No time

GRID

	Driver	Time
1	F Massa	1m15.034s
2	L Hamilton	1m15.104s
3	K Räikkönen	1m15.257s
4	R Kubica	1m15.493s
5	G Fisichella	1m15.674s
6	H Kovalainen	1m15.826s
7	N Heidfeld	1m15.900s
8	J Trulli	1m15.935s
9	N Rosberg	1m16.328s
10	F Alonso	no time
11	R Schumacher	1m15.534s
12	J Button	1m15.584s
13	R Barrichello	1m15.761s
14	M Webber	1m15.806s
15	S Speed	1m16.049s
16	D Coulthard	no time
17	V Liuzzi	1m16.142s
18	A Wurz	1m16.241s
19	A Davidson	1m16.366s
20	C Albers	1m17.826s
21	A Sutil	1m17.915s
22*	T Sato	1m16.244s

* INCLUDING A 10-PLACE PENALTY FOR PASSING UNDER WAVED YELLOWS AT US GP

RACE

	Driver	Car	Laps	Time	Avg. mph	Fastest	Stops
1	K Räikkönen	Ferrari F2007	70	1h30m54.200s	126.586	1m16.207s	2
2	F Massa	Ferrari F2007	70	1h30m56.614s	126.531	1m16.099s	2
3	L Hamilton	McLaren-Mercedes MP4-22	70	1h31m26.353s	125.844	1m16.587s	3
4	R Kubica	BMW Sauber F1.07	70	1h31m35.927s	125.626	1m17.153s	2
5	N Heidfeld	BMW Sauber F1.07	70	1h31m43.001s	125.464	1m16.875s	2
6	G Fisichella	Renault R27	70	1h31m46.410s	125.386	1m16.703s	2
7	F Alonso	McLaren-Mercedes MP4-22	70	1h31m50.716s	125.288	1m16.495s	2
8	J Button	Honda RA107	70	1h31m53.085s	125.235	1m16.770s	2
9	N Rosberg	Williams-Toyota FW29	70	1h32m02.705s	125.016	1m17.011s	2
10	R Schumacher	Toyota TF107	69	1h30m59.199s	124.663	1m16.966s	2
11	R Barrichello	Honda RA107	69	1h31m21.223s	124.162	1m17.220s	2
12	M Webber	Red Bull-Renault RB3	69	1h31m23.346s	124.114	1m17.249s	2
13	D Coulthard	Red Bull-Renault RB3	69	1h31m27.577s	124.018	1m17.447s	2
14	A Wurz	Williams-Toyota FW29	69	1h31m32.392s	123.910	1m17.240s	2
15	H Kovalainen	Renault R27	69	1h31m55.762s	123.385	1m17.206s	2
16	T Sato	Super Aguri-Honda SA07	68	1h31m07.775s	122.662	1m17.796s	2
17	A Sutil	Spyker-Ferrari F8-VII	68	1h31m34.551s	122.064	1m18.091s	3
R	S Speed	Toro Rosso-Ferrari STR02	55	Gearbox	-	1m17.934s	2
R	C Albers	Spyker-Ferrari F8-VII	28	Fuel rig attached	-	1m18.955s	1
R	A Davidson	Super Aguri-Honda SA07	1	Crash damage	-	-	0
R	J Trulli	Toyota TF107	1	Crash damage	-	-	0
R	V Liuzzi	Toro Rosso-Ferrari STR02	0	Accident	-	-	0

CHAMPIONSHIP

	Driver	Pts
1	L Hamilton	64
2	F Alonso	50
3	F Massa	47
4	K Räikkönen	42
5	N Heidfeld	30
6	R Kubica	17
7	G Fisichella	16
8	H Kovalainen	12
9	A Wurz	8
10	J Trulli	7
11	N Rosberg	5
12	D Coulthard	4
13	T Sato	4
14	M Webber	2
15	R Schumacher	2
16	J Button	1
	S Vettel	1

Fastest Lap
F Massa 1m16.099s
(129.661mph) on lap 42

Fastest speed trap
N Rosberg 190.6mph
Slowest speed trap
A Davidson 124.5mph

Fastest pit stop
1	H Kovalainen	22.684s
2	R Schumacher	22.783s
3	L Hamilton	22.788s

Constructor

	Constructor	Pts
1	McLaren-Mercedes	114
2	Ferrari	89
3	BMW Sauber	48
4	Renault	28
5	Williams-Toyota	13
6	Toyota	9
7	Red Bull-Renault	6
8	Super Aguri-Honda	4
9	Honda	1

David Coulthard
"With my longer strategy, I should have been able to pass some people, but I'm not sure if my in-laps weren't fast enough, or the stops, but I didn't gain any advantage."

Nico Rosberg
"Button was slightly faster, so he finished ahead of me and took the point. It's a shame for everyone to leave with no reward. We need to start scoring consistently."

Vitantonio Liuzzi
"My race didn't last long. Someone, probably Davidson, hit me, and that spun me after which we hit again. It's a shame, as we had a strategy that could have paid off."

Christijan Albers
"Thankfully, nobody was hurt. I made a mistake in the pits, I thought the lollipop was going up. It was chaotic as Adrian had just been in, and I just drove away."

Takuma Sato
"I could not get a proper start. The first stint was OK, but we lost time during my first stop with another fuel-rig problem. In the end, I just fought to finish my race."

Mark Webber
"I got to Turn 5 and had to go between Ralf and Rubens and nearly lost my wing. We tried to go shorter in the second stint to jump Rubens, but it didn't work out."

Alexander Wurz
"Fourteenth is not what I wanted. The only problem was traffic. I was stuck in the train behind Coulthard and neither our strategy, nor our pace, allowed us to get past him."

Scott Speed
"I had a lot of graining on my fronts, as our front wing setting was not the best. This made the first 15 laps hard, after which it improved. I had no warning about the gearbox failure."

Adrian Sutil
"We had an electrical problem and I changed to the T-car. Then I got a drive-through penalty for exceeding the pitlane speed limit. In the end, we were just not fast enough."

Anthony Davidson
"Into Turn 1, the cars in front of me braked early. Wurz went inside Liuzzi, which made him brake heavily, causing a chain reaction. I locked up and spun Liuzzi round."

2007 FORMULA 1™ SANTANDER BRITISH GRAND PRIX
SILVERSTONE

HAMILTON AT HOME

With a sense of drama, Hamilton snatched pole position, but there was to be no fairytale home debut as he fell to third in the race behind Räikkönen and Alonso

The British GP was one of the best races of 2007 in terms of the sheer intensity of the competition. It also caught us out a little as, while most of the paddock spent the weekend distracted by the controversy involving Nigel Stepney and Mike Coughlan, the real story was about tyres.

Among those who ran the full distance, no fewer than five different permutations of hards and mediums were used as everyone sought the best way of juggling around the tyre that suited their car most with the need to use, at some point, the one that didn't.

Just as McLaren gained the upper hand with the supersofts in Monaco and Montréal, so Ferrari was on top of the game at Silverstone. Kimi Räikkönen followed up his win in France with a second success, indicating that he was still very much a championship contender.

Silverstone was the first track since Barcelona at which the teams had enjoyed a chance to test their race tyres at a race venue (bar Honda and Super Aguri, who went to Jerez). The place is notorious for its fickle weather, though, and strong winds and overcast conditions made it hard to get a real handle on the tyres on Friday. It was warmer on Saturday, but even McLaren had doubts about exactly which way to jump for qualifying...

In the end, everyone used the option medium
tyre in Q3. It was a great qualifying session, and
Lewis Hamilton fulfilled the expectations of the extra
thousands of fans who had turned out to see him
with a brilliant pole lap. Not for the first time this year,
Fernando Alonso had been quicker throughout the day,
only to lose out when it really mattered. After Hamilton
was bumped down to second and the dirty side of the
track at Magny-Cours, with disastrous results, there was
a concerted effort to get a McLaren on pole at all costs.

Hamilton had a weight advantage over his rivals, but
the team was also well aware that he was not entirely
happy with the balance of the car, and had a different
set-up at the rear to Alonso. Given the commitment
required to go fast at Silverstone, McLaren had no
doubts that Hamilton's had been a great lap.

The tyre question continued into the race. Unusually,
McLaren and Ferrari made different choices. All the top
runners had saved a set of the medium tyres, and Ferrari
chose to put them on at the start of the race, while
McLaren went for new hard tyres.

Disastrously, Felipe Massa stalled at the first time
of asking on the grid, changing the complexion of
the race. The reason remained unknown as of Sunday
night, but the driver was exonerated.

"His procedure was perfect, he did absolutely
nothing wrong," said Massa's engineer Rob Smedley.
"He did absolutely the standard procedure, and then he
informed us on the radio that he had a problem and the
engine had stopped. We don't know where it's come
from, whether it's engine electronics. We've no idea."

The cause was traced to a 'combustion problem',
and a very expensive one at that. It also robbed us of a
key player, as he would have to start from the rear of
the grid instead of from fourth. As at many other races
this year, one of the big-four names was out of the
picture from the early stages.

Hamilton made full use of his pole position to hold
off Räikkönen into Copse, although it took a little
ducking and diving to keep the Finn behind. However,
it didn't take long for us to realise that this was going
to be a tough race for Hamilton, as Räikkönen stayed
glued to the back of the McLaren's rear wing. Indeed,
he was close enough on lap 14 to have a cheeky look
down the inside at Priory. It didn't work and the Finn
lost a little bit of ground, but his chance to take the lead
came two laps later, when Hamilton came into the pits
– by coincidence the same lap on which both McLarens
stopped in France.

It was then that things began to go awry for

TALKING POINT
SPYING SCANDAL ROCKS McLAREN

It's British Grand Prix week. Sitting atop the drivers' and constructors' championships with Lewis Hamilton heading for his first home grand prix, McLaren knew they would be under the media spotlight. But they couldn't quite have imagined how it would turn out...

For some weeks, Ferrari's Nigel Stepney had been in the news. He'd wanted to be Technical Director when Ross Brawn went on his sabbatical. He didn't approve of Mario Almondo. He'd told Ferrari boss Jean Todt that he didn't want to travel anymore. It hadn't been well received. After openly saying he would consider offers from other teams, Stepney had been accused of sabotaging the Ferraris ahead of the Monaco GP, when white powder was supposedly found in the vicinity of the fuel tank. Something didn't feel quite right.

On the eve of a Barcelona test in late April, Stepney was spotted having dinner with McLaren Chief Designer Mike Coughlan, an old buddy from their days at John Barnard's FDD concern. Suspicious? Maybe, and maybe not.

Suddenly, Ferrari was in a British court of law demanding a warrant to search Coughlan's house. They allegedly found computer discs and 780 pages of documentation relating to the Ferrari F2007. Ferrari dismissed Stepney on the Tuesday before the British GP and McLaren suspended Coughlan on the very same day.

On the surface, it looked bad for McLaren: as if they had breached the international sporting code the penalty could range from a reprimand to exclusion from the championship.

Amid Lewismania, Bernie Ecclestone said that even if McLaren was punished, there was no possibility of Hamilton losing points. No, said Max Mosley, that was incorrect. There would be an FIA investigation and it was very rare indeed that a penalty for a team was different from a penalty for a driver.

Ron Dennis, a man who places great importance on integrity and loyalty, was launching McLaren's palatial new hospitality building, 'The Brand Centre' in the paddock. Highly emotional, he was having trouble getting the words out. He couldn't say too much but McLaren, everyone would see, would be vindicated.

Enter Honda Racing's Nick Fry, who admitted meeting Stepney and Coughlan on 1 June as they explored 'job opportunities'. Now it started to make sense but, insisted Fry, no confidential information had been offered or received.

Coughlan, it seemed, was following his own agenda and McLaren, by dint of being responsible for its employees, was unwittingly involved. How had Ferrari found out? Allegedly via a tip-off from a Lightwater copy shop where Trudy Coughlan had gone with the documents. You couldn't make it up...

Hamilton, and he made the first obvious race mistake of his rookie year. He attempted to leave the pits prematurely when distracted by a lollipop man turning the board over, but he did a rather better job of checking himself than Christijan Albers had in France.

"Eagerness," said McLaren Chief Operating Officer Martin Whitmarsh. "Lewis is an uncomplicated fellow. At that point, he was quite keen to get back out into the fray, crept forward a couple of times on the clutch and it made it quite hard for the crew. I think the crew did a great job to hang on in there in that situation. The refuelling apparatus is difficult enough to unplug from a car when you're pulling it normal to the plane of the car, but they managed to get it off at an angle, so no harm done."

However, precious fractions slipped away just as Räikkönen was enjoying running in clean air and was banging in a couple of quick laps. On lap 17, the only complete lap he ran after Hamilton's stop and before his own, he did a 1m20.638s, a full second faster than anything he'd done when behind Hamilton's McLaren. In contrast, Hamilton lost pace when he returned to the track, heavy with fuel and still equipped with the harder prime tyre.

INSIDE LINE
KIMI RÄIKKÖNEN
FERRARI DRIVER

"I was disappointed not to be on pole position for the British GP because I made a mistake exiting the last corner. I ran a bit wide onto the grass and lost traction. The sand was flying everywhere.

There was definitely enough speed for pole. I wasn't happy with myself because I knew how competitive this year is and that it could have damaged our race.

I was expecting to be quick in the race and I really thought we could start from pole. Happily, we recovered from it and won, but for sure I made life more difficult than it needed to be.

The car was actually really good all weekend and at the start of the race I was just trying to save some fuel and look after my tyres and the car. Once Lewis pitted, I tried to push and gain some time on him, and that went well. But then Fernando did a very short stop and came out of the pits in front of me.

We knew that we were going to run longer in the second stint, and so I just pushed as hard as I could when he came in and it was enough. After that, it was pretty easy.

People have mentioned tyres graining when you try to follow another car closely, but I didn't experience that today at all, not even on the second set of tyres.

The tyres worked very well, including the last set – the harder (prime) tyre – which was very good but, by then, I wasn't pushing. Even driving well within myself, it seemed to give a good lap time. The gap to Fernando came down at the end, but I was just conserving the car and didn't push at all for the last 10 laps.

These two wins in a row – at Magny-Cours then Silverstone – are important. We gained some points on Lewis and Fernando for the drivers' championship and even if we didn't make up any ground in the constructors' championship, the result is significant.

We seem to have got the car a bit better suited to me now and everything seems to be a bit easier than it was earlier in the season. The car definitely feels better now than in the first few races, but I think it's still a long season. Right now, it's looking good, but everything can change again at the next race, so we just need to keep on pushing."

Räikkönen's pit stop went without any problems. Intriguingly, he spent 26.975s in the pitlane, while for Hamilton the figure was 26.140s, including the mishap. The difference was that Hamilton had taken on fuel to run 20 more laps and, aware that they now had the advantage, Ferrari fuelled Räikkönen to run 25 laps. He took on another set of the preferred medium tyres, although now the team only had scrubbed qualifying sets left for later in the race.

Ferrari's satisfaction at getting Räikkönen ahead of Hamilton was short-lived, because Alonso was still going. He did two further laps before coming in on lap 20, and again the value of those empty-tank laps was shown as he sneaked ahead of the Ferrari man to become the third leader of the race. To ensure he would hit the front, though, the team had short-fuelled him for just 17 laps. The team also chose to use this short stint for the compulsory run on the medium tyre.

It didn't really work out and, despite being lighter, Alonso could not pull out enough of an advantage to stay ahead to the finish and, as ever, traffic didn't help his progress. The main problem was that the medium tyre was not ideal.

"We could have used it then, or we could have used it at the end of the race," said Whitmarsh. "It was during that critical stage that we took a decision, we took a gamble. It was a much more teasing decision than we've had in other races."

Hamilton had stayed on the harder tyre for the middle stint, and he started to go backwards. "With the set-up, he was giving the rear tyres a reasonably hard time and it was a great job on his part to be able to live with that through the weekend," said Whitmarsh.

Despite running with a heavier fuel load that was in effect worth 0.4–0.5s a lap, Räikkönen stayed in touch with Alonso. For much of the time, the margin was a little over 4s, although it went up to 5.5s on the lap before Alonso came in for his second pit stop, because Räikkönen had to pass David Coulthard.

Then the Ferrari man reaped the benefits of that extra fuel when he had fully six laps on near-empty tanks with which to jump Alonso, and this he did with ease. His last three laps were especially quick and, of course, he didn't have to take on as much fuel as Alonso had, so he was stationary for less time. Traffic didn't help the Spaniard's cause, but it was always going to be difficult.

"This race was a race to that second pit stop," said Whitmarsh. "By then, Kimi had a 2.5s gap, and after

OPPOSITE Alex Wurz's Williams meets Scott Speed's Toro Rosso, putting the American out of the race with broken front suspension

BELOW Kimi Räikkönen hunted down the McLarens with great skill for his second win in succession

ABOVE The spotlight shone on
Lewis Hamilton all meeting, but his
legions of fans would have to make
do with a distant third place

that it was very difficult to change the race outcome."

Räikkönen had made his compulsory move to
the hard tyre, but any loss of performance for the
remaining 16 laps was incidental, because he was in
front and there was nothing Alonso could do about it.

"The mediums were absolutely fine to be honest,"
said Smedley. "They gave you a little bit less understeer
in the first couple of laps, because you don't have
graining, and they're absolutely fine."

The gap drifted out to as much as 7.7s, before
closing up right at the end when Räikkönen began to
coast. Not surprisingly, he had a big grin on his face on
the podium, one that even the sight of a rather cheap-
looking trophy could not remove.

In that third stint, Hamilton dropped off the radar to
finish 39s down on the winner, but all that mattered at
the finish was collecting another helping of points.

Massa had been caught out by heavy traffic in
the French GP and, thanks to that stall at the start,
he never had a chance at Silverstone. He made the
most of a super-quick car and his own commitment,
however, and his charge up to fifth – stopped only
by a determined Robert Kubica – was quite an
achievement. He could well have won both these
races, and the points differential to the McLaren

drivers would have looked rather different.

"It was a shame, as the car was fantastic," Massa
said as he walked from *parc fermé*. "The car was flying
all race. It was a shame to lose the engine at the start.
I had a great car to fight for a good position and I had a
great strategy as well. It's a shame because today was a
great race, but it was supposed to be even better."

His engineer had no doubt that his man had done
his best: "Felipe drove bloody fantastic to be honest,"
said Smedley in his typical forthright way, "and you can
quote me on that! He was passing car after car. When
he came out of the second stop he was obviously a lot
heavier, he gave away a second on the fuel to Fisichella.
But he then just couldn't get past, because that car was
a lot closer to his car in terms of performance. As you
saw in the first stint, though, Felipe passed car after
car after car."

Nick Heidfeld was not far behind Massa's Ferrari in
sixth, while Heikki Kovalainen and Giancarlo Fisichella
completed the points scorers for Renault. Rubens
Barrichello and Jenson Button finished ninth and 10th
for Honda after one of the more respectable showings
for the team to this point in the season, to the extent
that it was only the lack of attrition among the top four
teams that kept them out of the points.

SNAPSHOT FROM
BRITAIN

CLOCKWISE FROM RIGHT The Red Arrows put on their usual, stunning display; Posh and Becks also drew attention; to raise money for the Wings for Life Foundation, each Red Bull race car was covered with the portraits of 30,000 donors; Jenson Button receives the Hawthorn Trophy from the MSA's Colin Hilton; Nigel Mansell burns rubber as he puts a BMW Sauber F1.06 through its paces in BMW's Pit Lane park; race marshals and cutting-edge style continue to be at opposite ends of the spectrum; actress Gemma Atkinson was the face of the British GP, apart from Lewis that is...

WEEKEND NEWS

■ The arrival of David and Victoria Beckham caused mayhem in the Silverstone paddock on Sunday morning. The pair were guests of Honda, which was no surprise as they are managed by Simon Fuller, whose 19 concern doubles as a marketing consultant to the team. The pair enjoyed lunch with team boss Nick Fry then a head-turning grid walk.

■ Jenson Button suffered the recurrence of a back problem on Friday morning, and was advised to sit out the afternoon session in order to receive treatment. This year's rules allow for the use of replacement drivers on Friday, so Honda Racing's test driver Christian Klien had an unexpected opportunity to take part in the session.

■ The most dramatic news during a summer round of personnel swapping was that former BAR and Honda Racing Technical Director Geoff Willis had joined Red Bull Racing to perform a similar role alongside Adrian Newey. Meanwhile, Honda re-hired BMW chief designer Jorg Zander.

■ Immediately after the British GP, Spyker confirmed that its association with Christijan Albers had come to a premature end. The Dutch driver had been outpaced by Adrian Sutil and embarrassed by his error in the pits during the French GP but, as ever, what really mattered was a major shortfall in the sponsorship dollars he was due to be bringing.

■ A few days after the British GP, the Indianapolis Motor Speedway confirmed that there would be no United States GP in 2008, after failing to come to an agreement with Bernie Ecclestone. Despite landing a MotoGP event, the IMS insisted that the door was still open for F1 for 2009 and beyond.

RACE RESULTS
GREAT BRITAIN SILVERSTONE

Official Results © [2007]
Formula One Administration Limited,
6 Princes Gate, London, SW7 1QJ.
No reproduction without permission.
All copyright and database rights reserved.

RACE DATE July 8th
CIRCUIT LENGTH 3.194 miles
NO. OF LAPS 59
RACE DISTANCE 188.446 miles
WEATHER Sunny and dry, 20°C
TRACK TEMP 32°C
RACE DAY ATTENDANCE 85,000
LAP RECORD Michael Schumacher, 1m18.739s, 146.052mph, 2004

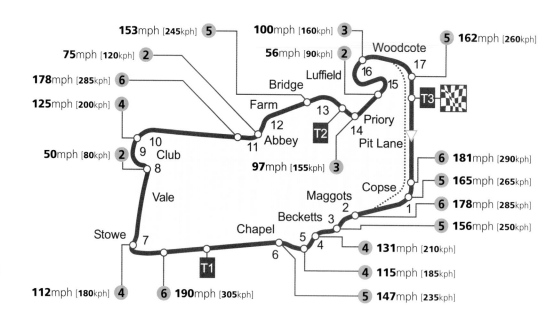

PRACTICE 1

	Driver	Time	Laps
1	L Hamilton	1m21.100s	24
2	K Räikkönen	1m21.211s	26
3	F Massa	1m21.285s	26
4	F Alonso	1m21.675s	21
5	N Rosberg	1m22.006s	24
6	R Kubica	1m22.107s	25
7	N Heidfeld	1m22.176s	13
8	A Wurz	1m22.216s	23
9	R Schumacher	1m22.878s	21
10	R Barrichello	1m22.956s	27
11	J Trulli	1m23.030s	26
12	A Davidson	1m23.037s	24
13	H Kovalainen	1m23.099s	25
14	G Fisichella	1m23.179s	21
15	J Button	1m23.517s	17
16	T Sato	1m23.548s	18
17	M Webber	1m23.564s	21
18	D Coulthard	1m23.618s	15
19	S Speed	1m23.854s	20
20	A Sutil	1m23.954s	25
21	V Liuzzi	1m24.154s	23
22	C Albers	1m24.172s	30

PRACTICE 2

	Driver	Time	Laps
1	K Räikkönen	1m20.639s	35
2	F Massa	1m21.138s	30
3	R Schumacher	1m21.381s	34
4	L Hamilton	1m21.381s	39
5	J Trulli	1m21.467s	35
6	F Alonso	1m21.616s	35
7	N Rosberg	1m21.619s	40
8	A Wurz	1m21.650s	37
9	M Webber	1m22.137s	31
10	A Davidson	1m22.143s	40
11	H Kovalainen	1m22.189s	42
12	G Fisichella	1m22.257s	39
13	R Kubica	1m22.372s	41
14	D Coulthard	1m22.428s	23
15	N Heidfeld	1m22.486s	34
16	T Sato	1m22.487s	38
17	R Barrichello	1m22.511s	39
18	C Klien	1m22.833s	45
19	S Speed	1m22.840s	42
20	V Liuzzi	1m23.105s	35
21	C Albers	1m23.113s	35
22	A Sutil	1m23.720s	30

PRACTICE 3

	Driver	Time	Laps
1	K Räikkönen	1m19.751s	17
2	F Alonso	1m19.920s	12
3	F Massa	1m19.969s	17
4	L Hamilton	1m20.344s	12
5	N Rosberg	1m20.666s	17
6	R Schumacher	1m20.770s	21
7	V Liuzzi	1m20.876s	21
8	H Kovalainen	1m20.882s	17
9	N Heidfeld	1m20.882s	19
10	A Davidson	1m20.915s	23
11	G Fisichella	1m20.983s	19
12	M Webber	1m21.002s	16
13	S Speed	1m21.039s	19
14	R Barrichello	1m21.140s	22
15	A Wurz	1m21.148s	17
16	R Kubica	1m21.156s	17
17	J Trulli	1m21.321s	18
18	D Coulthard	1m21.343s	16
19	J Button	1m21.583s	24
20	T Sato	1m21.745s	23
21	C Albers	1m22.101s	23
22	A Sutil	1m22.180s	24

QUALIFYING 1

	Driver	Time
1	F Alonso	1m19.330s
2	K Räikkönen	1m19.753s
3	F Massa	1m19.790s
4	L Hamilton	1m19.885s
5	R Kubica	1m20.294s
6	R Schumacher	1m20.513s
7	N Heidfeld	1m20.534s
8	H Kovalainen	1m20.570s
9	M Webber	1m20.583s
10	A Wurz	1m20.830s
11	S Speed	1m20.834s
12	G Fisichella	1m20.842s
13	J Trulli	1m21.150s
14	D Coulthard	1m21.154s
15	V Liuzzi	1m21.160s
16	R Barrichello	1m21.169s
17	N Rosberg	1m21.219s
18	J Button	1m21.335s
19	A Davidson	1m21.448s
20	A Sutil	1m22.019s
21	T Sato	1m22.045s
22	C Albers	1m22.589s

QUALIFYING 2

	Driver	Time
1	F Alonso	1m19.152s
2	K Räikkönen	1m19.252s
3	L Hamilton	1m19.400s
4	F Massa	1m19.421s
5	R Schumacher	1m19.860s
6	G Fisichella	1m20.042s
7	R Kubica	1m20.054s
8	H Kovalainen	1m20.077s
9	J Trulli	1m20.133s
10	N Heidfeld	1m20.178s
11	M Webber	1m20.235s
12	D Coulthard	1m20.329s
13	A Wurz	1m20.350s
14	R Barrichello	1m20.364s
15	S Speed	1m20.515s
16	V Liuzzi	1m20.823s

Best sectors – Practice
Sec 1	K Räikkönen	25.473s
Sec 2	F Alonso	34.174s
Sec 3	K Räikkönen	19.983s

Speed trap – Practice
1	K Räikkönen	185.9mph
2	F Alonso	185.4mph
	L Hamilton	185.4mph

Best sectors – Qualifying
Sec 1	F Alonso	25.298s
Sec 2	K Räikkönen	33.890s
Sec 3	F Alonso	19.697s

Speed trap – Qualifying
1	F Alonso	185.4mph
2	K Räikkönen	185.2mph
3	V Liuzzi	184.9mph

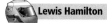 **Fernando Alonso**
"We decided to change during the race to a shorter fuel stop for the middle stint, hoping we'd be able to keep the lead, but we didn't build enough of a gap to Kimi."

 **Giancarlo Fisichella**
"I got Ralf at the start, then Nick passed me at Copse, but I passed him before Stowe. We put on the soft tyres for the last stint and the car felt like it had much less grip."

 **Felipe Massa**
"It could have been very different without the engine dying at the start. In the final stint, I quickly caught Kubica, but I was losing downforce in his slipstream."

 **Jenson Button**
"It was good to finish 10th from 18th. The one-stop strategy paid off, but I didn't get the best out of the car this weekend as I struggled with rear grip and had understeer."

 **Nick Heidfeld**
"I passed Giancarlo at Copse. Later he caught me on the Hangar Straight. I knew that Massa would have his second stop later than mine, but I couldn't stay in front."

 Ralf Schumacher
"We retired when I had a problem with the front-left wheel. I felt the failure as I came into the complex and had to retire. It is a pity, as we were confident of a good result."

Lewis Hamilton
"I made a mistake in the pit stop. Although I was more consistent later on, the team chose to save the engine. Starting with the hard tyre was not the way to go."

Heikki Kovalainen
"I managed to pass Ralf, which meant I was in fifth place after Massa stalled on the grid, but the rear tyre performance began to drop and I was really struggling."

Kimi Räikkönen
"If I had started from pole, things would have been easier. In the first stint, I looked after my tyres and saved fuel. I got close to Lewis, but didn't want to take any risks."

Rubens Barrichello
"I had one of my best Silverstone races, but it wasn't enough. Our one-stop strategy worked well for both of us, so it was a shame that we could not score any points."

Robert Kubica
"I found myself in front of Massa, but this wasn't as easy as in Magny-Cours as I had to keep him behind me for the final 13 laps. I just had to control the situation."

Jarno Trulli
"I struggled with tyre wear, so I was expecting a tough race, but it turned out even worse. The team brought me in as there was something we must investigate."

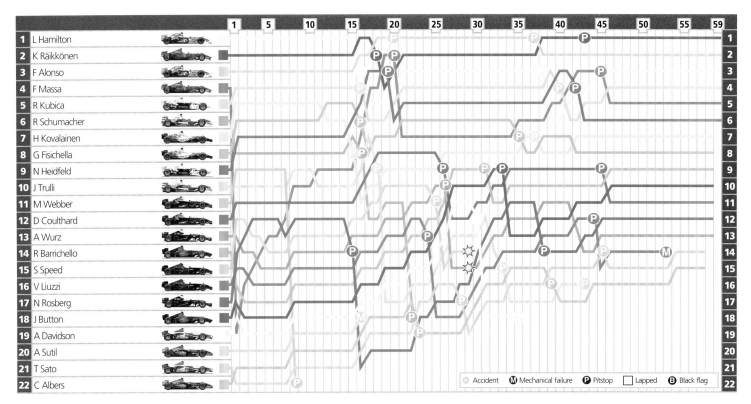

Lap-by-lap positions chart (laps 1–59):

Pos	Driver
1	L Hamilton
2	K Räikkönen
3	F Alonso
4	F Massa
5	R Kubica
6	R Schumacher
7	H Kovalainen
8	G Fisichella
9	N Heidfeld
10	J Trulli
11	M Webber
12	D Coulthard
13	A Wurz
14	R Barrichello
15	S Speed
16	V Liuzzi
17	N Rosberg
18	J Button
19	A Davidson
20	A Sutil
21	T Sato
22	C Albers

Legend: ✧ Accident Ⓜ Mechanical failure Ⓟ Pitstop ☐ Lapped Ⓑ Black flag

QUALIFYING 3

	Driver	Time
1	L Hamilton	1m19.997s
2	K Räikkönen	1m20.099s
3	F Alonso	1m20.147s
4	F Massa	1m20.265s
5	R Kubica	1m20.401s
6	R Schumacher	1m20.516s
7	H Kovalainen	1m20.721s
8	G Fisichella	1m20.775s
9	N Heidfeld	1m20.894s
10	J Trulli	1m21.240s

GRID

	Driver	Time
1	L Hamilton	1m19.997s
2	K Räikkönen	1m20.099s
3	F Alonso	1m20.147s
4	F Massa	1m20.265s
5	R Kubica	1m20.401s
6	R Schumacher	1m20.516s
7	H Kovalainen	1m20.721s
8	G Fisichella	1m20.775s
9	N Heidfeld	1m20.894s
10	J Trulli	1m21.240s
11	M Webber	1m20.235s
12	D Coulthard	1m20.329s
13	A Wurz	1m20.350s
14	R Barrichello	1m20.364s
15	S Speed	1m20.515s
16	V Liuzzi	1m20.823s
17	N Rosberg	1m21.219s
18	J Button	1m21.335s
19	A Davidson	1m21.448s
20	A Sutil	1m22.019s
21	C Albers	1m22.589s
22*	T Sato	1m22.045s

* SENT TO REAR FOR TAKING NEW CHASSIS

RACE

	Driver	Car	Laps	Time	Avg. mph	Fastest	Stops
1	K Räikkönen	Ferrari F2007	59	1h21m43.074s	138.364	1m20.638s	2
2	F Alonso	McLaren-Mercedes MP4-22	59	1h21m45.533s	138.295	1m21.117s	2
3	L Hamilton	McLaren-Mercedes MP4-22	59	1h22m22.447s	137.262	1m21.675s	2
4	R Kubica	BMW Sauber F1.07	59	1h22m36.393s	136.875	1m22.105s	2
5	F Massa	Ferrari F2007	59	1h22m37.137s	136.855	1m20.858s	2
6	N Heidfeld	BMW Sauber F1.07	59	1h22m39.410s	136.792	1m21.991s	2
7	H Kovalainen	Renault R27	58	1h21m47.621s	135.892	1m22.552s	2
8	G Fisichella	Renault R27	58	1h21m52.361s	135.761	1m22.136s	2
9	R Barrichello	Honda RA107	58	1h22m21.373s	134.964	1m23.387s	1
10	J Button	Honda RA107	58	1h22m27.851s	134.787	1m23.581s	1
11	D Coulthard	Red Bull-Renault RB3	58	1h22m28.494s	134.770	1m23.118s	2
12	N Rosberg	Williams-Toyota FW29	58	1h22m29.770s	134.735	1m22.896s	2
13	A Wurz	Williams-Toyota FW29	58	1h22m34.656s	134.602	1m22.693s	2
14	T Sato	Super Aguri-Honda SA07	57	1h21m57.702s	134.025	1m23.413s	2
15	C Albers	Spyker-Ferrari F8-VII	57	1h22m16.191s	132.776	1m24.390s	2
16	V Liuzzi	Toro Rosso-Ferrari STR02	53	Gearbox	133.819	1m23.628s	2
R	J Trulli	Toyota TF107	43	Handling	-	1m23.708s	2
R	A Davidson	Super Aguri-Honda SA07	35	Handling	-	1m24.144s	1
R	S Speed	Toro Rosso-Ferrari STR02	29	Accident	-	1m23.570s	1
R	R Schumacher	Toyota TF107	22	Handling	-	1m22.510s	1
R	A Sutil	Spyker-Ferrari F8-VII	16	Engine	-	1m25.015s	0
R	M Webber	Red Bull-Renault RB3	8	Hydraulics	-	1m23.767s	0

CHAMPIONSHIP

	Driver	Pts
1	L Hamilton	70
2	F Alonso	58
3	K Räikkönen	52
4	F Massa	51
5	N Heidfeld	33
6	R Kubica	22
7	G Fisichella	17
8	H Kovalainen	14
9	A Wurz	8
10	J Trulli	7
11	N Rosberg	5
12	D Coulthard	4
13	T Sato	4
14	M Webber	2
15	R Schumacher	2
16	J Button	1
	S Vettel	1

Fastest Lap
K Räikkönen 1m20.638s
(142.548mph) on lap 17

Fastest speed trap
F Alonso 186.3mph
Slowest speed trap
A Sutil 177.2mph

Fastest pit stop
1	F Alonso	24.065s
2	K Räikkönen	24.181s
3	F Massa	24.454s

Constructor Pts
	Constructor	Pts
1	McLaren-Mercedes	128
2	Ferrari	103
3	BMW Sauber	56
4	Renault	31
5	Williams-Toyota	13
6	Toyota	9
7	Red Bull-Renault	6
8	Super Aguri-Honda	4
9	Honda	1

David Coulthard
"I didn't drive very well. I made a few mistakes in the second stint and lost time. The car was tricky to drive, it had a lot of oversteer and the balance just wasn't there."

Nico Rosberg
"I managed to pass a few people, became stuck behind Coulthard and tried to pass him. He went wide and pushed me onto the grass. I didn't get another chance."

Vitantonio Liuzzi
"Yet another retirement, this time gearbox. I had problems from lap 15 as something got stuck between my back and my seat, so it was uncomfortable to drive."

Christijan Albers
"I enjoyed the race, as we could stay with the field, although it was a shame that in the end I lost the position to Sato. But I had a good race and am happy to finish."

Takuma Sato
"I changed to the T-car and had understeer, losing time until my first stop when we were able to adjust the front flap. Once I was clear of traffic, I was able to push."

Mark Webber
"My engineer told me to switch to a different gearbox map, but as I came into Becketts I had no power steering, then no hydraulics meant no throttle, steering or gearbox."

Alexander Wurz
"Around lap 30, I used the opportunity of blue flags to out-brake Speed, but after I went through, he hit my rear wheel. His race was over, but I continued."

Scott Speed
"The leaders were behind, but Alex wasn't letting them by. I knew that me, Alex and Trulli were close, so I let Fernando by. Then Alex made an optimistic move, but he ran into me."

Adrian Sutil
"It's frustrating that I could do only 17 laps before I had an engine problem. Everybody struggled in the first laps as the tyres had cooled from the second formation lap."

Anthony Davidson
"I had a good fight with Jenson when he got me back at Club. I kept in touch for 15 laps, and then started feeling that the car was touching at the rear."

2007 FORMULA 1™
GRAND PRIX OF EUROPE
NÜRBURGRING

HIGH AND A LOW

McLaren had a mixed weekend, ranging from Lewis Hamilton's accident to Fernando Alonso battling past Felipe Massa with four laps to go to take victory

Fernando Alonso and McLaren secured a superb team victory after an extraordinary wet race at the Nürburgring. While a defeated Felipe Massa at least came away with eight points, a retirement for Kimi Räikkönen made it a depressing afternoon for Ferrari.

The downside for the boys in silver was that Lewis Hamilton's unprecedented run of podium finishes finally came to an end – and yet, it didn't have to. In the early stages of the race, Hamilton survived a collision, puncture and trip into a gravel trap, and yet despite being lapped by the leader, he still had an opportunity to earn what ultimately could have been third place. Alas, McLaren made a strange strategy call that didn't work out, and he ended his dramatic afternoon without a point to his name, in ninth.

Hamilton's weekend began to go awry when he went off in final qualifying after a mechanical failure. McLaren rebuilt his car around a different tub, rather than just take the spare car that was ready and available, thus ensuring that he could start from the 10th grid position that he had earned.

It was quite a task for the crew to take a fourth 'reserve' chassis out of the truck, build it up, and equip it with the engine and gearbox from the crashed

coming down, he had dealt with Ralf Schumacher, Jarno Trulli, Heikki Kovalainen and Mark Webber. Then he clipped the rear of the spinning Kubica, and in an instant the McLaren's left-rear tyre went down. Hamilton held fourth position for a few seconds, but he was helpless as the field streamed past him.

Then luck swung Hamilton's way as, by the end of the lap, it was clear that wet tyres were necessary, and most of the field came into the pits to have them fitted. Leader Räikkönen didn't make it, slithering wide as he tried to come in and ending up back out on the track, so he was committed to another lap on dries, while several others plumped for a second lap and came to regret it.

Hamilton at least had a chance to change the punctured tyre at a time when everyone else had to stop too. Despite having to service Alonso first, McLaren did a better job than some other teams that were faced with having both of their cars in at the same time. Incredibly, the lead passed to none other than Markus Winkelhock, making his Formula One debut for Spyker and the only man to pit for wets at the end of the formation lap. This really was a strange one...

At the end of lap two, those who had not stopped the first time (either by design, or accident in the case of Räikkönen) had no choice but to come in after a treacherous extra tour. Hamilton charged across the line already in eighth place. From having a puncture just a couple of minutes earlier, that wasn't too bad a recovery.

Then it all went wrong as he hit a wall of water that had fallen suddenly on the approach to Turn 1, and went sailing straight on into the gravel trap.

Somehow, most of the front-runners had slithered through safely, but Jenson Button was already there, and Nico Rosberg, Adrian Sutil, Scott Speed and Vitantonio Liuzzi would soon join them as chaos ensued.

A safety car had been called for even before the Italian went off, and it was waiting at Turn 1. It was only the quick thinking of driver Bernd Maylander that

ABOVE Lewis Hamilton is taken away for a check-up after his 150mph accident in qualifying

OPPOSITE Carnage at Turn 1; Liuzzi gets too close to a tractor; Hamilton has the good fortune to be craned out of the gravel trap

BELOW Markus Winkelhock leads on his F1 debut, keeping his Spyker ahead of Massa, Alonso, Webber, Coulthard, Kovalainen et al

machine. After all that effort, it was just as well that Hamilton himself was passed fit to race.

Räikkönen had taken pole position ahead of Alonso, Massa and the BMW Saubers of Nick Heidfeld and Robert Kubica, but everyone was uneasy before the race, as rain had been threatening and there were already spots on the formation lap. Räikkönen duly led away, while behind there was confusion as Heidfeld ran into team-mate Kubica going into the second corner, pitching both cars into spins.

The incident was also to affect Hamilton. He had rocketed off the line away from his 10th grid position. By the exit of the first turn, and with the rain already

TALKING POINT
MAKING HIS FATHER PROUD

Manfred Winkelhock was always a popular man with German motorsport fans. He loved racing, but never really harboured ambitions to be a professional racing driver. Indeed, Manfred only started to compete after being urged in that direction by friends who were scared out of their wits as his passengers!

Manfred was never a political fellow and he never cared too much what he drove, displaying his skills in Formula One, sports cars and saloons. It was actually in cars with a roof, on the awesome Nürburgring Nordschleife, that he came to be so loved by the fans.

In 1985, Manfred raced in the German GP, held for the first time on the 'new' Nürburgring, a circuit that was a poor replacement for its predecessor. A few days later, he headed off for a sports-car race at Mosport Park, wherehe crashed heavily at the notorious Turn 2 and succumbed to his injuries. At the time, his young son Markus was just five.

Every so often, motor racing throws up a story so romantic that it is barely credible. At the Nürburgring in 2007, while the eyes of the world were on the post-race spat between Fernando Alonso and Felipe Massa, who had made contact disputing the 10 points for victory, a misty-eyed Markus reflected on a day that had seen him lead his first and, possibly, only grand prix.

He had tested for the Midland team before it had been renamed Spyker, impressing the team with his approach. Then, when the team parted company with Christijan Albers after the British GP, it made sense to bring in the German for a home debut. Ultimately, the ride for the remainder of the season would go to Sakon Yamamoto, who brought with him some healthy backing, but for the Nürburgring the seat was Markus's.

With the cars at the back of the grid, Chief Technical Officer Mike Gascoyne took a gamble on rain arriving as soon as the race got underway and elected to start Markus from the pits on wet tyres. When the elements obliged, Markus scythed through the slithering pack and into the lead of his first grand prix. At the end of the third lap, he led by more than half a minute. The safety car wiped out that, but he took the restart from the front of the field.

"Who'd have thought it," he smiled, shaking his head. "Whatever happens, I led my first F1 race and nobody can take that away from me!"

Whether Markus ever gets another start is anybody's guess but, 22 years on from Manfred's farewell grand prix, his father would have been a proud man.

INSIDE LINE
MARK WEBBER

**RED BULL
DRIVER**

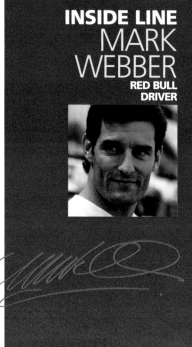

"A podium! It's a bloody huge relief for the whole team and for myself.

The start was not good at all, because I had a huge amount of clutch slip, so I was on the back foot going into Turn 1. Then in Turn 2, though, the BMW Saubers got together, which was a welcome bonus.

The rain started pretty quickly and was absoutely phenomenal. We obviously had to make some decisions pretty quickly and went onto intermediate tyres, but the aquaplaning we had in second or third gear on the run down to Turn 5, and in some other sections, was almost impossible to comprehend...

The FIA did a good job to put the safety car out and suspend the race at this point.

After the restart, I went onto intermediate tyres again and then grooved ones. We did a really, really long stint on the grooves, and I struggled a little bit with the rear tyres, but that stint was when I did the damage in terms of running a lot further than the others and securing what was going to be a podium finish.

When I saw Kimi retire, I must say I wasn't that disappointed!

Towards the end, I thought 'we've got it all in the bank, it's all fine, let's maybe start to wind the engine down and look after a few things.'

Then I saw the rain coming again and I thought 'my God, they're not going to give it to us easy!'

I had massive vibrations on the intermediates and I'd have been happier if it had stayed a bit drier given what was at stake.

Alex (Wurz) was pretty close towards the end of the race, but I was delighted to get the podium. These guys had been through a torrid start to the season, no question about it, and the whole Red Bull team deserved to have both cars in the points – with David coming home fifth – after the amount of effort that's gone in.

You can say it's a case of improving, but we continued to come back each race with the same old broken record stuff. We didn't drive to a podium in terms of pace, but we were there to get a podium in a very, very difficult motor race.

The team did a good job in terms of calling the race from the pit wall, and obviously you have to make some decisions yourself from the cockpit. Results are what count and today we've got a few points on the board, which moves us ahead of Toyota in the constructors' points table."

avoided a potential catastrophe as he accelerated out of the way of the spinning Toro Rosso. After missing the Mercedes safety car, Liuzzi could easily have gone under the tractor making its way across the gravel, or struck one of the marshals running alongside it.

Hamilton had decided to stay put in the gravel trap with the engine running. To everyone's astonishment, a crane returned him to the track, and he drove on. All was not lost after all...

"I think it started with a great bit of driving to get up to fourth," said McLaren supremo Ron Dennis. "But Lewis just clipped one of the BMWs and picked up a puncture. He came back around to the pits very slowly. Then, of course, by that time it had started to rain. So we switched him to intermediates, but Lewis was a long way back. Of course he spun off, but there was quite quick thinking on the pit wall and he kept the engine running. He just sat there and got picked up by the crane, but of course lost a lap."

A grateful Hamilton selected first gear and went on his way. "It was just unfortunate," he said, "as it was very, very slippery, I got caught out, and just went straight on. But 'thank you' to the safety team who helped me to get back on."

Just before the crane set him down on the track, Hamilton was passed by Winkelhock. Despite just coming out of the pits after a second change from intermediate tyres to extreme wets, the German still had a huge lead, and as he passed Hamilton, he put the McLaren man a lap down.

Both then got in line behind the safety car before a red flag signalled the suspension of the race, so bad had conditions become. They stopped on the grid at the end of the lap and there was a long wait until the rest of the drivers arrived, led by Massa.

This was when there was some degree of confusion, as McLaren were adamant that Hamilton had not been lapped, despite the fact that the timing showed

Winkelhock as leader and the McLaren was clearly circulating behind him. So, Hamilton was erroneously pushed to the back of the grid, when in fact he should have stayed where he was, passed the safety car at the restart, and been allowed to rejoin the back of the pack before the green flag flew.

The FIA had a lot to deal with at this point, trying to untangle what had happened, and dealing with urgent enquiries from all of the teams. When the field finally moved away, Hamilton was eventually allowed to regain his lap, although now he had to pass the whole field and the safety car. He was supposed to then rejoin the back of the queue, but McLaren made an ill-judged call to put him on to dry tyres while he was in the process of catching the queue. In stopping, he forfeited his right to rejoin the queue, so the green flag flew early and he was instantly more than half a lap down. Even worse, it was way too early for dries, and he lost even more time.

At the front, though, Massa looked pretty well set, and he seemed to have the race under control as dry tyres became the obvious choice within a few laps of the resumption of the race. Alonso and Räikkönen led the pursuit, but the Finn's day ended early with a hydraulic problem as his Nürburgring bad luck returned.

Thus Massa looked to have matters under control until the return of rain, with just eight laps of the race to go, turned things upside-down.

Everyone charged in for intermediate tyres, and it was soon apparent that Massa was less than comfortable on his. Alonso reeled him in and, after a couple of close calls, forced his way by with four laps to go. It was an incredible conclusion to a mad afternoon, and in *parc fermé* the pair had words, as Alonso made it clear that Massa's defence had been a little too forceful.

"I enjoyed the race so much because I like the different weather conditions," said winner Alonso, playing down the confrontation. "I always enjoy these types of races and at one point, when I was second,

Mark Webber splashes his Red Bull RB3 towards third place

Fernando Alonso leaves his fourth and final pit stop right into the path of Fisichella's Renault

With the track still dry, Lewis Hamilton dives inside Heikki Kovalainen in an impressive charge from 10th to sixth by Turn 1

Fernando Alonso points out bodywork damage to a TV cameraman, after his contact with Felipe Massa when he passed for the lead with four laps to go

I said maybe it's not the right time to rain, because I was happy with second place.

"Lewis was out of the points and Kimi as well, so for me eight points were good enough. But then, obviously now with my final result of victory, I like the rain, there's no doubt. I'm always quite happy when it rains and I have some fun. I was so happy on the podium, because the race was quite exciting."

"The car was just very good in the dry," reported Massa. "It had a little bit of understeer at the beginning of the stint, but then it was really, really good. I was able to pull away at a very nice and controlled pace. But then, unfortunately, the rain came

again. I think our car was not so bad even in the rain, but then I don't know what happened. I took a set of tyres which was vibrating a lot from the beginning of the stint and I couldn't manage to find the pace. Then Fernando was just getting closer and closer and we had a fight."

With Räikkönen, Hamilton and the BMWs all hitting trouble of one kind or another, the chance was there for others to take advantage, and it was certainly a day for the veterans. The one who profited the most was Mark Webber, who made all the right calls and took a deserved third place for Red Bull Racing. He just headed home Alex Wurz, the Austrian adding another good result to his third place in Montréal. David Coulthard was fifth in the other Red Bull entry, after losing out to his team-mate in the pit-stop sequence.

Such was the rate of attrition that Heidfeld and Kubica were able to claw back to sixth and seventh, although everyone was aware that without their first-lap clash, it would have been a lot better. Heidfeld was also lucky to escape either damage or a penalty after later shoving Ralf Schumacher's Toyota off the road.

Heikki Kovalainen had a good run to eighth place, helped by switching to wet tyres at his final scheduled stop before the second rain shower had started, as the team knew it was coming and took a gamble.

Hamilton finished ninth, off the podium for the first time in his F1 career.

"I enjoyed the race, to be honest," said Lewis. "It wasn't the best race, but it was still quite good fun, trying to come through the field, and sort of not really knowing where you were or where you were going to end up. It was quite close at the end. I could have got a point, but it just didn't happen this time."

Had McLaren not made that odd decision to go to dries, and just let him catch the queue and then change tyres with everyone else, he could well have made it up to third, so it was an expensive call...

SNAPSHOT FROM
EUROPE

CLOCKWISE FROM RIGHT Schloss Nürburg provides an historic backdrop to the Nürburgring; images of Hamilton illuminate the media centre; film director Quentin Tarantino was present as a guest of Red Bull; Ferrari's wheel covers necessitate the use of modified wheel guns; black and round versus in-black and rounded; smoke on the water courtesy of Alex Wurz's Williams-Toyota; there was much guesswork before the restart as to when the rain would strike next

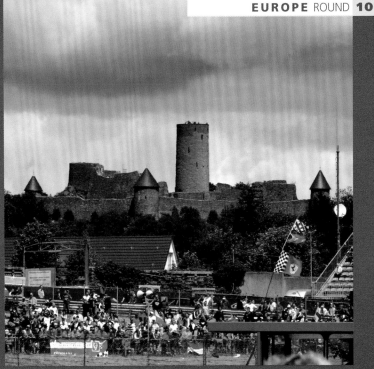

WEEKEND NEWS

■ Before the European GP, all 11 teams attended a three-day test at Spa-Francorchamps – the first at the venue since the 1980s. Rain spoiled the second and third days, but the test gave the teams a chance to sample the impressive new pits and the new chicane, which was very different from the old Bus Stop.

■ Sébastien Bourdais had two days of running with Scuderia Toro Rosso at Spa, increasing speculation that he was about to be signed up by the team for 2008. An unusual sight was that of Christian Klien in a Spyker, the Austrian having been released by Honda for the day. In the end, nothing came of the outing.

■ Eccentric Hollywood director Quentin Tarantino was a guest of Red Bull Racing on Sunday. In Europe to promote his latest release, the *Pulp Fiction* director posed with Mark Webber and David Coulthard. Originally from Tennessee, he admitted that he knew more about NASCAR than F1.

■ The high-speed S-bend after Nürburgring's hairpin was renamed in honour of Michael Schumacher in a ceremony on Sunday morning, the former World Champion driving himself around to the site in a Ferrari road car. Angered at being asked to keep well clear of the great man, F1's photographers elected to boycott the event and walked away.

■ After spinning off in the third-lap monsoon, Scott Speed was involved in a physical altercation in the Scuderia Toro Rosso garage with furious team boss Franz Tost. The aggrieved American tested at Mugello the following week, but it was clear to all that his days with the team were numbered.

RACE
RESULTS
EUROPE
NÜRBURGRING

Official Results © [2007]
Formula One Administration Limited,
6 Princes Gate, London, SW7 1QJ.
No reproduction without permission.
All copyright and database rights reserved.

RACE DATE July 22nd
CIRCUIT LENGTH 3.199 miles
NO. OF LAPS 60
RACE DISTANCE 191.940 miles
WEATHER Wet, dry then wet, 20°C
TRACK TEMP 30°C
RACE DAY ATTENDANCE 125,000
LAP RECORD Michael Schumacher
1m29.468s, 128.721mph, 2004

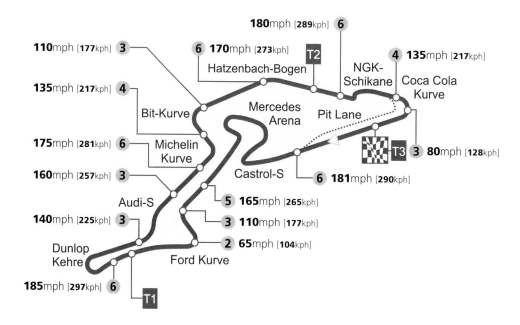

110mph [177kph] 3
135mph [217kph] 4
175mph [281kph] 6
160mph [257kph] 3
140mph [225kph] 3
185mph [297kph] 6
T1
Dunlop Kehre
Bit-Kurve
Michelin Kurve
Audi-S
Ford Kurve
6 170mph [273kph] T2
180mph [289kph] 6
Hatzenbach-Bogen
Mercedes Arena
Castrol-S
5 165mph [265kph]
3 110mph [177kph]
2 65mph [104kph]
6 181mph [290kph]
NGK-Schikane
Pit Lane
4 135mph [217kph]
Coca Cola Kurve
3 80mph [128kph] T3

PRACTICE 1		
Driver	**Time**	**Laps**
1 L Hamilton	1m32.515s	26
2 K Räikkönen	1m32.751s	24
3 F Alonso	1m32.932s	27
4 N Heidfeld	1m32.975s	35
5 R Kubica	1m33.205s	34
6 F Massa	1m33.605s	24
7 R Schumacher	1m33.825s	32
8 J Button	1m33.936s	28
9 D Coulthard	1m34.062s	25
10 R Barrichello	1m34.142s	25
11 J Trulli	1m34.152s	34
12 A Wurz	1m34.345s	32
13 N Rosberg	1m34.563s	32
14 A Davidson	1m34.567s	30
15 M Webber	1m34.683s	22
16 T Sato	1m34.708s	36
17 V Liuzzi	1m34.907s	31
18 H Kovalainen	1m34.921s	21
19 G Fisichella	1m35.077s	22
20 S Speed	1m35.643s	15
21 A Sutil	1m36.340s	22
22 M Winkelhock	1m37.116s	30

PRACTICE 2		
Driver	**Time**	**Laps**
1 K Räikkönen	1m33.339s	28
2 L Hamilton	1m33.478s	28
3 F Massa	1m33.590s	27
4 F Alonso	1m33.637s	30
5 R Schumacher	1m33.668s	18
6 J Trulli	1m33.746s	22
7 N Rosberg	1m33.845s	24
8 J Button	1m33.880s	36
9 N Heidfeld	1m34.146s	22
10 R Kubica	1m34.221s	19
11 M Webber	1m34.235s	29
12 A Wurz	1m34.264s	21
13 T Sato	1m34.357s	26
14 R Barrichello	1m34.411s	26
15 G Fisichella	1m34.431s	28
16 H Kovalainen	1m34.446s	25
17 D Coulthard	1m34.504s	19
18 A Davidson	1m34.554s	26
19 S Speed	1m35.320s	26
20 V Liuzzi	1m35.653s	24
21 A Sutil	1m36.527s	25
22 M Winkelhock	1m37.319s	19

PRACTICE 3		
Driver	**Time**	**Laps**
1 K Räikkönen	1m31.396s	18
2 L Hamilton	1m31.627s	12
3 F Alonso	1m32.039s	11
4 R Kubica	1m32.039s	18
5 F Massa	1m32.217s	18
6 N Rosberg	1m32.344s	16
7 N Heidfeld	1m32.581s	20
8 M Webber	1m32.632s	16
9 D Coulthard	1m32.679s	18
10 R Schumacher	1m32.788s	21
11 V Liuzzi	1m32.841s	20
12 J Button	1m32.869s	18
13 J Trulli	1m32.936s	20
14 S Speed	1m32.974s	14
15 A Wurz	1m33.154s	16
16 G Fisichella	1m33.214s	17
17 R Barrichello	1m33.229s	19
18 H Kovalainen	1m33.484s	13
19 A Davidson	1m33.792s	20
20 T Sato	1m33.945s	19
21 A Sutil	1m34.423s	20
22 M Winkelhock	1m36.090s	19

QUALIFYING 1	
Driver	**Time**
1 F Alonso	1m31.074s
2 F Massa	1m31.447s
3 K Räikkönen	1m31.522s
4 L Hamilton	1m31.587s
5 N Heidfeld	1m31.889s
6 R Kubica	1m31.961s
7 N Rosberg	1m32.117s
8 A Wurz	1m32.173s
9 G Fisichella	1m32.378s
10 J Trulli	1m32.381s
11 R Schumacher	1m32.446s
12 H Kovalainen	1m32.594s
13 M Webber	1m32.629s
14 R Barrichello	1m32.674s
15 T Sato	1m32.678s
16 A Davidson	1m32.793s
17 J Button	1m32.983s
18 S Speed	1m33.038s
19 V Liuzzi	1m33.148s
20 D Coulthard	1m33.151s
21 A Sutil	1m34.500s
22 M Winkelhock	1m35.940s

QUALIFYING 2	
Driver	**Time**
1 F Massa	1m30.912s
2 F Alonso	1m30.983s
3 L Hamilton	1m31.185s
4 K Räikkönen	1m31.237s
5 R Kubica	1m31.444s
6 N Heidfeld	1m31.652s
7 M Webber	1m31.661s
8 H Kovalainen	1m31.783s
9 R Schumacher	1m31.843s
10 J Trulli	1m31.859s
11 N Rosberg	1m31.978s
12 A Wurz	1m31.996s
13 G Fisichella	1m32.010s
14 R Barrichello	1m32.221s
15 A Davidson	1m32.451s
16 T Sato	1m32.838s

Best sectors – Practice			Speed trap – Practice		
Sec 1 L Hamilton	29.960s		1 L Hamilton	187.2mph	
Sec 2 K Räikkönen	37.952s		2 N Rosberg	186.6mph	
Sec 3 K Räikkönen	23.449s		3 F Alonso	186.5mph	

Best sectors – Qualifying			Speed trap – Qualifying		
Sec 1 F Massa	29.736s		1 K Räikkönen	186.2mph	
Sec 2 F Alonso	37.761s		F Alonso	186.2mph	
Sec 3 M Webber	22.239s		3 F Massa	186.1mph	

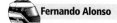

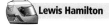

Fernando Alonso
"In the dry, the Ferraris were faster, but when the rain started again, I was able to pass Felipe to take the lead. We touched twice, but that is motor racing."

Giancarlo Fisichella
"I lost places with an extra lap on slicks, and then queuing in the pits. After that, we took on heavy fuel loads, and though the balance was OK, the performance wasn't."

Felipe Massa
"A second place that leaves a bitter taste. When I was on rain tyres after the last rain, I felt vibrations. The discussion with Fernando? I was on edge, but he apologised."

Jenson Button
"I fell to 20th, but was up to sixth when I pitted for wets. After that, Turn 1 was a lake. I was fourth behind Massa and Alonso, but my wheels locked, then I hit the wall."

Nick Heidfeld
"Robert forced me onto the dirt at the first two corners and again, when we touched. As the race was interrupted, we fixed the car. The crash with Ralf was unlucky."

Ralf Schumacher
"Even after the rain, we were as quick as the cars in front. I made a little mistake and Nick was able to close up. He made a move at the final corner and we collided."

Lewis Hamilton
"I made a good start and was fourth when the BMWs went off. Then I had a puncture. The team fitted rain tyres. I still went off, but kept the engine running."

Heikki Kovalainen
"We took some gambles, especially with wet tyres at my final pit stop, but they didn't pay off, as I had to look after them on a dry track, and it took it out of them."

Kimi Räikkönen
"I was right behind Felipe and Alonso and the car was quick. I was convinced I could win, but the hydraulic system malfunctioned and I was forced to stop."

Rubens Barrichello
"The car felt bad from the start and never improved, most likely due to damage caused when Rosberg hit me. I love these dry-wet conditions and we had some chances."

Robert Kubica
"Nick arrived too fast at the second corner. He touched me and I spun. It then started to rain and I asked if I should pit. I had no answer so I continued, which was wrong."

Jarno Trulli
"I was always in the wrong place at the wrong time, with the wrong decision at the wrong moments. I had a very good start and was fifth, but that is racing in the rain."

POSITIONS

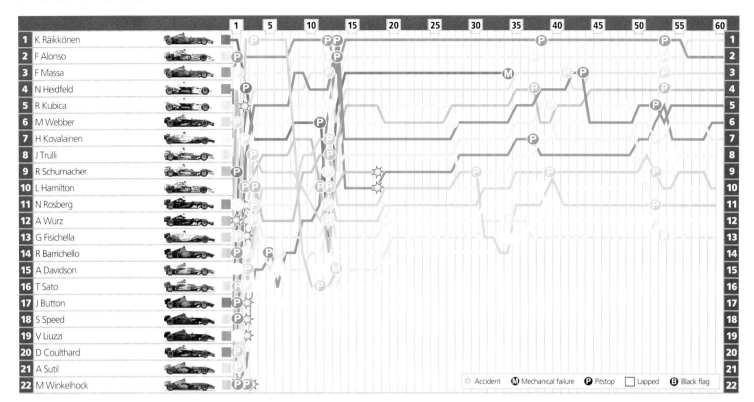

	Driver	1	5	10	15	20	25	30	35	40	45	50	55	60	
1	K Räikkönen														1
2	F Alonso														2
3	F Massa														3
4	N Heidfeld														4
5	R Kubica														5
6	M Webber														6
7	H Kovalainen														7
8	J Trulli														8
9	R Schumacher														9
10	L Hamilton														10
11	N Rosberg														11
12	A Wurz														12
13	G Fisichella														13
14	R Barrichello														14
15	A Davidson														15
16	T Sato														16
17	J Button														17
18	S Speed														18
19	V Liuzzi														19
20	D Coulthard														20
21	A Sutil														21
22	M Winkelhock														22

☼ Accident ⓜ Mechanical failure ⓟ Pitstop ▢ Lapped ⓑ Black flag

QUALIFYING 3

	Driver	Time
1	K Räikkönen	1m31.450s
2	F Alonso	1m31.741s
3	F Massa	1m31.778s
4	N Heidfeld	1m31.840s
5	R Kubica	1m32.123s
6	M Webber	1m32.476s
7	H Kovalainen	1m32.478s
8	J Trulli	1m32.501s
9	R Schumacher	1m32.570s
10	L Hamilton	1m33.833s

GRID

	Driver	Time
1	K Räikkönen	1m31.450s
2	F Alonso	1m31.741s
3	F Massa	1m31.778s
4	N Heidfeld	1m31.840s
5	R Kubica	1m32.123s
6	M Webber	1m32.476s
7	H Kovalainen	1m32.478s
8	J Trulli	1m32.501s
9	R Schumacher	1m32.570s
10	L Hamilton	1m33.833s
11	N Rosberg	1m31.978s
12	A Wurz	1m31.996s
13	G Fisichella	1m32.010s
14	R Barrichello	1m32.221s
15	A Davidson	1m32.451s
16	T Sato	1m32.838s
17	J Button	1m32.983s
18	S Speed	1m33.038s
19	V Liuzzi	1m33.148s
20	D Coulthard	1m33.151s
21	A Sutil	1m34.500s
22	M Winkelhock	1m35.940s

RACE

	Driver	Car	Laps	Time	Avg. mph	Fastest	Stops
1	F Alonso	McLaren-Mercedes MP4-22	60	2h06m26.358s	91.091	1m33.231s	2
2	F Massa	Ferrari F2007	60	2h06m34.513s	90.993	1m32.853s	4
3	M Webber	Red Bull-Renault RB3	60	2h07m32.032s	90.309	1m34.449s	4
4	A Wurz	Williams-Toyota FW29	60	2h07m32.295s	90.306	1m34.235s	4
5	D Coulthard	Red Bull-Renault RB3	60	2h07m40.014s	90.215	1m34.316s	4
6	N Heidfeld	BMW Sauber F1.07	60	2h07m46.656s	90.137	1m34.354s	6
7	R Kubica	BMW Sauber F1.07	60	2h07m48.773s	90.112	1m34.451s	4
8	H Kovalainen	Renault R27	59	2h06m37.437s	89.442	1m34.603s	4
9	L Hamilton	McLaren-Mercedes MP4-22	59	2h06m39.019s	89.438	1m33.401s	4
10	G Fisichella	Renault R27	59	2h06m39.782s	89.416	1m34.893s	4
11	R Barrichello	Honda RA107	59	2h07m21.333s	88.928	1m35.632s	5
12	A Davidson	Super Aguri-Honda SA07	59	2h07m52.997s	88.561	1m35.282s	6
13	J Trulli	Toyota TF107	59	2h07m57.073s	88.514	1m34.496s	6
R	K Räikkönen	Ferrari F2007	34	Hydraulics	-	1m33.904s	2
R	T Sato	Super Aguri-Honda SA07	19	Hydraulics	-	1m37.401s	3
R	R Schumacher	Toyota TF107	18	Collision	-	1m36.195s	3
R	M Winkelhock	Spyker-Ferrari F8-VII	13	Hydraulics	-	1m42.783s	2
R	J Button	Honda RA107	2	Spun off	-	2m20.041s	1
R	A Sutil	Spyker-Ferrar F8-VII	2	Spun off	-	2m25.798s	1
R	N Rosberg	Williams-Toyota FW29	2	Spun off	-	2m50.950s	1
R	S Speed	Toro Rosso-Ferrari STR02	2	Spun off	-	3m01.900s	1
R	V Liuzzi	Toro Rosso-Ferrari STR02	2	Suspension	-	3m22.300s	2

CHAMPIONSHIP

	Driver	Pts
1	L Hamilton	70
2	F Alonso	68
3	F Massa	59
4	K Räikkönen	52
5	N Heidfeld	36
6	R Kubica	24
7	G Fisichella	17
8	H Kovalainen	15
9	A Wurz	13
10	M Webber	8
11	D Coulthard	8
12	J Trulli	7
13	N Rosberg	5
14	T Sato	4
15	R Schumacher	2
16	J Button	1
	S Vettel	1

Fastest Lap
F Massa 1m32.853s
(124.020mph) on lap 34

Fastest speed trap
F Alonso 188.5mph
Slowest speed trap
V Liuzzi 151.4mph

Fastest pit stop
1	R Kubica	25.190s
2	D Coulthard	25.324s
3	N Heidfeld	25.545s

	Constructor	Pts
1	McLaren-Mercedes	138
2	Ferrari	111
3	BMW Sauber	61
4	Renault	32
5	Williams-Toyota	18
6	Red Bull-Renault	16
7	Toyota	9
8	Super Aguri-Honda	4
9	Honda	1

David Coulthard
"After such a bad qualifying, it was only ever going to be a change of conditions that was going to give us a chance to move forward, and we ended with fifth place for me."

Nico Rosberg
"We knew the rain was coming, but fitted my car with inters not wets. There were yellows going into the first corner. I slowed a lot, but I aquaplaned into the gravel."

Vitantonio Liuzzi
"It was really weird my spin, and I thought there was something wrong. To start with, I thought it was the suspension, rear left, as it felt as if it dropped a bit at the rear."

Adrian Sutil
"I couldn't hold the car on the wet track and was just a passenger in the hairpin. I braked and lost the rear. It was a hard impact, but I'm alright, just disappointed."

Takuma Sato
"I made up a lot of places on the dry tyre at the start and was 10th by the end of lap 1. At the restart, we had reasonable pace, but then I had hydraulic failure."

Mark Webber
"The rain came earlier than we expected. Near the end I thought 'oh God' when I saw rain coming and I had vibration from the rears, and that's why Alex got so close."

Alexander Wurz
"Near the end, I could almost taste the champagne, but I am very happy with fourth place. I had to use all my brain power and push at the right times and keep calm."

Scott Speed
"When we left the pit wall, Franz [Tost] was furious that I'd crashed in Turn 1, regardless of the fact that nearly every single driver behind Button did exactly the same thing."

Markus Winkelhock
"I thank the team for letting me start my first grand prix at home. Starting on wets was a fantastic decision. Leading an F1 race is something nobody can take away."

Anthony Davidson
"It was hard to know what tyre to be on, but in the dry we seemed to have the pace over the Honda and I had a nice fight with Rubens. We then made the wrong tyre choice."

FORMULA 1™
MAGYAR NAGYDIJ 2007
BUDAPEST

WAVES AT McLAREN

Starting with pole position and ending up with victory ought to have left McLaren happy, but the team from Woking suffered a weekend of unimaginable turmoil

Lewis Hamilton scored the third victory of his rookie season in Hungary, but his success came in controversial circumstances for the McLaren team and celebrations were certainly somewhat muted.

Hamilton's own team-mate Fernando Alonso had been dumped from pole position to sixth on the grid after impeding him in the pitlane during a heated qualifying session. The team's usual calculated approach was abandoned, and it seemed to have become every man for himself. Ron Dennis – the man who always likes to be in control – was caught on the hop.

The full story of the McLaren civil war would fill several pages of this annual, but in essence it started to go wrong when Hamilton chose not to follow a pre-arranged plan in the final qualifying session, and rather than let his team-mate by and allow him to complete an extra fuel-burning lap, set off quickly himself.

Hamilton held pole position after the first runs of Q3, but when he came in for his final set of tyres Alonso's car was being serviced. Alonso was being held by the lollipop man, ostensibly to find a clear piece of road. When Alonso was finally waved out, there was still just enough time for Hamilton to have his new tyres fitted and complete his out-lap.

ABOVE It's safe to say that there was tension between the McLaren drivers after qualifying...

However, to most people's astonishment, Alonso stayed firmly put for some 10 extra seconds before driving out of the pitlane. He got around the lap just in time to start what turned out to be the pole lap, but a furious Hamilton couldn't make it, being shown the chequered flag at the end of his out-lap. Angry words were exchanged between Dennis and Hamilton on the radio on his slowing-down lap and, after the session, tensions ran high in the camp.

Both drivers expressed their frustration to the media, and there was clearly a critical breakdown in communications. Dennis had no hesitation in blaming

Hamilton for kicking it all off. Then the FIA stewards got involved and it became a whole different game. Interestingly, the stewards chose not to focus entirely on those critical 10 extra seconds, but also took an extensive look at the wait at the first stop, and the initial 20 seconds' wait at the second before the lollipop went up.

They found that there were some inconsistencies in McLaren's story about looking for gaps and, armed with the FIA's GPS recordings showing the positions of the cars, they were able to pinpoint these – not least the fact that when Alonso went out at the end there were only four cars on the track, and they were not an issue.

TALKING POINT
CIVIL WAR AT McLAREN

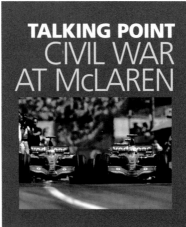

It was, by any measure, a bizarre Saturday at the Hungarian Grand Prix. Due to the narrowness of the circuit, pole position at the Hungaroring is more important than any bar Monte Carlo. Fernando Alonso was struggling to get a whole lap out of the option tyre. Despite managing to set quickest Q2 time on the option, he went for the

prime for his second run, which ruled out any realistic chance of beating team-mate Lewis Hamilton to pole.

After the first Q3 run, on the option tyre, Alonso was quickest. At the end of the session, with the final runs to come, he pitted for his new tyres, the lollipop was raised and Fernando went nowhere. Hamilton, coming in behind him, was delayed to the point where he could not get serviced and then hare around the circuit in time to start what would have been his flying lap. It looked like an example of blatant gamesmanship.

That was only the beginning, as it was not that simple. A beleaguered Ron Dennis explained that at some circuits it is not possible for both drivers to do the same number of fuel burn-off laps in Q3 and, when that happens, they take it in turns in

the interests of equality. Why does it matter? Because when you get your fuel credit from the FIA (2.1kg of fuel per completed lap in Hungary), it means that you can run a longer first stint in the race, which is often significant. The British GP had been Hamilton's turn to get the extra lap, said Dennis. Here, Alonso had priority.

Hamilton had got down to the end of the pitlane first and was instructed to let Alonso by. But he didn't. The British driver said initially that he was concerned that Räikkönen was too close and he didn't want to risk the Ferrari going by him as well, which could compromise McLaren's timings. Alonso, said Hamilton, backed off, and so he carried on, ignoring the instruction.

In fact, the fuel burn-off talk looked like a red herring. When you did the

maths it was perfectly feasible for both cars to do 12 laps, a fact proven by Räikkönen, who did just that despite being delayed behind Alonso.

The FIA called Alonso to explain himself, and he said he was being counted down to find the right gap in traffic, McLaren backed him up, but the FIA didn't buy it. Result: a five-place grid penalty.

At McLaren's press conference, Hamilton was missing. Hot under the collar, Dennis explained the situation. After 10 minutes Dennis was called to the stewards, whereupon Hamilton emerged from a side room and said, "Sorry, I'd forgotten we had this..." He then contradicted everything Alonso said before Martin Whitmarsh called an early halt to proceedings.

Diplomacy had failed and war had broken out.

Much emphasis was placed on the on-track radio conversations related to the last stop, and especially what Hamilton was told as he was coming in. There was a definite suspicion that, irrespective of anything Alonso might have done of his own volition, there was something strange about the 'official' 20 seconds countdown, even though it was not that but the extra 10 seconds that specifically caused Hamilton to miss his final lap.

Shortly before midnight, a lengthy FIA report confirmed that Alonso had unfairly impeded Hamilton and affected his chances of a fair crack at his final qualifying run, so a five-place penalty was awarded to the Spaniard, relegating him to sixth on the grid. Even worse for McLaren was a deduction of any constructors' points that might be scored in the race, which was a decision that was immediately appealed.

Hamilton thus inherited the pole position that many felt was rightfully his, while Nick Heidfeld moved up to the front row. It was not a great day for Ferrari either, as Kimi Räikkönen qualified a subdued third and Felipe Massa a frustrated 14th. The Brazilian hadn't made it out of Q2 after the team initially forgot to refuel him and in the ensuing panic he was sent out again on tyres that had cooled down.

After the excitement of Saturday and with the grid having something of an unusual look, a dramatic race appeared to be in prospect, but things didn't quite turn out that way. Like many Hungarian GPs, it was an afternoon of very little overtaking and little real drama.

At least things looked vaguely interesting after the start as, crucially, Räikkönen got ahead of Heidfeld (starting on the dirty side of the grid) and was able to chase Hamilton. This duo stopped together on lap 19 and, confident that they could get him out in front, McLaren fuelled Hamilton to lap 50. Trying to be more aggressive, Ferrari fuelled Räikkönen only to lap 46. So, after the Finn stopped and returned to the track behind Hamilton, without much of a weight advantage, it was clear that Hamilton would stay safely ahead.

In fact, Räikkönen remained close to Hamilton all the way to the flag, although there was never really any question of the positions changing. Ferrari regarded this result as a good case of damage limitation at a track that was not expected to be favourable to their cause.

"It's been an eventful weekend and quite emotional for all the team, I think," said a relieved Hamilton. "We made a really good step forward, as the team has been working so hard to improve the car and we came here with a great package. We still weren't sure whether we

BELOW LEFT Nick Heidfeld enjoyed his second podium finish of the year, keeping Alonso in check

BELOW RIGHT The usual Räikkönen-supporting Finns packing the hillsides were joined by a new contingent – Polish fans cheering for Robert Kubica's BMW Sauber

BOTTOM The pack trickles around to the start, with Honda mixing it with Super Aguri and Spyker

would be ahead of the Ferraris but, as you could see in the race, they obviously had great pace.

"Quite early on in the race – in the second stint – I had a problem with my steering. I don't really know what it was, but it made it quite difficult to keep the pace. As you could see, I dropped off a little bit and I was a bit nervous that something was going to break, but thank goodness it didn't. However, I was told over the radio that everything was fine, so I just had to keep on pushing.

"Kimi was on my tail for quite a long time and so I was pushing right to the last lap. He drove a fantastic race. I really enjoyed it, but it's good that we're back at the top after an eventful time at the last race."

Räikkönen opined: "We knew that they would be strong here, especially in qualifying. I expected the good race car that we had, but unfortunately it wasn't enough. Next year, we need to get the car sorted for one lap, but then I know from past experience with them [McLaren] that they are fast here. They are going to be fast in some other places, too. It has been the same thing every year, so it wasn't a surprise for me that they were strong here. Fortunately, I think the next circuit [Istanbul] will be OK for us, but I'm pretty happy with my second place. For sure I needed to win today, but unfortunately we were not up for it.

"I would certainly have tried if I'd had any chance, because I don't have much to lose. Even if we had ended up off the circuit, it wouldn't have changed much for me. But I didn't have any kind of chance to have even a reasonable go, so there is no point in being stupid. If I could have had a nice try, then for sure I would have gone for it, but with the race how it was, we were too close to each other speed-wise. On these kinds of circuits, you don't really have chances."

Heidfeld had a good run to third place, and through the final stint he did a great job to hold off the attentions of Alonso, as once again BMW Sauber

proved that it was always on hand to take advantage of trouble among the front-runners.

Alonso had made life hard for himself by dropping from sixth position to eighth at the start, and being committed to an early pit stop (on lap 17) didn't help his cause. However, he ran strongly thereafter and a late stop on lap 50 (the same as team-mate Hamilton) helped to bump him up to fourth place.

Robert Kubica had a drivetrain problem in qualifying and started only seventh, but he picked up pace during the race and advanced to fifth. Ralf Schumacher had qualified in that position, and gained a place when Alonso was demoted. The Toyota driver then took full advantage of the bonus and ran a strong fifth in the early part of the race. He got ahead of Nico Rosberg thanks to the Williams man opting for a three-stop race, but traffic delayed him, allowing Kubica and Alonso to get by, demoting Ralf to an eventual sixth.

Rosberg did a good job to qualify fifth, and then had the bonus of moving up to fourth on the grid when Alonso was penalised. He held that position through the opening stint. Along with Heidfeld, he was one of the first to pit and, after running an oddball three-stop strategy, he slipped back to a disappointed seventh.

The final point went to Heikki Kovalainen. The Finn qualified 12th, but moved up a place when his Renault team-mate Giancarlo Fisichella was moved back five places for impeding Spyker new boy Sakon Yamamoto in qualifying. Both drivers made the unusual decision to start on the less-favoured supersoft tyres. Kovalainen moved into ninth at the start and made it into the points by jumping ahead of Mark Webber. Fisichella was stuck with a light fuel load at the start and was always going to struggle. His race included a clumsy collision with Anthony Davidson (which put the Super Aguri man out of the race), but he eventually finished 12th.

After the double points finish at the Nürburgring, the Hungarian GP was a major disappointment for Red Bull.

OPPOSITE ABOVE Neither Adrian Sutil, shown being lapped by Felipe Massa, nor new team-mate Sakon Yamamoto made much progress

OPPOSITE BELOW Ralf Schumacher qualified strongly and raced well to finish sixth for Toyota

---

INSIDE LINE
RALF SCHUMACHER
TOYOTA DRIVER

"It was the best race of the season for me and equalled the team's best result, the sixth place that Jarno got at Indianapolis.

We got both TF107s into Q3 for the third consecutive race and we have definitely made a step forward, as at the start of the season I was struggling a little bit in adapting to the new Bridgestone tyres. I don't like an understeering car and, at first, it was difficult to get the front end into the corner.

I think I had the toughest time at Monte Carlo and some people assumed that because this was a high-downforce place we'd also struggle at the Hungaroring. But we have done a lot of work to improve the situation and I have also tried to adapt my style a little bit.

I qualified sixth fastest here and that became fifth when Alonso received his five-place penalty after qualifying. That was a bonus, because the dirty side of the grid is notoriously slippery at the Hungaroring and Fernando's problems put me on the clean side of the grid.

I made a decent start and was able to keep Fernando behind me for a long time. In the end, I finished just 3s behind Robert Kubica's BMW, and I think I might have beaten him if I hadn't lost time behind Nick Heidfeld in the other BMW. Nick finished on the podium and was obviously quick, but the BMWs went for a three-stop strategy, I presume to limit the amount of time they had to run on the option tyre, and I was trapped behind Nick with a lighter car before my second pit stop.

Overall, though, it was a strong race for me. The car felt a little bit nervous during the first stint, but we added some front wing at my first pit stop and that improved things. Despite what happened with Nick, I'm sure two stops was the right strategy for us.

We had a tough start to the season, there's no doubt about that, but the car is consistently in the top 10 now and we have done a lot of work and made progress.

Some think that F1 is easy, and that with a decent budget and good facilities you are going to be winning races, but experience is important as well and some of the teams we are racing against have 10 times as much experience as us.

There are no short cuts and everyone in Cologne and Japan is doing everything they can to close the gap to the top teams."

ABOVE Nico Rosberg was back in the points as Williams started to show an improvement in form

BELOW LEFT Sebastian Vettel took over from Scott Speed at Scuderia Toro Rosso and finished the race in 16th position

BELOW RIGHT Lewis Hamilton loves winning, but this one was the perfect end to a difficult weekend

Mark Webber started ninth and passed both Alonso and Jarno Trulli on the first lap. It looked as though he would be able to bag some points from there, but running a three-stop strategy saw him lose out and he dropped back to ninth, although he felt the car was becoming quicker as the race went on.

It was all change at Scuderia Toro Rosso as Scott Speed was dropped after the European GP and replaced by Sebastian Vettel. The German did not even try the car until Friday practice, and had to settle for 20th on the grid. He still had a lot to learn in the race, but had a steady run to 16th.

The race was the first anniversary of Honda's brilliant win with Jenson Button, but the weekend was a total disaster for the Japanese manufacturer. Once again, Button failed to get through Q3, and was stuck in 17th place on the grid, but at least he was ahead of team-mate Rubens Barrichello. Both men then made their Sunday afternoon even harder by making bad starts. Incredibly, Barrichello spent most of the race running around in last place, unable to challenge Adrian Sutil's Spyker. Button had some relief from his misery when his car failed after 35 laps. What a difference a year makes...

SNAPSHOT FROM
HUNGARY

CLOCKWISE FROM RIGHT The view from Pest across to Buda remains one of the best on F1's circus; for some, it was carnival time; relaxation for FIA Medical Delegate Dr Gary Hartstein; there were more FIA bulletins than normal...; Ferrari forgot to fuel Felipe Massa's car in qualifying; Lewis Hamilton checks for damage after an off in Friday practice; Fernando Alonso had to endure even more media attention than usual; Jenson Button found that a year can be a very long time

WEEKEND NEWS

■ The FIA World Motor Sport Council met on July 26 to discuss the Ferrari spy scandal. McLaren was found guilty because there was no question that employee Mike Coughlan had possession of Ferrari documents, but the team escaped punishment because there was no proof that the information had been used. Ferrari was furious with this verdict, and FIA President Max Mosley referred it to the Court of Appeal.

■ The WMSC also approved the 2008 Formula One World Championship calendar. As already announced, the United States GP was missing, while the two new street races in Valencia (August) and Singapore (September) were confirmed. The only other major change to the calendar was a switch for the Turkish GP from August to early May.

■ After the one-off appearance by Markus Winkelhock at the European GP, Spyker signed a more permanent replacement for the departed Christijan Albers. Sakon Yamamoto hadn't driven an F1 car in anger since his final Super Aguri outing in Brazil the previous October, but made steady progress through the weekend before spinning off in the race.

■ After the flare-up at the European GP, it came as no great surprise when Scuderia Toro Rosso announced that Scott Speed had been dropped prior to the Hungarian GP. He was replaced by BMW tester and Red Bull protégé Sebastian Vettel, who had also agreed terms with the team for 2008. Speed meanwhile began looking at a future in NASCAR.

■ In the days following the Hungarian GP, Scuderia Toro Rosso announced that Sébastien Bourdais had been signed up for 2008, after the Frenchman had impressed in a series of tests. Bourdais had moved to the USA after winning the 2002 FIA F3000 title, and at the time of the announcement was heading for his fourth straight Champ Car title. The news meant that Tonio Liuzzi was on the market for 2008.

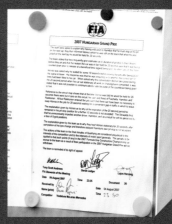

RACE RESULTS

HUNGARY
HUNGARORING

Official Results © [2007]
Formula One Administration Limited,
6 Princes Gate, London, SW7 1QJ.
No reproduction without permission.
All copyright and database rights reserved.

RACE DATE August 5th
CIRCUIT LENGTH 2.722miles
NO. OF LAPS 70
RACE DISTANCE 190.551 miles
WEATHER Bright and dry, 31°C
TRACK TEMP 43°C
RACE DAY ATTENDANCE 78,000
LAP RECORD Michael Schumacher
1m19.071s, 123.929mph, 2004

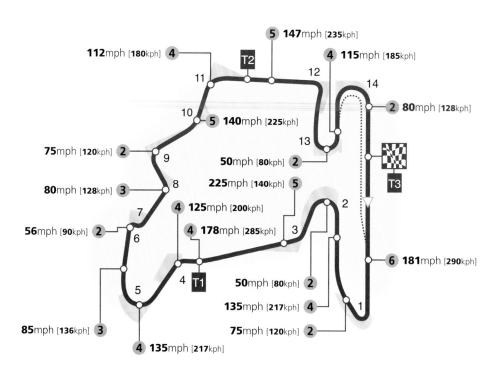

112mph [180kph] **4**
5 147mph [235kph]
4 115mph [185kph]
2 80mph [128kph]
75mph [120kph] **2**
5 140mph [225kph]
80mph [128kph] **3**
50mph [80kph] **2**
225mph [140kph] **5**
56mph [90kph] **2**
4 125mph [200kph]
4 178mph [285kph]
6 181mph [290kph]
4
50mph [80kph] **2**
85mph [136kph] **3**
135mph [217kph] **4**
75mph [120kph] **2**
4 135mph [217kph]

PRACTICE 1			
	Driver	Time	Laps
1	R Kubica	1m22.390s	25
2	F Massa	1m22.519s	18
3	K Räikkönen	1m22.540s	21
4	F Alonso	1m22.585s	18
5	L Hamilton	1m22.654s	19
6	N Heidfeld	1m22.891s	24
7	N Rosberg	1m22.983s	19
8	J Button	1m23.294s	20
9	R Barrichello	1m23.601s	20
10	R Schumacher	1m23.802s	27
11	A Davidson	1m24.102s	13
12	J Trulli	1m24.318s	30
13	A Wurz	1m24.321s	12
14	D Coulthard	1m24.474s	17
15	H Kovalainen	1m24.733s	18
16	S Vettel	1m24.905s	26
17	G Fisichella	1m24.920s	19
18	V Liuzzi	1m24.976s	20
19	T Sato	1m25.307s	13
20	M Webber	1m25.584s	14
21	A Sutil	1m26.332s	29
22	S Yamamoto	1m28.118s	30

PRACTICE 2			
	Driver	Time	Laps
1	F Alonso	1m20.919s	29
2	H Kovalainen	1m21.283s	39
3	L Hamilton	1m21.338s	32
4	N Rosberg	1m21.485s	40
5	N Heidfeld	1m21.517s	37
6	K Räikkönen	1m21.589s	29
7	F Massa	1m21.620s	29
8	G Fisichella	1m21.698s	36
9	J Trulli	1m21.857s	35
10	R Kubica	1m21.906s	37
11	R Schumacher	1m21.912s	29
12	A Wurz	1m21.987s	29
13	M Webber	1m22.325s	28
14	D Coulthard	1m22.483s	33
15	A Davidson	1m22.510s	41
16	J Button	1m22.550s	47
17	T Sato	1m22.556s	42
18	R Barrichello	1m22.727s	29
19	V Liuzzi	1m23.136s	42
20	S Vettel	1m23.148s	39
21	A Sutil	1m23.673s	34
22	S Yamamoto	1m26.307s	29

PRACTICE 3			
	Driver	Time	Laps
1	F Massa	1m20.183s	15
2	F Alonso	1m20.414s	11
3	L Hamilton	1m20.461s	11
4	N Heidfeld	1m20.565s	18
5	K Räikkönen	1m20.741s	15
6	N Rosberg	1m20.868s	16
7	J Trulli	1m20.878s	22
8	R Schumacher	1m20.933s	21
9	M Webber	1m21.220s	13
10	A Wurz	1m21.323s	15
11	A Davidson	1m21.501s	20
12	R Kubica	1m21.652s	18
13	H Kovalainen	1m21.666s	22
14	D Coulthard	1m21.752s	15
15	T Sato	1m21.839s	18
16	V Liuzzi	1m21.909s	21
17	G Fisichella	1m22.131s	22
18	J Button	1m22.202s	23
19	S Vettel	1m22.394s	20
20	R Barrichello	1m22.596s	18
21	A Sutil	1m23.560s	22
22	S Yamamoto	1m24.062s	24

QUALIFYING 1		
	Driver	Time
1	L Hamilton	1m19.570s
2	H Kovalainen	1m20.285s
3	R Kubica	1m20.366s
4	F Massa	1m20.408s
5	F Alonso	1m20.425s
6	K Räikkönen	1m20.435s
7	R Schumacher	1m20.449s
8	J Trulli	1m20.481s
9	N Rosberg	1m20.547s
10	N Heidfeld	1m20.751s
11	M Webber	1m20.794s
12	A Davidson	1m21.018s
13	A Wurz	1m21.243s
14	D Coulthard	1m21.291s
15	G Fisichella	1m21.645s
16	V Liuzzi	1m21.730s
17	J Button	1m21.737s
18	R Barrichello	1m21.877s
19	T Sato	1m22.143s
20	S Vettel	1m22.177s
21	A Sutil	1m22.737s
22	S Yamamoto	1m23.774s

QUALIFYING 2		
	Driver	Time
1	L Hamilton	1m19.301s
2	F Alonso	1m19.661s
3	J Trulli	1m19.951s
4	K Räikkönen	1m20.107s
5	N Rosberg	1m20.188s
6	N Heidfeld	1m20.322s
7	M Webber	1m20.439s
8	R Schumacher	1m20.455s
9	G Fisichella	1m20.590s
10	R Kubica	1m20.703s
11	D Coulthard	1m20.718s
12	H Kovalainen	1m20.779s
13	A Wurz	1m20.865s
14	F Massa	1m21.021s
15	A Davidson	1m21.127s
16	V Liuzzi	1m21.993s

Best sectors – Practice			Speed trap – Practice			Best sectors – Qualifying			Speed trap – Qualifying		
Sec 1	L Hamilton	28.550s	1	F Alonso	182.2mph	Sec 1	L Hamilton	28.397s	1	F Alonso	179.8mph
Sec 2	F Massa	28.659s		L Hamilton	182.2mph	Sec 2	L Hamilton	28.390s	2	L Hamilton	179.1mph
Sec 3	L Hamilton	22.483s	3	K Räikkönen	182.1mph	Sec 3	L Hamilton	22.424s		V Liuzzi	179.1mph

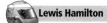

Fernando Alonso

"The most I could have achieved from sixth was a podium, especially on this track where passing is hard. In the last stint, I eased off to save my engine for Turkey."

Giancarlo Fisichella

"My race was more or less decided by the [grid] penalty. When I was able to a have few clear laps, I was on the pace, but I damaged my car when I tagged Davidson."

Felipe Massa

"It was a horrible race. I passed a few cars at the start, but lost them again at Turn 1. I had a very heavy car and lost downforce when I tried to close on other cars."

Jenson Button

"The problem that brought my race to an end appears to be a sensor problem, as I couldn't get full throttle for a few laps before I slowed for blues and stalled."

Nick Heidfeld

"I had a bad start on the dirty side of the track and lost a place to Kimi, but anyway both Lewis and he were faster, so a better start wouldn't have changed much."

Ralf Schumacher

"The race was great. I made a strong start and was fighting for fourth in the first few corners. The car was a bit nervous, so we made some front flap adjustments."

Lewis Hamilton

"A very emotional race and an eventful weekend. I pulled out a slight gap in the first stint, but then had a small problem with the steering, which let Kimi close in."

Heikki Kovalainen

"It was difficult starting from 11th place, but I made a good start and never gave up. I pushed as hard as I could and succeeded in finishing the race in the points."

Kimi Räikkönen

"When you find yourself very close to a car with similar speed, unless its driver makes a mistake, it's very difficult to overtake, especially on a track like the Hungaroring."

Rubens Barrichello

"The race started badly when I was pushed wide at the exit of Turn 2 and ended up at the back of the field. With overtaking next to impossible, that was my race."

Robert Kubica

"I had to start the race with new tyres, so the early laps were very difficult. However, after the first stop, my pace was really good and I closed the gap to Nick to 3s."

Jarno Trulli

"I lost a lot of positions at the start and from there I couldn't really do anything, as it is so hard to overtake at this circuit. We tried to make up time with strategy."

	Lap	1	5	10	15	20	25	30	35	40	45	50	55	60	65	70	
1	L Hamilton																1
2	N Heidfeld																2
3	K Räikkönen																3
4	N Rosberg																4
5	R Schumacher																5
6	F Alonso																6
7	R Kubica																7
8	J Trulli																8
9	M Webber																9
10	D Coulthard																10
11	H Kovalainen																11
12	A Wurz																12
13	G Fisichella																13
14	F Massa																14
15	A Davidson																15
16	V Liuzzi																16
17	J Button																17
18	R Barrichello																18
19	T Sato																19
20	S Vettel																20
21	A Sutil																21
22	S Yamamoto																22

☆ Accident Ⓜ Mechanical failure Ⓟ Pitstop ☐ Lapped Ⓑ Black flag

QUALIFYING 3

	Driver	Time
1	F Alonso	1m19.674s
2	L Hamilton	1m19.781s
3	N Heidfeld	1m20.259s
4	K Räikkönen	1m20.410s
5	N Rosberg	1m20.632s
6	R Schumacher	1m20.714s
7	R Kubica	1m20.876s
8	G Fisichella	1m21.079s
9	J Trulli	1m21.206s
10	M Webber	1m21.256s

GRID

	Driver	Time
1	L Hamilton	1m19.781s
2	N Heidfeld	1m20.259s
3	K Räikkönen	1m20.410s
4	N Rosberg	1m20.632s
5	R Schumacher	1m20.714s
6*	F Alonso	1m19.674s
7	R Kubica	1m20.876s
8	J Trulli	1m21.206s
9	M Webber	1m21.256s
10	D Coulthard	1m20.718s
11	H Kovalainen	1m20.779s
12	A Wurz	1m20.865s
13*	G Fisichella	1m21.079s
14	F Massa	1m21.021s
15	A Davidson	1m21.127s
16	V Liuzzi	1m21.993s
17	J Button	1m21.737s
18	R Barrichello	1m21.877s
19	T Sato	1m22.143s
20	S Vettel	1m22.177s
21	A Sutil	1m22.737s
22	S Yamamoto	1m23.774s

* DEMOTED FIVE PLACES ON GRID

RACE

	Driver	Car	Laps	Time	Avg. mph	Fastest	Stops
1	L Hamilton	McLaren-Mercedes MP4-22	70	1h35m52.991s	119.239	1m20.171s	2
2	K Räikkönen	Ferrari F2007	70	1h35m53.706s	119.225	1m20.047s	2
3	N Heidfeld	BMW Sauber F1.07	70	1h36m36.120s	118.352	1m20.582s	3
4	F Alonso	McLaren-Mercedes MP4-22	70	1h36m37.849s	118.317	1m20.324s	2
5	R Kubica	BMW Sauber F1.07	70	1h36m40.607s	118.260	1m20.419s	3
6	R Schumacher	Toyota TF107	70	1h36m43.660s	118.198	1m20.961s	2
7	N Rosberg	Williams-Toyota FW29	70	1h36m52.130s	118.026	1m20.672s	3
8	H Kovalainen	Renault R27	70	1h37m01.095s	117.844	1m20.935s	2
9	M Webber	Red Bull-Renault RB3	70	1h37m09.322s	117.678	1m20.915s	3
10	J Trulli	Toyota TF107	69	1h36m10.495s	117.179	1m21.253s	2
11	D Coulthard	Red Bull-Renault RB3	69	1h36m12.080s	117.147	1m21.553s	2
12	G Fisichella	Renault R27	69	1h36m17.976s	117.059	1m21.695s	2
13	F Massa	Ferrari F2007	69	1h36m18.626s	117.015	1m20.981s	2
14	A Wurz	Williams-Toyota FW29	69	1h36m19.158s	117.003	1m21.264s	2
15	T Sato	Super Aguri-Honda SA07	69	1h36m33.552s	116.713	1m20.980s	2
16	S Vettel	Toro Rosso-Ferrari STR02	69	1h37m04.656s	116.090	1m21.915s	2
17	A Sutil	Spyker-Ferrari F8-VII	68	1h36m28.802s	115.116	1m22.263s	2
18	R Barrichello	Honda RA107	68	1h36m32.481s	115.043	1m22.004s	2
R	V Liuzzi	Toro Rosso-Ferrari STR02	42	Electronics	-	1m22.410s	1
R	A Davidson	Super Aguri-Honda SA07	41	Accident	-	1m22.166s	1
R	J Button	Honda RA107	35	Throttle sensor	-	1m22.906s	1
R	S Yamamoto	Spyker-Ferrari F8-VII	4	Accident	-	1m26.741s	0

CHAMPIONSHIP

	Driver	Pts
1	L Hamilton	80
2	F Alonso	73
3	K Räikkönen	60
4	F Massa	59
5	N Heidfeld	42
6	R Kubica	28
7	G Fisichella	17
8	H Kovalainen	16
9	A Wurz	13
10	M Webber	8
11	D Coulthard	8
12	N Rosberg	7
13	J Trulli	7
14	R Schumacher	5
15	T Sato	4
16	J Button	1
17	S Vettel	1

Fastest Lap
K Räikkönen 1m20.047s
(122.428mph) on lap 70

Fastest speed trap
F Alonso 186.2mph
Slowest speed trap
S Yamamoto 173.2mph

Fastest pit stop
1	M Webber	21.444s
2	R Kubica	21.566s
3	R Kubica	21.833s

	Constructor	Pts
1	McLaren-Mercedes	138
2	Ferrari	119
3	BMW Sauber	71
4	Renault	33
5	Williams-Toyota	20
6	Red Bull-Renault	16
7	Toyota	12
8	Super Aguri-Honda	4
9	Honda	1

David Coulthard

"It was very inconsistent between sets of tyres out on track, so it was difficult to judge our performance. Other than that, there wasn't too much to report from this race."

 Nico Rosberg

"I have to be pleased, even if I'd hoped for more than seventh. Our strategy was good – I didn't come across any traffic and that allowed me to run at my own pace."

Vitantonio Liuzzi

"My race was OK, but I was stuck behind Massa, running with a heavier fuel load. We changed our strategy to counter this, but then my car had an electronic problem."

Adrian Sutil

"We were quite competitive with the cars in front of us. We could race with Honda, which meant I really had to push and attack every lap, keeping them behind to the end."

Takuma Sato

"Through the first few turns I was side-by-side with a few cars and made up some positions. But then I struggled as the car started to slide with the heavy fuel load."

 Mark Webber

"We thought that if we could get some clean air between lap 20-something and 30, we'd switch to a three-stop strategy, but it wasn't enough to get us a point today."

 **Alexander Wurz**

"I lost a place to Davidson at the start and this cost me a lot of time. I was fighting with Fisichella and Massa, but came to lap Sutil and he put me onto the grass."

 **Sebastian Vettel**

"I had quite a good start and found it quite exciting, though it felt like a long race. Overall, it was a good weekend, considering that Friday was the first time I drove the car."

Sakon Yamamoto

"I really pushed, but suddenly I lost grip in Turn 11 and spun and crashed. I just made a mistake, so I'm really disappointed as I really wanted to finish the race."

Anthony Davidson

"Challenging Wurz and Fisichella was great, but when I was racing Fisichella out of the pitlane, he ran out of road on cold tyres and we touched, breaking my suspension."

2007 FORMULA 1™ PETROL
OFISI TURKISH GRAND PRIX
ISTANBUL

FELIPE FLIES

A supreme qualifying lap set Felipe Massa up for this second win in Turkey in 12 months, as Ferrari reigned supreme and closed the gap on McLaren to 11 points

It wasn't so long ago that Michael Schumacher used to sign and seal world titles by July, and yet after Felipe Massa's win in Istanbul five drivers were still in contention as the World Championship headed into September. Yes, even Nick Heidfeld could still – mathematically, at least – come out on top.

Perhaps the most impressive thing was that after 12 races Massa, Lewis Hamilton, Fernando Alonso and Kimi Räikkönen had won three races apiece.

The other great arbiter of performance is qualifying, and the story was rather different there. Post-Turkey, Massa was clearly on top with five pole positions to the four of Hamilton, two of Räikkönen and one of Alonso. Of course, pole isn't quite the yardstick that it was in the Clark or Senna eras, due to the vagaries of fuel load opted for by the teams, but nevertheless those numbers said a lot about Massa's performance. Bear in mind, too, that he had a car failure in qualifying in Melbourne and was hampered by a team operational error in Hungary, so the league table could have favoured him even more.

Massa's pole-to-flag win in Istanbul was a further sign of how much he had improved since his maiden success a year earlier. Especially bearing in mind that the Brazilian was under strong pressure from his team-mate throughout, and until a late tyre problem Hamilton was also close enough to keep both Ferrari men on their toes.

As noted, Massa's 2007 qualifying performances had always been very strong, and Istanbul was one of his best. He was 0.217s ahead of Räikkönen and, as we were to find out on race day, he was carrying an extra lap of fuel. It's no exaggeration to say that he won the race with that qualifying lap and, even before he got back to *parc fermé*, Räikkönen knew just how hard it would be to retrieve the situation.

Massa was also a lap heavier than Alonso, and one lighter than Hamilton. That turned out to be a great call by Ferrari, because had Massa been fuelled for one more lap in qualifying, everything else being equal, that extra weight alone would have given the pole position to Hamilton.

The next job for Massa was to convert pole into first place by Turn 1. It helped that the 'wrong' side of the grid in Turkey is notoriously dirty and slow, but Ferrari had another ace up its sleeve. As we had seen previously, the team was able to make the option tyre – in this case officially the medium tyre – work better than its main rivals.

The two tyres were certainly very close in Turkey, and it was one of those weekends when balance, feel and driver preference were just as important in determining the choice as lap time and degradation. Indeed, Alonso took a punt and did his crucial final qualifying lap on the harder tyre – which turned out to be a gamble that didn't do him any favours.

Having the softer of the two tyres fitted at the start of the race gave a slight advantage off the grid, and that clearly didn't hurt either Ferrari driver. Especially Räikkönen, who was able to outdrag Hamilton.

"We made a long run on both tyres on Friday," said Massa, "and it was pretty similar, with maybe just

one or two tenths between them. We knew that the track changes a great deal between Friday and Sunday and the soft [ie medium] tyre should improve even more, so we took a bit of a gamble, although it was a pretty safe risk. Especially for the start of the race, we knew that the soft would be better and we had fantastic starts: Kimi overtook Lewis and we had a very good race on the soft tyre."

"As we've seen a few times this year, our car tends to look after the tyres quite well in the race," noted Massa's engineer, Rob Smedley. "We knew that we would probably be able to fit the soft tyre and we knew that other people probably wouldn't be able to, so we were going to accept that advantage.

"Felipe was absolutely inch-perfect in qualifying, when it was very easy to make a mistake on the tyres, as we saw other drivers were doing. He did the right job and that paid dividends today. He was heavier than Kimi, and that was an added bonus. We were on pole and we had a reasonable amount of fuel in."

Nevertheless, it was a relief to both Smedley and his charge to see Massa make it to Turn 1 clearly ahead.

"We knew that starting on the clean side was going to play into our hands," added Smedley. "That's why it's so important to have the pole. We did that, and we got into the first corner ahead. How much of a relief is it? It was huge, to be honest!"

After that, it was a question of not making any mistakes, although having his team-mate rather than a McLaren behind, and the knowledge that he would be pitting later than Räikkönen, made all the difference.

Massa did have a little extra to think about before his second pit stop, however. "The gap was pretty similar throughout the stint," reported the Brazilian, "but then Kimi started to run two tenths quicker and I started to push again. Then I made a small mistake going into Turn 7, and Kimi was just able to close the gap completely. Luckily the gap was OK to control, the

BELOW Mayhem on the opening lap as Jarno Trulli is tipped into a spin in the middle of pack. Renault's Giancarlo Fisichella was the culprit

OPPOSITE A poor start left Fernando Alonso behind Nick Heidfeld's BMW, but he was ahead after the first of their two pit stops

TALKING POINT
RENAULT'S UPS & DOWNS

After Renault's back-to-back championships, the 2007 season had become a harsh reminder that competitiveness cannot be taken for granted. Executive Director of Engineering Pat Symonds (above left) admitted that it had taken the team much longer to get to grips with the R27 chassis than had been expected.

There had been a couple of factors in this. Firstly, the correlation between what the team was being told by its wind-tunnel figures and what it was seeing on the track in testing were two different things (for more detailed explanation, see Symonds's Renault technical review in the 'Teams' feature).

Secondly, the R27's concept meant that on the Michelin tyres run prior to 2007, it paid dividends to have the weight distribution with a more rearward bias than is the case on this year's control Bridgestones. The outcome was a difficult car, which was not an ideal situation for Heikki Kovalainen, in his first season at the sport's top level.

The team got more of a handle on its problems at the North American races in June, since when Kovalainen's performances had changed "like the flicking of a switch".

The car was never going to become a McLaren/Ferrari challenger, but at least it was looking more capable of leading the midfield group consistently, or even challenging the BMW Saubers.

There was a distraction in the paddock at the Turkish GP with the news that team chief Flavio Briatore (left, on the right) was trying to buy Queens Park Rangers Football Club. The cynics suggested that he was just a front man for his mate Bernie (Ecclestone), who fancied a nicely located bit of London real estate and would shortly be filing a 'change of use' application and turning a nice profit on some houses and supermarkets. Briatore insisted that it was just a group of football friends tabling an offer to help out the club.

And, he said, it wouldn't be allowed to get in the way of Renault, which he wants back at the front of the grid in 2008. Either with or without the services of Fernando Alonso...

On the track, the cars both qualified in the top 10 for the first time since the British GP and Kovalainen charged home sixth. It may not sound much but, in light of the team's season, it was satisfying to get to the flag just 6s behind Nick Heidfeld in the stronger of the two BMW Saubers.

"I'm as proud of what we've done getting on top of our problems this year as when we have been winning championships," said Technical Director Bob Bell. "It's not so much how you handle the ups, it's rather how you cope with the downs that shows your quality. In a different way, we've done a strong job this year."

balance was OK and the car was easy to drive, so it was not so hard, but the small mistake made my life just that little bit more difficult."

It could still have gone wrong – traffic or some other glitch on the crucial in-laps before each of his pit stops – but it didn't. This time, the strategy favoured Massa, just as it hadn't in Magny-Cours.

"As you saw in France," said Smedley, "it's very, very difficult to win the race, as they're both very evenly matched, both in the same car. The one with more fuel usually gets away with it in a situation like that.

"Felipe drove a fantastic race from the green light to the flag, absolutely not a single mistake. It was always close, and the two drivers are very evenly matched, so it was always going to be a close fight, but fortunately we came out on top in the end."

The option tyre worked so well that the Ferraris also took them for the second stint, when they could have gone for the more conservative choice of the harder tyre. Räikkönen did get closer at certain stages, but he was never close enough to contemplate a passing move.

Massa's only real drama throughout was a highly unusual one: a plastic air vent on the top of his helmet cracked and acted like an air brake, which wasn't good

INSIDE LINE
ANTHONY DAVIDSON
SUPER AGURI DRIVER

"Qualifying 11th was great. The prime tyre was easy to get a lap out of, but the option tyre had the ultimate pace, although it tended to destroy itself before the end of the lap.

Turn 8 was the problem. The tyres take really high g-loadings and the temperatures go up. I thought hard about how to do the out-laps on the option tyre. We saw that the warm-up characteristics were good, so maybe that would allow a slow out-lap to protect the tyre, but still with the necessary temperature from the start of the flying lap.

I did my first run in the first qualifying session fairly fast and the warm-up was good, Turn 8 was good, but the tyre graining was there by the end of the lap. The tyre was giving up at just the very section of the lap where you're really relying on it for grip and traction. Those slow Turns 12, 13 and 14 make it such a technical end to the lap, but the car was just sliding and that really costs you.

So for the next lap in first qualifying I tried an even slower out-lap and really focused on trying to keep the tyre together for the whole lap. However, because I hadn't warmed the tyre up enough, the pressures dropped and the car bottomed out through Turn 8. I had a massive moment and was so close to going out there and then.

Into the second qualifying session, I asked the team to increase the pressures to try to get a bit more warm-up so I could still do a slow out-lap without the car bottoming. Turn 8 was alright this time, but the graining was back at the end of the lap. The higher pressures had meant that it grained up easier. So, there wasn't really a window where you could have a stable, easy car in Turn 8 and not have the graining at the end of the lap as well. You had to accept either one or the other.

On my last run in Q2, I went halfway house. I knew Turn 8 was going to be tough and was close to going off, but it came back, gripped, and I knew I was on for a mega lap. I'd taken the pain and now it was all gain.

The last sector was fantastic. I saw some onboard footage from other cars and really believe my lap was the best anyone did at the Turkish GP. I saw Felipe Massa's pole-position lap and I thought mine was better. He was faster because he's in a faster car but, in terms of precision, my lap was better."

either for his neck or for his concentration, but he had the presence of mind to rip it off and chuck the offending item overboard...

After the dramas of the Hungarian GP, McLaren boss Ron Dennis brought his two drivers together and tried to make peace between them, and the Turkish GP proved a far calmer occasion for the team. However, Ferrari had the edge on performance in qualifying, and Hamilton and Alonso had to settle for second and fourth on the grid.

Hamilton lost out to Räikkönen at the start and seemed destined for third place until a late front-right tyre failure. He made it back to the pits and managed to salvage fifth place. "As the tyre was delaminating, it exploded," he explained. "Basically, it was flapping around and broke the front wing. I don't know if it was the front flap, I think it was a piece of trim on the outside of the front wing, but it made a huge difference. I lost front downforce and just couldn't get the car around the corners.

"I think without a doubt we would have finished third at least, but I was pushing obviously... I still had, I think, six laps more fuel than the Ferraris, and I was hoping that in those six laps I would at least maybe

get Kimi. However, the tyre went and I was a bit unlucky. But that's racing.

"Considering what happened, I think we were very, very fortunate to bring it back to the pits. The team did a great job to get the tyres on as quickly as possible and not lose too many places, so I don't think the team should be disappointed. I think we need to look forward and try doing a better job next time."

Alonso was beaten off the line by both BMW Saubers and looked set for a disastrous result in Turkey, but he managed to get past both as the race progressed, before Hamilton's problem gave him an extra bonus and put him on the podium.

"The start did not go to plan and to be overtaken by two cars and find yourself sixth at the first corner was not great," Alonso explained. "My race was a little bit over from there. I was following Nick [Heidfeld] for 17 laps, and these days in F1 it is very, very difficult to overtake. You need to wait for a mistake from the driver in front of you, but Nick was very consistent and driving very well, so I waited for the pit stop and I was lucky to overtake him.

"Then my race started, but I was half-a-minute behind everybody at that point. I just took my pace

OPPOSITE Jenson Button pats team-mate Rubens Barrichello on the back, but it was another fruitless afternoon for the Honda racers

BELOW Anthony Davidson keeps his Super Aguri ahead of Toyota's Ralf Schumacher and Honda's Rubens Barrichello in the early laps

Lewis Hamilton could do nothing about the Ferraris, but his third place was scuppered by this flailing tyre and he fell to fifth

and concentrated on being consistent, on not making a mistake and waiting for the miracle, which only happened with Hamilton."

It was no great surprise that when one of the 'big four' had a delay, a BMW Sauber driver was there to step in and finish fourth. It was a familiar pattern in qualifying as well, as Robert Kubica and Heidfeld claimed fifth and sixth. Both men got away well and slipped past Alonso. However, it soon emerged that Kubica was running very light. Indeed, an early pit stop put him out of sequence and contributed to

him tumbling down to eighth by the end of the race. Heidfeld was on a more normal strategy and was close enough to Hamilton to get ahead when the McLaren driver was delayed, and thereafter he made sure Hamilton couldn't get back past.

Heikki Kovalainen had another good run for Renault and wasn't far behind at the flag in finishing sixth, while the final points went to Nico Rosberg for Williams and Kubica. In a race of few incidents that saw just one retirement, the top 10 was completed by Giancarlo Fisichella and David Coulthard.

Felipe Massa was delighted with his second straight win in Turkey, but Ferrari team-mate Kimi Räikkönen behind him appears to be having trouble with the bubbly

SNAPSHOT FROM
TURKEY

CLOCKWISE FROM RIGHT On the F1 tour, this sunset scene could only be found in Turkey; Heikki Kovalainen larks around; "Here are two types of tyres for your perusal, sir?"; Kimi Räikkönen cuts himself down to the same height as Ferrari boss Jean Todt and team-mate Felipe Massa; girls, girls, girls; Fernando Alonso's manager, Luis Garcia Abad, leaves the Renault inner sanctum, fuelling the rumour mill; pretty, shady character

WEEKEND NEWS

■ Most of the drivers had taken advantage of the break since the Hungarian GP to have a holiday, but none was more adventurous than Jenson Button. The Honda star did a tour of France and Italy with his girlfriend aboard a classic VW bus, staying in a tent they pitched alongside. However, they drew the line at catering for themselves...

■ The Malaysian GP organisers confirmed that the extension of their deal with Bernie Ecclestone had been signed off. Concerned about the threat from the new grand prix in Singapore, the organisers secured their race until 2015 – on the understanding that at FOM's discretion it could become a night event.

■ Toyota indicated that it was in no hurry to confirm its driver line-up for 2008. Jarno Trulli was safe because of his ongoing contract, but Ralf Schumacher's deal was coming to an end and, after a lacklustre season, his appeal had waned. The German said he would be happy to wait for as long as it took.

■ Meanwhile, veteran engineer and sometime technical director Frank Dernie joined Toyota as an adviser on technical matters. The long-time Williams employee, who also enjoyed spells at Lotus, Benetton and Ligier, had no plans to attend races with the team.

■ Renault announced that it had backed off on development of its 2007 car in order to ensure that it was fully prepared for 2008. As part of that programme, the team was pushing ahead with adapting to the new common ECU. At Monza a few days after the Turkish GP, Renault followed Ferrari as only the second team to run the system on track.

RACE RESULTS
TURKEY ISTANBUL

RACE DATE August 26th
CIRCUIT LENGTH 3.317 miles
NO. OF LAPS 58
RACE DISTANCE 192.388 miles
WEATHER Dry, bright, 33°C
TRACK TEMP 48°C
RACE DAY ATTENDANCE 50,000
LAP RECORD Juan Pablo Montoya
1m24.770s, 138.056mph, 2005

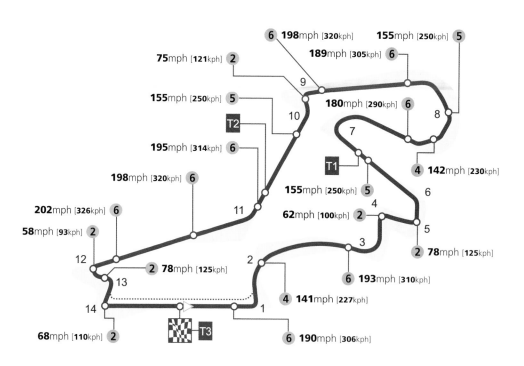

#	PRACTICE 1 Driver	Time	Laps
1	K Räikkönen	1m27.988s	22
2	F Massa	1m28.391s	20
3	F Alonso	1m29.222s	20
4	L Hamilton	1m29.261s	10
5	H Kovalainen	1m29.346s	19
6	N Rosberg	1m29.403s	23
7	R Schumacher	1m29.414s	24
8	G Fisichella	1m29.541s	19
9	N Heidfeld	1m29.641s	20
10	J Trulli	1m29.685s	26
11	R Kubica	1m29.710s	23
12	A Davidson	1m30.384s	17
13	D Coulthard	1m30.398s	23
14	J Button	1m30.483s	17
15	R Barrichello	1m30.580s	25
16	V Liuzzi	1m30.612s	21
17	T Sato	1m30.624s	15
18	A Wurz	1m30.876s	12
19	M Webber	1m30.917s	22
20	S Vettel	1m31.383s	22
21	A Sutil	1m31.445s	31
22	S Yamamoto	1m32.270s	35

#	PRACTICE 2 Driver	Time	Laps
1	L Hamilton	1m28.469s	28
2	K Räikkönen	1m28.762s	21
3	R Schumacher	1m28.773s	23
4	J Trulli	1m28.874s	28
5	F Massa	1m28.884s	25
6	F Alonso	1m28.947s	24
7	N Rosberg	1m28.995s	27
8	H Kovalainen	1m29.025s	28
9	A Wurz	1m29.093s	27
10	R Kubica	1m29.368s	31
11	D Coulthard	1m29.435s	12
12	G Fisichella	1m29.456s	28
13	N Heidfeld	1m29.792s	30
14	J Button	1m29.945s	26
15	R Barrichello	1m30.055s	31
16	T Sato	1m30.104s	27
17	M Webber	1m30.315s	25
18	A Davidson	1m30.530s	24
19	V Liuzzi	1m30.702s	24
20	S Vettel	1m30.801s	16
21	A Sutil	1m31.153s	32
22	S Yamamoto	1m31.175s	32

#	PRACTICE 3 Driver	Time	Laps
1	L Hamilton	1m27.325s	12
2	F Massa	1m27.366s	15
3	K Räikkönen	1m27.506s	16
4	F Alonso	1m27.743s	13
5	N Rosberg	1m28.056s	16
6	N Heidfeld	1m28.184s	18
7	R Kubica	1m28.224s	21
8	G Fisichella	1m28.261s	20
9	M Webber	1m28.337s	15
10	H Kovalainen	1m28.364s	17
11	A Wurz	1m28.413s	16
12	D Coulthard	1m28.448s	14
13	R Schumacher	1m28.481s	20
14	J Trulli	1m28.520s	21
15	J Button	1m28.548s	16
16	R Barrichello	1m28.715s	18
17	A Davidson	1m28.755s	16
18	V Liuzzi	1m28.937s	20
19	S Vettel	1m29.408s	19
20	T Sato	1m29.436s	14
21	A Sutil	1m30.044s	22
22	S Yamamoto	1m30.712s	21

#	QUALIFYING 1 Driver	Time
1	K Räikkönen	1m27.294s
2	F Alonso	1m27.328s
3	F Massa	1m27.488s
4	L Hamilton	1m27.513s
5	R Kubica	1m27.997s
6	N Heidfeld	1m28.099s
7	H Kovalainen	1m28.127s
8	N Rosberg	1m28.275s
9	A Davidson	1m28.304s
10	G Fisichella	1m28.313s
11	J Trulli	1m28.318s
12	A Wurz	1m28.360s
13	J Button	1m28.373s
14	D Coulthard	1m28.395s
15	M Webber	1m28.500s
16	R Barrichello	1m28.792s
17	V Liuzzi	1m28.798s
18	R Schumacher	1m28.809s
19	T Sato	1m28.953s
20	S Vettel	1m29.408s
21	A Sutil	1m29.861s
22	S Yamamoto	1m31.479s

#	QUALIFYING 2 Driver	Time
1	F Alonso	1m26.841s
2	K Räikkönen	1m26.902s
3	L Hamilton	1m26.936s
4	F Massa	1m27.039s
5	R Kubica	1m27.253s
6	N Heidfeld	1m27.253s
7	N Rosberg	1m27.750s
8	H Kovalainen	1m27.784s
9	J Trulli	1m27.801s
10	G Fisichella	1m27.880s
11	A Davidson	1m28.002s
12	M Webber	1m28.013s
13	D Coulthard	1m28.100s
14	R Barrichello	1m28.188s
15	J Button	1m28.220s
16	A Wurz	1m28.390s

Best sectors – Practice
Sec 1 K Räikkönen 32.436s
Sec 2 L Hamilton 30.709s
Sec 3 F Alonso 23.927s

Speed trap – Practice
1 L Hamilton 199.1mph
2 J Trulli 199.0mph
3 H Kovalainen 198.2mph

Best sectors – Qualifying
Sec 1 K Räikkönen 32.076s
Sec 2 F Alonso 30.633s
Sec 3 K Räikkönen 24.033s

Speed trap – Qualifying
1 F Alonso 201.3mph
2 L Hamilton 200.1mph
3 J Trulli 199.6mph

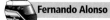

Fernando Alonso
"My race was pretty much over when I came into the first corner in sixth. I followed Heidfeld for 17 laps. We were able to pass him in the first stops, but I was 30s down."

Giancarlo Fisichella
"My race was compromised at the first corner. Jarno braked suddenly in front of me, I had nowhere to go and hit him. That ruined his race, but it cost me points."

Felipe Massa
"This is becoming a special place for me! Only towards the end of the second stint did I make a mistake which cost me the gap I had over Kimi, who closed right up."

Jenson Button
"It was fun passing 10 cars! I had a good time and was able to pass quite a few of the midfield entries that we've been struggling to keep pace with in recent races."

Nick Heidfeld
"I braked very late for Turn 1 and came very close to Alonso. I dreamt I could keep him behind me, but we knew he'd refuel later. After the stop, he was in front."

Ralf Schumacher
"The car was not ideal on hard tyres. Also, as I was on a one-stop strategy, my car was heavy. If our qualifying had been better, we would have been able to score."

Lewis Hamilton
"I saw bits fly off the tyre and then it just blew into Turn 9. It was lucky that I didn't put it in the gravel and managed to get it back to the pits. In the end, I only lost two places."

Heikki Kovalainen
"Heidfeld pushed me wide on the run to the first corner, and I had to back off. But I defended my position and once the tyres started working, the car was stable."

Kimi Räikkönen
"The race was probably decided in qualifying. The quick lap at the end? I was bored with spending the race behind another car and so I tried to see how quick I could go."

Rubens Barrichello
"It was always going to be hard starting from the back. The car was moving around quite a bit from corner to corner and there wasn't much I could do from the back."

Robert Kubica
"I could not build up a big enough gap when I was running light in the first stint. Every time I pitted, someone passed me. My problems were really a bit of everything."

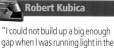

Jarno Trulli
"The start went well, but Fisichella hit me in the back at Turn 1 and I lost a lot of places. I passed a lot of cars, but when you end up at the back it is so hard to catch up."

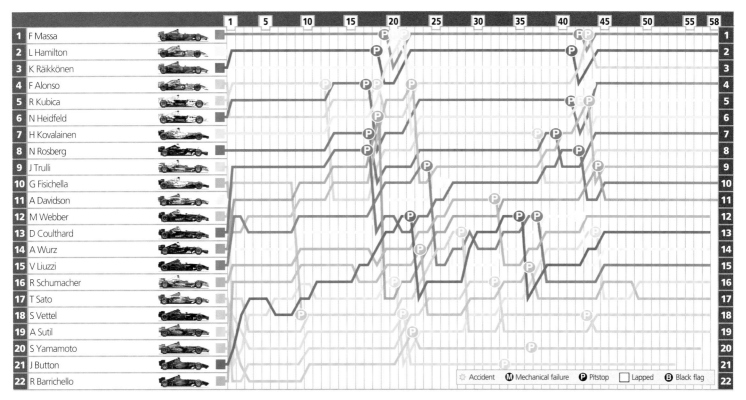

	Driver				1	5	10	15	20	25	30	35	40	45	50	55	58	
1	F Massa																	1
2	L Hamilton																	2
3	K Räikkönen																	3
4	F Alonso																	4
5	R Kubica																	5
6	N Heidfeld																	6
7	H Kovalainen																	7
8	N Rosberg																	8
9	J Trulli																	9
10	G Fisichella																	10
11	A Davidson																	11
12	M Webber																	12
13	D Coulthard																	13
14	A Wurz																	14
15	V Liuzzi																	15
16	R Schumacher																	16
17	T Sato																	17
18	S Vettel																	18
19	A Sutil																	19
20	S Yamamoto																	20
21	J Button																	21
22	R Barrichello																	22

Accident   Ⓜ Mechanical failure   Ⓟ Pitstop   ☐ Lapped   Ⓑ Black flag

QUALIFYING 3

	Driver	Time
1	F Massa	1m27.329s
2	L Hamilton	1m27.373s
3	K Räikkönen	1m27.546s
4	F Alonso	1m27.574s
5	R Kubica	1m27.722s
6	N Heidfeld	1m28.037s
7	H Kovalainen	1m28.491s
8	N Rosberg	1m28.501s
9	J Trulli	1m28.740s
10	G Fisichella	1m29.322s

GRID

	Driver	Time
1	F Massa	1m27.329s
2	L Hamilton	1m27.373s
3	K Räikkönen	1m27.546s
4	F Alonso	1m27.574s
5	R Kubica	1m27.722s
6	N Heidfeld	1m28.037s
7	H Kovalainen	1m28.491s
8	N Rosberg	1m28.501s
9	J Trulli	1m28.740s
10	G Fisichella	1m29.322s
11	A Davidson	1m28.002s
12	M Webber	1m28.013s
13	D Coulthard	1m28.100s
14	R Barrichello	1m28.188s
15	A Wurz	1m28.390s
16	V Liuzzi	1m28.798s
17	R Schumacher	1m28.809s
18	T Sato	1m28.953s
19	S Vettel	1m29.408s
20	A Sutil	1m29.861s
21	S Yamamoto	1m31.479s
22*	J Button	1m28.220s

* 10-PLACE ENGINE-CHANGE PENALTY

RACE

	Driver	Car	Laps	Time	Avg. mph	Fastest	Stops
1	F Massa	Ferrari F2007	58	1h26m42.161s	133.040	1m27.922s	2
2	K Räikkönen	Ferrari F2007	58	1h26m44.436s	132.983	1m27.295s	2
3	F Alonso	McLaren-Mercedes MP4-22	58	1h27m08.342s	132.374	1m28.070s	2
4	N Heidfeld	BMW Sauber F1.07	58	1h27m21.835s	132.034	1m28.319s	2
5	L Hamilton	McLaren-Mercedes MP4-22	58	1h27m27.246s	131.898	1m27.963s	2
6	H Kovalainen	Renault R27	58	1h27m28.330s	131.870	1m28.603s	2
7	N Rosberg	Williams-Toyota FW29	58	1h27m37.939s	131.629	1m28.536s	2
8	R Kubica	BMW Sauber F1.07	58	1h27m38.868s	131.606	1m28.918s	2
9	G Fisichella	Renault R27	58	1h27m41.652s	131.536	1m28.793s	2
10	D Coulthard	Red Bull-Renault RB3	58	1h27m53.170s	131.245	1m29.068s	2
11	A Wurz	Williams-Toyota FW29	58	1h28m01.789s	131.035	1m28.737s	2
12	R Schumacher	Toyota TF107	57	1h26m42.779s	130.729	1m28.924s	1
13	J Button	Honda RA107	57	1h26m56.426s	130.388	1m28.873s	2
14	A Davidson	Super Aguri-Honda SA07	57	1h27m02.147s	130.245	1m29.658s	2
15	V Liuzzi	Toro Rosso-Ferrari STR02	57	1h27m11.636s	130.009	1m29.563s	2
16	J Trulli	Toyota TF107	57	1h27m12.168s	129.996	1m29.459s	2
17	R Barrichello	Honda RA107	57	1h27m13.195s	129.969	1m29.513s	2
18	T Sato	Super Aguri-Honda SA07	57	1h27m36.215s	129.400	1m29.916s	1
19	S Vettel	Toro Rosso-Ferrari STR02	57	1h27m47.110s	129.133	1m29.983s	2
20	S Yamamoto	Spyker-Ferrari F8-VII	56	1h27m48.209s	126.840	1m30.951s	2
21	A Sutil	Spyker-Ferrari F8-VII	53	1h25m43.944s	122.939	1m30.617s	2
R	M Webber	Red Bull-Renault RB3	9	Hydraulics	–	1m30.808s	0

CHAMPIONSHIP

	Driver	Pts
1	L Hamilton	84
2	F Alonso	79
3	F Massa	69
4	K Räikkönen	68
5	N Heidfeld	47
6	R Kubica	29
7	H Kovalainen	19
8	G Fisichella	17
9	A Wurz	13
10	N Rosberg	9
11	M Webber	8
12	D Coulthard	8
13	J Trulli	7
14	R Schumacher	5
15	T Sato	4
16	J Button	1
17	S Vettel	1

Fastest Lap
K Räikkönen 1m27.295s
(136.786mph) on lap 57

Fastest speed trap
Hamilton 199.0mph
Slowest speed trap
Vettel 191.5mph

Fastest pit stop
1 A Wurz 26.120s
2 A Davidson 26.625s
3 F Alonso 26.802s

	Constructor	Pts
1	McLaren-Mercedes	148
2	Ferrari	137
3	BMW Sauber	77
4	Renault	36
5	Williams-Toyota	22
6	Red Bull-Renault	16
7	Toyota	12
8	Super Aguri-Honda	4
9	Honda	1

David Coulthard
"I think I made up four places at the start, but the car was a bit inconsistent which did not help me maintain a good pace, especially when I had a bit of fuel on board."

Nico Rosberg
"I am very happy to have beaten Kubica – I didn't expect him to pit first. We beat him fair and square. It became harder towards the end, but the car handled pretty well."

Vitantonio Liuzzi
"The most important thing is that I finished. I had upshift problems and towards the end I eased off to look after the engine. It was really good to see the chequered flag."

Adrian Sutil
"I stalled and got stuck in gear and, as Sakon was coming in, they had to put the car in the garage to restart it. I had to stop on the last lap with fuel pressure problems."

Takuma Sato
"I did not have a good start, but held my position. I was optimistic that I would gain some places into Turn 1, but one of the Toyotas spun and I lost many positions."

Mark Webber
"It looks like it was hydraulics. It's a shame as I was fuelled to go longer than those ahead of us. On the lap before I stopped, I started to have problems downshifting."

Alexander Wurz
"I felt good on my first set of tyres which let me attack. After the first stop, it was close as a lot of people on a one-stop strategy went past me and that cost me time."

Sebastian Vettel
"I got away well, but as I upshifted I lost momentum. Apart from that, my biggest problem was at the pit stop when the engine stalled, so we had to re-start it and I was in neutral."

Sakon Yamamoto
"I would like to thank the team, as my aim was to finish the grand prix. I stalled in the pit stop as the fuel pressure was low, but I did not lose too much time."

Anthony Davidson
"I got sandwiched between Coulthard and Fisichella. Fisi and Trulli touched and I had to go off track. I clipped another car when I rejoined and suffered damage."

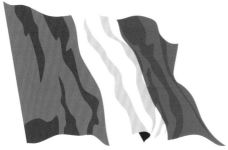

FORMULA 1™
GRAN PREMIO D'ITALIA 2007
MONZA

TWO STOPS FOR GLORY

McLaren's pride was dented by the spying scandal gripping Formula One, so it had to win at Monza, and it did as Fernando Alonso drove an imperious race to victory

McLaren ignored the ongoing controversy surrounding the spying scandal to score a dominant 1–2 finish on Ferrari's home ground at Monza, as victor Fernando Alonso clawed back a little more of Lewis Hamilton's advantage.

The Italian GP was not the best race of the year, but for once the fans saw a race in which differing strategies created real intrigue, and we even saw a spectacular pass for position involving two of the leading contenders.

On top of this, the victory at least gave McLaren a boost prior to the World Motor Sport Council's second investigation into the spy scandal, due just four days after the race in Paris.

McLaren's performance advantage was already apparent in the previous week's testing, and the MP4-22's performance over Monza's kerbs was key.

"We worked very hard to address the challenges of Monza," said McLaren team principal Ron Dennis, "and that is one of the challenges, the ability for the car to ride the kerbs."

Ferrari suffered a blow on Saturday morning when Kimi Räikkönen had his huge crash just a few laps into the practice session. The first impression was

"It's been a very difficult season for us, but you just have to keep your head down and keep working. I don't think it's a secret that the RA107 has been lacking downforce and aerodynamic efficiency, so obviously Monza, which is very low downforce, is a track where we were going to be hurt a bit less than at other places.

We did a three-day Monza test before the grand prix and we knew from that that we should be in better shape. There had been some changes to the suspension, which helped, and we also had some aerodynamic mods.

Despite the mods, we were still slow in a straight line, but that wasn't going to hurt us too much in qualifying and I made it into Q3 for the first time since Monte Carlo, which, interestingly enough, is right at the other end of the aerodynamic spectrum. That was satisfying, but I used up my full quota of the softer tyres in Q1 and Q2, so I was under no illusions about any heroics in Q3. It was always going to be 10th for me.

It's always a very busy first corner at Monza, after the long drag down to the first chicane, but I got through unscathed and picked up a place when I beat Trulli away from the grid. I was right in behind Nico and we had a fantastic scrap for most of the first stint. I passed him on lap eight when I was as late as possible down the inside into the first chicane. Nico ran straight on across the chicane trying to defend the place and came out ahead, but realised that he risked a penalty and was forced to get off the throttle and let me back past.

That put me into the points and I picked up another place a couple of laps later when Massa's Ferrari retired. It was tough to keep Nico behind me though, because the Williams was a bit quicker than us and Nico had qualified 0.8s quicker. Part of that was down to fuel load and I ended up going three laps further than him as we both did one-stoppers. I obviously wanted to keep him behind, but he got me back again on lap 20, which gave him enough time to take advantage of his lighter load.

It was good to score just our second point of the year, but I had quite a bit of understeer all afternoon and, if we'd got the most out of the set-up, another couple of places might have been possible. Still, it was progress."

that he'd suffered a mechanical failure, but later the Finn insisted that he'd locked a brake on a bump. The spare car was pressed into service, with the race engine from the crashed car fitted to avoid penalty. Räikkönen himself had a sore neck.

Come qualifying, Alonso pipped Hamilton to pole position, while there was a safe margin to Massa in third place. In fact, this was more than McLaren had anticipated. On top of this, Räikkönen had qualified significantly behind his team-mate in fifth place, with BMW Sauber's Nick Heidfeld having sneaked in front of him. Even allowing for his uncomfortable morning, it was apparent that Räikkönen had qualified with a little extra fuel on board. The key question was whether it was enough to suggest that he was going to go for just one, early, stop – a perfectly legitimate strategy, even for a front-runner.

For McLaren, stopping once was never going to be an option, as Dennis explained: "We were just trying to look after our tyres. If you've got inherent pace, then there's obviously something absorbing that pace, which is the tyres. Of all the teams, I think we're probably giving the tyres the hardest time, and therefore that's why we opted for two pit stops and

felt, after all our testing, that was a better way to win the race. And this proved to be the case."

If there were any doubts about Räikkönen's choice, they were answered when his selection of the softer tyre for the first stint was revealed on the grid. Since this would be the shorter of his two planned stints, it was logical to use up the less favoured tyre and then have the more reliable medium tyre for the second, longer stint.

"Ferrari took an intelligent decision on that car," said McLaren Chief Operating Officer Martin Whitmarsh. "We thought that they might one-stop. I think they weren't quite as quick as us here, so we believed that's what they might do. We were fairly sure when the tyre heaters came off on the grid, seeing that Kimi was on the option tyre, we assumed that he was probably stopping between lap 20 and lap 25, and would then one-stop it from there."

A couple of crucial things happened at the start of the race. Firstly, Räikkönen got ahead of Heidfeld, which meant that the German wouldn't be a factor. Secondly, Hamilton stayed ahead of Massa, although it was close. We had seen some aggressive first laps from Hamilton earlier in the year, and this

OPPOSITE TOP Media interest in Fernando Alonso was intense, as McLaren found itself under the spotlight due to spying charges

OPPOSITE BOTTOM Takuma Sato rounds Monza's Parabolica en route to finishing a lap down

ABOVE Jenson Button scored his second point of the year after a good battle with Nico Rosberg

TALKING POINT
WHAT NEXT FOR NICO?

After an opening season at Williams in which Nico Rosberg was shaded by Mark Webber in a car that gave the team the worst ever constructors' championship finish (eighth) in its history, he has emerged as one of the hot properties of 2007.

While Lewis Hamilton was taking most of the plaudits, Rosberg's qualifying performances overshadowed those of his Williams team-mate Alexander Wurz and his name has been on many lips as a star of the future.

When, mid-season, rumours of a potential Ferrari B-team emerged, run by Nicolas Todt, son of the Ferrari supremo, Nico's name was mentioned. When rumours of the difficulties between Hamilton and Fernando Alonso became reality and the chances of the two staying together at McLaren in 2008 started looking slim, his was the name whispered as a potential McLaren man.

He was also linked with Toyota, as Ralf Schumacher was reaching the end of his contract and Nico – young, quick and German – appeared to fit the bill.

Added credence was lent by the fact that Williams uses Toyota engines.

At the Italian GP, where Nico finished in the points for the third successive race, in sixth place, the talk gathered momentum. However, Sir Frank Williams, never a man to have his driver line-up dictated to him, was adamant that he was in no way interested in selling Nico.

"He's doing a great job for us," Frank said. "If you put him in a Ferrari or a McLaren, I'm absolutely sure that he would be qualifying it on the front row of the grid. He's definitely a man to watch, that's sure."

The man himself was equally firm in his commitment to the team: "It's nice to be talked about, as it shows you are making the right impression, and I do feel that I have driven very well this year, but I am not interested in leaving Williams. The team is working well and I have seen some of the plans for next year – and they are exciting. I'm very happy where I am."

Rosberg, multi-lingual and with the looks befitting a grand prix driver, has been labelled a marketing dream by none other than Sir Jackie Stewart, a man who always had an appreciation of the sport's commercial possibilities. "He could be to motor racing what David Beckham is to football," said JYS.

Whether the mutual solidarity between Rosberg and the Williams team was the real thing or a price-maximising opening stance for future negotiations was much discussed up and down the paddock.

was another good one as he refused to give up after Massa briefly got ahead on the run to the first corner, the right-left chicane. He even had a little luck, surviving a nudge from the Ferrari without a puncture, and the ensuing trip across the chicane also went without penalty after the FIA deemed that he had little choice after the bump from Massa.

"It was a fantastic overtaking manoeuvre at the start," said Whitmarsh. "Having lost out in the initial launch to Massa, I think Lewis did everything that was expected of him at the first corner..."

David Coulthard wasn't quite as lucky after tapping Giancarlo Fisichella's Renault, and the loss of his front wing and massive crash at Curva Grande on the second lap led to a safety-car interlude. This was a major blow to McLaren, because any such intervention hindered the two-stoppers as it reduced the number of laps they had to open a gap, and helped one-stoppers because it effectively lengthened their first stints. In fact, the full-course yellow stretched out to lap six, enough to give everyone a couple of extra laps to their first stops.

The complexion of the race changed right after the safety car withdrew, with Massa's sudden retirement due to a rear damper-related problem. With Massa gone, Räikkönen came into the picture as Ferrari's principal candidate, and he stayed uncomfortably close to the McLarens.

The safety car had given everyone extra mileage, so Hamilton came in on lap 18 and Alonso two laps later, having once again done an excellent job of conserving fuel. Räikkönen enjoyed a spell in the lead until pitting on lap 25, with 28 laps of the race still to run. He was then fuelled to the finish, and it was now all about how far ahead the McLarens could get before their second stops.

As the stops approached, it seemed that Alonso was safe, but Hamilton wasn't quite. Then, just to make things complicated, McLaren brought him in a lap or two earlier than planned. The reason was a tyre vibration and, after the expensive failure in the Turkish GP, neither team nor driver wanted to take any risks.

"The target was to get 28 seconds clear before the second stop," explained Whitmarsh. "That's the gap you need here to come out in front, but in Lewis's case we didn't quite achieve that. Lewis reported some vibration so we took an arguably conservative decision to pit him early. Whether we needed to or not, the fact is that Lewis was able to cope with the situation quite brilliantly.

"Everything was moved from schedule because with a safety-car period things move around and we felt at the time that was the way to go. We were on the edge with the tyres here in the way that we were pushing them, and we were right to take a conservative view after the issues we've had recently."

Dennis elaborated on the thinking in the pits: "We stopped a little early with Lewis. He was suffering a little with vibration, but since the incident with Kimi at the Nürburgring in 2005 we now monitor very carefully not so much how much vibration you get on a flat-spotted tyre, but we've done a lot of rig-testing to determine what sort of forces become challenging for the suspension to accommodate. So we knew there was nothing unsafe with the vibration Lewis was feeling, but it was a little bit uncomfortable, so we brought the stop earlier to handle that problem."

The bottom line was that the team knew that the premature stop would drop Hamilton behind Räikkönen. The question was what would happen after that? Both men would have identical fuel loads, that's to say enough to get to the flag, but Hamilton would have new tyres that would be superior for a few laps, while Räikkönen's had already run 15.

Dennis was adamant that everything was under control: "Even though we calculated that he would

OPPOSITE Felipe Massa missed an opportunity to please the *tifosi* when he retired with a rear damper-related problem after 10 laps

BELOW Nico Rosberg battled with Jenson Button before the Williams driver prevailed and took sixth place

ABOVE Hamilton and Alonso put their intra-team rivalry behind them to acknowledge a 1–2 result that boosted beleaguered McLaren

BELOW Polish, British, Swedish, Finnish, Irish and Spanish flags, and not an Italian one in sight...

lose the second place to Kimi, with fresh tyres and our pace which was very good, we knew he should be able to get past him. It was a bit of a calculated risk, but Lewis did a good job."

Hamilton hit back almost immediately with a superb pass into the first chicane that appeared to catch Räikkönen unawares. It certainly wasn't as straightforward as he made it look when he dived down the inside into the chicane at the start of lap 43. He still had to scrub off speed by putting the car sideways, but did it with aplomb and the move was

nailed. Räikkönen was left with no answer.

"We're talking about Lewis Hamilton, so no situation is absolutely hopeless," said Whitmarsh, "but it was clearly quite tough. We know how good Kimi is, and therefore it was a big ask to go out there and do what he did.

"Lewis has a great tactical mind, and he recognised that at that stage he was on the option tyre, recognised that he had two laps and then potentially a bit of graining or the tyres going off, so he knew when to take the risk. That was his opportunity. Had he not nailed it then, it may have been difficult subsequently. It was Lewis's skill, will power, determination and bravery that just hustled through. It was a great bit of overtaking."

After that, Räikkönen slowed his pace, and the gap grew dramatically.

"Kimi was suffering with his neck," said Dennis, "and then he obviously slowed dramatically. He dropped his pace by nearly two seconds per lap, and that allowed us to conserve our engines for Spa.

"I think that it was a little difficult to say what their strategy would have been in normal circumstances, but clearly Kimi's accident was not very conducive to them getting the best out of their own situation. In the end, we showed through testing and qualifying that we really had the pace here and I feel that it was a well-deserved win for the team as a whole."

Alonso was certainly pleased: "The team told me Kimi was on a one-stop strategy and we decided to do two stops to avoid any risk with the tyres. That was the main concern. We knew we had the pace. We knew that with two stops the victory was in our hands with no problems, so there was no point in taking risks with a one-stopper."

Although Heidfeld lost out to Räikkönen at the start, he gained a spot when Massa retired. Heidfeld pitted later than many expected, on lap 21, which showed how good his qualifying performance had been. Team-mate Robert Kubica ran just behind him, but lost time when his car dropped off its jack at his first pit stop. Heidfeld then had an untroubled and relatively lonely race to yet another fourth-place finish, while Kubica recovered to be just 4s behind him at the chequered flag in fifth.

Nico Rosberg ran in eighth place in the first stint, and became embroiled in a battle with Jenson Button. He finally made it by the Honda driver on lap 21. A single stop then moved him ahead of Renault's Heikki Kovalainen and he finished a very respectable sixth. Kovalainen continued his good recent form by securing seventh place as one of very few drivers outside the top-six qualifiers to opt for two stops.

The unique high-speed/low-downforce nature of Monza seemed to flatter the unloved Honda as Button managed to qualify 10th, this the first time a Honda had made the top 10 since Monaco. He then had a strong first stint, getting ahead of Rosberg to run in seventh place. The Englishman pitted on lap 33 and lost out to Rosberg once again, but nevertheless made it home in eighth to score the team's second point of the year. That said, Super Aguri still had double that number to their tally...

SNAPSHOT FROM
ITALY

CLOCKWISE FROM RIGHT How to find the circuit in this royal park; Forza Ferrari; Luca di Montezemolo looks serious as the McLaren challenge mounts; Fernando Alonso appears on top of the world after closing the points gap to Lewis Hamilton; for grandstand, read tree; since when did gorillas come from Finland?; McLaren principal Ron Dennis and the team's press officer Ellen Kolby feel the pressure; lonely lenses await some action

WEEKEND NEWS

■ McLaren had a scare at the start of the weekend when it was revealed that Lewis Hamilton had won the Hungarian GP with a revised gearbox that had not been through a crash test. It subsequently passed and the FIA accepted that there had been some confusion on the matter. The team was fined $50,000 for its slip-up.

■ A rare press release from Formula One supremo Bernie Ecclestone announced that from 2009 Suzuka would alternate the Japanese GP with the Toyota-owned Fuji Speedway. All parties claimed that the move had been made in the interest of the sport in Japan.

■ Discussions about the unpopular fuel-burn phase of qualifying produced a potentially simple solution for the 2008 World Championship: the final session would be shorter and there would be no fuel credit. In other words, if you needed a second qualifying run you would simply eat into your race fuel allowance.

■ Research into a possible night race continued when Nelson Piquet Jr drove a GP2 car at a floodlit Paul Ricard circuit, mainly to evaluate how the car appeared on TV. The Renault test driver reported that it felt 'normal', and there appeared to be no major handicaps.

■ After discussions at the Turkish GP, it was revealed that the Dutch Mol family was to team up with Indian billionaire Vijay Mallya to buy the Spyker team from its struggling owner of just one year, Spyker cars. Mallya's Kingfisher Airlines was already involved in the sport as a sponsor of the Toyota Formula One team.

RACE RESULTS
ITALY
MONZA

Official Results © [2007]
Formula One Administration Limited,
6 Princes Gate, London, SW7 1QJ.
No reproduction without permission.
All copyright and database rights reserved.

RACE DATE September 9th
CIRCUIT LENGTH 3.600 miles
NO. OF LAPS 53
RACE DISTANCE 190.587 miles
WEATHER Dry and bright, 25°C
TRACK TEMP 35°C
RACE DAY ATTENDANCE 90,000
LAP RECORD Rubens Barrichello
1m21.046s, 159.726mph, 2004

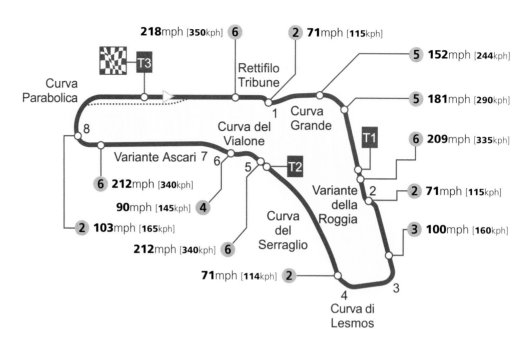

	PRACTICE 1				PRACTICE 2				PRACTICE 3				QUALIFYING 1			QUALIFYING 2	
	Driver	Time	Laps		Driver	Time	Laps		Driver	Time	Laps		Driver	Time		Driver	Time
1	K Räikkönen	1m22.446s	20	1	F Alonso	1m22.386s	30	1	F Alonso	1m22.054s	10	1	F Alonso	1m21.718s	1	F Alonso	1m21.356s
2	F Massa	1m22.590s	17	2	L Hamilton	1m23.209s	33	2	L Hamilton	1m22.200s	11	2	L Hamilton	1m21.956s	2	L Hamilton	1m21.746s
3	L Hamilton	1m22.618s	18	3	G Fisichella	1m23.584s	38	3	F Massa	1m22.615s	11	3	F Massa	1m22.309s	3	F Massa	1m21.993s
4	F Alonso	1m22.840s	12	4	R Kubica	1m23.599s	44	4	N Heidfeld	1m22.855s	15	4	K Räikkönen	1m22.673s	4	K Räikkönen	1m22.369s
5	N Rosberg	1m23.472s	21	5	N Rosberg	1m23.679s	33	5	R Kubica	1m23.287s	14	5	R Kubica	1m23.088s	5	R Kubica	1m22.400s
6	J Button	1m23.668s	21	6	F Massa	1m23.722s	27	6	N Rosberg	1m23.454s	13	6	N Heidfeld	1m23.107s	6	N Heidfeld	1m22.466s
7	G Fisichella	1m23.671s	22	7	N Heidfeld	1m23.821s	38	7	A Wurz	1m23.596s	15	7	N Rosberg	1m23.333s	7	N Rosberg	1m22.748s
8	R Kubica	1m23.703s	22	8	K Räikkönen	1m23.833s	12	8	J Trulli	1m23.672s	16	8	R Barrichello	1m23.474s	8	J Button	1m23.021s
9	N Heidfeld	1m23.886s	17	9	H Kovalainen	1m23.848s	32	9	H Kovalainen	1m23.672s	12	9	H Kovalainen	1m23.505s	9	J Trulli	1m23.107s
10	J Trulli	1m23.965s	29	10	A Wurz	1m23.881s	32	10	M Webber	1m23.708s	13	10	G Fisichella	1m23.559s	10	H Kovalainen	1m23.134s
11	H Kovalainen	1m24.076s	21	11	J Trulli	1m23.919s	39	11	J Button	1m23.803s	15	11	M Webber	1m23.578s	11	M Webber	1m23.166s
12	R Barrichello	1m24.564s	19	12	R Schumacher	1m23.922s	29	12	R Barrichello	1m23.830s	14	12	S Vettel	1m23.578s	12	R Barrichello	1m23.176s
13	T Sato	1m24.587s	15	13	J Button	1m24.137s	36	13	S Vettel	1m23.853s	14	13	J Button	1m23.639s	13	A Wurz	1m23.209s
14	M Webber	1m24.595s	22	14	M Webber	1m24.328s	31	14	G Fisichella	1m23.877s	12	14	A Davidson	1m23.646s	14	A Davidson	1m23.274s
15	R Schumacher	1m24.660s	20	15	R Barrichello	1m24.462s	40	15	A Davidson	1m23.942s	12	15	J Trulli	1m23.724s	15	G Fisichella	1m23.325s
16	A Wurz	1m24.689s	29	16	D Coulthard	1m24.605s	31	16	T Sato	1m24.022s	16	16	A Wurz	1m23.739s	16	S Vettel	1m23.351s
17	A Davidson	1m24.694s	17	17	T Sato	1m25.328s	27	17	D Coulthard	1m24.055s	12	17	T Sato	1m23.749s			
18	D Coulthard	1m24.810s	19	18	S Vettel	1m25.459s	36	18	R Schumacher	1m24.167s	13	18	R Schumacher	1m23.787s			
19	A Sutil	1m25.130s	24	19	A Sutil	1m25.531s	24	19	V Liuzzi	1m24.208s	15	19	V Liuzzi	1m23.886s			
20	S Vettel	1m25.439s	25	20	V Liuzzi	1m25.567s	26	20	K Räikkönen	1m24.442s	3	20	D Coulthard	1m24.019s			
21	S Yamamoto	1m25.448s	25	21	S Yamamoto	1m25.863s	40	21	S Yamamoto	1m24.736s	17	21	A Sutil	1m24.699s			
22	V Liuzzi	1m25.762s	25	22	A Davidson	1m26.021s	6	22	A Sutil	1m24.943s	18	22	S Yamamoto	1m25.084s			

Best sectors – Practice			Speed trap – Practice			Best sectors – Qualifying			Speed trap – Qualifying		
Sec 1	L Hamilton	26.783s	1	R Kubica	217.2mph	Sec 1	F Alonso	26.605s	1	N Heidfeld	217.2mph
Sec 2	F Alonso	27.764s	2	N Heidfeld	217.1mph	Sec 2	L Hamilton	27.709s	2	R Kubica	216.7mph
Sec 3	F Alonso	27.364s	3	F Alonso	216.8mph	Sec 3	F Alonso	26.949s	3	J Trulli	216.1mph

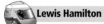

Fernando Alonso

"To win at Monza for the first time is special. My start wasn't perfect, and I had to defend my lead in to the first corner. To win in front of the Italian fans is very emotional."

Giancarlo Fisichella

"I lost a place to Davidson. Then Coulthard hit the back of my car and it damaged a rear endplate. There was nothing to gain, so we turned the engine down."

Felipe Massa

"It's horrible to see your chances go early on. There was something not working with the rear suspension and I pitted, thinking it might be a puncture, but it wasn't."

Jenson Button

"It was nice to get a point, but it was frustrating as I flat-spotted the front right and this meant that I couldn't fend off Rosberg and the long first stint compromised me."

Nick Heidfeld

"I was on the outside at Turn 2 and lost out to Kimi. Our strategy was to gain advantage over the one-stoppers, but this didn't work out because of the safety car."

Ralf Schumacher

"That was a very disillusioning result. It didn't work very well and it was a struggle. We still have problems with kerbs and that makes a big difference at Monza."

Lewis Hamilton

"Felipe got past at the start. I outbraked him and Fernando into Turn 1, and thought I was going to get past, but then Felipe clipped me and sent me over the chicane."

Heikki Kovalainen

"I passed Kubica and was fighting with Heidfeld going into the Curva Grande, but he put me on the grass and I had to back off, which meant I lost ground to Kubica too."

Kimi Räikkönen

"This was tough due to the pain in my neck after my crash, which made it hard under braking. Hamilton's passing move? I tried to defend, but he was quicker."

Rubens Barrichello

"It was a good race and I put in some good laps on the prime tyres, but my challenge was effectively over when Webber was just able to get out ahead at the second stop."

Robert Kubica

"I didn't arrive straight for my pit stop, so the car slid from the jack. After the stop, we couldn't get the jack out from under the front wing, so it cost me a lot of time."

Jarno Trulli

"It was a pity that we made such a poor getaway, as our pace was good. Again, we had problems at the start. I lost three places and from then on it was difficult."

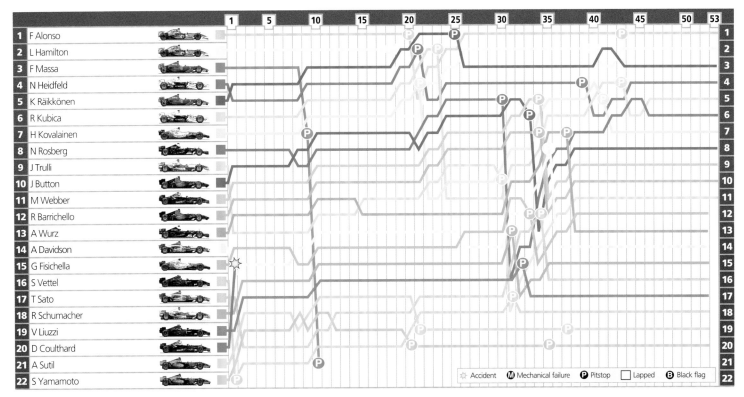

			1	5	10	15	20	25	30	35	40	45	50	53		
1	F Alonso															1
2	L Hamilton															2
3	F Massa															3
4	N Heidfeld															4
5	K Räikkönen															5
6	R Kubica															6
7	H Kovalainen															7
8	N Rosberg															8
9	J Trulli															9
10	J Button															10
11	M Webber															11
12	R Barrichello															12
13	A Wurz															13
14	A Davidson															14
15	G Fisichella															15
16	S Vettel															16
17	T Sato															17
18	R Schumacher															18
19	V Liuzzi															19
20	D Coulthard															20
21	A Sutil															21
22	S Yamamoto															22

☼ Accident   Ⓜ Mechanical failure   Ⓟ Pitstop   ☐ Lapped   Ⓑ Black flag

QUALIFYING 3

	Driver	Time
1	F Alonso	1m21.997s
2	L Hamilton	1m22.034s
3	F Massa	1m22.549s
4	N Heidfeld	1m23.174s
5	K Räikkönen	1m23.183s
6	R Kubica	1m23.446s
7	H Kovalainen	1m24.102s
8	N Rosberg	1m24.382s
9	J Trulli	1m24.555s
10	J Button	1m25.165s

GRID

	Driver	Time
1	F Alonso	1m21.997s
2	L Hamilton	1m22.034s
3	F Massa	1m22.549s
4	N Heidfeld	1m23.174s
5	K Räikkönen	1m23.183s
6	R Kubica	1m23.446s
7	H Kovalainen	1m24.102s
8	N Rosberg	1m24.382s
9	J Trulli	1m24.555s
10	J Button	1m25.165s
11	M Webber	1m23.166s
12	R Barrichello	1m23.176s
13	A Wurz	1m23.209s
14	A Davidson	1m23.274s
15	G Fisichella	1m23.325s
16	S Vettel	1m23.351s
17	T Sato	1m23.749s
18	R Schumacher	1m23.787s
19	V Liuzzi	1m23.886s
20	D Coulthard	1m24.019s
21	A Sutil	1m24.699s
22	S Yamamoto	1m25.084s

RACE

	Driver	Car	Laps	Time	Avg. mph	Fastest	Stops
1	F Alonso	McLaren-Mercedes MP4-22	53	1h18m37.806s	145.460	1m22.871s	2
2	L Hamilton	McLaren-Mercedes MP4-22	53	1h18m43.868s	145.284	1m22.936s	2
3	K Räikkönen	Ferrari F2007	53	1h19m05.131s	144.622	1m23.370s	1
4	N Heidfeld	BMW Sauber F1.07	53	1h19m34.368s	143.747	1m23.681s	2
5	R Kubica	BMW Sauber F1.07	53	1h19m38.364s	143.617	1m23.908s	2
6	N Rosberg	Williams-Toyota FW29	53	1h19m43.616s	143.459	1m24.472s	1
7	H Kovalainen	Renault R27	53	1h19m44.557s	143.341	1m24.226s	2
8	J Button	Honda RA107	53	1h19m49.974s	143.269	1m24.532s	1
9	M Webber	Red Bull-Renault RB3	53	1h19m53.685s	143.158	1m24.824s	1
10	R Barrichello	Honda RA107	53	1h19m54.764s	143.126	1m24.767s	1
11	J Trulli	Toyota TF107	53	1h19m55.542s	143.102	1m24.622s	1
12	G Fisichella	Renault R27	52	1h18m39.466s	142.663	1m24.849s	1
13	A Wurz	Williams-Toyota FW29	52	1h18m45.759s	142.473	1m25.000s	1
14	A Davidson	Super Aguri-Honda SA07	52	1h18m49.356s	142.365	1m25.116s	1
15	R Schumacher	Toyota TF107	52	1h18m50.818s	142.320	1m24.951s	1
16	T Sato	Super Aguri-Honda SA07	52	1h18m53.034s	142.254	1m24.669s	1
17	V Liuzzi	Toro Rosso-Ferrari STR02	52	1h18m59.339s	142.064	1m25.373s	1
18	S Vettel	Toro Rosso-Ferrari STR02	52	1h19m04.650s	141.906	1m25.313s	2
19	A Sutil	Spyker-Ferrari F8-VII	52	1h19m49.036s	140.590	1m25.377s	2
20	S Yamamoto	Spyker-Ferrari F8-VII	52	1h20m00.701s	140.249	1m25.478s	2
R	F Massa	Ferrari F2007	10	Suspension	-	1m23.971s	1
R	D Coulthard	Red Bull-Renault RB3	1	Collision	-	-	0

CHAMPIONSHIP

	Driver	Pts
1	L Hamilton	92
2	F Alonso	89
3	K Räikkönen	74
4	F Massa	69
5	N Heidfeld	52
6	R Kubica	33
7	H Kovalainen	21
8	G Fisichella	17
9	A Wurz	13
10	N Rosberg	12
11	M Webber	8
12	D Coulthard	8
13	J Trulli	7
14	R Schumacher	5
15	T Sato	4
16	J Button	2
17	S Vettel	1

Fastest Lap
F Alonso 1m22.871s
(156.370mph) on lap 15

Fastest speed trap
Kubica 218.6mph
Slowest speed trap
Barrichello 212.0mph

Fastest pit stop
1 F Alonso 27.245s
2 R Kubica 27.388s
3 L Hamilton 27.428s

	Constructor	Pts
1	Ferrari	143
2	BMW Sauber	86
3	Renault	38
4	Williams-Toyota	25
5	Red Bull-Renault	16
6	Toyota	12
7	Super Aguri-Honda	4
8	Honda	2

David Coulthard
"I touched Fisichella's car at the first chicane and broke my front wing. The downforce pushed it underneath the car and broke the steering and I went straight off."

Nico Rosberg
"The team's made good progress following last week's test here, and the hard work paid off with a big step forward. Well done Toyota, as Monza is an engine track."

Vitantonio Liuzzi
"We saw the chequered flag again, but we didn't have enough pace to get ahead of the cars in front. I had understeer in the first stint, which cost me a lot of time."

Adrian Sutil
"Today was not so good, but we got to the finish with the new car. Its balance was not great and it was difficult to keep the temperature in the tyres under the safety car."

Takuma Sato
"On the way to the grid, I felt the brake pedal go soft, but there was nothing we could do. After the formation lap, the brakes caught fire when I got back to the grid."

Mark Webber
"I had a pretty good start and a scrap with Button and Rosberg. I tried to be consistent on the heavy load fuel, and to keep the best rhythm I could, but it wasn't easy."

Alexander Wurz
"It was a difficult first stint for me. We went with a very aggressive strategy, but being heavy with fuel had a negative effect on my rears and I just couldn't get the speed."

Sebastian Vettel
"My start was OK and then I saw David coming up my right-hand side, which forced me to go round the outside, and then in the second chicane I ran into Davidson."

Sakon Yamamoto
"We made the most of the two-stop strategy. I could keep up with the field without problems with our B-spec car, but we lost a bit of time compared to the others."

Anthony Davidson
"Vettel made contact with the rear of my car into Turn 1 which damaged the diffuser. The car seemed to be quite good and I was able to challenge Wurz and Fisichella."

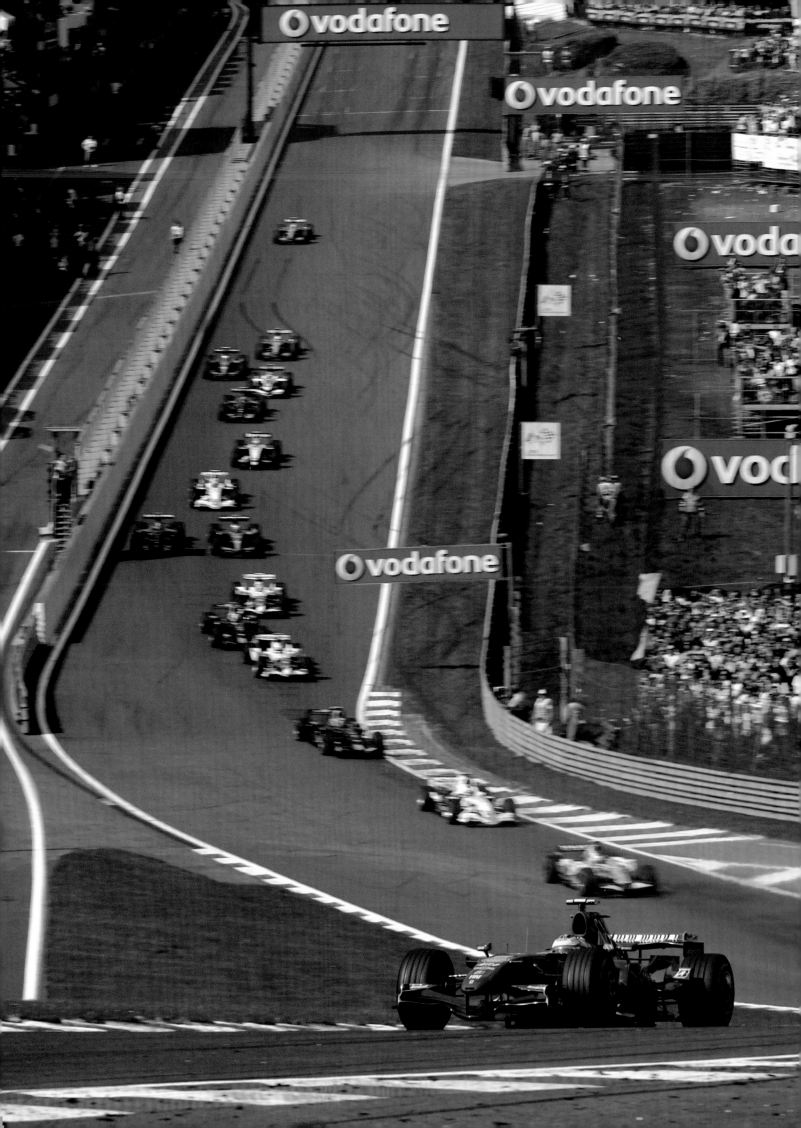

2007 FORMULA 1™
ING BELGIAN GRAND PRIX
SPA-FRANCORCHAMPS

RÄIKKÖNEN STRIKES

Embarrassed at home, Ferrari struck back with a 1–2 on Formula One's return to Spa after a year away, making it a double blow against arch-rivals McLaren

After all the off-track fuss that preceded the Belgian GP, it would have been highly appropriate if the return to a revamped Spa-Francorchamps had created a classic encounter between Ferrari and McLaren. Alas, it wasn't to be, and within two or three laps of the start it was clear that the race was going to be processional.

The really frustrating thing was that the 14th race of the season featured ingredients that we had rarely enjoyed through 2007. The four main contenders qualified at the front, they all got away well (and thus the group was not infiltrated by a BMW Sauber), and they all ran reliably throughout to fill the top four places.

The only other time they had started and finished first through to fourth was at Indianapolis – but even then Kimi Räikkönen spent his first stint behind slower cars after a bad start and wasn't part of the fight.

At Spa, Ferrari was simply quicker than McLaren, and Räikkönen – whose raw speed is never better expressed than at this challenging Belgian circuit – was a step ahead of team-mate Felipe Massa. This was the Finn's third straight victory at the Belgian track, following his wins with McLaren before the hiatus of 2006.

Everyone was happy to be back at Spa, where smart new pit facilities and a tricky chicane at the final corner

INSIDE LINE
JARNO TRULLI
TOYOTA DRIVER

"We had a good test at Spa-Francorchamps earlier in the year and I was really confident that I could have a good race here.

We scored points five times in the first half of the season but, through various circumstances, some of which were beyond our control, we have only scored once in the second half of the season up to now.

We all love driving here at Spa-Francorchamps. I think all drivers like it because of a combination of lots of things – the location, the history and of course the track itself. As well as the challenging corners, it has changes of elevation and it's not like anywhere else we go.

Viewers don't get a full idea of the challenge it offers from the pictures they see on television, but anyone who goes to the track and sees the Eau Rouge section for the first time can't quite believe it. It's so steep.

I've made it through into the top 10 qualifiers in every session except one this year, and I managed it again at Spa-Francorchamps and was ninth on the grid.

Having achieved that, I was planning a two-stop strategy and I was hopeful of scoring points.

It all went wrong at La Source hairpin on the opening lap. I got a decent start and was just turning into the corner when I saw some tyre smoke and realised that someone had braked too late and locked up.

I had no choice but to go to the outside and I lost a lot of time. I lost positions to both Ralf and David Coulthard's Red Bull – who were both heavy and on one-stop strategies.

We had put quite a bit of wing on the car and our straight-line speed was not so high in the race, so basically that first corner totally compromised my race.

I was potentially a lot quicker than Coulthard, but there was no way that I could get by and I lost a lot of time in the middle section of the lap where I was potentially much quicker. It was really frustrating. Any chance of points was gone and I could only finish in 10th position.

It was typical of the things that have been going wrong through 2007. The midfield is so competitive that everything has to go right; qualifying, the start, strategy, the way you run the race and the teamwork. If any one thing is not right, you don't score points. Everyone is working as hard as they ever have and I hope we can get back to some point-scoring before the end of the season."

were the main features of an expensive rebuild.

Practice on Friday didn't present a clear picture, as Räikkönen was on top in the morning, then Fernando Alonso and Lewis Hamilton led the way in the afternoon. Ferrari's preparations certainly weren't helped by an 'off' for Massa at the start of the morning session, but everything seemed to change in Ferrari's favour on Saturday. Räikkönen was fastest from Massa, Alonso and Hamilton in the morning, and oddly enough the result that mattered, in the final qualifying session, mirrored that precisely.

In the end, it was pretty close, as Massa admitted to losing time at the final chicane and yet was just 0.015s behind Räikkönen. The extra lap of fuel he was carrying more than accounted for that.

Pole was critical for Räikkönen because it ultimately negated the need for team orders come the race. As long as he got to the first corner in front, there would be little that Massa could do to reverse the situation.

The race itself was hardly a gripper, apart from the start, and afterwards Hamilton made it clear that he wasn't very happy. Certainly the TV pictures showed a 'Schumacher-esque' lunge towards him from team-mate Alonso as they exited the first corner, the La Source hairpin. It sent Hamilton out wide over the kerbs, but Alonso nearly wrecked his own chances by getting on the artificial grass, which was somewhat lacking in traction compared to the grey stuff. He still just managed to beat Hamilton on the run down to Eau Rouge, moving ahead in the second part of the corner, but it was mighty close.

"We all got quite equal starts, perhaps a little bit better for me than Fernando," said Hamilton. "I braked quite late, and I was on the outside, quite close to the Ferrari, and I was just behind Felipe and started to accelerate. All of a sudden, Fernando came swooping across me. He knew I was there.

"The guy on the outside doesn't always have the corner, but there was enough room for us to get round fair and square. In the past few years I've watched F1, and for someone who is always complaining about other people doing unfair manoeuvres and wanting everyone to be fair, and someone I look up to, to suddenly swipe me and push me as wide as he could was a shock. I was lucky that there was run-off area."

"I think they were both racing, that's what we pay them for," deadpanned McLaren's Martin Whitmarsh after the race. "I think that's one of the issues of the team and the way we run it. It didn't do anything for our health, momentarily, but they were racing each other. I think they're both skilled drivers and they were pushing it to the limit. They were both reasonably robust with one another. Both probably felt that the other was more robust. There was no doubt that there were no team orders being practised there."

Alonso might have assured himself of third place, but he also cost both McLarens momentum and took away any chance, however slight, that they might challenge the Ferraris later around the opening lap.

"I think that's true," Whitmarsh rejoined. "Obviously, we were very concerned when Fernando was off and lost momentum, but he actually did a very good job to come back on the track from that. That's the cost of motor racing. I think they both did a good job to push it to the limit without pushing it over."

The speed with which the two silver cars dropped away from their rivals was astonishing, for Alonso was 4.4s down on the leader after just five laps, and 7.9s after 10 laps. In fact, at that stage, the first four drivers were all running between 3–4s apart and, with the pit stops approaching, it was evident that something would have to go seriously wrong for anything to change significantly. Indeed, after the first round of pit stops the McLarens continued to drop away, and even extra laps before Hamilton's second stop failed to make any difference to the outcome.

OPPOSITE All 22 drivers prepare to fire themselves towards La Source. Amazingly, all got around the hairpin, but only just...

BELOW Jarno Trulli's hopes of a shot at points were scuppered when he lost ground at the start and ended up behind slower cars

some people it was pretty difficult, because here it's pretty low downforce so you seem to lose a lot of grip, making it hard to get past people. But it was the same for everybody. Apart from that, the car was very good, everything went well and it was a nice race.

"We knew that we were going to be much stronger here than we were in Monza. We know the reasons why we can't challenge on circuits like Monaco, Monza and Montréal and we will try to fix that problem for next year. This is mainly to do with aerodynamics and our car is strong in that area, so any circuits like Spa are going to be alright for us."

"I think I started with maybe too much front wing," explained Massa, who could see his slim title hopes ebbing away. "My car was a bit oversteery in the first stint. The second stint was pretty good as we could manage to keep the same margin from the beginning to the end of the run. Then, in the end, the car was just perfect on the soft tyres, so maybe we made a little bit of a wrong choice looking at how the track improved. We needed to take some risks at the beginning, but I think the race was pretty good, the car was fairly quick and consistent, and I think we set a very good pace compared to McLaren."

Alonso was happy enough to finish ahead of Hamilton and claw back a little more of his team-mate's lead, reducing it from three points to two.

"They were too quick for us today," he said of the Ferraris. "I tried quite hard in the first stint to keep pace with Felipe, just hoping around the pit stop time to make up a position, but they were slowly breaking clear and after the first stop, for sure, we didn't see them any more. We lacked a little bit of pace in the race. We had been quite OK in qualifying, but for sure in the race we were off the pace by a couple of tenths.

"Maybe in Turkey there was no possibility at all to fight with them. Today, OK, they were quicker than us, but maybe we have reduced the gap a little. There's

ABOVE Fernando Alonso was able to get away from the press when he had his helmet on and raced to third

Räikkönen was around 18s ahead of Alonso before he backed off on the final lap. All four drivers had the engines they'd used in the Italian GP, and as ever reliability played some part in the stalemate.

"We backed off just a little bit towards the end," said Dennis, "but that was more to make sure we had 100% reliability. If there was an opportunity for one of the drivers [to gain a place], we would have taken a risk."

Räikkönen celebrated his victory with a spectacular donut as the cars were flagged straight into the pit exit, so as to avoid a long slowing-down lap.

"There were not really any issues during the race," he said. "Only sometimes when you came up to lap

OPPOSITE Kimi Räikkönen drove such a strong race that his Ferrari pit crew had the luxury of not having to hurry at either of his pit stops

Nick Heidfeld was again the best of the rest for BMW, taking his 12th points finish in 14 starts

With three wins from the past three starts at Spa, no wonder Räikkönen earned applause aplenty

still a long way to go, but circuits are coming now that maybe suit our car a little bit better, so I think we still have possibilities to win the races from now on."

Third and fourth places weren't ideal for McLaren, but it was enough to leave Ferrari with a lot of chasing to do over the final three grands prix, albeit they now had the constructors' championship sewn up due to the removal of all of McLaren's points by the FIA.

"At the end of the day I'm happy, as we had 100% reliability on the cars," said Dennis. "We were trying to go a bit long, and then it's hard in the opening laps behind people, and it's a very long circuit. Ferrari didn't win by that much, although they were quite commanding at some parts of the race. The balance will swing around over the remainder of the season."

As far as Ferrari was concerned, the main thing was to hit back after their Monza defeat and give McLaren a beating on the track to match the one it received on Thursday in Paris. Sporting Director Stefano Domenicali made it quite clear that this wasn't just a normal win.

"We're very happy," he smiled. "It's always difficult, much more than what you can see outside. It was good to give an answer like that to the fact that in Monza we didn't perform so well. We knew that we had everything in place to keep on fighting for the championship, so we do all that we can to try to achieve the other title."

There was rather more interest behind the top four. Nico Rosberg ran an impressive fifth for Williams initially, but was later passed by Nick Heidfeld in the pit stops, the BMW Sauber racer having lost ground on the first lap.

Mark Webber moved up to a solid seventh for Red Bull, while one-stopper Heikki Kovalainen took the final point for Renault after holding off the determined challenge of BMW's Robert Kubica. The Pole had suffered an engine-change penalty, costing him 10 places on the grid, and a bad first lap, so had to work hard to regain ground.

It was not a great day for Giancarlo Fisichella, who also had an engine-change penalty, started from the pitlane with a revised set-up and then crashed out on the first lap because his brakes were cold...

One of the stars of the race was Adrian Sutil, who started his B-specification Spyker from 19th and got up to 15th on the first lap. After that, he picked up more positions as the team's strategy of making two stops and starting with the softer tyre paid dividends. By lap five, he had risen to 12th when he passed the Toyota of Jarno Trulli! He eventually finished 14th.

SNAPSHOT FROM
BELGIUM

CLOCKWISE FROM RIGHT FIA President Max Mosley and McLaren supremo Ron Dennis try to look friendly, for the sake of the sport; mine is a Martini, make it a double...; ...hear no evil; it's a busy time of year for the chiefs; fans prepare to put their money where their mouths are; Bernie Ecclestone helps Toyota celebrate its 50 years in motorsport; even marshals have to take a break; "so, how is your lad getting on?"

WEEKEND NEWS

■ The spy scandal and its fallout dominated the Belgian GP after the result of the World Motor Sport Council hearing in Paris was revealed on Thursday evening. McLaren was fined $100m and excluded from the constructors' championship, while the FIA promised to examine its 2008 car for any signs of Ferrari influence.

■ The role of Fernando Alonso in the case added fuel to the fire in terms of his uncomfortable relationship with McLaren boss Ron Dennis. The team chief had said in Paris that he had not talked to the Spaniard since the Hungarian GP, and the second hearing was a direct result of Alonso apparently threatening to reveal information he had on the case to the FIA.

■ A few days after the Belgian GP, Dennis confirmed that the team would not appeal against the FIA's judgement, and would accept the fine. As part of his quest for closure, Dennis also decided to withdraw the team's appeal against the constructors' points penalty it had received at the Hungarian GP, as there was no real reason to pursue it.

■ News reached Spa on Saturday evening of the death of 1995 World Rally Champion Colin McRae in a helicopter crash near his home in Scotland. McRae's son and two others – including another child – also died in the accident. Many paddock notables were quick to pay tribute to the fearless Scot.

■ McRae's former boss David Richards was at Spa on Sunday, and bizarrely had a helicopter crash of his own on the way home, from which he and his wife escaped unhurt. At the track, he had talked up Prodrive's prospects of concluding its customer deal with McLaren for 2008, but there was still no firm news.

RACE RESULTS

Official Results © [2007]
Formula One Administration Limited,
6 Princes Gate, London, SW7 1QJ.
No reproduction without permission.
All copyright and database rights reserved.

September 16th
4.352 miles
44
191.491 miles
Dry and cloudy, 21°C
31°C
60,000
Massa 1m48.036s,
145.021mph, 2007

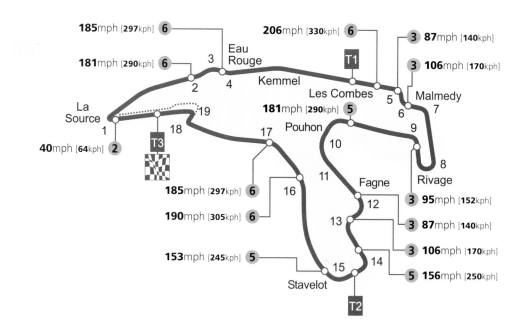

185mph [297kph] 6
181mph [290kph] 6
206mph [330kph] 6
3 87mph [140kph]
3 106mph [170kph]
Eau Rouge
Kemmel
Les Combes
Malmedy
3
2 4
5 6
7
La Source
19
181mph [290kph] 5
Pouhon
T1
1
40mph [64kph] 2
18
17
T3
10
9
8
Rivage
185mph [297kph] 6
16
11
Fagne
3 95mph [152kph]
12
3 87mph [140kph]
190mph [305kph] 6
13
3 106mph [170kph]
153mph [245kph] 5
15
14
5 156mph [250kph]
Stavelot
T2

PRACTICE 1

	Driver	Time	Laps
1	K Räikkönen	1m47.339s	16
2	L Hamilton	1m47.881s	19
3	F Alonso	1m47.994s	17
4	N Heidfeld	1m48.052s	20
5	N Rosberg	1m48.372s	18
6	R Kubica	1m48.605s	20
7	A Wurz	1m48.920s	20
8	J Trulli	1m48.994s	19
9	H Kovalainen	1m49.138s	22
10	J Button	1m49.330s	22
11	G Fisichella	1m49.380s	25
12	R Schumacher	1m49.548s	21
13	M Webber	1m49.894s	23
14	D Coulthard	1m49.931s	19
15	R Barrichello	1m50.264s	22
16	S Vettel	1m50.482s	27
17	T Sato	1m50.640s	16
18	A Davidson	1m50.648s	20
19	A Sutil	1m50.768s	22
20	V Liuzzi	1m51.628s	12
21	S Yamamoto	1m52.379s	21
22	F Massa	no time	2

PRACTICE

	Driver	Time	Laps
1	F Alonso	1m46.654s	29
2	L Hamilton	1m46.765s	29
3	F Massa	1m46.953s	27
4	K Räikkönen	1m47.166s	26
5	J Trulli	1m47.491s	33
6	R Schumacher	1m47.946s	34
7	G Fisichella	1m48.086s	30
8	M Webber	1m48.271s	29
9	R Kubica	1m48.279s	37
10	H Kovalainen	1m48.567s	38
11	N Heidfeld	1m48.606s	36
12	N Rosberg	1m48.840s	32
13	D Coulthard	1m48.883s	17
14	J Button	1m48.919s	29
15	R Barrichello	1m49.364s	31
16	A Wurz	1m49.393s	28
17	S Yamamoto	1m49.697s	32
18	S Vettel	1m49.720s	34
19	T Sato	1m50.168s	23
20	A Sutil	1m50.399s	24
21	A Davidson	1m50.542s	24
22	V Liuzzi	1m50.865s	9

PRACTICE 3

	Driver	Time	Laps
1	K Räikkönen	1m46.137s	17
2	F Massa	1m46.388s	17
3	F Alonso	1m46.507s	10
4	L Hamilton	1m46.782s	14
5	H Kovalainen	1m47.065s	13
6	J Trulli	1m47.218s	11
7	N Rosberg	1m47.251s	16
8	N Heidfeld	1m47.359s	16
9	R Schumacher	1m47.454s	19
10	M Webber	1m47.527s	15
11	G Fisichella	1m47.564s	16
12	J Button	1m47.767s	18
13	D Coulthard	1m47.806s	10
14	S Vettel	1m47.838s	19
15	A Wurz	1m47.902s	16
16	T Sato	1m48.129s	16
17	V Liuzzi	1m48.163s	21
18	A Sutil	1m48.348s	18
19	R Barrichello	1m48.528s	16
20	A Davidson	1m48.955s	15
21	S Yamamoto	1m49.179s	14
22	R Kubica	no time	2

QUALIFYING 1

	Driver	Time
1	F Alonso	1m46.058s
2	F Massa	1m46.060s
3	K Räikkönen	1m46.242s
4	L Hamilton	1m46.437s
5	R Kubica	1m46.707s
6	N Heidfeld	1m46.923s
7	N Rosberg	1m46.950s
8	H Kovalainen	1m46.971s
9	M Webber	1m47.084s
10	J Trulli	1m47.143s
11	G Fisichella	1m47.143s
12	R Schumacher	1m47.300s
13	D Coulthard	1m47.340s
14	J Button	1m47.474s
15	A Wurz	1m47.522s
16	V Liuzzi	1m47.576s
17	S Vettel	1m47.581s
18	R Barrichello	1m47.954s
19	T Sato	1m47.980s
20	A Sutil	1m48.044s
21	A Davidson	1m48.199s
22	S Yamamoto	1m49.577s

QUALIFYING 2

	Driver	Time
1	K Räikkönen	1m45.070s
2	L Hamilton	1m45.132s
3	F Massa	1m45.173s
4	F Alonso	1m45.442s
5	R Kubica	1m45.885s
6	N Heidfeld	1m45.994s
7	H Kovalainen	1m46.240s
8	M Webber	1m46.426s
9	N Rosberg	1m46.469s
10	J Trulli	1m46.480s
11	G Fisichella	1m46.603s
12	R Schumacher	1m46.618s
13	D Coulthard	1m46.800s
14	J Button	1m46.955s
15	V Liuzzi	1m47.115s
16	A Wurz	1m47.394s

Best sectors – Practice

Sec 1	K Räikkönen	30.722s
Sec 2	K Räikkönen	46.449s
Sec 3	S Yamamoto	28.572s

Speed trap – Practice

1	K Räikkönen	198.0mph
2	F Alonso	196.4mph
3	L Hamilton	194.2mph

Best sectors – Qualifying

Sec 1	F Massa	30.484s
Sec 2	L Hamilton	45.724s
Sec 3	K Räikkönen	28.616s

Speed trap – Qualifying

1	H Kovalainen	195.5mph
2	K Räikkönen	195.4mph
3	M Webber	194.2mph

Fernando Alonso
"I stuck to the inside as long as I could. Lewis ran wide, as there was no space and I knew there was run-off. I was stopping earlier, so it was very important to be in front."

Giancarlo Fisichella
"We started from the pits, so we could use a lower-downforce set-up. But when I came to Turn 5, I braked and the car didn't slow down and it just went straight on."

Felipe Massa
"I had oversteer but then the soft tyres worked well and it might have been better to use them even from the start, but you can only see such things after the race."

Jenson Button
"It's always disappointing to retire, but it was six laps less pain, as the car was changing from huge oversteer to understeer on any lap. Then the power steering failed."

Nick Heidfeld
"I had a poor start, then braked too late. I had to pass Heikki, as he was on a one-stopper. When Rosberg and Webber pitted earlier than me, I knew I could beat them."

Ralf Schumacher
"I think we got the best out of the car, but unfortunately it was not quite enough for any points. It's frustrating as we pushed the car to the limit and hoped for more."

Lewis Hamilton
"I thought I had a chance to get past at the first corner, but I had to run wide as Fernando kept to the inside line. I thought 'oh thanks', but I guess these things happen."

Heikki Kovalainen
"I had a fantastic start, but I was just defending all the way through. There was a lot of wheel-to-wheel action but that kind of thing is more fun when you are attacking!"

Kimi Räikkönen
"I had doubts about the handling after qualifying, but I was quick enough in the first part to control the race. It is nice to win on my top track for the third time in a row."

Rubens Barrichello
"This has been frustrating for us because we have been struggling with the car. Carrying that amount of fuel for a one-stop strategy, the rears were locking up badly."

Robert Kubica
"Sometimes you push and get nothing. It was very difficult behind Kovalainen, as he had more top speed. Also, I lost time behind Coulthard for almost 10 laps."

Jarno Trulli
"I lost a few places, as I had to go on the outside after another car braked late and I fell behind other cars who had more fuel on board and were much slower than me."

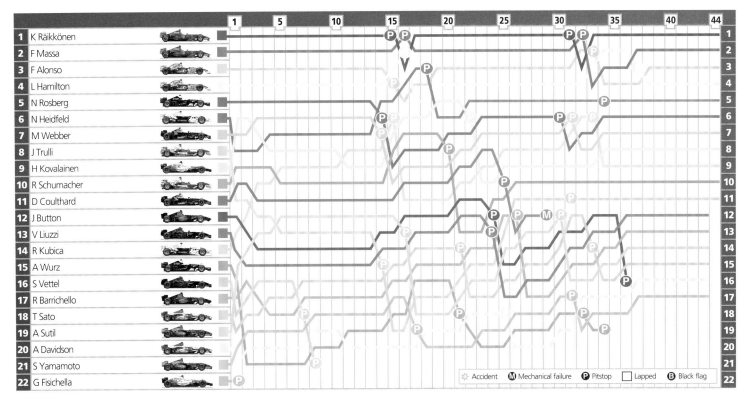

Lap-by-lap positions chart, starting order:

Pos	Driver
1	K Räikkönen
2	F Massa
3	F Alonso
4	L Hamilton
5	N Rosberg
6	N Heidfeld
7	M Webber
8	J Trulli
9	H Kovalainen
10	R Schumacher
11	D Coulthard
12	J Button
13	V Liuzzi
14	R Kubica
15	A Wurz
16	S Vettel
17	R Barrichello
18	T Sato
19	A Sutil
20	A Davidson
21	S Yamamoto
22	G Fisichella

Legend: ☼ Accident Ⓜ Mechanical failure Ⓟ Pitstop ☐ Lapped Ⓑ Black flag

QUALIFYING 3

	Driver	Time
1	K Räikkönen	1m45.994s
2	F Massa	1m46.011s
3	F Alonso	1m46.091s
4	L Hamilton	1m46.406s
5	R Kubica	1m46.996s
6	N Rosberg	1m47.334s
7	N Heidfeld	1m47.409s
8	M Webber	1m47.524s
9	J Trulli	1m47.798s
10	H Kovalainen	1m48.505s

GRID

	Driver	Time
1	K Räikkönen	1m45.994s
2	F Massa	1m46.011s
3	F Alonso	1m46.091s
4	L Hamilton	1m46.406s
5	N Rosberg	1m47.334s
6	N Heidfeld	1m47.409s
7	M Webber	1m47.524s
8	J Trulli	1m47.798s
9	H Kovalainen	1m48.505s
10	R Schumacher	1m46.618s
11	D Coulthard	1m46.800s
12	J Button	1m46.955s
13	V Liuzzi	1m47.115s
14*	R Kubica	1m46.996s
15	A Wurz	1m47.394s
16	S Vettel	1m47.581s
17	R Barrichello	1m47.954s
18	T Sato	1m47.980s
19	A Sutil	1m48.044s
20+	A Davidson	1m48.199s
21	S Yamamoto	1m49.577s
22*	G Fisichella	1m46.603s

* 10-PLACE GRID PENALTY + STARTED FROM THE PITLANE

RACE

	Driver	Car	Laps	Time	Avg.mph	Fastest	Stops
1	K Räikkönen	Ferrari F2007	44	1h20m39.066s	142.432	1m48.095s	1
2	F Massa	Ferrari F2007	44	1h20m43.761s	142.294	1m48.036s	2
3	F Alonso	McLaren-Mercedes MP4-22	44	1h20m53.409s	142.011	1m48.182s	2
4	L Hamilton	McLaren-Mercedes MP4-22	44	1h21m02.681s	141.740	1m48.215s	2
5	N Heidfeld	BMW Sauber F1.07	44	1h21m30.945s	140.921	1m48.663s	2
6	N Rosberg	Williams-Toyota FW29	44	1h21m55.942s	140.204	1m49.769s	2
7	M Webber	Red Bull-Renault RB3	44	1h21m59.705s	140.097	1m50.049s	2
8	H Kovalainen	Renault R27	44	1h22m04.172s	139.970	1m49.600s	1
9	R Kubica	BMW Sauber F1.07	44	1h22m04.727s	139.954	1m48.894s	2
10	R Schumacher	Toyota TF107	44	1h22m07.640s	139.872	1m50.022s	1
11	J Trulli	Toyota TF107	44	1h22m22.719s	139.445	1m48.990s	2
12	V Liuzzi	Toro Rosso-Ferrari STR02	43	1h21m01.646s	138.547	1m50.730s	1
13	R Barrichello	Honda RA107	43	1h21m12.817s	138.229	1m50.678s	1
14	A Sutil	Spyker-Ferrari F8-VII	43	1h21m15.180s	138.162	1m50.902s	2
15	T Sato	Super Aguri-Honda SA07	43	1h21m15.825s	138.144	1m50.886s	2
16	A Davidson	Super Aguri-Honda SA07	43	1h21m43.683s	137.359	1m51.391s	1
17	S Yamamoto	Spyker-Ferrari F8-VII	43	1h21m58.817s	136.936	1m51.648s	2
R	J Button	Honda RA107	36	Hydraulics	-	1m51.141s	2
R	A Wurz	Williams-Toyota FW29	34	Fuel pressure	-	1m51.270s	2
R	D Coulthard	Red Bull-Renault RB3	29	Throttle	-	1m51.156s	1
R	S Vettel	Toro Rosso-Ferrari STR02	8	Steering	-	1m52.724s	1
R	G Fisichella	Renault R27	1	Suspension	-	-	0

CHAMPIONSHIP

	Driver	Pts
1	L Hamilton	97
2	F Alonso	95
3	K Räikkönen	84
4	F Massa	77
5	N Heidfeld	56
6	R Kubica	33
7	H Kovalainen	22
8	G Fisichella	17
9	N Rosberg	15
10	A Wurz	13
11	M Webber	10
12	D Coulthard	8
13	J Trulli	7
14	R Schumacher	5
15	T Sato	4
16	J Button	2
17	S Vettel	1

Fastest Lap
F Massa 1m48.036s
(145.021mph) on lap 34

Fastest speed trap		Fastest pit stop		
K Räikkönen	194.8mph	1	F Alonso	25.612s
Slowest speed trap		2	A Wurz	25.655s
G Fisichella	173.8mph	3	T Sato	25.777s

David Coulthard
"I lost throttle control and power steering. It happened on a straight, so I had room to move out of the way of the others. There's no way you can get it back to the pits."

Nico Rosberg
"I'm delighted, as we were again the fourth-placed team, showing that we are making progress. It's also positive for me, as a good car allows me to show what I can do."

Vitantonio Liuzzi
"I made some nice passing moves. We had a good pace compared to the Red Bulls. It was a job well done apart from a problem with the right-front wheel in my stop."

Adrian Sutil
"This is the first time I am smiling after getting out! It was a good race. Every lap there were cars in front and behind that I was racing so I had to push, but also defend."

Takuma Sato
"I made up a few places, but on the Kemmel straight, when I was next to a Toro Rosso, I was pushed off and lost momentum. I then had to make up my lost positions."

Mark Webber
"It's good to get points, as it's not always easy for us, and it was great to beat the Renault fair and square. David did a great job as a buffer in front of Kubica."

Alexander Wurz
"Starting 15th, it was all uphill and then we had fuel pressure problems. The problem got worse and worse, so I had to do an extra stop to try and recover pressure."

Sebastian Vettel
"I retired because I could not steer the car to the right. We thought it might be related to the tyres, but as soon as I left the pits with new tyres, I could feel the same problem."

Sakon Yamamoto
"I could set the same pace as the others, but the soft tyre gave a lot of understeer. We went to the harder tyre and made a wing change and the car improved."

Anthony Davidson
"I had to start from the pitlane after feeling a problem on the front end of the car. I caught the back of the pack and fought hard on my one-stop strategy."

	Constructor	Pts
1	Ferrari	161
2	BMW Sauber	90
3	Renault	39
4	Williams-Toyota	28
5	Red Bull-Renault	18
6	Toyota	12
7	Super Aguri-Honda	4
8	Honda	2

2007 FORMULA 1™ FUJI
TELEVISION JAPANESE GRAND PRIX
FUJI SPEEDWAY

LEWIS ON THE BRINK

It was wet, wet, wet at Fuji Speedway, but
Lewis Hamilton kept his cool at the head
of the ball of spray and recorded a vital
win to put him on the brink of the title

The return to a rebuilt Fuji Speedway after a 30-year
absence inevitably revived memories of James Hunt
clinching the title there in 1976, and it was appropriate
therefore that a British driver in a McLaren stole the
show. A fabulous wet-weather performance from
Lewis Hamilton left the rookie with a healthy points
lead over his team-mate Fernando Alonso with just
two races to run. As in 1976, Ferrari was left to rue a
frustrating weekend.

Somehow, the FIA managed to squeeze qualifying
in on schedule on a soggy Saturday, despite fog
grounding the medical helicopter. Hamilton did a great
job to take pole position on a wet track, ahead of
Alonso, Kimi Räikkönen and Felipe Massa.

Fog was less of an issue on race day, but it rained all
morning. In fact, by Fuji standards it wasn't too bad.
Nevertheless, it was apparent that safety-car driver
Bernd Maylander would lead the field into lap 1.

What came as a surprise was a last-minute, *ad hoc*
ruling that everyone should start on extreme-wet tyres
should the safety car be used. This was an eminently
sensible decision given that safety was an absolute
priority for the FIA in the potentially treacherous
conditions, but one that came couched in complex

INSIDE LINE
MARK WEBBER
RED BULL DRIVER

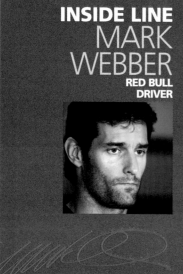

"I felt lousy before the race and even sicker after it! I had been closing on Lewis [Hamilton] before the second safety-car period and I really thought that I was in with a good chance of racing him for the win.

I think it was tuna I'd eaten the night before but, whatever, I had a bout of food poisoning and I was very ill on Sunday morning. I was ill before the race and ill during the race. It was very difficult for me, but I was 100% fit again on the Monday morning, which was frustrating. It was just a 24-hour bug that hit me quite hard.

It was one of the lowest points of my career, no question about it. I was in a position to challenge for my first victory and it was taken away – not even in a racing incident, but sitting behind a safety car. That was hard to swallow and explained my frustration

with Sebastian [Vettel] immediately afterwards, before I calmed down a bit.

It's pretty easy when the safety-car lights are on because you can see everything. If you're the next guy behind the silver Mercedes, you just have to try to keep to a sensible rhythm behind. Obviously, during the first safety-car deployment and clearly in the second, there was not a sensible rhythm.

I'm all up for not a great rhythm when the safety-car lights are off, because we're all preparing for a restart, and when the lights were off there were a few times when I believe Button was being backed up by Heidfeld. I think sometimes Jenson passed Nick and I passed Jenson sometimes, because the pace was yo-yoing massively.

We know what pace the safety

car can do and I accept a little bit that maybe you get a bit bored in that situation because we did a lot of laps, and sometimes you are ready to go. But it definitely contributed to Sebastian hitting me up the back that he was confused at what the other car was doing. Because he wasn't doing what he was supposed to be doing behind the safety car – clearly.

I think Hamilton did a s*** job behind the safety car. He did a s*** job and that's it. He spoke in the drivers' briefing about how good a job he was going to do and then he did the job the opposite way. We know for next time, no problem...

But we have to pick ourselves up from tough weekends. It's the game we're in. It's not lawn bowls, it's Formula One. It's under the bridge now. Gone. We'll never get that one back..."

legal language as Chief Steward Tony Scott Andrews sought to justify this unusual intervention. That was presumably why it took so long for the decision to be signed off for circulation via the FIA e-mail system that is used to send messages to teams. Somehow, Ferrari failed to get the message before the start.

Hamilton, Alonso and Räikkönen went to the grid on intermediates. In the case of the first two, it was just to give the tyres a try, and the team knew it had to switch to extremes for the start proper. Ferrari decided to start both cars on intermediates, on the assumption that the track would dry and they would come into their own.

But, even behind the safety car, with tyre pressures and temperature suffering, they were a real handful once the 'action' got underway. Massa spun (and later got a drive-through penalty for regaining positions), and Räikkönen had a moment too. It wasn't just Charlie Whiting's insistence that brought them in on laps 2 and 3 – the tyres were simply unusable in the conditions. The fact that everyone else stayed on extremes for the duration was pretty good evidence for that.

McLaren's Chief Operating Officer Martin Whitmarsh certainly thought it an odd decision: "Honestly, I don't think we would have stayed on extreme wets actually, but an instruction was issued at 12.37pm that we thought made it fairly clear that we didn't have a choice.

"We received what we thought were relatively clear instructions that you needed to start the race on extreme wets. To find that both the Ferraris were on standard wets was a bit disturbing!"

"We were surprised that they started on something other than the monsoon tyres," said McLaren chief Ron Dennis, "because effectively there was a communication that everybody had to start on those tyres. So it was very confusing to us."

The Ferraris also took on fuel at those early stops, and topped up again at second stops while the safety car was still running. That made for a fascinating strategic conundrum. As the laps went by, it became apparent that there was a scenario where one-by-one the leading cars would stop and drop down the order, and the Ferraris would creep to the front by virtue of having so much more fuel on board...

Fortunately, by lap 19, the cars had dispersed enough water for the safety car to pull off, but there was drama at the first turn when Jenson Button collected Nick Heidfeld. Both carried on, but Button soon had to pit for a new nose. Meanwhile, Alexander Wurz spun and nudged the unfortunate Massa into a spin. Still, at last we had a race.

"I don't think many cars fell off the road on their own," said Dennis of the conditions. "Most of the incidents were caused by drivers trying to overtake. Our drivers radioed that they were very comfortable to start the race. The FIA asked us to, as the drivers said it would be no problem to start. Visibility was a little bad, but the grip was fine."

The McLaren drivers had only a few laps in which to try and make an escape before their stops were due. With the Ferraris making their way through from the back, the chase was led by none other than Sebastian Vettel, doing a sensational job for Toro Rosso, Mark Webber, Giancarlo Fisichella and Heikki Kovalainen.

The safety-car period had allowed the McLarens to at least save some fuel and extend their range, but Alonso had only eight laps under green before he came in, and Hamilton had just one more. Both cars were fuelled for the long run to the flag, which meant 40- and 39-lap second stints respectively.

The stop sequence was to make life hard for Alonso. He dropped as low as eighth, not helping himself with a moment on his 'out'-lap, and got caught behind a group of several cars. Pitting a lap later, and with a 3s advantage on Alonso before the stops, Hamilton came out safely in front of that group.

"It was a rather unlucky moment," Alonso

OPPOSITE It didn't rain on every day of Formula One's return to Fuji Speedway. Look, you can even see the slopes of the volcano behind Ralf Schumacher's Toyota...

BELOW Heikki Kovalainen claimed his first podium, but had to fight to keep second position from Kimi Räikkönen in the closing laps

TALKING POINT
THE SECOND SAFETY CAR

When Formula One rolled out of Fuji Speedway late on Sunday night after the Japanese GP, the talk was of Lewis Hamilton's Ayrton Senna-like mastery of monsoon conditions.

That and Mark Webber's ire at being taken out by Sebastian Vettel during the second safety-car period.

Webber, at the time, blamed the young German's inexperience. But, by the time everyone re-assembled in Shanghai four days later, the goalposts had moved.

Everybody was looking at a *You Tube* video shot by a spectator at Fuji during one of the safety-car deployments. It clearly showed Hamilton pulling over to the right-hand side of the track behind the safety car, slowing his pace considerably and clearly not staying within five car-lengths of Bernd Maylander's Mercedes, as required by the regulations.

The news came at the Chinese GP that the stewards were going to open an investigation into Hamilton's conduct behind the safety car.

Webber thought Hamilton had done "a s*** job" and Vettel added: "You react to movement and all of a sudden I saw Lewis pulling to the right and slowing down a lot. I was looking at him, wondering just what was happening and thinking that his car must have lost power and that he was retiring. By the time I looked back in front of me, I was already in Mark's rear end."

Through Thursday and Friday in Shanghai, it was all speculation about what would happen to Hamilton. Would he lose his Japanese GP victory? Would he be penalised 10 places on the grid for the Chinese GP, as Vettel had been? Or would it be 20 places in view of the fact that Vettel had effectively been punished twice as a result of Hamilton's driving?

The video evidence clearly showed there was a case to answer. Hamilton, himself a rookie coping with difficult conditions behind the safety car and trying to stop his brakes glazing and his engine from drowning, didn't think that he deserved a penalty, but suspected that he would get one.

The British daily press was outraged. This, they said, amounted to manipulation of the World Championship, so that it would all conveniently go down to the wire in the final round in Brazil in front of a peak-time TV audience.

It was as bad as Alonso's ridiculous qualifying penalty for impeding Massa while 93 metres ahead of him at Monza in 2006, they said. One 'red top' wrote a strong piece accusing F1's bosses of being unfit to run a garage in Chipping Sodbury. Perhaps against the run of play, no penalty was ultimately forthcoming. Instead, Vettel had his 10-place penalty wiped out. Hamilton, for the moment, could breathe again...

explained, "as I was fighting with Lewis. I was a little bit quicker in the first part, but it was difficult to follow that close, because I didn't see the corners with the spray and the water. And then when I pitted I was behind four cars, and when he pitted he was in front of them."

Hamilton was soon 10s ahead of his team-mate, and looking set for victory. But then came the bizarre scenario of Hamilton being assaulted by Kubica and Alonso by Vettel within minutes of each other. Hearts were pounding in the McLaren camp...

"Kubica made life interesting," said Dennis. "It was a very strange thing to do in such poor conditions. So Lewis was very lucky not to damage the car. There was some vibration coming from the car, which we were monitoring, but we could see it wasn't suspension, so we anticipated some body damage."

Both drivers survived, but within a few laps Alonso's race was run after a heavy impact with the wall. He didn't use the earlier contact as an excuse, but he would have been justified in so doing.

"Both our drivers were hit from behind today," said Whitmarsh. "Unfortunately for Fernando, he was hit harder than Lewis. The floor was very badly damaged and flapping around, its rear pick-ups damaged. We

could see on the data that he had lost a significant amount of downforce and the overall balance of the car, so the likelihood of him aquaplaning was always going to be greater than it was for anyone else out there. He lost approaching 10% of the downforce, a sizeable amount."

Alonso was out of the race, but life was far from easy for Hamilton, even under the safety car that his team-mate had triggered.

"Lewis had quite a lot of pressure during those safety-car periods," admitted Whitmarsh. "He had a driver behind him who wasn't fighting for the championship and might have fancied his chances at a win. Mark looked like he was thinking of having a go, and you can imagine if you were Lewis that that was a bit of pressure. It's ironic that while Lewis was concerned about having Mark up his tail, Webber should get another Red Bull-backed car up his backside!"

Indeed, the battle for the podium slots was turned on its head when Vettel ran into the back of Webber's car, putting both of them out. Already struggling with food poisoning, the Australian driver was furious, but Vettel blamed Hamilton for slowing abruptly.

"One of the challenges that you had was tyre

OPPOSITE, ABOVE LEFT The FIA declared that all teams should fit monsoon tyres, but Ferrari didn't...

OPPOSITE, ABOVE RIGHT Lewis Hamilton realises that his title bid has been made easier, as Fernando Alonso's stricken McLaren is lifted from the track after its crash

OPPOSITE, BELOW Mark Webber can't believe what has happened after being taken out of second place by Sebastian Vettel when the field was behind the safety car

ABOVE Even pit stops, such as this Honda one, were extra hazardous under the atrocious conditions

Visibility was horrendous, and sitting water awaited even the most wary and attentive of drivers

McLaren's Ron Dennis congratulates Renault's Pat Symonds on Heikki Kovalainen's second place

pressures and brake temperatures," said Whitmarsh. "We did alert the FIA that we thought the cars were very close, and when you think the safety car is coming in you've got to be prepared, you've got to get some temperatures back into the brakes, put the pressures in, and that's very difficult. Your carbon brakes can glaze over as well, especially in these sorts of conditions. The reality is everyone was braking, and if you follow too closely, you get the typical motorway incident..."

With the safety car gone, Hamilton still had another 18 laps of racing to do, and plenty of opportunity to make a mistake, but he barely put a foot wrong.

"The challenge for a driver, especially leading the race, is not to drive too quickly," said Dennis. "And the challenge for the team is not to go over the top on slowing him down. The real message was not to take risks, and keep him informed of where the puddles were. So we were encouraging him to back off at Turn 4 and Turn 10, where we could see there was the most standing water. Of course, we really had to look after the tyres, it's a long stint to do on the monsoon tyres.

"We had to be careful with information overload. There was so much, visibility was so bad you couldn't rely on pit signals, so we were feeding him the data. It was difficult to know how much to give him. But, overall, it was a tremendously well-disciplined race."

Hamilton was ecstatic: "Over the last few laps, the team was telling me to slow down, that I was a second faster than anyone, and I was saying that I was going as slow as I feel comfortable doing. In the last couple of laps, I took it easy because it was so wet and my tyres were getting old, and I was aquaplaning. But I'm thrilled to take it home, and it's great for the team."

There was much more going on behind. A single, and very late, pit stop had worked wonders for Heikki Kovalainen and put the Renault man second. Then, in the closing laps, he held off a strong challenge from Räikkönen, who drove superbly from the back.

Fourth went to David Coulthard, ahead of Fisichella, Massa (who needed a late splash-and-dash) and Kubica.

Over the final lap, Massa and Kubica were embroiled in a sensational battle that saw them off the road more often than not, and revived memories of Gilles Villeneuve and René Arnoux at Dijon in 1979.

The final championship point went initially to Tonio Liuzzi, who had lost a lap by starting from the pitlane as Toro Rosso failed to realise that there is no formation lap under the safety car. He got it back after a safety-car wave by, but was penalised for passing Adrian Sutil under yellows. So, instead, after a great drive, Spyker man Sutil landed his first point.

SNAPSHOT FROM
JAPAN

CLOCKWISE FROM RIGHT Japanese fans came dressed for rain; Kovalainen walks the track; five photographers trying to be individual...; in a race that was a triumph just to finish, Heikki Kovalainen was delighted with second place for Renault; it's safe to say that visibility was poor; led by David Coulthard, the F1 paddock united to commemorate rally ace Colin McRae; Lewis in profile; smile for Aguri; Alonso found smiles harder to come by

WEEKEND NEWS

■ In an attempt to alleviate traffic problems, the race organisers required all spectators to drive to car parks some distance from the Fuji Speedway, and then take a bus. This massively reduced traffic in the environs of the circuit and the local town of Gotemba, although actually getting from the paddock to the front gate was a painful experience.

■ Queues for the buses and a long trek from the stops to the grandstands did not go down very well with the fans, though. To make matters worse, some found themselves with seats from which the view was all but obliterated by mist. It was announced on the day after the race that refunds would be made to those worst affected.

■ The social highlight of the Japanese GP weekend was the Sunday-night party at the famed Lexington Queen nightclub in Tokyo's Roppongi district. Organised by Tsukasa Shiga – a friend of Eddie Irvine and many other visiting racers over the years – the informal affair saw 13 F1 drivers (and two team principals) letting their hair down in a major way. Sakon Yamamoto served as DJ.

■ Ralf Schumacher made a pre-emptive strike just after the Japanese GP by announcing the not-unexpected news that he would not be staying at Toyota in 2008, thus denying the team the chance to drop him. The German appeared to have few serious options left, but he remained upbeat about his prospects.

■ While the F1 circus was in Japan, the GP2 teams gathered in Valencia for the season finale and the category's only stand-alone race. BMW Sauber test driver Timo Glock clinched the title after main rival and Flavio Briatore protégé Lucas di Grassi had a nightmare weekend. Glock continued to be linked with a Toyota race seat for 2008.

RACE RESULTS

Official Results © [2007]
Formula One Administration Limited,
6 Princes Gate, London, SW7 1QJ.
No reproduction without permission.
All copyright and database rights reserved.

RACE DATE September 30th
CIRCUIT LENGTH 2.835 miles
NO. OF LAPS 67
RACE DISTANCE 191.488 miles
WEATHER Heavy rain, 17°C
TRACK TEMP 20°C
RACE DAY ATTENDANCE 80,000
LAP RECORD Hamilton 1m28.193s,
115.736mph, 2007

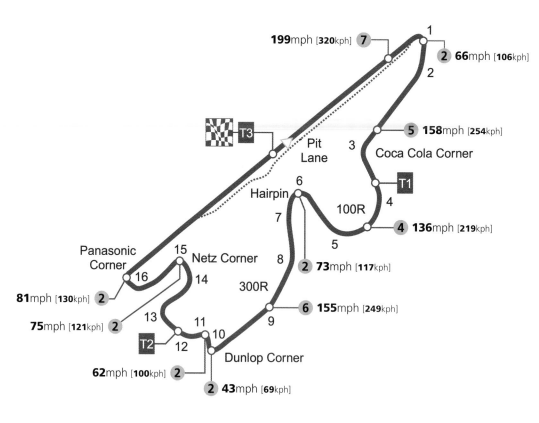

199mph [320kph] 7

66mph [106kph] 2

5 158mph [254kph]

Coca Cola Corner

T3

Pit Lane

T1

Hairpin

100R

4 136mph [219kph]

Panasonic Corner

Netz Corner

2 73mph [117kph]

81mph [130kph] 2

300R

6 155mph [249kph]

75mph [121kph] 2

T2

Dunlop Corner

62mph [100kph] 2

2 43mph [69kph]

PRACTICE 1		
Driver	**Time**	**Laps**
1 K Räikkönen	1m19.119s	26
2 F Massa	1m19.498s	27
3 F Alonso	1m19.667s	27
4 L Hamilton	1m19.807s	24
5 N Rosberg	1m20.058s	26
6 R Kubica	1m20.297s	26
7 A Wurz	1m20.411s	24
8 J Trulli	1m20.483s	32
9 A Sutil	1m20.516s	29
10 A Davidson	1m20.601s	22
11 R Barrichello	1m20.686s	24
12 H Kovalainen	1m20.718s	27
13 N Heidfeld	1m20.728s	26
14 V Liuzzi	1m20.808s	29
15 R Schumacher	1m20.828s	28
16 G Fisichella	1m20.851s	23
17 T Sato	1m21.186s	15
18 M Webber	1m21.437s	18
19 J Button	1m21.541s	22
20 S Vettel	1m21.854s	18
21 D Coulthard	1m22.436s	18
22 S Yamamoto	1m22.902s	17

PRACTICE 2		
Driver	**Time**	**Laps**
1 L Hamilton	1m18.734s	38
2 F Alonso	1m18.948s	34
3 F Massa	1m19.483s	36
4 J Trulli	1m19.711s	35
5 K Räikkönen	1m19.714s	29
6 H Kovalainen	1m19.789s	40
7 G Fisichella	1m19.926s	39
8 D Coulthard	1m19.949s	33
9 R Schumacher	1m19.969s	40
10 R Kubica	1m20.069s	45
11 M Webber	1m20.069s	35
12 A Wurz	1m20.233s	37
13 N Rosberg	1m20.270s	43
14 J Button	1m20.336s	44
15 N Heidfeld	1m20.462s	36
16 A Sutil	1m20.736s	37
17 R Barrichello	1m20.889s	33
18 V Liuzzi	1m20.985s	44
19 S Vettel	1m20.997s	38
20 D Coulthard	1m21.007s	34
21 S Yamamoto	1m21.305s	38
22 T Sato	1m21.352s	34

PRACTICE 3		
Driver	**Time**	**Laps**
1 A Wurz	1m32.746s	3
2 N Rosberg	1m34.758s	3
3 J Trulli	1m36.150s	3
4 S Vettel	no time	1
5 A Sutil	no time	1
6 S Yamamoto	no time	1
7 V Liuzzi	no time	1
8 R Kubica	no time	1
9 G Fisichella	no time	1
10 H Kovalainen	no time	1
11 R Schumacher	no time	2
12 N Heidfeld	no time	1
13 T Sato	no time	2
14 M Webber	no time	1
15 A Davidson	no time	2
16 J Button	no time	2
17 D Coulthard	no time	1
18 F Alonso	no time	2
19 R Barrichello	no time	2
20 L Hamilton	no time	1
21 F Massa	no time	1
22 K Räikkönen	no time	0

QUALIFYING 1	
Driver	**Time**
1 F Massa	1m25.359s
2 F Alonso	1m25.379s
3 K Räikkönen	1m25.390s
4 L Hamilton	1m25.489s
5 M Webber	1m25.970s
6 N Heidfeld	1m25.971s
7 S Vettel	1m26.025s
8 R Kubica	1m26.300s
9 N Rosberg	1m26.579s
10 J Button	1m26.614s
11 J Trulli	1m26.711s
12 D Coulthard	1m26.904s
13 G Fisichella	1m26.909s
14 R Schumacher	1m27.191s
15 H Kovalainen	1m27.223s
16 V Liuzzi	1m27.234s
17 R Barrichello	1m27.323s
18 A Wurz	1m27.454s
19 A Davidson	1m27.564s
20 A Sutil	1m28.628s
21 T Sato	1m28.792s
22 S Yamamoto	1m29.668s

QUALIFYING 2	
Driver	**Time**
1 L Hamilton	1m24.753s
2 F Alonso	1m24.806s
3 K Räikkönen	1m24.988s
4 F Massa	1m25.049s
5 N Heidfeld	1m25.248s
6 J Button	1m25.454s
7 R Kubica	1m25.530s
8 M Webber	1m25.535s
9 N Rosberg	1m25.816s
10 S Vettel	1m25.909s
11 G Fisichella	1m26.033s
12 H Kovalainen	1m26.232s
13 D Coulthard	1m26.247s
14 J Trulli	1m26.253s
15 V Liuzzi	1m26.948s
16 R Schumacher	no time

Best sectors – Practice			Speed trap – Practice	
Sec 1 L Hamilton	21.494s		1 M Webber	208.0mph
Sec 2 L Hamilton	28.721s		2 D Coulthard	206.4mph
Sec 3 L Hamilton	28.409s		3 V Liuzzi	203.8mph

Best sectors – Qualifying			Speed trap – Qualifying	
Sec 1 L Hamilton	23.160s		1 G Fisichella	195.0mph
Sec 2 L Hamilton	31.275s		2 H Kovalainen	194.6mph
Sec 3 F Alonso	30.054s		3 F Massa	194.6mph

Fernando Alonso
"It was hard to see due to the spray. So I didn't see Vettel and was shocked when he hit me. I was able to continue, but when I was braking for Turn 5 I aquaplaned and spun."

Giancarlo Fisichella
"It was one of the most difficult races I've ever driven, the conditions were just so wet all the way. The balance was inconsistent, particularly at low speeds."

Felipe Massa
"I took the risk of running different tyres to our rivals, but it was not the right choice. I made good progress, but I had to pit again as I did not have enough fuel."

Jenson Button
"We weren't able to take advantage of our qualifying position. I lost my wing after a clash with Heidfeld, then I had a sensor problem and later needed a new nose."

Nick Heidfeld
"I was only in sixth gear on the straight, so I tried to find a line where I'd be safe. That's why Räikkönen passed me on the left. But then Button damaged my car."

Ralf Schumacher
"My radio stopped working, but then water got into our electrics and that forced me to pit again. My crew fixed the problem, but we had a puncture so that was that."

Lewis Hamilton
"I am so happy to have won. I was lucky that nothing serious happened to my car when Kubica hit me. I didn't see him come, so the impact caught me by surprise."

Heikki Kovalainen
"In the last laps with Kimi, my mirrors had steamed up, but I was watching my board. He got past me into Turn 6 on the final lap, but I got him back before Turn 10."

Kimi Räikkönen
"We raced with zero visibility. My race was ruined by the enforced pit stop on lap 3. We started on standard rain tyres, but will never know if this could have paid off."

Rubens Barrichello
"I'm disappointed our strategy did not work out, but the race should have been stopped very early on. The conditions were so difficult and it was impossible to see anything."

Robert Kubica
"Hamilton went wide, then cut into the apex and I was there. Massa overtook me before Turn 6, then I got him back. Into Turn 10, if I had turned in, he would have hit me."

Jarno Trulli
"I made a mistake at the hairpin behind the safety car. While I was warming the tyres, I shifted down but it shifted one gear too much and I spun, losing a few places."

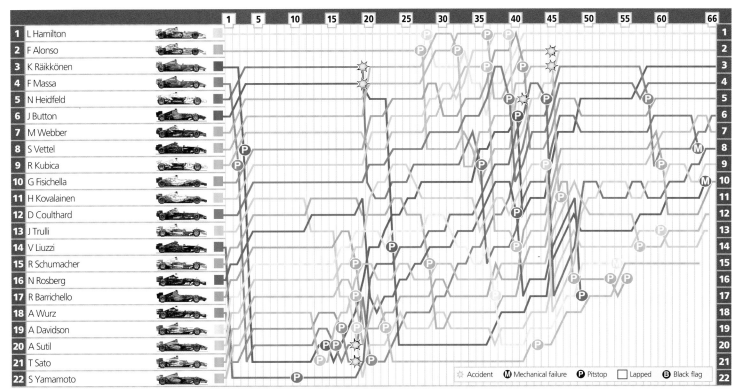

	Driver		
1	L Hamilton		
2	F Alonso		
3	K Räikkönen		
4	F Massa		
5	N Heidfeld		
6	J Button		
7	M Webber		
8	S Vettel		
9	R Kubica		
10	G Fisichella		
11	H Kovalainen		
12	D Coulthard		
13	J Trulli		
14	V Liuzzi		
15	R Schumacher		
16	N Rosberg		
17	R Barrichello		
18	A Wurz		
19	A Davidson		
20	A Sutil		
21	T Sato		
22	S Yamamoto		

Accident ☆   Mechanical failure Ⓜ   Pitstop Ⓟ   Lapped ▢   Black flag Ⓑ

QUALIFYING 3

	Driver	Time
1	L Hamilton	1m25.368s
2	F Alonso	1m25.438s
3	K Räikkönen	1m25.516s
4	F Massa	1m25.765s
5	N Heidfeld	1m26.505s
6	N Rosberg	1m26.728s
7	J Button	1m26.913s
8	M Webber	1m26.914s
9	S Vettel	1m26.973s
10	R Kubica	1m27.225s

GRID

	Driver	Time
1	L Hamilton	1m25.368s
2	F Alonso	1m25.438s
3	K Räikkönen	1m25.516s
4	F Massa	1m25.765s
5	N Heidfeld	1m26.505s
6	J Button	1m26.913s
7	M Webber	1m26.914s
8	S Vettel	1m26.973s
9	R Kubica	1m27.225s
10	G Fisichella	1m26.033s
11	H Kovalainen	1m26.232s
12	D Coulthard	1m26.247s
13	J Trulli	1m26.253s
14+	V Liuzzi	1m26.948s
15	R Schumacher	no time
16*	N Rosberg	1m26.728s
17	R Barrichello	1m27.323s
18	A Wurz	1m27.454s
19	A Davidson	1m27.564s
20	A Sutil	1m28.628s
21	T Sato	1m28.792s
22	S Yamamoto	1m29.668s

* 10-PLACE GRID PENALTY   + STARTED FROM THE PITLANE

RACE

	Driver	Car	Laps	Time	Avg. mph	Fastest	Stops
1	L Hamilton	McLaren-Mercedes MP4-22	67	2h00m34.579s	94.439	1m28.193s	1
2	H Kovalainen	Renault R27	67	2h00m42.956s	94.329	1m29.655s	1
3	K Räikkönen	Ferrari F2007	67	2h00m44.057s	94.315	1m29.619s	3
4	D Coulthard	Red Bull-Renault RB3	67	2h00m54.876s	94.174	1m30.086s	1
5	G Fisichella	Renault R27	67	2h01m13.443s	93.934	1m30.387s	1
6	F Massa	Ferrari F2007	67	2h01m23.621s	93.802	1m29.588s	4
7	R Kubica	BMW Sauber F1.07	67	2h01m23.864s	93.799	1m29.021s	2
8	A Sutil	Spyker-Ferrari F8-VII	67	2h01m34.708s	93.660	1m31.891s	1
9	V Liuzzi+	Toro Rosso-Ferrari STR02	67	2h01m55.201s	93.487	1m30.653s	2
10	R Barrichello	Honda RA107	67	2h02m02.921s	93.299	1m31.060s	2
11	J Button	Honda RA107	66	Suspension	93.205	1m31.951s	1
12	S Yamamoto	Spyker-Ferrari F8-VII	66	2h00m54.187s	92.776	1m32.130s	2
13	J Trulli	Toyota TF107	66	2h01m06.449s	92.619	1m32.414s	2
14	N Heidfeld	BMW Sauber F1.07	65	Electronics	93.376	1m29.084s	1
15	T Sato	Super Aguri-Honda SA07	65	Puncture	91.783	1m31.507s	2
R	R Schumacher	Toyota TF107	55	Puncture	-	1m30.865s	3
R	A Davidson	Super Aguri-Honda SA07	54	Throttle sensor	-	1m31.803s	1
R	N Rosberg	Williams-Toyota FW29	49	Electronics	-	1m29.926s	2
R	S Vettel	Toro Rosso-Ferrari STR02	46	Crash damage	-	1m29.057s	1
R	M Webber	Red Bull-Renault RB3	45	Accident	-	1m28.940s	1
R	F Alonso	McLaren-Mercedes MP4-22	41	Accident	-	1m28.511s	2
R	A Wurz	Williams-Toyota FW29	19	Accident	-	2m05.636s	1

CHAMPIONSHIP

	Driver	Pts
1	L Hamilton	107
2	F Alonso	95
3	K Räikkönen	90
4	F Massa	80
5	N Heidfeld	56
6	R Kubica	35
7	H Kovalainen	30
8	G Fisichella	21
9	N Rosberg	15
10	A Wurz	13
11	D Coulthard	13
12	M Webber	10
13	J Trulli	7
14	R Schumacher	5
15	T Sato	4
16	J Button	2
17	A Sutil	1
18	S Vettel	1

Fastest Lap
L Hamilton 1m28.193s
(115.736mph) on lap 27

Fastest speed trap
S Vettel 192.9mph
Slowest speed trap
A Wurz 114.7mph

Fastest pit stop
1 R Barrichello 30.873s
2 K Räikkönen 32.031s
3 F Massa 32.499s

	Constructor	Pts
1	Ferrari	170
2	BMW Sauber	92
3	Renault	51
4	Williams-Toyota	28
5	Red Bull-Renault	23
6	Toyota	12
7	Super Aguri-Honda	4
8	Honda	2
9	Spyker-Ferrari	1

David Coulthard
"It's a crazy thing to be a racing driver: on the one hand you're scared, but on the other, you're having the time of your life as every moment you're on the edge."

Nico Rosberg
"I couldn't see, I was aquaplaning and had two big moments. Then I had an electronic failure. Most significant was the loss of traction control and consistent gearshift."

Vitantonio Liuzzi
"It was 67 laps of pure tension. I chose to start from the pitlane in the T-car that was set up for the wet. Conditions were critical for everyone, but it is our job to race."

Adrian Sutil
"We fought a lot and ended up with our first point, even if we did not get it on the track. There was no green flag after the yellow from Turn 1 and that's why we scored."

Takuma Sato
"Someone braked in front of me and I damaged my nose. When the rain got lighter, I had fuel to the end and a new set of extreme tyres, but they overheated."

Mark Webber
"We were in good shape to fight Lewis. Alonso's crash caused the second safety-car period. Vettel, who had been wild during the first period, hit me hard in the second."

Alexander Wurz
"I was next to Massa when I was hit. Whoever it was couldn't see me, just like I couldn't see anything else. It was like closing your eyes and running through your house."

Sebastian Vettel
"I was behind Lewis and Mark and, exiting Turn 13, I looked right and saw Lewis going slowly. Then, by the time I looked forward again, I was in the back of Mark's car."

Sakon Yamamoto
"This was the toughest race I have ever had, even behind the safety car. We also should think of the fans as they watched right to the end when it was so cold and wet!"

Anthony Davidson
"Very wet conditions made it hard for all the drivers. I was pleased to make it through without mistakes, but unfortunately I had to retire due to a throttle-sensor failure."

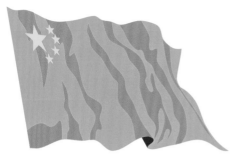

2007 FORMULA 1™ SINOPEC CHINESE GRAND PRIX
SHANGHAI

THROWN AWAY

Kimi Räikkönen raced to victory in the wet-dry Chinese GP, but the big story was Lewis Hamilton blowing his chance to land the title by sliding into a gravel trap

After his brilliant success in Japan, Lewis Hamilton came to China with the world title within his grasp. After he took pole and pulled away in the wet conditions that prevailed at the start of the race, it appeared that he would clinch it in the best possible style.

However, the dream result turned into a nightmare, as he ended his race perched ignominiously in a gravel trap at the pit entry, having slid off when he was finally called in to change tyres that had been run way beyond their useful life. Victory went instead to Ferrari's Kimi Räikkönen and, with Lewis's team-mate and closest title rival Fernando Alonso taking second, the result could hardly have been worse for Lewis, as it set up the thrilling prospect of a three-way battle in Brazil.

Hamilton's weekend did not get off to a comfortable start for, in the wake of the Webber/Vettel collision behind the safety car at Fuji, he had emerged as the bad guy, criticised severely by his fellow drivers for his stop-start antics as he tried to keep his brakes and tyres warm. Attention focused on a video posted by a spectator on the *YouTube* website that appeared to vindicate Vettel and place the blame on Hamilton, who was clearly affected by the saga, especially after his rivals gave him a hard time in the drivers' briefing on Friday.

After the Japanese Grand Prix, Scuderia Toro Rosso was in despair. Sebastian Vettel had been running third and heading for the podium when he whacked Mark Webber's Red Bull behind the safety car, taking both out.

To make matters worse, after the delight of Tonio Liuzzi scoring the team's first point by finishing eighth, he lost it when he had 25s added to his race time for overtaking Adrian Sutil's Spyker under a yellow.

The penalty handed that precious final World Championship point to Sutil and the Spyker team instead, meaning that Spyker and not Toro Rosso had one solitary point in the constructors' championship. According to those who knew the working of the Concorde Agreement, that point may have been worth as much as $20 million to Spyker over the next two seasons… Toro Rosso, unsurprisingly, lodged an appeal.

After the Chinese GP, though, this was all irrelevant, as Toro Rosso left Shanghai ecstatic, since no fewer than eight points had come their way as Vettel finished a fabulous fourth after running a one-stop strategy, and Liuzzi came home sixth after pitting twice.

"It's a great day for me and the whole team," the effervescent Vettel enthused. "After last weekend in Japan, everyone told me to keep my head up because I'd driven a good race, but obviously as a driver you need time to recover and get over disappointments. This was a great result, though – payback! What we lost in Fuji, we certainly got back today.

"I had a great first lap. I went around the outside and almost lost the car because the track was very slippery. From there, I had a great first stint with a very heavy car. It felt perfect and it was great to see that I wasn't losing out too much to the cars ahead, because I knew they were stopping twice and I was going to come in only once. Only two cars dropped out ahead of us, so we would have scored points on merit anyway. It's been a special day.

"The team really deserves this result. When I left Faenza, all the guys said, 'Hey, Sebastian, try to bring back some points'. I said I'd do my best. This team is one big, happy family and we stick together no matter what.

On the radio at the end, I was shouting, 'Yes, yes, yes, yes!' The chequered flag is really just a stupid wooden stick and a piece of cloth, but crossing the finish line meant so much. I saw the guys on the pit wall – and also the guys from BMW, who were cheering for me. That was a great moment. I think most of the Toro Rosso team were more or less falling onto the track!"

The FIA stewards picked up on the matter and had a look at this 'new evidence' in Shanghai, but fears that Hamilton would be penalised proved unfounded and there were to be no repercussions.

Buoyed by the news, Hamilton did a storming job in qualifying to take pole position, ahead of Räikkönen, Felipe Massa and Alonso. The race was to prove that the Spaniard was carrying three laps more fuel than his team-mate, but that didn't fully explain the time gap. After the session, Alonso lost his rag and vented his frustration with some vandalism in the McLaren hospitality building. As before, he wasted no chance to suggest that something strange had gone on that he could not explain.

All weekend, the forecasts had pointed to rain on Sunday and, as at the Nürburgring, it arrived right at the start of the race. This time everyone was prepared, and the entire field started on intermediates, save for the Spyker drivers, who went for extremes. In the event, the rain was not hard enough to justify that choice, and they soon changed back.

Hamilton immediately established himself in the lead, and pulled away from Räikkönen, Massa and Alonso in convincing style. The last pair had quite a

fight off the line, as Fernando explained: "The first lap was interesting with Felipe in Turn 1, Turn 2, Turn 4 and basically every corner. I didn't manage to finish the lap in front of him, and this cost me a bit of time in the early part of the race because I was behind him and not very comfortable, because I had a bit too much downforce in Turns 7 and 8."

A very early pit stop for Hamilton, on lap 15, showed how the team had focused on landing him pole. He took on fuel, but kept the same intermediate tyres, a ploy then adopted by the other front-runners.

The sequence didn't shuffle the order at the front and, despite running four laps longer, Räikkönen was still some 4s shy of Hamilton when he re-emerged, while Massa and Alonso were a further 12s down.

Things began to get interesting around the lap-22 mark. Running what turned out to be his final grand prix, Alex Wurz was the first to stop for dry tyres. He was immediately quick, so others in the midfield who were due a stop soon followed suit. It was a harder choice for those who had just made a scheduled stop, but Ferrari gambled and brought Massa in on lap 26, giving him fuel to get to the end. But, just as he stopped, a little more rain fell, taking the edge off his

Jenson Button hoped for points, as he was starting 10th on the grid, but fifth place was an unexpected bonus

Only the first few drivers are spared the spray as Lewis Hamilton leads Kimi Räikkönen into Turn 1 on the first lap

Spurred on by the slating that he received in Japan, Sebastian Vettel showed that his front-running form was no fluke and finished an astounding fourth for Toro Rosso

dry tyres as he struggled for temperature and grip.

Meanwhile, it was apparent to the naked eye that Hamilton's rear tyres were badly worn, and Räikkönen reeled him in. After a couple of laps of cat-and-mouse games, the Ferrari man charged past, and Hamilton lost precious seconds as he slid around. It was clear that he had to pit for tyres, but McLaren kept him out, thinking that the worn inters would be a better bet for those crucial damp laps than new grooves. When he was finally called in on lap 30, Hamilton made the biggest mistake of his career to date, sliding helplessly into the gravel trap at the tight left in the pit entry. He tried to drive out, but became stuck fast. Unlike at the Nürburgring, there was to be no rescue.

McLaren boss Ron Dennis tried hard to justify the decision to leave Hamilton out: "We just disregarded all the cars other than the Ferraris and ourselves. And we were unconcerned with Kimi, we just let him past. Everyone was just trying to get through that last rain period, which we knew would last two or three laps. He was just struggling with a bit of tyre vibration, but we weren't concerned about pace. He was being quite careful on the circuit. Into the pitlane, he got a bit crossed up. It was one of those things.

"It's easy to say that we could have stopped earlier, that it would have made a difference, but everybody had exactly the same thought, which was if you remember last year when Alonso swapped on to intermediate tyres they grained immediately and he was extremely slow. Both top teams, Ferrari and ourselves, were trying to get through the rain and be able to go straight onto a dry tyre."

A couple of laps later, Räikkönen and Alonso both stopped for dry tyres without problem, and thereafter they ran without incident to the flag.

"We were in a pretty comfortable position to be honest," said Räikkönen's engineer Chris Dyer. "When it looked as though it was time to change to dry tyres,

we could see the other guys were quicker, but we knew also that there was rain coming. We passed Lewis and we had more fuel than him, so there was no need for us to rush anything and put dry tyres on the car. We just had to cover Lewis and stop the lap after him and we were OK."

After his earlier pit stop, Massa regained ground and pushed Alonso in the latter stages of the race, but he was never going to get past the McLaren.

This was Räikkönen's fifth win of the year, and it left him seven points shy of Hamilton going into Brazil. Ferrari folk could barely believe it.

"At the start, I had some problems with the front tyres graining and was understeering too much," said Räikkönen. "I just kept pushing as much as I could. We expected to run quite a bit longer than Lewis and so it worked out well. After the pit stop, I saw that he could not pull away any more and I was catching him little by little, and with a little rain my car was pretty good. One time I went to pass him, but there were too many yellow flags and I backed off, but in the end I could pass him and quite easily pull away. I waited for the right moment to change on to dry tyres, then everything worked well and there was no problem."

Alonso was pleased to have turned the title chase around but, as ever, took a cautious approach: "I am very happy, but I am not extremely happy with the qualifying and with things that happened yesterday, so this second place, eight points, is good and the championship is a little closer. But, again, if I want to win the championship it will be extremely difficult. If I want to win, I need some strange results and some very lucky moves and, for that, eight points today are very important but not changing the chances to win the championship too much."

Massa was a little frustrated with third, but it was important for the team that Räikkönen finished ahead.

"We were just missing a tiny little bit of speed,

BELOW Alexander Wurz powers his Williams past Takuma Sato's Super Aguri early in the race. He didn't know it at the time, but this would be his final grand prix

OPPOSITE What must have been going through Lewis Hamilton's head after he put his 'rubber-light' McLaren into the gravel at the pitlane entry and out of the race?

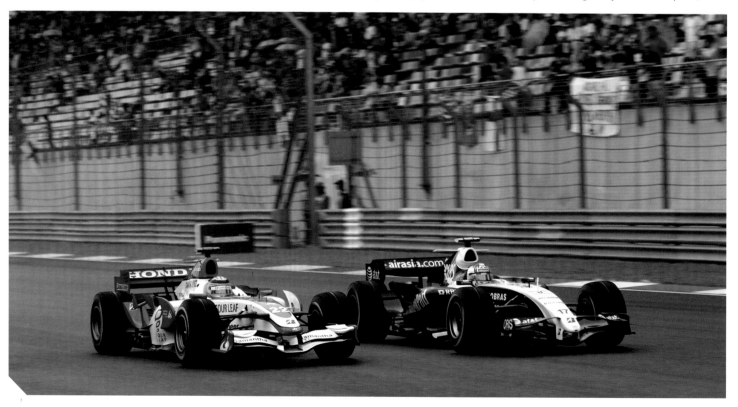

INSIDE LINE
ALEXANDER WURZ
WILLIAMS DRIVER

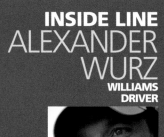

"My retirement has many little aspects to it, but I always wanted to stop when I was on good terms with the sport and enjoying it. As a sportsman, you have to be open and really see when it's the best time. I see many people passing that point and some athletes really nailing that point.

I had a fantastic time in F1 for 11 years. I loved the highs and the lows of such an intense business. The one best thing, my biggest trophy, was my wife, who I met when I was at Benetton. We now have a great family, three young, healthy boys and, thank God, I'm healthy and never had an injury.

I get asked if family had an impact. Well, I think it only makes you a richer person. I'm really angry when people say that with kids you are a second slower. It's bollocks. I could always separate family from racing.

For example, in some of my races this year, I've done some crazy, aggressive overtaking.

People ask about my highs and lows and it would be a long story but, to cut it short, I loved that in F1 you can have highs and lows within days of each other. F1 is famous for that. This intense life is really something I enjoyed for all the time I did it but, in the end, I didn't like the ups and downs and constant change any more. But it gave me a lot for my later life and it makes you a very rich man.

I drove for the three British World Championship-winning teams and was the only one in the history of the sport contracted to Benetton, McLaren and Williams. I raced for all three and stood on the podium for them all. I enjoyed that and I'm proud of it.

The highlight of 2007 was simply going racing again. Malaysia, I loved, overtaking 10 or 11 people in 15 laps – just great. I had a really good race in Monaco, simply because I pushed like crazy on every lap. I slid wide once at the harbour chicane, but that was the only mistake. Canada was another highlight, using all my experience to cope with the tyre problems and getting a podium.

The constant travelling, talking, smiling and waving eats you up, though. It was eating a little too much of my will, my power and my energy, so it's the right time to stop."

A relieved Fernando Alonso joins the Ferrari duo of Kimi Räikkönen and Felipe Massa in their champagne-spraying podium celebrations, his title hopes intact

to be honest, especially with respect to Kimi today," said Massa's engineer, Rob Smedley. "We were right there on the Friday, and then Kimi picked up his game on Saturday and today. To be honest, Kimi has been fantastic, I can't take anything away from him. He's done an absolutely stunning job today.

"That was exactly the result we wanted: Kimi had to win the race. Obviously, we wanted Felipe second. You can't control what's going to go on with Lewis, and what happened to him was a complete unknown, but it's been, let's say, a nice piece of luck for Ferrari…"

An astonishing fourth place went to none other than Sebastian Vettel, who more than made up for the

accident he had with Webber at Fuji. Toro Rosso got the strategy just right, making a single stop and switching from intermediates to dries at the same time as Massa, and then staying out as others made second stops.

Fifth place was just as much of a surprise, as Jenson Button also made the right calls and hustled his Honda up the order. Four precious points finally put the works team ahead of Super Aguri. However, a good run to sixth for Tonio Liuzzi made it eight for Toro Rosso on the day, and thus the Italian team leaped up the table

The final points went to Nick Heidfeld, after a below-par afternoon for BMW Sauber, and David Coulthard, the Scot once again making the most of a mixed-up wet day to creep into the points. He headed home team-mate Mark Webber, with Heikki Kovalainen in between the pair and right under Coulthard's rear wing.

Hamilton aside, the biggest loser on the day was probably Robert Kubica, who had a long first stint and was actually leading the race after the principal players made their second stops, only for a hydraulic failure to stop his BMW Sauber. Also not running at the end was Ralf Schumacher, who spun his Toyota off after another mediocre performance. The clock was running out on the German's career.

Overall, though, the focus was on what went wrong for Hamilton. "Lewis wanted to win here," said Martin Whitmarsh. "That's how he is. I don't think after the season that we've had that we'd want to modify Lewis. He'll want to go to Brazil to win that race and win the championship. If he didn't have that as a driving force within him, he wouldn't be the great driver that he is.

"So it's a mixture of feelings as we leave here, but we're first and second in the drivers' championship, we've got two great drivers, both of whom are capable of winning the World Championship, and Kimi we know well is a formidable opponent. So it's great for F1 that there are three drivers there in Interlagos who can win this World Championship…"

Finishing fourth was like a race win for Toro Rosso's clearly delighted Sebastian Vettel

SNAPSHOT FROM
CHINA

CLOCKWISE FROM RIGHT
The sheer scale of the circuit infrastructure at Shanghai never ceases to impress, as shown in particular by the huge edifice that dominates the start/finish straight; Renault racer Giancarlo Fisichella's son Cristofer came along to lend his dad a little support at work; actor Keanu Reeves tries Jenson Button's Honda for size; the grammar is weak, but the sentiment is clear; one of Formula One's friendly faces; the Chinese security crew march into position

WEEKEND NEWS

■ As well as letting Lewis Hamilton off the hook by electing not to punish him for alleged erratic driving behind the safety car at Fuji, the FIA stewards decided to cancel the 10-place grid penalty awarded to Sebastian Vettel after his collision there with Mark Webber. Ironically, the German then lost five places for impeding Heikki Kovalainen in qualifying. Meanwhile, Anthony Davidson was docked five places for a pitlane offence.

■ The FIA announced that there would be a Court of Appeal hearing in London in late October to review the legality of Prodrive's entry in 2008, at the instigation of Williams. Shortly afterwards came word that Prodrive's negotiations with McLaren had collapsed.

■ Alexander Wurz let it be known in Shanghai that he would be retiring at the end of what had been a difficult season for the Austrian at Williams. Nevertheless, it came as a surprise when the team later announced that Kazuki Nakajima would replace him for the Brazilian GP, denying the popular veteran the chance of a proper send-off.

■ The Stepneygate spying scandal took yet another twist immediately after the Chinese GP when McLaren's Fernando Alonso paid a visit to the Modena magistrates in Italy, to discuss his role in the affair. His team-mate Lewis Hamilton was not required for interview, though. Nigel Stepney, meanwhile, was reportedly pressing ahead with plans for a book, despite being dropped by his original publisher.

■ Max Mosley and Sir Jackie Stewart were embroiled in a war of words after the FIA President had made some colourful remarks to the British media about the former World Champion, who had been critical of the penalty applied to McLaren. Stewart hinted that he might be prepared to take legal action by way of response.

RACE RESULTS
CHINA
SHANGHAI

Official Results © [2007]
Formula One Administration Limited,
6 Princes Gate, London, SW7 1QJ.
No reproduction without permission.
All copyright and database rights reserved.

RACE DATE October 7th
CIRCUIT LENGTH 3.390 miles
NO. OF LAPS 56
RACE DISTANCE 189.680 miles
WEATHER Overcast then wet, 28°C
TRACK TEMP 27°C
RACE DAY ATTENDANCE 150,000
LAP RECORD Michael Schumacher,
1m32.238s, 132.202mph, 2004

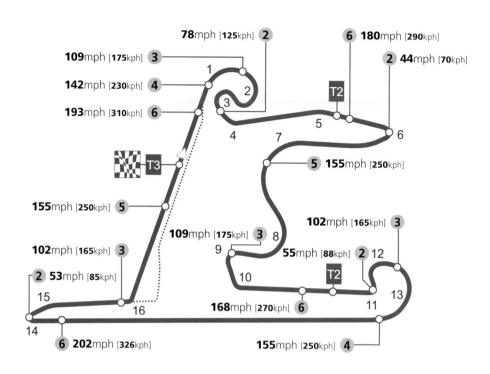

PRACTICE 1		
Driver	**Time**	**Laps**
1 K Räikkönen	1m37.024s	24
2 F Alonso	1m37.108s	18
3 F Massa	1m37.125s	21
4 L Hamilton	1m37.210s	20
5 N Rosberg	1m37.707s	23
6 R Kubica	1m38.055s	23
7 J Trulli	1m38.208s	30
8 G Fisichella	1m38.217s	16
9 K Nakajima	1m38.270s	30
10 N Heidfeld	1m38.445s	13
11 H Kovalainen	1m38.551s	17
12 R Schumacher	1m38.661s	23
13 D Coulthard	1m38.700s	25
14 J Button	1m38.942s	18
15 R Barrichello	1m38.945s	22
16 T Sato	1m39.238s	23
17 V Liuzzi	1m39.497s	22
18 M Webber	1m39.535s	23
19 A Davidson	1m39.539s	20
20 S Vettel	1m39.898s	24
21 S Yamamoto	1m40.126s	27
22 A Sutil	1m40.149s	26

PRACTICE 2		
Driver	**Time**	**Laps**
1 K Räikkönen	1m36.607s	31
2 F Alonso	1m36.613s	28
3 F Massa	1m36.630s	29
4 L Hamilton	1m36.876s	33
5 J Trulli	1m37.151s	36
6 M Webber	1m37.450s	34
7 R Schumacher	1m37.524s	32
8 D Coulthard	1m37.617s	27
9 N Rosberg	1m37.646s	36
10 G Fisichella	1m37.970s	32
11 H Kovalainen	1m38.062s	21
12 J Button	1m38.205s	41
13 R Barrichello	1m38.304s	40
14 R Kubica	1m38.379s	39
15 N Heidfeld	1m38.388s	16
16 A Wurz	1m38.531s	32
17 A Davidson	1m38.975s	38
18 V Liuzzi	1m39.065s	36
19 A Sutil	1m39.224s	37
20 T Sato	1m39.360s	37
21 S Vettel	1m39.404s	34
22 S Yamamoto	1m40.051s	3

PRACTICE 3		
Driver	**Time**	**Laps**
1 K Räikkönen	1m36.100s	15
2 F Alonso	1m36.126s	13
3 L Hamilton	1m36.227s	14
4 F Massa	1m36.405s	14
5 R Schumacher	1m36.959s	18
6 D Coulthard	1m36.964s	13
7 R Kubica	1m37.024s	23
8 H Kovalainen	1m37.106s	14
9 N Heidfeld	1m37.176s	18
10 M Webber	1m37.315s	13
11 N Rosberg	1m37.323s	16
12 V Liuzzi	1m37.463s	14
13 J Button	1m37.564s	19
14 J Trulli	1m37.679s	20
15 A Davidson	1m37.732s	15
16 S Vettel	1m37.759s	19
17 G Fisichella	1m37.791s	17
18 R Barrichello	1m37.920s	20
19 A Wurz	1m37.926s	16
20 T Sato	1m38.577s	16
21 A Sutil	1m38.868s	20
22 S Yamamoto	1m39.517s	21

QUALIFYING 1	
Driver	**Time**
1 K Räikkönen	1m35.692s
2 F Massa	1m35.792s
3 L Hamilton	1m35.798s
4 F Alonso	1m35.809s
5 R Kubica	1m36.309s
6 N Heidfeld	1m36.737s
7 D Coulthard	1m36.930s
8 S Vettel	1m37.006s
9 V Liuzzi	1m37.047s
10 J Button	1m37.092s
11 R Schumacher	1m37.135s
12 N Rosberg	1m37.144s
13 M Webber	1m37.199s
14 A Davidson	1m37.203s
15 J Trulli	1m37.209s
16 H Kovalainen	1m37.225s
17 R Barrichello	1m37.251s
18 G Fisichella	1m37.290s
19 A Wurz	1m37.456s
20 T Sato	1m38.218s
21 A Sutil	1m38.668s
22 S Yamamoto	1m39.336s

QUALIFYING 2	
Driver	**Time**
1 K Räikkönen	1m35.381s
2 F Massa	1m35.796s
3 F Alonso	1m35.845s
4 L Hamilton	1m35.898s
5 R Kubica	1m36.116s
6 N Heidfeld	1m36.217s
7 D Coulthard	1m36.252s
8 M Webber	1m36.602s
9 R Schumacher	1m36.709s
10 J Button	1m36.771s
11 V Liuzzi	1m36.862s
12 S Vettel	1m36.891s
13 J Trulli	1m36.959s
14 H Kovalainen	1m36.991s
15 A Davidson	1m37.247s
16 N Rosberg	1m37.483s

Best sectors – Practice	
Sec 1 K Räikkönen	25.216s
Sec 2 F Massa	28.439s
Sec 3 K Räikkönen	41.972s

Speed trap – Practice	
1 K Räikkönen	200.3mph
2 F Massa	200.1mph
3 N Rosberg	196.6mph

Best sectors – Qualifying	
Sec 1 K Räikkönen	25.146s
Sec 2 K Räikkönen	28.093s
Sec 3 F Massa	42.124s

Speed trap – Qualifying	
1 K Räikkönen	195.5mph
2 F Massa	194.9mph
3 F Alonso	194.1mph

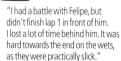

Fernando Alonso
"I had a battle with Felipe, but didn't finish lap 1 in front of him. I lost a lot of time behind him. It was hard towards the end on the wets, as they were practically slick."

Giancarlo Fisichella
"We could have done better with the strategy. We changed to dry tyres at the right moment. I knew I had one more stop, so I pushed to the limit, but we ran out of time."

Felipe Massa
"The moment I switched to dries, the rain came back and it was difficult to stay on track. It can pay off to take risks, but finishing on the podium in a race like this is vital."

Jenson Button
"I'm very happy to collect four points. The car wasn't working well in the wet and I had no grip. When the track dried, I went for the option tyre and a light load."

Nick Heidfeld
"Fourth was possible. It was a mistake to take a second set of wets, as I lost 12s a lap. It also looked as though we would have more rain, but I had to pit again for dries."

Ralf Schumacher
"I spun on lap 1 avoiding another car. After that, I passed a lot of cars, but Liuzzi hit me. The track was drying, so we switched to dries, but I lost grip and the engine died."

Lewis Hamilton
"My first stop went well. Though my tyres were in poor condition, we decided to get through the last shower before changing, but I made a mistake coming into the pitlane."

Heikki Kovalainen
"I lost time in a strange way: Kimi had lapped me but was on old wets, while my dries were new. I couldn't pass off-line as it was wet, so I lost 7–8s until I got past."

Kimi Räikkönen
"I had understeer, but it improved. I was one of the last to switch to dry tyres, but this was a help as the rain returned. I knew Alonso was very quick, but I was in control."

Rubens Barrichello
"We made one decision too many, which ruined my chances. When the rain fell after my first stop, I thought it would stay wet, so I came in for wets but this proved to be wrong."

Robert Kubica
"We stayed out for three or four laps after it started raining, which was difficult, then were making good ground on the wet tyres, but I had to retire with a hydraulic leak."

Jarno Trulli
"I was making ground on the wet tyres, given the conditions. But after the stop we lost a few places. It was a difficult race for everyone and it just didn't work out for me."

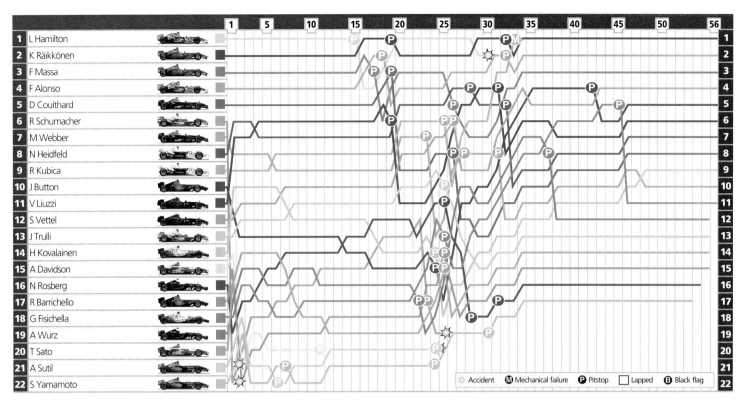

		1	5	10	15	20	25	30	35	40	45	50	56	
1	L Hamilton													1
2	K Räikkönen													2
3	F Massa													3
4	F Alonso													4
5	D Coulthard													5
6	R Schumacher													6
7	M Webber													7
8	N Heidfeld													8
9	R Kubica													9
10	J Button													10
11	V Liuzzi													11
12	S Vettel													12
13	J Trulli													13
14	H Kovalainen													14
15	A Davidson													15
16	N Rosberg													16
17	R Barrichello													17
18	G Fisichella													18
19	A Wurz													19
20	T Sato													20
21	A Sutil													21
22	S Yamamoto													22

☆ Accident Ⓜ Mechanical failure Ⓟ Pitstop ☐ Lapped Ⓑ Black flag

QUALIFYING 3

	Driver	Time
1	L Hamilton	1m35.908s
2	K Räikkönen	1m36.044s
3	F Massa	1m36.221s
4	F Alonso	1m36.576s
5	D Coulthard	1m37.619s
6	R Schumacher	1m38.013s
7	M Webber	1m38.153s
8	N Heidfeld	1m38.455s
9	R Kubica	1m38.472s
10	J Button	1m39.285s

GRID

	Driver	Time
1	L Hamilton	1m35.908s
2	K Räikkönen	1m36.044s
3	F Massa	1m36.221s
4	F Alonso	1m36.576s
5	D Coulthard	1m37.619s
6	R Schumacher	1m38.013s
7	M Webber	1m38.153s
8	N Heidfeld	1m38.455s
9	R Kubica	1m38.472s
10	J Button	1m39.285s
11	V Liuzzi	1m36.862s
12	J Trulli	1m36.959s
13	H Kovalainen	1m36.991s
14	A Davidson	1m37.247s
15	N Rosberg	1m37.483s
16	R Barrichello	1m37.251s
17*	S Vettel	1m36.891s
18	G Fisichella	1m37.290s
19	A Wurz	1m37.456s
20	T Sato	1m38.218s
21	A Sutil	1m38.668s
22	S Yamamoto	1m39.336s

*5-PLACE GRID PENALTY FOR IMPEDING

RACE

	Driver	Car	Laps	Time	Avg. mph	Fastest	Stops
1	K Räikkönen	Ferrari F2007	56	1h37m58.935s	116.088	1m38.285s	2
2	F Alonso	McLaren-Mercedes MP4-22	56	1h38m08.201s	115.894	1m37.991s	2
3	F Massa	Ferrari F2007	56	1h38m11.286s	115.834	1m37.454s	2
4	S Vettel	Toro Rosso-Ferrari STR02	56	1h38m51.904s	115.041	1m39.890s	1
5	J Button	Honda RA107	56	1h39m07.061s	114.747	1m38.913s	2
6	V Liuzzi	Toro Rosso-Ferrari STR02	56	1h39m12.068s	114.651	1m39.654s	2
7	N Heidfeld	BMW Sauber F1.07	56	1h39m12.619s	114.640	1m39.325s	2
8	D Coulthard	Red Bull-Renault RB3	56	1h39m19.145s	114.515	1m39.640s	2
9	H Kovalainen	Renault R27	56	1h39m19.581s	114.507	1m39.331s	1
10	M Webber	Red Bull-Renault RB3	56	1h39m23.080s	114.439	1m39.371s	3
11	G Fisichella	Renault R27	56	1h39m25.078s	114.401	1m38.900s	2
12	A Wurz	Williams-Toyota FW29	55	1h38m02.945s	113.925	1m39.743s	2
13	J Trulli	Toyota TF107	55	1h38m19.947s	113.597	1m39.911s	1
14	T Sato	Super Aguri-Honda SA07	55	1h38m40.162s	113.209	1m40.126s	1
15	R Barrichello	Honda RA107	55	1h39m33.455s	112.199	1m40.516s	3
16	N Rosberg	Williams-Toyota FW29	54	1h38m24.721s	111.440	1m39.233s	3
17	S Yamamoto	Spyker-Ferrari F8-VII	53	1h39m13.633s	108.476	1m40.764s	4
R	R Kubica	BMW Sauber F1.07	33	Hydraulics	-	1m40.926s	1
R	L Hamilton	McLaren-Mercedes MP4-22	30	Spun off	-	1m43.131s	1
R	R Schumacher	Toyota TF107	25	Spun off	-	1m44.062s	1
R	A Sutil	Spyker-Ferrari F8-VII	24	Accident	-	1m47.603s	2
R	A Davidson	Super Aguri-Honda SA07	11	Brakes	-	1m51.765s	1

CHAMPIONSHIP

	Driver	Pts
1	L Hamilton	107
2	F Alonso	103
3	K Räikkönen	100
4	F Massa	86
5	N Heidfeld	58
6	R Kubica	35
7	H Kovalainen	30
8	G Fisichella	21
9	N Rosberg	15
10	D Coulthard	14
11	A Wurz	13
12	M Webber	10
13	J Trulli	7
14	S Vettel	6
15	J Button	6
16	R Schumacher	5
17	T Sato	4
18	V Liuzzi	3
19	A Sutil	1

Fastest Lap
F Massa 1m37.454s
(125.120mph) on lap 56

Fastest speed trap
F Alonso 194.8mph
Slowest speed trap
T Sato 183.6mph

Fastest pit stop
1	G Fisichella	25.693s
2	M Webber	26.469s
3	V Liuzzi	26.508s

	Constructor	Pts
1	Ferrari	186
2	BMW Sauber	94
3	Renault	51
4	Williams-Toyota	28
5	Red Bull-Renault	24
6	Toyota	12
7	Toro Rosso-Ferrari	8
8	Honda	6
9	Super Aguri-Honda	4
10	Spyker-Ferrari	1

 David Coulthard
"To start fifth and finish eighth is disappointing, but at least we take a point and close on Williams. When I changed to dry tyres it started to rain, costing me 30s."

Nico Rosberg
"I had a poor start, but then I got by several cars. In the next stint, we had switched to dries. On lap 29, I got a left-rear puncture, so it cost me to come in for an extra stop."

Vitantonio Liuzzi
"I think Sebastian's one-stop strategy was better, but it's great for the team that we both scored. I had some great fights with Williams, Renault and BMW."

Adrian Sutil
"We started on extremes, hoping for more rain, but it didn't come, so we changed to wets, then dries at the second stop, but rain returned and the car hit the barriers."

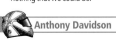 **Takuma Sato**
"I made a good start, gaining a few places. But we had a problem and the car was bouncing a lot. I radioed the team, but there was nothing that we could do."

Mark Webber
"I made the call to go to dries, at about the right time. Once on the dries, the rain returned. I came in for wets, but the rain didn't last long, so I had to go back to dries."

Alexander Wurz
"The conditions worked well for me at the beginning. I was the first to put on dry tyres, which worked, so we thought we'd pulled a rabbit out of the hat, but the grip went."

Sebastian Vettel
"P4! I used my momentum to go round several cars. After I passed Kovalainen, I was able to push harder. Just as I changed to dries the rain came, but it went away quickly."

Sakon Yamamoto
"We made mistakes over tyre choice, but nobody knows how it will go and you have to take risks. If it works out, then it will be a success and if not, a tough race."

Anthony Davidson
"Going into Turn 1 on lap 2, Rubens tagged my right rear and we spun, damaging the bodywork that covered my brake duct, sending the temperatures sky high."

FORMULA 1™ GRANDE PRÊMIO DO BRASIL 2007
SÃO PAULO

RÄIKKÖNEN RULES, OK?

Kimi Räikkönen was the outside bet, Lewis Hamilton the pre-race favourite, but a slip-up, then a gearbox glitch, helped the Ferrari ace win the day and the year

An extraordinary season came to an appropriately dramatic conclusion in Brazil as Kimi Räikkönen did the impossible and stole the 2007 Formula One World Championship from under the noses of the McLaren drivers. Some 17 points behind Lewis Hamilton after the Japanese GP, the Finn collected two maximum scores and came out on top, while everything that could go wrong for Hamilton did go wrong, and Fernando Alonso simply didn't have the pace.

Hamilton's hopes began to fade with a mistake on the opening lap, and then a delay caused by a curious gearbox glitch did the rest. He fought his way back to seventh place, but it wasn't quite enough. Even then, there was a glimmer of hope as three cars that finished ahead of his McLaren – a Williams and the BMW Saubers – were investigated for a fuel irregularity, and their exclusion would have handed him the title. It wasn't until around 9.45pm, though, that the FIA stewards confirmed that they would take no action, and Ferrari could restart their celebrations.

After his disastrous race in China, Hamilton came to Brazil full of confidence. He was four points clear of Alonso and seven ahead of Räikkönen. To become the sport's first rookie champion, all he had to do was finish right behind them. Räikkönen didn't have to play a percentage game for, with his points deficit, he knew that he had to win, with team-mate Felipe Massa behind him. That would take care of Alonso, and then it was a question of Hamilton having a problem.

Qualifying produced a degree of controversy when, on his critical lap, Räikkönen had to pass Hamilton, who was coming out of the pits. The Finn ran wide on the next corner, losing precious time, and to those keen to find a stick to beat Hamilton with, it appeared that he had been a little clumsy in allowing Räikkönen space. In the end, no action was taken. Pole position went to local hero and 2007 winner Massa, ahead of Hamilton, Räikkönen and Alonso. The stage seemed set for some first-lap drama...

And that's what we got. Off the line, Hamilton tucked in behind Massa, while Räikkönen swept by on the outside. The Brazilian made it to the first corner in front, as Räikkönen slipped into second place. Räikkönen then had to lift a little so as not to clip Massa, and Hamilton got a little crossed-up behind him. In an instant, looking to make the most of this loss of momentum, Alonso dived for the inside and relegated Hamilton to third.

It already looked interesting, and got more so when Hamilton, seemingly flummoxed by his loss of positions, locked up and ran wide at Turn 4, Descida do Lago. In an instant, Mark Webber, Robert Kubica, Nick Heidfeld and Jarno Trulli swept past.

Now down in eighth place, Hamilton really had a job on. He quickly disposed of Trulli, but it took him until the start of lap 7 to hustle Heidfeld into a mistake at the first corner. He was now just a place away from fifth, the position that would in effect make the title safe. But then the McLaren slowed suddenly, the result of a gearbox problem. For what seemed an age, he coasted along until, following directions from the team, he found the procedure that kicked the system back into life. But now he was 18th, and more than 40 seconds down on race-leader Massa.

Now he really had to go for it, but he lost precious time picking his way through the backmarkers.

Meanwhile, up front, Massa led in accomplished style, and the only question was when and how Ferrari would perform a 'correction' and put Räikkönen in front and in a title-winning position. Alonso clearly didn't have the pace of the Ferraris and had dropped 12s back before the first stops. Clearly, his hopes now

BELOW **Felipe Massa leads into the Senna S, but Kimi Räikkönen has had to lift to avoid him and Lewis Hamilton is briefly blocked, which will allow Fernando Alonso to use his unchecked momentum to take third at the following corner**

OPPOSITE **Sakon Yamamoto was left with nowhere to go when Giancarlo Fisichella came back on to the circuit right in front of him**

TALKING POINT
THE FINAL
SHOWDOWN

You could not have scripted the championship finale better, with drama aplenty and the end result the closest finish in the history of the Formula 1 World Championship. When the chequered flag fell after 71 laps, it stood as Kimi Räikkönen, 110 points; Lewis Hamilton, 109; Fernando Alonso, 109.

Right until the very last lap of the 17th and last race of the year, the destiny of the World Championship was up in the air. Kimi Räikkönen's task was simple enough: he had to win. And he did precisely that. In order to beat him, Hamilton had to be fifth or better.

Ordinarily, of course, it wouldn't have been a problem. But after his opening-lap misjudgement with Alonso into Turn 4, and then his gearbox glitch seven laps later, Hamilton was left to drive through from 18th, with fifth place his target if he wanted to be champion. When Jarno Trulli's Toyota peeled into the pits for super-soft Bridgestones with eight laps to go, that put Hamilton seventh.

In the Ferrari pit, Räikkönen's managers David and Steve Robertson could not bear to watch. Nico Rosberg had already pulled a great late-braking move into Turn 1 to pass Nick Heidfeld's BMW, but was now under pressure from a determined Robert Kubica. Both are young chargers and if they took each other off, Hamilton could still rob Räikkönen at the death.

"I just thought, 'Oh my God, what are they doing' when the screen picked up that battle," gasped David Robertson. "It was the longest three or four laps I have ever known.

"I'm just so pleased for Kimi. It was going to be a long shot for him over the last two races, but he did a brilliant job and he's a proper World Champion. He just kept his head down and got on with the job.

"He's won six races this year, which is two more than anyone else, and he's won the championship after a couple of DNFs earlier in the year. He deserves it and nobody can take anything away from him."

By finishing third, Alonso had missed out on joining Formula One greats Juan Manuel Fangio and Michael Schumacher as the only drivers to achieve championship hat-tricks. The two additional points for second place would have been enough, but it was not to be.

"For the first three laps, I could run with the Ferraris no problem and I started to be optimistic," said Alonso, "but they were probably looking after the tyres at that point and when they started to push I just didn't have the pace to keep up and there was nothing more I could do. But congratulations to Kimi – he did a good job."

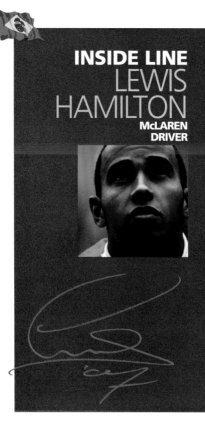

INSIDE LINE
LEWIS HAMILTON
McLAREN DRIVER

"I went into the race thinking that whatever happens today, it has been a phenomenal year. Who'd have thought I'd be leading the World Championship going into the final race? With a little luck I might have done it, but it's a great feeling to have been in that position.

The team has done a phenomenal job all year, absolutely amazing. We all wanted to win the Rugby World Cup and the F1 World Championship, but it obviously wasn't England's turn this weekend. It's my first year of F1, though, and next year we'll bounce back even stronger, for sure.

To be honest, I didn't get a great start to the race. I locked up to avoid hitting Fernando at Turn 4 and ran a bit wide. I think I was eighth after that, but was quite relaxed when I came back on because I knew I had the pace to get my positions back. Then, a few laps later, I was downshifting into Turn 4 and the car just selected neutral.

I coasted for what seemed like an eternity and while that was going on I just felt that someone, somewhere, didn't want me to win the title. But that's racing. To think I've come from GP2 to be ranked number two in the world is a positive thing and I know we'll be strong next year. We'll do a better job, for sure, and I can't wait.

From that moment, I also had to manage the engine temperature as well, so I was running quite low rpm at times. I only felt that it was over when I saw the chequered flag. I never stopped pushing and just kept trying as hard as I could right to the end. I was told at the start that I could still get it and I believed that. Pace-wise we weren't too bad: not as good as the Ferraris, but part of that was down to the way we were running our engine.

I feel a little emotional, but it's been an incredible season. Kimi has done a great job all year, drove well today and deserves his success. I honestly can't say I'm really gutted, because I'm not. The car was phenomenal during the race. Apart from the first lap, I think I drove one of my best races, so I can't be disappointed. Everyone has had their fair share of bad luck this year, it's just a shame mine all came at the end."

rested solely on a retirement for Räikkönen.

Massa opened the pit-stop sequence when he came in on lap 20, followed by his team-mate a lap later. McLaren demonstrated that there had been parity in qualifying when Alonso and Hamilton both came in on lap 22, the delay for the British driver meaning that both cars could be serviced on the same lap.

Intriguingly, McLaren put Hamilton straight on to the less-favoured super-soft tyres that everyone had been putting off using due to soaring track temperatures. With a short fuel load, the idea was to get him in clean air and get that unwanted stint on the super-softs out of the way sooner rather than later.

Through the middle part of the race, Alonso continued to fade, while Hamilton charged and passed any car that he came up against. He pitted for a second time on lap 36. There were still 35 laps to run and he could have made it to the end from there, but again McLaren short-fuelled him, to many people's surprise. It was now apparent that he would need a third stop. The team's ploy was to give him a lightish car and relatively fresh tyres throughout, but many observers felt that the extra stop was not the most logical way to get him back up to the fifth place he needed.

Out front, the Ferraris continued their serene progress, but with revs turned down and everyone's

BELOW Rubens Barrichello (sporting a new helmet livery) was one of many drivers who Lewis Hamilton had to brave it past on his climb back through the field

fingers crossed. The 'correction' was beautifully choreographed, with Massa pitting three laps earlier than his team-mate, and Räikkönen emerging from his stop just in front. But there was no time to relax.

Hamilton worked his way up to seventh, and needed just two more places. The cars ahead were out of reach – and he would have to unlap himself on both Ferraris to get to them – but Heidfeld, Kubica and Williams's Nico Rosberg were involved in a heated battle that could well have ended with a shunt that let Hamilton into that crucial position.

In the end, this didn't happen, and the positions remained unchanged, with Räikkönen leading Massa across the line, while a subdued Alonso dropped 57s back at the flag. Hamilton remained seventh, and that meant Räikkönen had a tally of 110 points, and his two rivals had 109. It couldn't have been much closer...

"For sure, it was really like any other race for me," said Räikkönen. "There were some people who said for sure I was going to win, but I didn't take them too seriously really. There were so many things that needed to go our way today, but it all really happened on the first lap. We made a good start and certain things went in our direction and then after that we had a very good

car, we were able to keep the pace as we wanted to try to just make sure we were one and two and hope that the rest went right for us.

"I don't believe in luck too much. It is down to hard work, and sometimes you do things wrong and sometimes you have problems, but today we needed help from the others and it turned out to be good for us. Sometimes this year we have had hard times in the races when we have been leading and something has gone wrong, but today everything went right and worked out for us beautifully. I don't know if it is luck or whatever, but I'll take it. It was good and that is the main thing."

Alonso seemed pretty philosophical about the outcome, and it was all too clear that he was delighted that the title had not gone to his team-mate.

"I knew it was going to be very difficult, and not only because I had to take four or five points off Lewis, but also because with the problem for Lewis in the race, I knew that Ferrari could finish one and two and that was not enough for me. So I tried at the start, I had a good start and I managed to be third.

"For the first two or three laps, I was keeping the pace with them, so I was extremely optimistic at that

ABOVE Fernando Alonso drove a good, clean race, but with Kimi Räikkönen winning, third was never going to be enough for the title

point, because I was hoping that the pace was just that. The Ferrari drivers were probably taking care of their tyres in the first couple of laps, and then when they pushed I was not able to keep the pace, but you never know. It was the same in China, and anything can happen, so I was keeping the pace with fingers crossed that maybe one of the Ferraris has a problem or something and I can take second place. But it didn't happen in the end, so there was nothing I could do."

Despite his bitter disappointment, Hamilton tried to put a brave face on both his first-lap mishap and the technical glitch that followed a handful of laps later (see 'Inside Line'). "I was downshifting into Turn 4 and the car just selected neutral," he explained. "Once I regained the gears, I still didn't think that was it, I still thought I could do it, even though I was dead last and nearly a lap behind. I just kept my hopes up. It's never over until the fat lady sings, until you see the chequered flag, so I just kept on pushing."

The title battle drew everyone's attention away from what was going on behind. Rosberg did a great job to outfumble both BMW Sauber drivers, with Kubica (who also three-stopped) heading home Heidfeld. All three had to sweat after the race, though, after the FIA found that their fuel had been cooler than is permitted. However, they escaped penalty because of some apparent incongruities in the rules. Not everyone was convinced that justice had been done...

Behind Hamilton, Trulli had his best race for a while, taking the final point for Toyota ahead of David Coulthard's Red Bull and impressive Williams rookie Kazuki Nakajima. The latter set the fifth-fastest lap of the race, after scattering his mechanics when he messed up his first pit stop. Fortunately, none was seriously injured.

Meanwhile, it was a disastrous end to the season for Renault. Heikki Kovalainen tangled with Ralf Schumacher at the first corner, and later had a big off into a tyre wall when a tyre failed. Team-mate Giancarlo Fisichella was hit hard from behind on lap 2 after going off and then spearing back on to the track in front of Sakon Yamamoto's Spyker. It was the second race of the year in which the team had failed to score, having also struck out at the previous round, in China.

For Renault, it was certainly very different from 12 months before, when the team was celebrating its second double title with Alonso. And of course at that stage Alonso was looking forward to a bright future and a new challenge at McLaren in 2007, and the world was still waiting to hear who his team-mate would be. A year can be an inordinately long time in motor racing...

TOP **Mark Webber knows this feeling only too well, as he climbs from his broken Red Bull and says goodbye to another points score**

LEFT **Kimi Räikkönen celebrates his unexpected world title with his race engineer Chris Dyer, who achieved so much with Michael Schumacher**

SNAPSHOT FROM
BRAZIL

CLOCKWISE FROM RIGHT São Paulo expands with every year and provides a distinctive backdrop to the circuit; Bernie and Flavio find that it isn't always sunny in Brazil; Heikki Kovalainen celebrated his 26th birthday on the Friday; a welcoming smile; after the race, the cars, two BMW Saubers and a Williams, that finished fourth, fifth and sixth, were locked away while under investigation for a fuel irregularity; McLaren had an FIA official stationed in their garage to ensure that both of their cars were afforded equality; Toyota bade farewell to Ralf Schumacher and its test driver Franck Montagny

WEEKEND NEWS

- Lewis Hamilton, Jenson Button and Takuma Sato infringed the rules by using two sets of standard wet tyres in Friday's damp morning practice session, when only one set is allowed. They each escaped with a 15,000 Euro fine and had to hand back the least-used set to Bridgestone.

- With suggestions that McLaren had been favouring Lewis Hamilton reaching fever pitch after the Chinese GP, the FIA took the unusual step of allocating a special observer to keep tabs on the team's actions. A senior Brazilian scrutineer was given a team radio headset and stationed in the garage from Saturday morning onwards.

- As ever, the Interlagos paddock was full of past Brazilian F1 drivers, led of course by former World Champions Emerson Fittipaldi and Nelson Piquet. Also in attendance were Alex Ribeiro, Luciano Burti, Raul Boesel and Ricardo Rosset. Meanwhile, Gil de Ferran made his first appearance since leaving Honda earlier in the season.

- Early in the weekend, Ron Dennis was invited into the McLaren garage to give his team a pre-race pep talk. He was surprised when the tables were turned and the mechanics presented him with their own version of the constructors' trophy that the team had been denied by the FIA. Dennis said later he would keep it in his office at home.

- The result of the Brazilian GP remained in flux at the time of closing for press, as McLaren had appealed against the stewards' decision not to exclude the BMW Saubers or Williams from the results after the discovery of their fuel-temperature irregularities. The hearing was scheduled for November.

RACE RESULTS
BRAZIL
INTERLAGOS

Official Results © [2007]
Formula One Administration Limited,
6 Princes Gate, London, SW7 1QJ.
No reproduction without permission.
All copyright and database rights reserved.

RACE DATE October 21st
CIRCUIT LENGTH 2.677 miles
NO. OF LAPS 71
RACE DISTANCE 190.067 miles
WEATHER Sunny and dry, 36°C
TRACK TEMP 63°C
RACE DAY ATTENDANCE 63,000
LAP RECORD Juan Pablo Montoya,
1m11.473s, 134.837mph, 2004

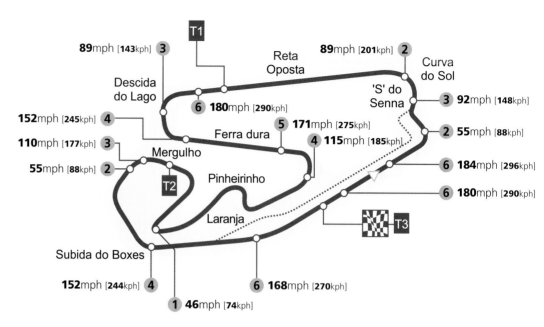

Descida do Lago — 89mph [143kph] (3)
Reta Oposta — 89mph [201kph] (2)
Curva do Sol
'S' do Senna — 92mph [148kph] (3)
180mph [290kph] (6)
152mph [245kph] (4)
171mph [275kph] (5)
Ferra dura
110mph [177kph] (3)
115mph [185kph] (4)
55mph [88kph] (2)
Mergulho
T2
Pinheirinho
55mph [88kph] (2)
184mph [296kph] (6)
180mph [290kph] (6)
Laranja
T3
Subida do Boxes
152mph [244kph] (4)
168mph [270kph] (6)
46mph [74kph] (1)
T1

	PRACTICE 1		
	Driver	Time	Laps
1	K Räikkönen	1m19.580s	9
2	F Massa	1m20.062s	10
3	H Kovalainen	1m20.829s	19
4	N Rosberg	1m21.064s	14
5	L Hamilton	1m21.121s	10
6	R Schumacher	1m21.243s	22
7	S Vettel	1m21.598s	22
8	M Webber	1m22.104s	12
9	J Trulli	1m22.104s	26
10	V Liuzzi	1m22.250s	17
11	R Barrichello	1m22.434s	23
12	J Button	1m22.477s	22
13	D Coulthard	1m22.667s	16
14	T Sato	1m22.929s	19
15	A Sutil	1m23.248s	30
16	K Nakajima	1m23.261s	26
17	A Davidson	1m23.551s	20
18	S Yamamoto	1m24.366s	25
19	G Fisichella	no time	2
20	F Alonso	no time	1
21	N Heidfeld	no time	1
22	R Kubica	no time	1

	PRACTICE 2		
	Driver	Time	Laps
1	L Hamilton	1m12.767s	27
2	F Alonso	1m12.889s	28
3	F Massa	1m13.075s	30
4	K Räikkönen	1m13.112s	30
5	G Fisichella	1m13.549s	22
6	R Kubica	1m13.587s	34
7	N Rosberg	1m13.655s	33
8	K Nakajima	1m13.664s	38
9	D Coulthard	1m13.706s	30
10	N Heidfeld	1m13.785s	44
11	R Schumacher	1m13.829s	29
12	H Kovalainen	1m13.879s	28
13	R Barrichello	1m13.892s	45
14	J Button	1m14.095s	44
15	V Liuzzi	1m14.152s	33
16	J Trulli	1m14.179s	25
17	S Vettel	1m14.409s	37
18	T Sato	1m14.431s	27
19	A Davidson	1m14.477s	31
20	M Webber	1m14.543s	35
21	A Sutil	1m15.095s	35
22	S Yamamoto	1m15.715s	32

	PRACTICE 3		
	Driver	Time	Laps
1	F Massa	1m11.810s	22
2	L Hamilton	1m11.934s	18
3	K Räikkönen	1m11.942s	21
4	M Webber	1m12.446s	14
5	J Trulli	1m12.461s	23
6	R Barrichello	1m12.478s	24
7	N Heidfeld	1m12.579s	25
8	F Alonso	1m12.594s	12
9	S Vettel	1m12.767s	18
10	N Rosberg	1m12.823s	20
11	V Liuzzi	1m12.893s	20
12	G Fisichella	1m12.913s	20
13	J Button	1m13.015s	22
14	R Schumacher	1m13.046s	23
15	H Kovalainen	1m13.090s	20
16	D Coulthard	1m13.117s	12
17	A Davidson	1m13.299s	16
18	T Sato	1m13.331s	16
19	K Nakajima	1m13.474s	17
20	R Kubica	1m13.525s	14
21	A Sutil	1m13.684s	21
22	S Yamamoto	1m13.872s	21

	QUALIFYING 1	
	Driver	Time
1	F Massa	1m12.303s
2	F Alonso	1m12.895s
3	K Räikkönen	1m13.016s
4	L Hamilton	1m13.033s
5	M Webber	1m13.081s
6	R Kubica	1m13.085s
7	D Coulthard	1m13.264s
8	J Trulli	1m13.470s
9	N Heidfeld	1m13.472s
10	G Fisichella	1m13.482s
11	V Liuzzi	1m13.607s
12	R Barrichello	1m13.661s
13	N Rosberg	1m13.707s
14	R Schumacher	1m13.767s
15	S Vettel	1m13.853s
16	J Button	1m14.054s
17	H Kovlainen	1m14.078s
18	T Sato	1m14.098s
19	K Nakajima	1m14.417s
20	A Davidson	1m14.596s
21	A Sutil	1m15.217s
22	S Yamamoto	1m15.487s

	QUALIFYING 2	
	Driver	Time
1	K Räikkönen	1m12.161s
2	L Hamilton	1m12.296s
3	F Massa	1m12.374s
4	F Alonso	1m12.637s
5	R Kubica	1m12.641s
6	M Webber	1m12.683s
7	N Rosberg	1m12.752s
8	J Trulli	1m12.832s
9	D Coulthard	1m12.846s
10	N Heidfeld	1m12.888s
11	R Barrichello	1m12.932s
12	G Fisichella	1m12.968s
13	S Vettel	1m13.058s
14	V Liuzzi	1m13.251s
15	R Schumacher	1m13.315s
16	J Button	1m13.469s

Best sectors – Practice

Sec 1	K Räikkönen	18.263s
Sec 2	F Massa	36.398s
Sec 3	F Massa	17.039s

Speed trap – Practice

1	G Fisichella	196.4mph
2	L Hamilton	195.9mph
3	K Räikkönen	195.5mph

Best sectors – Qualifying

Sec 1	F Massa	18.287s
Sec 2	L Hamilton	36.405s
Sec 3	F Massa	17.031s

Speed trap – Qualifying

1	F Alonso	197.2mph
2	L Hamilton	197.0mph
3	F Massa	196.8mph

Fernando Alonso
"The result is disappointing, but we knew that it would be difficult starting from fourth. During the first laps, I thought I was able to match the Ferraris; but they were too fast."

Giancarlo Fisichella
"On lap 2, I went off fighting with a Williams into Turn 1. The car was hard to control, and when I came back on to the track I was involved in a collision with another car."

Felipe Massa
"Today is a great day for the team and for Kimi. I'd have liked to have won my home race again, but I am happy to have helped Kimi, who still had a chance of the title."

Jenson Button
"Not a great end to the season. We had a problem with the engine overheating in the very high temperatures. We have to look forward now and focus on 2008."

Nick Heidfeld
"I was fourth until Rosberg outbraked me. The move was hard. If I hadn't opened the door we would have crashed. We both went on the dirt and Robert squeezed by."

Ralf Schumacher
"At the start, I was in a Toro Rosso sandwich and I lost ground. But it was a relatively good race from there. It is my last race for Toyota and it is a pity to be leaving."

Lewis Hamilton
"I am pretty disappointed, having led for so much of the season. But I have to put it into perspective, as this is only my first year in F1 and it has just been phenomenal."

Heikki Kovalainen
"I think Fisi got hit as his car came over and Ralf hit my car, giving me a puncture. Later, going through Turn 2, I felt a vibration, and the back end snapped and put me off."

Kimi Räikkönen
"It is very difficult to explain the incredible emotion I'm feeling. Today, Felipe's help was vital. We had to get into a 1–2 and then see what the others did."

Rubens Barrichello
"A disappointing end to a very hard season for us. Our position wasn't looking too bad before I came in to make my second stop, but unluckily there was an engine problem."

Robert Kubica
"I had to push right from the start, due to my three-stop strategy. I got a call to reduce the rpm because the temperatures were too high. Then I lost time behind Rosberg."

Jarno Trulli
"I am happy, as we finished with our first points for ages. We all had a battle with the tyres. We took the gamble to go for a three-stopper, and eighth was a good result."

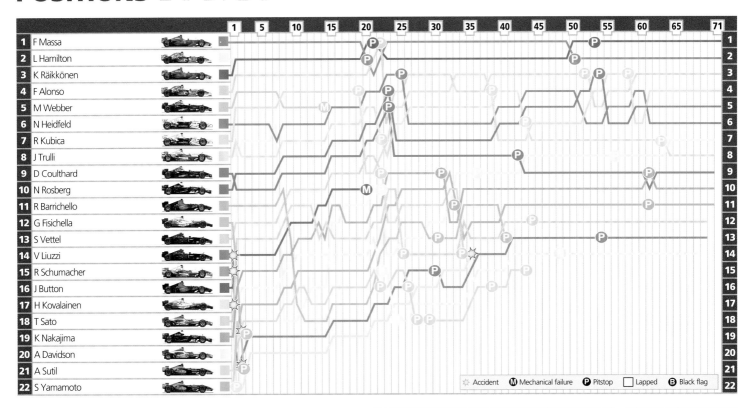

	Driver
1	F Massa
2	L Hamilton
3	K Räikkönen
4	F Alonso
5	M Webber
6	N Heidfeld
7	R Kubica
8	J Trulli
9	D Coulthard
10	N Rosberg
11	R Barrichello
12	G Fisichella
13	S Vettel
14	V Liuzzi
15	R Schumacher
16	J Button
17	H Kovalainen
18	T Sato
19	K Nakajima
20	A Davidson
21	A Sutil
22	S Yamamoto

Legend: ☼ Accident   Ⓜ Mechanical failure   Ⓟ Pitstop   ☐ Lapped   Ⓑ Black flag

QUALIFYING 3

	Driver	Time
1	F Massa	1m11.931s
2	L Hamilton	1m12.082s
3	K Räikkönen	1m12.322s
4	F Alonso	1m12.356s
5	M Webber	1m12.928s
6	N Heidfeld	1m13.081s
7	R Kubica	1m13.129s
8	J Trulli	1m13.195s
9	D Coulthard	1m13.272s
10	N Rosberg	1m13.477s

GRID

	Driver	Time
1	F Massa	1m11.931s
2	L Hamilton	1m12.082s
3	K Räikkönen	1m12.322s
4	F Alonso	1m12.356s
5	M Webber	1m12.928s
6	N Heidfeld	1m13.081s
7	R Kubica	1m13.129s
8	J Trulli	1m13.195s
9	D Coulthard	1m13.272s
10	N Rosberg	1m13.477s
11	R Barrichello	1m12.932s
12	G Fisichella	1m12.968s
13	S Vettel	1m13.058s
14	V Liuzzi	1m13.251s
15	R Schumacher	1m13.315s
16	J Button	1m13.469s
17	H Kovalainen	1m14.078s
18	T Sato	1m14.098s
19	K Nakajima	1m14.417s
20	A Davidson	1m14.596s
21*	A Sutil	1m15.217s
22	S Yamamoto	1m15.487s

*STARTED FROM THE PITLANE

RACE

	Driver	Car	Laps	Time	Avg. mph	Fastest	Stops
1	K Räikkönen	Ferrari F2007	71	1h28m15.270s	129.228	1m12.445s	2
2	F Massa	Ferrari F2007	71	1h28m16.763s	129.192	1m12.584s	2
3	F Alonso	McLaren-Mercedes MP4-22	71	1h29m12.289s	127.851	1m13.150s	2
4	N Rosberg	Williams-Toyota FW29	71	1h28m18.118s	127.712	1m13.159s	2
5	R Kubica	BMW Sauber F1.07	71	1h28m26.227s	127.519	1m12.686s	3
6	N Heidfeld	BMW Sauber F1.07	71	1h28m26.587s	127.511	1m13.452s	2
7	L Hamilton	McLaren-Mercedes MP4-22	70	1h28m19.350s	127.309	1m12.506s	3
8	J Trulli	Toyota TA107	70	1h28m30.730s	127.037	1m13.361s	3
9	D Coulthard	Red Bull-Renault RB3	70	1h28m54.817s	126.463	1m14.195s	2
10	K Nakajima	Williams-Toyota FW29	70	1h28m55.985s	126.435	1m13.116s	2
11	R Schumacher	Toyota TA107	70	1h28m58.235s	126.382	1m13.368s	2
12	T Sato	Super Aguri-Honda SA07	69	1h28m44.249s	124.903	1m14.914s	2
13	V Liuzzi	Toro Rosso-Ferrari STR02	69	1h29m29.773s	123.845	1m13.643s	3
14	A Davidson	Super Aguri-Honda SA07	68	1h29m14.983s	122.387	1m14.329s	3
R	A Sutil	Spyker-Ferrari F8-VII	43	Brakes	-	1m15.202s	5
R	R Barrichello	Honda RA107	40	Engine	-	1m14.742s	2
R	H Kovalainen	Renault 27	35	Accident	-	1m14.891s	1
R	S Vettel	Toro Rosso-Ferrari STR02	34	Hydraulics	-	1m14.423s	1
R	J Button	Honda RA107	20	Engine	-	1m14.039s	0
R	M Webber	Red Bull-Renault RB3	14	Transmission	-	1m14.398s	0
R	G Fisichella	Renault R27	2	Accident	-	1m50.404s	0
R	S Yamamoto	Spyker-Ferrari F8-VII	2	Accident	-	2m02.680s	0

CHAMPIONSHIP

	Driver	Pts
1	K Räikkönen	110
2	L Hamilton	109
3	F Alonso	109
4	F Massa	94
5	N Heidfeld	61
6	R Kubica	39
7	H Kovalainen	30
8	G Fisichella	21
9	N Rosberg	20
10	D Coulthard	14
11	A Wurz	13
12	M Webber	10
13	J Trulli	8
14	S Vettel	6
15	J Button	6
16	R Schumacher	5
17	T Sato	4
18	V Liuzzi	3
19	A Sutil	1

Fastest Lap
K Räikkönen 1m12.445s
(133.051mph) on lap 66

Fastest speed trap
L Hamilton 197.3mph
Slowest speed trap
S Yamamoto 170.8mph

Fastest pit stop
1	R Kubica	25.220s
2	L Hamilton	25.261s
3	R Kubica	25.569s

	Constructor	Pts
1	Ferrari	204
2	BMW Sauber	101
3	Renault	51
4	Williams-Toyota	33
5	Red Bull-Renault	24
6	Toyota	13
7	Toro Rosso-Ferrari	8
8	Honda	6
9	Super Aguri-Honda	4
10	Spyker-Ferrari	1

David Coulthard
"I thought we might get into the points, but I didn't have enough pace. I came together with Nakijima towards the end, which knocked my front suspension out."

Nico Rosberg
"This is my best result. My strategy was on the limit: a heavy fuel load on the second stint was really tough on the tyres, but I could make up the pace with my last set."

Vitantonio Liuzzi
"I saw Giancarlo lock up and go straight at Turn 1 and I expected him to miss the corner, so I went down the inside, but he came back and clipped my nose so I had to pit."

Adrian Sutil
"After my first stop, I tried to brake for Turn 1, but there was no deceleration and I hit Davidson. The car was OK, but then I started to lose brake pressure. We couldn't fix it."

Takuma Sato
"It was a tough, but exciting race. I did not get a great start, but into Turns 1, 2 and 3 I was overtaking lots of people. I then started to struggle with balance and pace."

Mark Webber
"I had a good start, but something failed. It's unbelievable. The guys saw a disconnect between the engine and gearbox, which is another new issue by the looks of it."

Kazuki Nakajima
"I'm really sorry that some of my mechanics were injured during my pit stop. I lost places because of the collision in front of me in to Turn 1. I was then held up by Sato."

Sebastian Vettel
"I retired with a hydraulic problem. First I lost the gear shift, then the power steering. Up to then, I was competitive, and the last few races have shown we are getting better."

Sakon Yamamoto
"Unfortunately, at the start of lap 2, Fisichella went off the track and then just came back on to the racing line. I couldn't do anything other than crash into him."

Anthony Davidson
"The car didn't quite have the pace to match our midfield rivals, but we had reliability on our side. Considering I got taken out by Sutil early on, my pace was good."

DRIVER RESULTS

	Driver	Nationality	Car	ROUND 1 March 18 AUSTRALIAN GP	ROUND 2 April 8 MALAYSIAN GP	ROUND 3 April 15 BAHRAIN GP	ROUND 4 May 13 SPANISH GP	ROUND 5 May 27 MONACO GP
1	Kimi Räikkönen	FIN	Ferrari F2007	1PF	3	5	R	8
2	Lewis Hamilton	GBR	McLaren-Mercedes MP4-22	3	2F	2	2	2
3	Fernando Alonso	SPA	McLaren-Mercedes MP4-22	2	1	3	3	1PF
4	Felipe Massa	BRA	Ferrari F2007	6	5P	1PF	1PF	3
5	Nick Heidfeld	GER	BMW Sauber F1.07	4	4	4	R	6
6	Robert Kubica	POL	BMW Sauber F1.07	R	18	6	4	5
7	Heikki Kovalainen	FIN	Renault R27	10	8	9	7	13
8	Giancarlo Fisichella	ITA	Renault R27	5	6	8	9	4
9	Nico Rosberg	GER	Williams-Toyota FW29	7	R	10	6	12
10	David Coulthard	GBR	Red Bull-Renault RB3	R	R	R	5	14
11	Alexander Wurz	AUT	Williams-Toyota FW29	R	9	11	R	7
12	Mark Webber	AUS	Red Bull-Renault RB3	13	10	R	R	R
13	Jarno Trulli	ITA	Toyota TF107	9	7	7	R	15
14	Sebastian Vettel	GER	BMW Sauber F1.07					
			Toro Rosso-Ferrari STR02					
15	Jenson Button	GBR	Honda RA107	15	12	R	12	11
16	Ralf Schumacher	GER	Toyota TF107	8	15	12	R	16
17	Takuma Sato	JAP	Super Aguri-Honda SA07	12	13	R	8	17
18	Vitantonio Liuzzi	ITA	Toro Rosso-Ferrari STR02	14	17	R	R	R
19	Adrian Sutil	GER	Spyker-Ferrari F8-VII	17	R	15	13	R
	Rubens Barrichello	BRA	Honda RA107	11	11	13	10	10
	Scott Speed	USA	Toro Rosso-Ferrari STR02	R	14	R	R	9
	Kazuki Nakajima	JAP	Williams-Toyota FW29					
	Anthony Davidson	GBR	Super Aguri-Honda SA07	16	16	R	11	18
	Sakon Yamamoto	JAP	Spyker-Ferrari F8-VII					
	Christijan Albers	NED	Spyker-Ferrari F8-VII	R	R	14	14	19
	Markus Winkelhock	GER	Spyker-Ferrari F8-VII					

RACE SCORING

1st	10	POINTS
2nd	8	POINTS
3rd	6	POINTS
4th	5	POINTS
5th	4	POINTS
6th	3	POINTS
7th	2	POINTS
8th	1	POINT

DATA KEY

D	DISQUALIFIED
F	FASTEST LAP
NC	NON-CLASSIFIED
NQ	NON-QUALIFIER
NS	NON-STARTER
P	POLE POSITION
R	RETIRED
W	WITHDRAWN

QUALIFYING HEAD-TO-HEAD

Ferrari
Massa– Räikkönen **9–8**

BMW Sauber
Heidfeld–Kubica **11–5**
Heidfeld–Vettel **1–0**

Renault
Kovalainen–Fisichella **9–8**

Williams-Toyota
Rosberg–Wurz **15–1**
Rosberg–Nakajima **1–0**

Red Bull-Renault
Webber–Coulthard **15–2**

Toyota
Trulli–Schumacher **14–3**

Toro Rosso-Ferrari
Liuzzi–Speed **6–4**
Liuzzi–Vettel **4–3**

Honda
Button–Barrichello **9–8**

Super Aguri-Honda
Davidson–Sato **10–7**

Spyker-Ferrari
Sutil–Albers **7–2**
Sutil–Winkelhock **1–0**
Sutil–Yamamoto **7–0**

McLaren-Mercedes
Hamilton–Alonso **9–8**

Race results for both drivers, ie. first and second listed as 1/2 with team's best result listed first. *McLaren's points annulled as a result of one of their employees being in possession of Ferrari documentation

CONSTRUCTOR RESULTS

1	Ferrari
2	BMW Sauber
3	Renault
4	Williams-Toyota
5	Red Bull-Renault
6	Toyota
7	Toro Rosso-Ferrari
8	Honda
9	Super Aguri-Honda
10	Spyker-Ferrari
11	McLaren-Mercedes

ROUND 6 June 10 CANADIAN GP	ROUND 7 June 17 UNITED STATES GP	ROUND 8 July 1 FRENCH GP	ROUND 9 July 8 BRITISH GP	ROUND 10 July 22 EUROPEAN GP	ROUND 11 August 5 HUNGARIAN GP	ROUND 11 August 26 TURKISH GP	ROUND 13 September 9 ITALIAN GP	ROUND 14 September 16 BELGIAN GP	ROUND 15 September 30 JAPANESE GP	ROUND 16 October 7 CHINESE GP	ROUND 17 October 21 BRAZILIAN GP	TOTAL POINTS
5	4F	1	1F	RP	2F	2F	3	1P	3	1	1F	110
1P	1P	3	3P	9	1P	5	2	4	1PF	RP	7	109
7F	2	7	2	1	4	3	1PF	3	R	2	3	109
D	3	2PF	5	2F	13	1P	R	2F	6	3F	2P	94
2	R	5	6	6	3	4	4	5	14	7	6	61
R		4	4	7	5	8	5	9	7	R	5	39
4	5	15	7	8	8	6	7	8	2	9	R	30
D	9	6	8	10	12	9	12	R	5	11	R	21
10	16	9	12	R	7	7	6	6	R	16	4	20
R	R	13	11	5	11	10	R	R	4	8	9	14
3	10	14	13	4	14	11	13	R	R	12		13
9	7	12	R	3	9	R	9	7	R	10	R	10
R	6	R	R	13	10	16	11	11	13	13	8	8
	8											
					16	19	18	R	R	4	R	6
R	12	8	10	R	R	13	8	R	11	5	R	6
8	R	10	R	R	6	12	15	10	R	R	11	5
6	R	16	14	R	15	18	16	15	15	14	12	4
R	17	R	16	R	R	15	17	12	9	6	13	3
R	14	17	R	R	17	21	19	14	8	R	R	1
12	R	11	9	11	18	17	10	13	10	15	R	
R	13	R	R	R								
											10	
11	11	R	R	12	R	14	14	16	R	R	14	
					R	20	20	17	12	17	R	
R	15	R	15									
				R								

ROUND 1 March 18 AUSTRALIAN GP	ROUND 2 April 8 MALAYSIAN GP	ROUND 3 April 15 BAHRAIN GP	ROUND 4 May 13 SPANISH GP	ROUND 5 May 27 MONACO GP	ROUND 6 June 10 CANADIAN GP	ROUND 7 June 17 UNITED STATES GP	ROUND 8 July 1 FRENCH GP	ROUND 9 July 8 BRITISH GP	ROUND 10 July 22 EUROPEAN GP	ROUND 11 August 5 HUNGARIAN GP	ROUND 12 August 26 TURKISH GP	ROUND 13 September 9 ITALIAN GP	ROUND 14 September 16 BELGIAN GP	ROUND 15 September 30 JAPANESE GP	ROUND 16 October 7 CHINESE GP	ROUND 17 October 21 BRAZILIAN GP	TOTAL POINTS
1/6	3/5	1/5	2/R	3/8	5/D	3/4	1/2	1/5	2/R	2/13	1/2	3/R	1/2	3/6	1/3	1/2	204
4/R	4/18	4/6	4/R	5/6	2/R	8/R	4/5	4/6	6/7	3/5	4/8	4/5	5/9	7/14	7/R	5/6	101
5/10	6/8	8/9	7/9	4/13	4/D	5/9	6/15	7/8	8/10	8/12	6/9	7/12	8/R	2/5	9/11	R/R	51
7/R	9/R	10/11	6/R	7/12	3/10	10/16	9/14	12/13	4/R	7/14	7/11	6/13	6/R	R/R	16/12	4/10	33
13/R	10/R	R/R	5/R	14/R	9/R	7/R	12/13	11/R	3/5	9/11	10/R	9/R	7/R	4/R	8/10	9/R	24
8/9	7/15	7/12	R/R	15/16	8/R	6/R	10/R	R/R	13/R	6/10	12/16	11/15	10/11	13/R	13/R	8/11	13
14/R	14/17	R/R	R/R	9/R	R/R	13/17	R/R	16/R	R/R	16/R	15/19	17/18	12/R	9/R	4/6	13/R	8
11/15	11/12	13/R	10/12	10/11	12/R	12/R	8/11	9/10	11/R	18/R	13/17	8/10	13/R	11/10	5/15	R/R	6
12/16	13/16	R/R	8/11	17/18	6/11	11/R	16/R	14/R	12/R	15/R	14/18	14/16	15/16	15/R	14/R	12/14	4
17/R	R/R	14/15	13/14	19/R	R/R	14/15	17/R	15/R	R/R	17/R	20/21	19/20	14/17	8/12	17/R	R/R	1
2/3	1/2	2/3	2/3	1/2	1/7	1/2	3/7	2/3	1/9	1/4	3/5	1/2	3/4	1/R	2/R	3/7	0*

FORMULA ONE STATISTICS

STARTS

256	Riccardo Patrese
252	Rubens Barrichello
250	Michael Schumacher
229	David Coulthard
210	Gerhard Berger
208	Andrea de Cesaris
204	Nelson Piquet
201	Jean Alesi
199	Alain Prost
196	Giancarlo Fisichella
194	Michele Alboreto
187	Nigel Mansell
184	Jarno Trulli
180	Ralf Schumacher
176	Graham Hill
175	Jacques Laffite
171	Niki Lauda
165	Jacques Villeneuve
164	Thierry Boutsen
162	Mika Häkkinen
	Johnny Herbert
161	Ayrton Senna
159	Heinz-Harald Frentzen
158	Martin Brundle
	Olivier Panis
152	John Watson
149	René Arnoux
147	Eddie Irvine
	Derek Warwick
146	Carlos Reutemann
144	Emerson Fittipaldi
136	Jenson Button
135	Jean-Pierre Jarier
134	Nick Heidfeld
132	Eddie Cheever
	Clay Regazzoni
128	Mario Andretti
126	Jack Brabham
123	Ronnie Peterson
122	Kimi Räikkönen
119	Pierluigi Martini
116	Damon Hill
	Jacky Ickx
	Alan Jones

OTHERS

105	Fernando Alonso
104	Mark Webber
89	Takuma Sato
88	Felipe Massa
69	Alexander Wurz
46	Christijan Albers
39	Vitantonio Liuzzi
35	Nico Rosberg
28	Scott Speed
22	Robert Kubica
20	Anthony Davidson
17	Lewis Hamilton
	Heikki Kovalainen
	Adrian Sutil
14	Sakon Yamamoto
8	Sebastian Vettel
1	Kazuki Nakajima
	Markus Winkelhock

CONSTRUCTORS

758	Ferrari
631	McLaren
550	Williams
490	Lotus
418	Tyrrell
409	Prost
394	Brabham
383	Arrows
376	Toro Rosso (formerly Minardi)
317	Benetton
285	Spyker (formerly Jordan)
252	BMW Sauber
230	March
228	Renault
197	BRM
188	Red Bull (formerly Stewart then Jaguar)
153	Honda Racing (formerly BAR)

OTHERS

105	Toyota
35	Super Aguri

WINS

91	Michael Schumacher
51	Alain Prost
41	Ayrton Senna
31	Nigel Mansell
27	Jackie Stewart
25	Jim Clark
	Niki Lauda
24	Juan Manuel Fangio
23	Nelson Piquet
22	Damon Hill
20	Mika Häkkinen
19	Fernando Alonso
16	Stirling Moss
15	Kimi Räikkönen
14	Jack Brabham
	Emerson Fittipaldi
	Graham Hill
13	Alberto Ascari
	David Coulthard
12	Mario Andretti
	Alan Jones
	Carlos Reutemann
11	Jacques Villeneuve
10	Gerhard Berger
	James Hunt
	Ronnie Peterson
	Jody Scheckter

OTHERS

5	Felipe Massa
4	Lewis Hamilton
3	Giancarlo Fisichella
1	Jenson Button
	Jarno Trulli

CONSTRUCTORS

201	Ferrari
156	McLaren
113	Williams
79	Lotus
35	Brabham
33	Renault
27	Benetton
23	Tyrrell

17	BRM	
16	Cooper	
10	Alfa Romeo	
9	Ligier	
	Maserati	
	Matra	
	Mercedes	
	Vanwall	
4	Spyker (formerly Jordan)	
3	March	
	Wolf	
1	Eagle	
	Hesketh	
	Honda Racing (formerly BAR)	
	Penske	
	Porsche	
	Shadow	
	Red Bull (formerly Stewart then Jaguar)	

IN 2007

6	Kimi Räikkönen
4	Fernando Alonso
	Lewis Hamilton
3	Felipe Massa

CONSTRUCTORS

9	Ferrari
8	McLaren

WINS IN ONE SEASON

13	Michael Schumacher	2004
11	Michael Schumacher	2002
9	Nigel Mansell	1992
	Michael Schumacher	1995
	Michael Schumacher	2000
	Michael Schumacher	2001
8	Mika Häkkinen	1998
	Damon Hill	1996
	Michael Schumacher	1994
	Ayrton Senna	1988
7	Fernando Alonso	2005
	Fernando Alonso	2006
	Jim Clark	1963
	Alain Prost	1984
	Alain Prost	1988
	Alain Prost	1993
	Kimi Räikkönen	2005
	Michael Schumacher	2006
	Ayrton Senna	1991
	Jacques Villeneuve	1997

CONSTRUCTORS

15	Ferrari	2002
	Ferrari	2004
	McLaren	1988
12	McLaren	1984
	Williams	1986
11	Benetton	1995
10	Ferrari	2000
	McLaren	1989
	McLaren	2005
	Williams	1992
	Williams	1993
9	Ferrari	2001
	Ferrari	2006
	Ferrari	2007
	McLaren	1998
	Williams	1986

	Williams	1987
8	Benetton	1994
	Ferrari	2003
	Ferrari	2007
	Lotus	1978
	McLaren	1991
	McLaren	2007
	Renault	2005
	Renault	2006
	Williams	1997

POLE POSITIONS

68	Michael Schumacher
65	Ayrton Senna
33	Jim Clark
	Alain Prost
32	Nigel Mansell
29	Juan Manuel Fangio
26	Mika Häkkinen
24	Niki Lauda
	Nelson Piquet
20	Damon Hill
18	Mario Andretti
	René Arnoux
17	Jackie Stewart
16	Fernando Alonso
	Stirling Moss
14	Alberto Ascari
	James Hunt
	Ronnie Peterson
	Kimi Räikkönen
13	Rubens Barrichello
	Jack Brabham
	Graham Hill
	Jacky Ickx
	Juan Pablo Montoya
	Jacques Villeneuve
12	Gerhard Berger
	David Coulthard

OTHERS

9	Felipe Massa
6	Lewis Hamilton
	Ralf Schumacher
3	Jenson Button
	Giancarlo Fisichella
	Jarno Trulli
1	Nick Heidfeld

CONSTRUCTORS

195	Ferrari
133	McLaren
125	Williams
107	Lotus
50	Renault
39	Brabham
16	Benetton
14	Tyrrell
12	Alfa Romeo
11	BRM
	Cooper
10	Maserati
9	Prost
8	Mercedes
7	Vanwall
5	March
4	Matra

3	Honda Racing (formerly BAR)
	Shadow
2	Spyker (formerly Jordan)
	Lancia
	Toyota
1	Red Bull (formerly Stewart then Jaguar)

IN 2007

6	Lewis Hamilton
	Felipe Massa
3	Kimi Räikkönen
2	Fernando Alonso

CONSTRUCTORS

9	Ferrari
8	McLaren

FASTEST LAPS

75	Michael Schumacher
41	Alain Prost
30	Nigel Mansell
28	Jim Clark
25	Mika Häkkinen
	Kimi Räikkönen
24	Niki Lauda
23	Juan Manuel Fangio
	Nelson Piquet
21	Gerhard Berger
19	Damon Hill
	Stirling Moss
	Ayrton Senna
18	David Coulthard
15	Rubens Barrichello
	Clay Regazzoni
	Jackie Stewart
14	Jacky Ickx
13	Alberto Ascari
	Alan Jones
	Riccardo Patrese

OTHERS

11	Fernando Alonso
8	Felipe Massa
	Ralf Schumacher
2	Giancarlo Fisichella
	Lewis Hamilton
1	Nico Rosberg

CONSTRUCTORS

204	Ferrari
134	McLaren
129	Williams
71	Lotus
40	Brabham
35	Benetton
27	Renault
20	Tyrrell
15	BRM
	Maserati
14	Alfa Romeo
13	Cooper

IN 2007

6	Felipe Massa
	Kimi Räikkönen
3	Fernando Alonso
2	Lewis Hamilton

CONSTRUCTORS

12	Ferrari
5	McLaren

POINTS

(Figures given are for gross tally – ie, including scores that were later dropped.)

1369	Michael Schumacher
798.5	Alain Prost
614	Ayrton Senna
519	Rubens Barrichello
513	David Coulthard
485.5	Nelson Piquet
482	Nigel Mansell
480	Fernando Alonso
456	Kimi Räikkönen
420.5	Niki Lauda
420	Mika Häkkinen
386	Gerhard Berger
360	Damon Hill
	Jackie Stewart

OTHERS

267	Giancarlo Fisichella
228	Jenson Button
201	Felipe Massa
182	Jarno Trulli
140	Nick Heidfeld
109	Lewis Hamilton
79	Mark Webber
45	Robert Kubica
	Alexander Wurz
44	Takuma Sato
30	Heikki Kovalainen
24	Nico Rosberg
6	Sebastian Vettel
5	Vitantonio Liuzzi
4	Christijan Albers
1	Adrian Sutil

CONSTRUCTORS

3849.5	Ferrari
3150.5	McLaren
2545.5	Williams
1352	Lotus
976	Renault
877.5	Benetton
854	Brabham
617	Tyrrell
439	BRM
424	Prost
333	BMW Sauber
	Cooper
312	Honda Racing (formerly BAR)
288	Spyker (formerly Jordan)
171.5	March
167	Arrows
163	Toyota
162	Red Bull (formerly Stewart then Jaguar)

OTHERS

47	Toro Rosso (formerly Minardi)
4	Super Aguri

LAPS LED

5108	Michael Schumacher
2931	Ayrton Senna
2683	Alain Prost
2058	Nigel Mansell
1940	Jim Clark
1918	Jackie Stewart
1633	Nelson Piquet

1590	Niki Lauda
1490	Mika Häkkinen
1363	Damon Hill
1347	Juan Manuel Fangio
1164	Stirling Moss
1160	Fernando Alonso
1106	Graham Hill

OTHERS

896	David Coulthard
819	Kimi Räikkönen
722	Rubens Barrichello
456	Felipe Massa
401	Ralf Schumacher
322	Lewis Hamilton
209	Giancarlo Fisichella
147	Jarno Trulli
104	Jenson Button

IN 2007

322	Lewis Hamilton
300	Felipe Massa
212	Kimi Räikkönen
203	Fernando Alonso
9	Heikki Kovalainen
6	Markus Winkelhock
5	Mark Webber
3	Nick Heidfeld
1	David Coulthard
	Giancarlo Fisichella
	Robert Kubica

CONSTRUCTORS

525	McLaren
512	Ferrari
10	Renault
7	BMW Sauber
6	Red Bull (formerly Stewart then Jaguar)
	Spyker (formerly Jordan)

MILES LED

14992	Michael Schumacher
8345	Ayrton Senna
7751	Alain Prost
6282	Jim Clark
5905	Nigel Mansell
5789	Juan Manuel Fangio
5692	Jackie Stewart
4820	Nelson Piquet
4475	Mika Häkkinen
4386	Niki Lauda
3939	Damon Hill
3450	Fernando Alonso

OTHERS

2614	David Coulthard
2615	Kimi Räikkönen
2167	Rubens Barrichello
1365	Felipe Massa
1202	Ralf Schumacher
900	Lewis Hamilton
673	Giancarlo Fisichella
375	Jarno Trulli
324	Jenson Button
28	Mark Webber
25	Heikki Kovalainen
21	Robert Kubica
19	Markus Winkelhock
13	Nick Heidfeld

9	Sebastian Vettel
6	Takuma Sato

IN 2007

913	Felipe Massa
900	Lewis Hamilton
714	Kimi Räikkönen
599	Fernando Alonso
25	Heikki Kovalainen
19	Markus Winkelhock
14	Mark Webber
9	Nick Heidfeld
	Sebastian Vettel
3	David Coulthard
	Giancarlo Fisichella
	Robert Kubica

DRIVERS' TITLES

7	Michael Schumacher
5	Juan Manuel Fangio
4	Alain Prost
3	Jack Brabham
	Niki Lauda
	Nelson Piquet
	Ayrton Senna
	Jackie Stewart
2	Fernando Alonso
	Alberto Ascari
	Jim Clark
	Emerson Fittipaldi
	Mika Häkkinen
	Graham Hill
1	Mario Andretti
	Giuseppe Farina
	Mike Hawthorn
	Damon Hill
	Phil Hill
	Denny Hulme
	James Hunt
	Alan Jones
	Nigel Mansell
	Kimi Räikkönen
	Jochen Rindt
	Keke Rosberg
	Jody Scheckter
	John Surtees
	Jacques Villeneuve

CONSTRUCTORS' TITLES

15	Ferrari
9	Williams
8	McLaren
7	Lotus
2	Brabham
	Cooper
	Renault
1	Benetton
	BRM
	Matra
	Tyrrell
	Vanwall

NB: To avoid confusion, the Renault stats are based on the team that evolved from Benetton in 2002, and include those stats that have happened since, plus those from Renault's first F1 spell from 1977–85. The figures for Benetton, and Toleman from which it metamorphosed in 1986, are listed as Benetton